The Nature of Mathematics

Twelfth Edition

Karl J. Smith

CENGAGE
Learning·

Australia • Brazil • Japan • Korea • Mexico • Singapore • Spain • United Kingdom • United States

CENGAGE
Learning

The Nature of Mathematics: Twelfth Edition

Senior Manager, Student Engagement:

Linda deStefano

Janey Moeller

Manager, Student Engagement:

Julie Dierig

Marketing Manager:

Rachael Kloos

Manager, Production Editorial:

Kim Fry

Manager, Intellectual Property Project Manager:

Brian Methe

Senior Manager, Production and Manufacturing:

Donna M. Brown

Manager, Production:

Terri Daley

Printed in the United States of America

Nature of Mathematics, 12th Edition
Karl J. Smith

For product information and technology assistance, contact us at
Cengage Learning Customer & Sales Support, 1-800-354-9706

For permission to use material from this text or product,
submit all requests online at **cengage.com/permissions**
Further permissions questions can be emailed to
permissionrequest@cengage.com

This book contains select works from existing Cengage Learning resources and was produced by Cengage Learning Custom Solutions for collegiate use. As such, those adopting and/or contributing to this work are responsible for editorial content accuracy, continuity and completeness.

Compilation © 2014 Cengage Learning

ISBN-13: 978-1-305-29079-2

ISBN-10: 1-305-29079-8

WCN: 01-100-101

Cengage Learning

5191 Natorp Boulevard
Mason, Ohio 45040
USA

Cengage Learning is a leading provider of customized learning solutions with office locations around the globe, including Singapore, the United Kingdom, Australia, Mexico, Brazil, and Japan. Locate your local office at:
international.cengage.com/region.

Cengage Learning products are represented in Canada by Nelson Education, Ltd. For your lifelong learning solutions, visit **www.cengage.com/custom.**
Visit our corporate website at **www.cengage.com.**

Brief Contents

Preface

I frequently encounter people who tell me about their unpleasant experiences with mathematics. I have a true sympathy for those people, and I recall one of my elementary school teachers who assigned additional arithmetic problems as punishment. This can only create negative attitudes toward mathematics, which is indeed unfortunate. If elementary school teachers and parents have positive attitudes toward mathematics, their children cannot help but see some of the beauty of the subject. I want students to come away from this course with the feeling that mathematics can be pleasant, useful, and practical—and enjoyed for its own sake.

Since the first edition, my goal has been, and continues to be, to create a positive attitude toward mathematics. But the world, the students, and the professors are very different today than they were when I began writing this book. This is a very different book from its first printing, and this edition is very different from the previous edition. The world of knowledge is more accessible today (via the Internet) than at any time in history. Supplementary help is available on the World Wide Web, and can be accessed at the following Web address: www.mathnature.com

All of the Web addresses mentioned in this book are linked to the above Web address. If you have access to a computer and the world wide Web, check out this Web address. You will find links to several search engines, history, and reference topics. You will find, for each section, homework hints, and a listing of essential ideas, projects, and links to related information on the Web.

This book was written for students who need a mathematics course to satisfy the general university competency requirement in mathematics. Because of the university requirement, many students enrolling in a course that uses my book have postponed taking this course as long as possible. They dread the experience, and come to class with a great deal of anxiety. Rather than simply presenting the technical details needed to proceed to the next course, I have attempted to give insight into what mathematics is, what it accomplishes, and how it is pursued as a human enterprise. However, at the same time, in this eleventh edition I have included a great deal of material to help students estimate, calculate, and solve problems *outside* the classroom or textbook setting.

This book was written to meet the needs of all students and schools. How did I accomplish that goal? First, the chapters are almost independent of one another, and can be covered in any order appropriate to a particular audience. Second, the problems are designed as the core of the course. There are problems that every student will find easy and this will provide the opportunity for success; there are also problems that are very challenging. Much interesting material appears in the problems, and students should get into the habit of reading (not necessarily working) all the problems whether or not they are assigned.

Level 1: Mechanical or drill problems

Level 2: Problems that require understanding of the concepts

Level 3: Problems that require problem solving skills or original thinking

What Are the Major Themes of This Book?

The major themes of this book are *problem solving* and estimation in the context of presenting the great ideas in the history of mathematics.

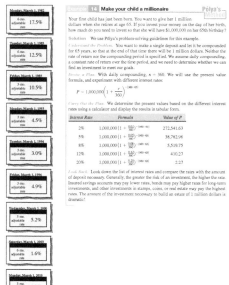

Pólya's Method

52. In 2009, the U.S. national soared to 11.0 trillion dollars.
a. If this debt is shared equally by the 300 million U.S. citizens, how much would it cost each of us (rounded to the nearest thousand dollars)?
b. If the interest rate is 6%, what is the interest on the national debt *each second*? Assume a 365-day year.

You can check on the current national debt at http://www.brillig.com/debt_clock/ This link, as usual, can be accessed through www.mathnature.com

Level 3 Problem

9. IN YOUR OWN WORDS It has been said that "computers influence our lives increasingly every year, and the trend will continue." Do you see this as a benefit or a detriment to humanity? Explain your reasons.

10. IN YOUR OWN WORDS A heated controversy rages about the possibility of a computer actually thinking. Do you believe that is possible? Do you think a computer can eventually be taught to be truly creative?

In Your Own Words

Historical NOTE

Karl Gauss (1777–1855)

Along with Archimedes and Isaac Newton, Gauss is considered one of the three greatest mathematicians of all time. When he w... old, he corrected an e... father's payroll calcula... time he was 21 he ha... more to mathematics... in a lifetime.

Historical Note

57. HISTORICAL QUEST The Historical Note on page 222 introduces the great mathematician Karl Gauss. Gauss kept a scientific diary containing 146 entries, some of which were independently discovered and published by others. On July 10, 1796, he wrote

EUREKA!
NUM = △ + △ + △

What do you think this meant? Illustrate with some numerical examples.

Historical Quest

I believe that *learning to solve problems is the principal reason for studying mathematics.* Problem solving is the process of applying previously acquired knowledge to new and unfamiliar situations. Solving word problems in most textbooks is one form of problem solving, but students also should be faced with non-text-type problems. In the first section of this edition I introduce students to Pólya's problem-solving techniques, and these techniques are used throughout the book to solve non-text-type problems. Problem-solving examples are found throughout the book (marked as **PÓLYA'S METHOD** examples).

You will find problems in *each* section that require Pólya's method for problem solving, and then you can practice your problem-solving skills with problems that are marked: **Level 3, Problem Solving.**

Students should learn the language and notation of mathematics. Most students who have trouble with mathematics do not realize that mathematics *does require hard work.* The usual pattern for most mathematics students is to open the book to the assigned page of problems, and begin working. Only after getting "stuck" is an attempt made to "find it in the book." The final resort is reading the text. In this book students are asked not only to "do math problems," but also to "experience mathematics." This means it is necessary to become involved with the **concepts** being presented, not "just get answers." In fact, the advertising slogan "Mathematics Is Not a Spectator Sport" is an invitation which suggests that the only way to succeed in mathematics is to become involved with it.

Students will learn to receive mathematical ideas through listening, reading, and visualizing. They are expected to present mathematical ideas by speaking, writing, drawing pictures and graphs, and demonstrating with concrete models. There is a category of problems in each section which is designated IN YOUR OWN WORDS, and which provides practice in communication skills.

Students should view mathematics in historical perspective. There is no argument that mathematics has been a driving force in the history of civilization. In order to bring students closer to this history, I've included not only Historical Notes, but a new category of problems called **Historical Quest** problems.

Students should learn to think critically. Many colleges have a broad educational goal of increasing critical thinking skills. Wikipedia defines **critical thinking** as "purposeful and reflective judgment about what to believe or do in response to observations, experience, verbal or written expressions or arguments." Critical thinking might involve determining the meaning and significance of what is observed or expressed, or, concerning a given inference or argument, determining whether there is adequate justification to accept the conclusion as true. Critical thinking begins in earnest in Section 1.1 when we introduce Pólya's problem solving method. These Pólya examples found throughout the book are not the usual "follow-the-leader"-type problems, but attempt, slowly, but surely, to teach critical thinking. The Problem Solving problems in almost every section continue this theme. The following sections are especially appropriate to teaching critical thinking skills: Problem Solving (1.1), Problem Solving with Logic (3.5), Cryptography (5.3), Modeling Uncategorized Problems (6.9), Summary of Financial Formulas (11.7), Probability Models (13.3), Voting Dilemmas (17.2), Apportionment Paradoxes (17.4), and What Is Calculus? (18.1).

A Note for Instructors

The prerequisites for this course vary considerably, as do the backgrounds of students. Some schools have no prerequisites, while other schools have an intermediate algebra prerequisite. The students, as well, have heterogeneous backgrounds. Some have little or no mathematics skills; others have had a great deal of mathematics. Even though the usual prerequisite for using this book is intermediate algebra, a careful selection of topics and chapters would allow a class with a beginning algebra prerequisite to study the material effectively.

Feel free to arrange the material in a different order from that presented in the text. I have written the chapters to be as independent of one another as possible. There is much more material than could be covered in a single course. This book can be used in classes designed for liberal arts, teacher training, finite mathematics, college algebra, or a combination of these.

Over the years, many instructors from all over the country have told me that they love the material, love to teach from this book, but complain that there is just too much material in this book to cover in one, or even two, semesters. In response to these requests, I have divided some of the material into two separate volumes:

> *The Nature of Problem Solving in Geometry and Probability*
> *The Nature of Problem Solving in Algebra*

The first volume, *The Nature of Geometry and Probability* includes chapters 1, 2, 3, 7, 8, 9, 11, 12, and 13 from this text.

The second volume, *The Nature of Algebra* includes chapters 1, 4, 5, 6, 9, 10, 14, 15, 16, and 17 from this text.

Since the first edition of this book, I have attempted to make the chapters as independent as possible to allow instructors to "pick and choose" the chapters to custom design the course. Because of advances in technology, it is now possible to design your own book for your class. The publisher offers a digital library, **TextChoice,** which helps you build your own custom version of *The Nature of Mathematics*. The details are included on the endpapers of this book.

One of the advantages of using a textbook that has traveled through many editions is that it is well seasoned. Errors are minimal, pedagogy is excellent, and it is easy to use; in other words, it works. For example, you will find that the sections and chapters are about the right length... each section will take about one classroom day. The problem sets are graded so that you can teach the course at different levels of difficulty, depending on the assigned problems. The problem sets are uniform in length (60 problems each), which facilitates the assigning of problems from day-to-day. The chapter reviews are complete and lead students to the type of review they will need to prepare for an examination.

Changes from the Previous Edition

As a result of extensive reviewer feedback, there are many new ideas and changes in this edition.

- The examples throughout the book have been redesigned. Each example now includes a title as well as a fresh easy-to read format.
- Each chapter now has a Chapter Challenge as an added problem-solving practice. These problems are out of context in order to give students additional challenge.
- Mathematical history has been an integral feature of this book since its inception, and we have long used Historical Notes to bring the human story into our venture through this text. In the last edition we experimented with a new type of problem called an Historical Quest and it has proved to be an overwhelming success, so we have greatly expanded its use in this edition. These problems are designed to *involve* the student in the historical development of the great ideas in mathematical history.

1 THE NATURE OF PROBLEM SOLVING

What in the World?

"Hey, Tom, what are you taking this semester?"
asked Susan. "I'm taking English, history, and math.
I can't believe my math teacher," responded Tom.
"The first day we were there, she walked in, wrote
her name on the board, and then she asked, 'How
much space would you have if you, along with
everyone else in the world, moved to California?'
What a stupid question ... I would not have enough

Overview

There are many reasons for reading a book, but the best
reason is because you want to read it. Although you are
probably reading this first page because you were required to
do so by your instructor, it is my hope that in a short while
you will be reading this book because you *want* to read it. It
was written for people who think they don't like mathematics, or people who think they can't work math problems, or

What in the World?

■ The chapter openings have been redesigned, but continue to offer the popular "What in the World?" introduction. They use common conversations between two students to introduce chapter material, helping to connect the content with students' lives.

■ The prologue and epilogue have been redesigned and offer unique "bookends" to the material in the book. The prologue asks, "Why Math?". This prologue not only puts mathematics into a historical perspective, but also is designed to get students thinking about problem solving. The problems accompanying this prologue could serve as a pre-test or diagnostic test, but I use these prologue problems to let the students know that this book will not be like other math books they may have used in the past. The epilogue, "Why Not Math?", is designed to tie together many parts of the book (which may or may not have been covered in the class) to show that there are many rooms in the mansion known as mathematics. The problems accompanying this epilogue could serve as a review to show that it would be difficult to choose a course of study in college without somehow being touched by mathematics. When have you seen a mathematics textbook that asks, "Why study mathematics?" and then actually produces an example to show it?[*]

*See Example 2, Section 11.5, 551.

Acknowledgments

I also appreciate the suggestions of the reviewers of this edition:

Vincent Edward Castellana, Eastern Kentucky University
Beth Greene Costner, Winthrop University
Charles Allen Matthews, Southeastern Oklahoma State University
James Waichiro Miller, Chaminade University of Honolulu
Tammy Potter, Gadsen State Community College
Jill S. Rafael, Sierra College
Leonora DePiola Smook, Suffolk Community College
Lynda Zenati, Robert Morris College

One of the nicest things about writing a successful book is all of the letters and suggestions I've received. I would like to thank the following people who gave suggestions for previous editions of this book: Jeffery Allbritten, Brenda Allen, Richard C. Andrews, Nancy Angle, Peter R. Atwood, John August, Charles Baker, V. Sagar Bakhshi, Jerald T. Ball, Carol Bauer, George Berzsenyi, Daniel C. Biles, Jan Boal, Elaine Bouldin, Kolman Brand, Chris C. Braunschweiger, Barry Brenin, T. A. Bronikowski, Charles M. Bundrick, T. W. Buquoi, Eugene Callahan, Michael W. Carroll, Joseph M. Cavanaugh, Rose Cavin, Peter Chen, James R. Choike, Mark Christie, Gerald Church, Robert Cicenia, Wil Clarke, Lynn Cleaveland, Penelope Ann Coe, Thomas C. Craven, Gladys C. Cummings, C.E. Davis, Steven W. Davis, Tony F. DeLia, Stephen DeLong, Ralph De Marr, Robbin Dengler, Carolyn Detmer, Maureen Dion, Charles Downey, Mickle Duggan, Samuel L. Dunn, Robert Dwarika, Beva Eastman, William J. Eccles, Gentil Estevez, Ernest Fandreyer, Loyal Farmer, Gregory N. Fiore, Robert Fliess, Richard Freitag, Gerald E. Gannon, Ralph Gellar, Sanford Geraci, Gary Gislason, Lourdes M. Gonzalez, Mark Greenhalgh, Martin Haines, Abdul Rahim Halabieh, Ward Heilman, John J. Hanevy, Michaael Helinger, Robert L. Hoburg, Caroline Hollingsworth, Scott Holm, Libby W. Holt, Peter Hovanec, M. Kay Hudspeth, Carol M. Hurwitz, James J. Jackson, Kind Jamison, Vernon H. Jantz, Josephine Johansen, Charles E. Johnson, Nancy J. Johnson, Judith M. Jones, Michael Jones, Martha C. Jordan, Ravindra N. Kalia, Judy D. Kennedy, Linda H. Kodama, Daniel Koral, Helen Kriegsman, Frances J. Lane, C. Deborah Laughton, William Leahey, John LeDuc, Richard Leedy, William A. Leonard, Beth Long, Adolf Mader, Winifred A. Mallam, John Martin, Maria M. Maspons, Cherry F. May, Paul McCombs, Cynthia L. McGinnis, George McNulty, Carol McVey, Max Melnikov, Valerie Melvin, Charles C. Miles, Allen D. Miller, Clifford D. Miller, Elaine I. Miller, Ronald H. Moore, John Mullen, Charles W. Nelson, Ann Ostberg, Barbara Ostrick, John Palumbo, Joanne V. Peeples, Gary Peterson, Michael Petricig, Mary Anne C. Petruska, Michael Pinter, Susan K. Puckett, Laurie Poe, Joan Raines, James V. Rauff, Richard Rempel, Pat Rhodes, Paul M. Riggs, Jane Rood, Peter Ross, O. Sassian, Mickey G. Settle, James R. Smart, Andrew Simoson, Glen T. Smith, Donald G. Spencer, Barb Tanzyus, Gustavo Valadez-Ortiz, John Vangor, Arnold Villone, Clifford H. Wagner, James Walters, Steve Warner, Steve Watnik, Pangyen Ben Weng, Barbara Williams, Carol E. Williams, Stephen S. Willoughby, Mary C. Woestman, Jean Woody, and Bruce Yoshiwara.

The creation of a textbook is really a team effort. My thanks to Beth Kluckhohn, Abigail Perrine, Carly Bergey, and Shaun Williams who led me through the process effortlessly. And I especially express my appreciation to Jack Morrell for carefully reading the entire manuscript while all the time offering me valuable suggestions.

I would especially like to thank Joe Salvati, from New School University in Manhattan, Robert J. Wisner of New Mexico State for his countless suggestions and ideas over the many editions of this book; Marc Bove, Shona Burke, John-Paul Ramin, Craig Barth, Jeremy Hayhurst, Paula Heighton, Gary Ostedt, and Bob Pirtle of Brooks/Cole; as well as Jack Thornton, for the sterling leadership and inspiration he has been to me from the inception of this book to the present.

Finally, my thanks go to my wife, Linda, who has always been there for me. Without her this book would exist only in my dreams, and I would never have embarked as an author.

Karl J. Smith
Sebastopol, CA
smithkjs@mathnature.com

Supplements

For the Student

Student Survival and Solutions Manual
AUTHOR: Karl Smith
ISBN: 0538495286
The Student Survival and Solutions Manual provides helpful study aids and fully worked-out solutions to all of the odd-numbered exercises in the text. It's a great way to check your answers and ensure that you took the correct steps to arrive at an answer.

Enhanced WebAssign
ISBN: 0538738103
Enhanced Webassign, used by over one million students at more than 1100 institutions, allows you to assign, collect, grade, and record homework assignments via the web. This proven and reliable homework system includes thousands of algorithmically generated homework problems, an eBook, links to relevant textbook sections, video examples, problem specific tutorials, and more.

For the Instructor

Annotated Instructor's Edition
AUTHOR: Karl Smith
ISBN: 0538738693
The Annotated Instructor's Edition features an appendix containing the answers to all problems in the book as well as icons denoting which problems can be found in Enhanced WebAssign.

Instructor's Manual
AUTHOR: Karl Smith
ISBN: 0538495278
Written by author Karl Smith, the Instructor's Manual provides worked-out solutions to all of the problems in the text. For instructors only.

Text-Specific DVDs
AUTHOR: Dana Mosely
ISBN: 1111571252
Hosted by Dana Mosley, these text-specific instructional videos provide students with visual reinforcement of concepts and explanations, presented in easy-to-understand terms with detailed examples and sample problems. A flexible format offers versatility for quickly accessing topics or catering lectures to self-paced, online, or hybrid courses. Closed captioning is provided for the hearing impaired.

Enhanced WebAssign
ISBN: 0538738103
Enhanced WebAssign, used by over one million students at more than 1,100 institutions, allows you to assign, collect, grade, and record homework assignments via the web. This proven and reliable homework system includes thousands of algorithmically generated homework problems, links to relevant textbook sections, video examples, problem-specific tutorials, and more.

New! Personal Study Plans and a Premium eBook
Diagnostic quizzing for each chapter identifies concepts that students still need to master, and directs them to the appropriate review material. Students will appreciate the interactive Premium eBook, which offers search, highlighting, and note-taking functionality, as well as links to multimedia resources, all available to students when you choose Enhanced WebAssign.

Note that the WebAssign problems for this text are highlighted by a ➤.

PowerLecture with ExamView®
ISBN: 0840053304
This CD-ROM provides the instructor with dynamic media tools for teaching. Create, deliver, and customize tests (both print and online) in minutes with ExamView® Computerized Testing Featuring Algorithmic Equations. Easily build solution sets for homework or exams using Solution Builder's online solutions manual. Microsoft® PowerPoint® lecture slides and figures from the book are also included on this CD-ROM.

Solution Builder
This online solutions manual allows instructors to create customizable solutions that they can print out to distribute or post as needed. This is a convenient and expedient way to deliver solutions to specific homework sets. Visit www.cengage.com/solutionbuilder.

Math Study Skills Workbook, 4th Edition
AUTHOR: Paul Nolting
ISBN-13: 978-0-840-05309-1
Paul Nolting's workbook will help you identify your strengths, weaknesses, and personal learning styles in math. Nolting offers proven study tips, test-taking strategies, a homework system, and recommendations for reducing anxiety and improving grades.

Book-companion Web site at **www.mathnature.com**
Author: Karl Smith
Created and updated by Karl Smith, the Web site offers supplementary help and practice for students. All of the Web addresses mentioned in the book are linked to the above Web address. You will find links to several search engines, history, and reference topics. You will find, for each section, homework hints, and a listing of essential ideas, projects, and links to related information on the Web.

To the Student

A FABLE

If people do not believe that mathematics is simple, it is only because they do not realize how complicated life is.

JOHN VAN NEUMANN

Once upon a time, two young ladies, Shelley and Cindy, came to a town called Mathematics. People had warned them that this was a particularly confusing town. Many people who arrived in Mathematics were very enthusiastic, but could not find their way around, became frustrated, gave up, and left town.

Shelley was strongly determined to succeed. She was going to learn her way through the town. For example, in order to learn how to go from her dorm to class, she concentrated on memorizing this clearly essential information: she had to walk 325 steps south, then 253 steps west, then 129 steps in a diagonal (south-west), and finally 86 steps north. It was not easy to remember all of that, but fortunately she had a very good instructor who helped her to walk this same path 50 times. In order to stick to the strictly necessary information, she ignored much of the beauty along the route, such as the color of the adjacent buildings or the existence of trees, bushes, and nearby flowers. She always walked blindfolded. After repeated exercising, she succeeded in learning her way to class and also to the cafeteria. But she could not learn the way to the grocery store, the bus station, or a nice restaurant; there were just too many routes to memorize. It was so overwhelming! Finally, she gave up and left town; Mathematics was too complicated for her.

Cindy, on the other hand, was of a much less serious nature. To the dismay of her instructor, she did not even intend to memorize the number of steps of her walks. Neither did she use the standard blindfold which students need for learning. She was always curious, looking at the different buildings, trees, bushes, and nearby flowers or anything else not necessarily related to her walk. Sometimes she walked down dead-end alleys in order to find out where they were leading, even if this was obviously superfluous. Curiously, Cindy succeeded in learning how to walk from one place to another. She even found it easy and enjoyed the scenery. She eventually built a building on a vacant lot in the city of Mathematics.*

*My thanks to Emilio Roxin of the University of Rhode Island for the idea for this fable.

A HISTORICAL OVERVIEW

Whether you love or loathe mathematics, it is hard to deny its importance in the development of the main ideas of this world! Read the BON VOYAGE invitation on the inside front cover. The goal of this text is to help you to discover an answer to the question, "Why study math?"

The study of mathematics can be organized as a history or story of the development of mathematical ideas, or it can be organized by topic. The intended audience of this book dictates that the development should be by topic, but mathematics involves real people with real stories, so you will find this text to be very historical in its presentation. This overview rearranges the material you will encounter in the text into a historical timeline. It is not intended to be read as a history of mathematics, but rather as an overview to make you want to do further investigation. Sit back, relax, and use this overview as a *starting place* to expand your knowledge about the beginnings of some of the greatest ideas in the history of the world!

We have divided this history of mathematics into seven chronological periods:

Babylonian, Egyptian, and Native American Period	3000 B.C. to 601 B.C.
Greek, Chinese, and Roman Periods	600 B.C. to A.D. 499
Hindu and Persian Period	500 to 1199
Transition Period	1200 to 1599
Age of Reason	1600 to 1699
Early Modern Period	1700 to 1799
Modern Period	1800 to present

Babylonian, Egyptian, and Native American Period: 3000 B.C. to 601 B.C.

Mesopotamia is an ancient region located in southwest Asia between the lower Tigris and Euphrates Rivers and is historically known as the birthplace of civilization. It is part of modern Iraq. Mesopotamian mathematics refers to the mathematics of the ancient Babylonians, and this mathematics is sometimes referred to as Sumerian mathematics. Over 50,000 tablets from Mesopotamia have been found and are exhibited at major museums around the world.

© Gianni Dagli Orti/CORBIS

Sumerian clay tablet

Babylonian, Egyptian, and Native American Period: 3000 BC to 601 BC

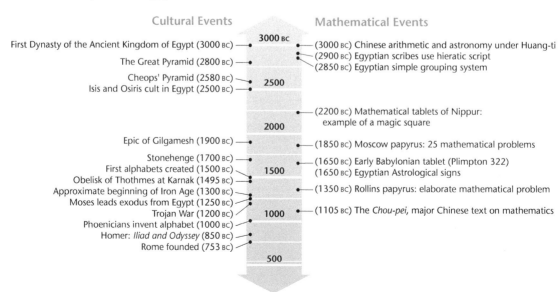

Cultural Events

First Dynasty of the Ancient Kingdom of Egypt (3000 BC)
The Great Pyramid (2800 BC)
Cheops' Pyramid (2580 BC)
Isis and Osiris cult in Egypt (2500 BC)
Epic of Gilgamesh (1900 BC)
Stonehenge (1700 BC)
First alphabets created (1500 BC)
Obelisk of Thothmes at Karnak (1495 BC)
Approximate beginning of Iron Age (1300 BC)
Moses leads exodus from Egypt (1250 BC)
Trojan War (1200 BC)
Phoenicians invent alphabet (1000 BC)
Homer: *Iliad and Odyssey* (850 BC)
Rome founded (753 BC)

Mathematical Events

(3000 BC) Chinese arithmetic and astronomy under Huang-ti
(2900 BC) Egyptian scribes use hieratic script
(2850 BC) Egyptian simple grouping system
(2200 BC) Mathematical tablets of Nippur: example of a magic square
(1850 BC) Moscow papyrus: 25 mathematical problems
(1650 BC) Early Babylonian tablet (Plimpton 322)
(1650 BC) Egyptian Astrological signs
(1350 BC) Rollins papyrus: elaborate mathematical problem
(1105 BC) The *Chou-pei*, major Chinese text on mathematics

3000 BC
2500
2000
1500
1000
500

Interesting readings about Babylon can be found in a book on the history of mathematics, such as *An Introduction to the History of Mathematics,* 6th edition, by Howard Eves (New York: Saunders, 1990), or by looking at the many sources on the World Wide Web. You can find links to such Web sites, as well as all Web sites in this book, by looking at the Web page for this text:

 **www.mathnature.com**

This Web page allows you to access a world of information by using the links provided.

The mathematics of this period was very practical and it was used in construction, surveying, recordkeeping, and in the creation of calendars. The culture of the Babylonians reached its height about 2500 B.C., and about 1700 B.C. King Hammurabi formulated a famous code of law. In 330 B.C., Alexander the Great conquered Asia Minor, ending the great, Persian (Achaemenid) Empire. Even though there was a great deal of political and social upheaval during this period, there was a continuity in the development of mathematics from ancient time to the time of Alexander.

The main information we have about the civilization and mathematics of the Babylonians is their numeration system, which we introduce in the text in Section 4.1 (p. 140). The Babylonian numeration system was positional with base 60. It did not have a 0 symbol, but it did represent fractions, squares, square roots, cubes, and cube roots. We have evidence that the Babylonians knew the quadratic formula and they had stated algebraic problems verbally. The base 60 system of the Babylonians led to the division of a circle into 360 equal parts that today we call degrees, and each degree was in turn divided into 360 parts that today we call seconds. The Greek astronomer Ptolemy (A.D. 85–165) used this Babylonian system, which no doubt is why we have minutes, seconds, and degree measurement today.

The Egyptian civilization existed from about 4000 B.C., and was less influenced by foreign powers than was the Babylonian civilization. Egypt was divided into two kingdoms until about 3000 B.C., when the ruler Menes unified Egypt and consequently became known as the founder of the first dynasty in 2500 B.C. This was the egyptians' pyramid-building period, and the Great Pyramid of Cheops was built around 2600 B.C. (Chapter 7, p. 369; see The Riddle of the Pyramids).

The Egyptians developed their own pictorial way of writing, called *hieroglyphics,* and their numeration system was consequently very pictorial (Chapter 4).

The Egyptian numeration system is an example of a simple grouping system. Although the Egyptians were able to write fractions, they used only unit fractions. Like the Babylonians, they had not developed a symbol for zero. Since the writing of the Egyptians was on papyrus, and not on tablets as with the Babylonians, most of the written history has been lost. Our information comes from the Rhind papyrus, discovered in 1858 and dated to about 1700 B.C., and the Moscow papyrus, which has been dated to about the same time period.

The mathematics of the Egyptians remained remarkably unchanged from the time of the first dynasty to the time of Alexander the Great who conquered Egypt in 332 B.C. The Egyptians did surveying using a unique method of stretching rope, so they referred to their surveyors as "rope stretchers." The basic unit used by the Egyptians for measuring length was the *cubit,* which was the distance from a person's elbow to the end of the middle finger. A *khet* was defined to equal 100 cubits; khets were used

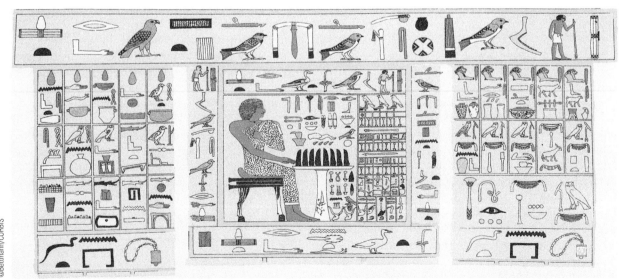

©Bettmann/CORBIS

Egyptian hieroglyphics: Inscription and relief from the grave of Prince Rahdep (ca. 2800 B.C.)

by the Egyptians when land was surveyed. The Egyptians did not have the concept of a variable, and all of their problems were verbal or arithmetic. Even though they solved many equations, they used the word *AHA* or *heap* in place of the variable. For an example of an Egyptian problem, see Ahmes' dilemma in Chapter 1 and the statement of the problem in terms of Thoth, an ancient Egyptian god of wisdom and learning.

The Egyptians had formulas for the area of a circle and the volume of a cube, box, cylinder, and other figures. Particularly remarkable is their formula for the volume of a truncated pyramid of a square base, which in modern notation is

$$V = \frac{h}{3}\left(a^2 + ab + b^2\right)$$

where h is the height and a and b are the sides of the top and bottom. Even though we are not certain the Egyptians knew of the Pythagorean theorem, we believe they did because the rope stretchers had knots on their ropes that would form right triangles. They had a very good reckoning of the calendar, and knew that a solar year was approximately $365\frac{1}{4}$ days long. They chose as the first day of their year the day on which the Nile would flood.

Contemporaneous with the great civilizations in Mesopotamia was the great Mayan civilization in what is now Mexico. A Mayan timeline is shown in Figure 1.

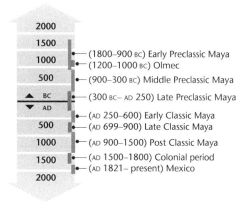

FIGURE 1 Mayan timeline

Just as with the Mesopotamian civilizations, the Olmeca and Mayan civilizations lie between two great rivers, in this case the Grijalva and Papaloapan Rivers. Sometimes the Olmecas are referred to as the Tenocelome. The Olmeca culture is considered the mother culture of the Americas. What we know about the Olmecas centers around their art. We do know they were a farming community. The Mayan civilization began around 2600 B.C. and gave rise to the Olmecas. The Olmecas had developed a written hieroglyphic language by 700 B.C., and they had a very accurate solar calendar. The Mayan culture had developed a positional numeration system.

You will find the influences from this period discussed throughout the book.

Greek, Chinese, and Roman Periods: 600 B.C. to A.D. 499

Greek mathematics began in 585 B.C. when Thales, the first of the Seven Sages of Greece (625–547 B.C.) traveled to Egypt.[*]

The Greek civilization was most influential in our history of mathematics. So striking was its influence that the historian Morris Kline declares, "One of the great problems of the history of civilization is how to account for the brilliance and creativity of the ancient Greeks."[†] The Greeks settled in Asia Minor, modern Greece, southern Italy, Sicily, Crete, and North Africa. They replaced the various hieroglyphic systems with the Phoenician alphabet, and with that they were able to become more literate and more capable of recording history and ideas. The Greeks had their own numeration system. They had fractions and some irrational numbers, including π.

The great mathematical contributions of the Greeks are Euclid's *Elements* and Apollonius' *Conic Sections* (p. 732, Figure 15.26). Greek knowledge developed in several centers or schools. (See Figure 3 on page P5 for depiction of one of these centers of learning.) The first was founded by Thales (ca. 640–546 B.C.) and known as the Ionian in Miletus. It is reported that while he was traveling and studying in Egypt, Thales calculated the heights of the pyramids by using similar triangles (see Section 7.4). You can read about these great Greek mathematicians in *Mathematics Thought from Ancient to Modern Times,* by Morris Kline.[‡] You can also refer to the World Wide Web at **www.mathnature.com.**

Between 585 B.C. and 352 B.C., schools flourished and established the foundations for the way knowledge is organized today. Figure 2 shows each of the seven major schools, along with each school's most notable contribution. Links to textual discussion are shown within each school of thought, along with the principal person for each of these schools. Books have been written about the importance of each of these Greek schools, and several links can be found at **www.mathnature.com.**

One of the three greatest mathematicians in the entire history of mathematics was Archimedes (287–212 B.C.). His accomplishments are truly remarkable, and you should seek out other sources about the magnitude of his accomplishments. He invented a pump (the Archimedean screw), military engines and weapons, and catapults; in addition, he used a parabolic mirror as a weapon by concentrating the sun's rays on the invading Roman ships. "The most famous of the stories about Archimedes is his discovery of the method of testing the debasement of a crown of gold. The king of Syracuse had ordered the crown. When it was delivered, he suspected that it was filled with baser metals and sent it to Archimedes to

[*]The Seven Sages in Greek history refer to Thales of Miletus, Bias of Priene, Chilo of Sparta, Cleobulus of Rhodes, Periander of Corinth, Pittacus of Mitylene, and Solon of Athens; they were famous because of their practical knowledge about the world and how things work.

[†]p. 24, *Mathematical Thought from Ancient to Modern Times* by Morris Kline (New York: Oxford University Press, 1972).

[‡] New York: Oxford University Press, 1972.

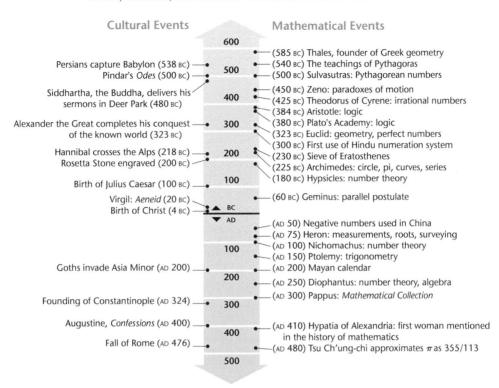

Greek, Chinese, and Roman Period: 600 BC to AD 499

Cultural Events / **Mathematical Events**

Persians capture Babylon (538 BC)
Pindar's *Odes* (500 BC)
Siddhartha, the Buddha, delivers his sermons in Deer Park (480 BC)
Alexander the Great completes his conquest of the known world (323 BC)
Hannibal crosses the Alps (218 BC)
Rosetta Stone engraved (200 BC)
Birth of Julius Caesar (100 BC)
Virgil: *Aeneid* (20 BC)
Birth of Christ (4 BC)
Goths invade Asia Minor (AD 200)
Founding of Constantinople (AD 324)
Augustine, *Confessions* (AD 400)
Fall of Rome (AD 476)

(585 BC) Thales, founder of Greek geometry
(540 BC) The teachings of Pythagoras
(500 BC) Sulvasutras: Pythagorean numbers
(450 BC) Zeno: paradoxes of motion
(425 BC) Theodorus of Cyrene: irrational numbers
(384 BC) Aristotle: logic
(380 BC) Plato's Academy: logic
(323 BC) Euclid: geometry, perfect numbers
(300 BC) First use of Hindu numeration system
(230 BC) Sieve of Eratosthenes
(225 BC) Archimedes: circle, pi, curves, series
(180 BC) Hypsicles: number theory
(60 BC) Geminus: parallel postulate
(AD 50) Negative numbers used in China
(AD 75) Heron: measurements, roots, surveying
(AD 100) Nichomachus: number theory
(AD 150) Ptolemy: trigonometry
(AD 200) Mayan calendar
(AD 250) Diophantus: number theory, algebra
(AD 300) Pappus: *Mathematical Collection*
(AD 410) Hypatia of Alexandria: first woman mentioned in the history of mathematics
(AD 480) Tsu Ch'ung-chi approximates π as 355/113

devise some method of testing the contents without, of course, destroying the workmanship. Archimedes pondered the problem; one day while bathing he observed that his body was partly buoyed up by the water and suddenly grasped the principle that enabled him to solve the problem. He was so excited by this discovery that he ran out into the street naked shouting, `Eureka!' ('I have found it!') He had discovered that a body immersed in water is buoyed up by a force equal to the weight of the water displaced, and by means of this principle was able to determine the contents of the crown."[*]

The Romans conquered the world, but their mathematical contributions were minor. We introduce the Roman numerals in Section 4.1, their fractions were based on a duodecimal (base 12) system and are still used today in certain circumstances. The unit of weight was the *as* and one-twelfth of this was the *uncia,* from which we get our measurements of *ounce* and *inch,* respectively. The Romans improved on our calendar, and set up the notion of leap year every four years. The Julian calendar was adopted in 45 B.C. The Romans conquered Greece and Mesopotamia, and in 47 B.C., they set fire to the Egyptian fleet in the harbor of Alexandria. The fire spread to the city and burned the library, destroying two and a half centuries of book-collecting, including all the important knowledge of the time.

Another great world civilization existed in China and also developed a decimal numeration system and used a decimal system with symbols 1, 2, 3, . . . , 9, 10, 100, 1000, and 10000. Calculations were performed using small bamboo counting rods, which eventually evolved into the abacus. Our first historical reference to the Chinese culture is the yin-yang symbol, which has its roots in ancient cosmology. The original meaning is representative of the mountains, both the bright side and the dark side. The "yin" represents the female, or shaded, aspect, the earth, the darkness, the moon, and passivity. The "yang" represents the male, light, sun, heaven, and the active principle in nature. These words can be traced back to the Shang and Chou Dynasty (1550–1050 B.C.), but most scholars credit them to the Han Dynasty (220–206 B.C.). One of the first examples of a magic square comes from Lo River around 200 B.C., where legend tells us that the emperor Yu of the Shang dynasty received a magic square on the back of a tortoise's shell.

From 100 B.C. to A.D. 100 the Chinese described the motion of the planets, as well as what is the earliest known proof of the Pythagorean theorem. The longest surviving and most influential Chinese math book is dated from the beginning of the Han Dynasty around A.D. 50. It includes measurement and area problems, proportions, volumes, and some approximations for π. Sun Zi (ca. A.D. 250) wrote his mathematical manual, which included the "Chinese remainder problem": Find *n* so that upon division by 3 you obtain a remainder of 2; upon division by 5 a remainder of 3; and upon division by 7 you get a remainder of 2. His solution: Add 140, 63, 30 to obtain 233,

[*]pp. 105–106, *Mathematical Thought from Ancient to Modern Times* by Morris Kline (New York: Oxford University Press, 1972).

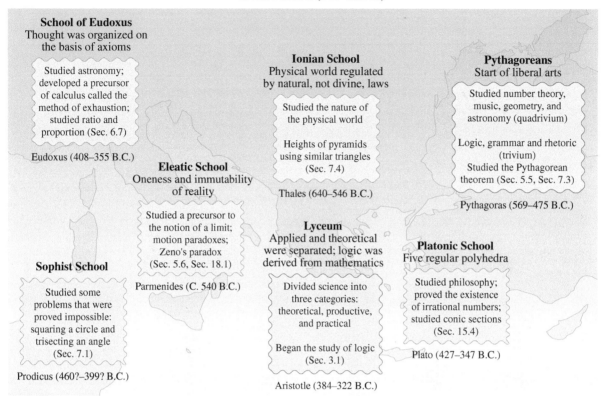

Greek Schools (585–352 BC)

School of Eudoxus
Thought was organized on the basis of axioms

> Studied astronomy; developed a precursor of calculus called the method of exhaustion; studied ratio and proportion (Sec. 6.7)

Eudoxus (408–355 B.C.)

Ionian School
Physical world regulated by natural, not divine, laws

> Studied the nature of the physical world
>
> Heights of pyramids using similar triangles (Sec. 7.4)

Thales (640–546 B.C.)

Pythagoreans
Start of liberal arts

> Studied number theory, music, geometry, and astronomy (quadrivium)
>
> Logic, grammar and rhetoric (trivium)
> Studied the Pythagorean theorem (Sec. 5.5, Sec. 7.3)

Pythagoras (569–475 B.C.)

Eleatic School
Oneness and immutability of reality

> Studied a precursor to the notion of a limit; motion paradoxes; Zeno's paradox (Sec. 5.6, Sec. 18.1)

Parmenides (C. 540 B.C.)

Lyceum
Applied and theoretical were separated; logic was derived from mathematics

> Divided science into three categories: theoretical, productive, and practical
>
> Began the study of logic (Sec. 3.1)

Aristotle (384–322 B.C.)

Platonic School
Five regular polyhedra

> Studied philosophy; proved the existence of irrational numbers; studied conic sections (Sec. 15.4)

Plato (427–347 B.C.)

Sophist School

> Studied some problems that were proved impossible: squaring a circle and trisecting an angle (Sec. 7.1)

Prodicus (460?–399? B.C.)

FIGURE 2 Greek schools from 585 B.C. to 352 B.C.

FIGURE 3 The School at Athens by Raphael, 1509. This fresco includes portraits of Raphael's contemporaries and demonstrates the use of perspective. Note the figures in the lower right, who are, no doubt, discussing mathematics.

and subtract 210 to obtain 23. Zhang Qiujian (ca. A.D. 450) wrote a mathematics manual that included a formula for summing the terms of an arithmetic sequence, along with the solution to a system of two linear equations in three unknowns. The problem is the "One Hundred Fowl Problem," and is included in Problem Set 5.7 (p. 240). At the end of this historic period, the mathematician and astronomer Wang Xiaotong (ca. A.D. 626) solved cubic equations by generalization of an algorithm for finding the cube root.

Check **www.mathnature.com** for links to many excellent sites on Greek mathematics.

Hindu and Persian Period: 500 to 1199

Much of the mathematics that we read in contemporary mathematics textbooks ignores the rich history of this period. Included on the World Wide Web are some very good sources for this period. Check our Web site **www.mathnature.com** for some links. The Hindu civilization dates back to 2000 B.C., but the first recorded mathematics was during the Śulvasūtra period from 800 B.C. to 200 A.D. In the third century, Brahmi symbols were used for 1, 2, 3, . . . , 9 and are significant because there was a single symbol for each number. There was no zero or positional notation at this time, but by A.D. 600 the

Hindus used the Brahmi symbols with positional notation. In Chapter 4, we will discuss a numeration system that eventually evolved from these Brahmi symbols. For fractions, the Hindus used sexagesimal positional notation in astronomy, but in other applications they used a ratio of integers and wrote $\frac{3}{4}$ (without the fractional bar we use today). The first mathematically important period was the second period, A.D. 200–1200. The important mathematicians of this period are Āryabhata (A.D. 476–550), Brahmagupta (A.D. 598–670), Mahāvīra (9th century), and Bhāskara (1114–1185). In Chapter 6, we include some historical questions from Bhāskara and Brahmagupta.

The Hindus developed arithmetic independently of geometry and had a fairly good knowledge of rudimentary algebra. They knew that quadratic equations had two solutions, and they had a fairly good approximation for π. Astronomy motivated their study of trigonometry. Around 1200, scientific activity in India declined, and mathematical progress ceased and did not revive until the British conquered India in the 18th century.

The Persians invited Hindu scientists to settle in Baghdad, and when Plato's Academy closed in A.D. 529, many scholars traveled to Persia and became part of the Iranian tradition of science and mathematics. Omar Khayyám (1048–1122) and Nasîr-Eddin (1201–1274), both renowned Persian scholars, worked freely with irrationals, which contrasts with the Greek idea of number. What we call Pascal's triangle dates

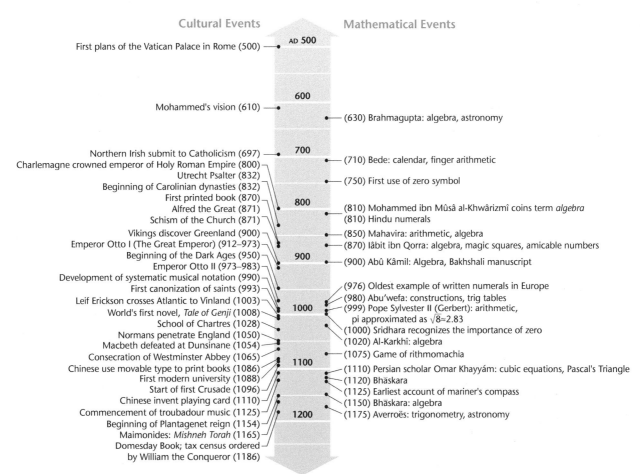

Hindu and Arabian Period: AD 500 to 1199

Cultural Events

First plans of the Vatican Palace in Rome (500)
Mohammed's vision (610)
Northern Irish submit to Catholicism (697)
Charlemagne crowned emperor of Holy Roman Empire (800)
Utrecht Psalter (832)
Beginning of Carolinian dynasties (832)
First printed book (870)
Alfred the Great (871)
Schism of the Church (871)
Vikings discover Greenland (900)
Emperor Otto I (The Great Emperor) (912–973)
Beginning of the Dark Ages (950)
Emperor Otto II (973–983)
Development of systematic musical notation (990)
First canonization of saints (993)
Leif Erickson crosses Atlantic to Vinland (1003)
World's first novel, *Tale of Genji* (1008)
School of Chartres (1028)
Normans penetrate England (1050)
Macbeth defeated at Dunsinane (1054)
Consecration of Westminster Abbey (1065)
Chinese use movable type to print books (1086)
First modern university (1088)
Start of first Crusade (1096)
Chinese invent playing card (1110)
Commencement of troubadour music (1125)
Beginning of Plantagenet reign (1154)
Maimonides: *Mishneh Torah* (1165)
Domesday Book; tax census ordered by William the Conqueror (1186)

AD 500
600
700
800
900
1000
1100
1200

Mathematical Events

(630) Brahmagupta: algebra, astronomy
(710) Bede: calendar, finger arithmetic
(750) First use of zero symbol
(810) Mohammed ibn Mûsâ al-Khwârizmî coins term *algebra*
(810) Hindu numerals
(850) Mahavira: arithmetic, algebra
(870) Iâbit ibn Qorra: algebra, magic squares, amicable numbers
(900) Abû Kâmil: Algebra, Bakhshali manuscript
(976) Oldest example of written numerals in Europe
(980) Abu'wefa: constructions, trig tables
(999) Pope Sylvester II (Gerbert): arithmetic, pi approximated as $\sqrt{8} \approx 2.83$
(1000) Sridhara recognizes the importance of zero
(1020) Al-Karkhî: algebra
(1075) Game of rithmomachia
(1110) Persian scholar Omar Khayyám: cubic equations, Pascal's Triangle
(1120) Bhāskara
(1125) Earliest account of mariner's compass
(1150) Bhāskara: algebra
(1175) Averroës: trigonometry, astronomy

back to this period. The word *algebra* comes from the Persians in a book by the Persian astronomer Mohammed ibn Musa al-Khâwarizmî (780–850) entitled *Hisâb al-jabr w'al muqâbala*. Due to the Arab conquest of Persia, Persian scholars (notably Nasir-Eddin and al-Khwarizmi) were obliged to publish their works in the Arabic language and not Persian, causing many historians to falsely label the texts as products of Arab scholars. Al-Khwarizmi solved quadratic equations and knew there are two roots, and even though the Persians gave algebraic solutions of quadratic equations, they explained their work geometrically. They solved some cubics, but could solve only simple trigonometric problems.

Check **www.mathnature.com** for links to many excellent sites on Hindu and Arabian mathematics.

Transition Period: 1200 to 1599

Mathematics during the Middle Ages was transitional between the great early civilizations and the Renaissance.

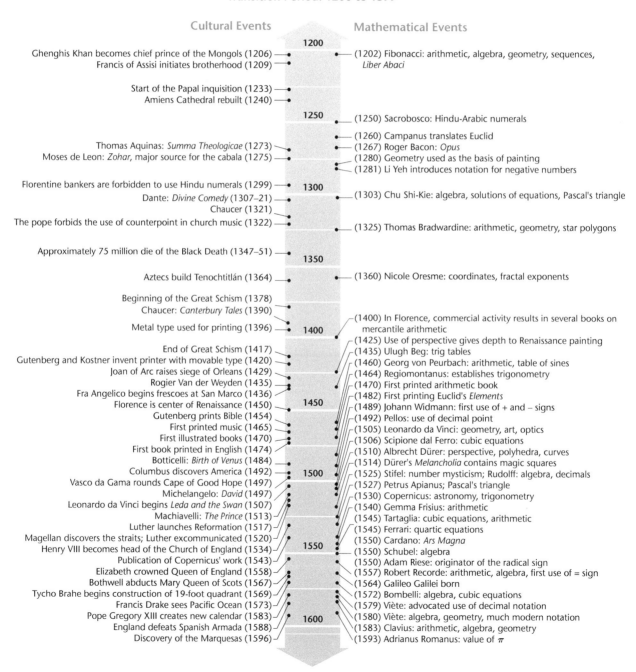

Transition Period: 1200 to 1599

Cultural Events

Ghenghis Khan becomes chief prince of the Mongols (1206)
Francis of Assisi initiates brotherhood (1209)

Start of the Papal inquisition (1233)
Amiens Cathedral rebuilt (1240)

Thomas Aquinas: *Summa Theologicae* (1273)
Moses de Leon: *Zohar*, major source for the cabala (1275)

Florentine bankers are forbidden to use Hindu numerals (1299)
Dante: *Divine Comedy* (1307–21)
Chaucer (1321)
The pope forbids the use of counterpoint in church music (1322)

Approximately 75 million die of the Black Death (1347–51)

Aztecs build Tenochtitlán (1364)

Beginning of the Great Schism (1378)
Chaucer: *Canterbury Tales* (1390)
Metal type used for printing (1396)

End of Great Schism (1417)
Gutenberg and Kostner invent printer with movable type (1420)
Joan of Arc raises siege of Orleans (1429)
Rogier Van der Weyden (1435)
Fra Angelico begins frescoes at San Marco (1436)
Florence is center of Renaissance (1450)
Gutenberg prints Bible (1454)
First printed music (1465)
First illustrated books (1470)
First book printed in English (1474)
Botticelli: *Birth of Venus* (1484)
Columbus discovers America (1492)
Vasco da Gama rounds Cape of Good Hope (1497)
Michelangelo: *David* (1497)
Leonardo da Vinci begins *Leda and the Swan* (1507)
Machiavelli: *The Prince* (1513)
Luther launches Reformation (1517)
Magellan discovers the straits; Luther excommunicated (1520)
Henry VIII becomes head of the Church of England (1534)
Publication of Copernicus' work (1543)
Elizabeth crowned Queen of England (1558)
Bothwell abducts Mary Queen of Scots (1567)
Tycho Brahe begins construction of 19-foot quadrant (1569)
Francis Drake sees Pacific Ocean (1573)
Pope Gregory XIII creates new calendar (1583)
England defeats Spanish Armada (1588)
Discovery of the Marquesas (1596)

1200
1250
1300
1350
1400
1450
1500
1550
1600

Mathematical Events

(1202) Fibonacci: arithmetic, algebra, geometry, sequences, *Liber Abaci*

(1250) Sacrobosco: Hindu-Arabic numerals

(1260) Campanus translates Euclid
(1267) Roger Bacon: *Opus*
(1280) Geometry used as the basis of painting
(1281) Li Yeh introduces notation for negative numbers

(1303) Chu Shi-Kie: algebra, solutions of equations, Pascal's triangle

(1325) Thomas Bradwardine: arithmetic, geometry, star polygons

(1360) Nicole Oresme: coordinates, fractal exponents

(1400) In Florence, commercial activity results in several books on mercantile arithmetic
(1425) Use of perspective gives depth to Renaissance painting
(1435) Ulugh Beg: trig tables
(1460) Georg von Peurbach: arithmetic, table of sines
(1464) Regiomontanus: establishes trigonometry
(1470) First printed arithmetic book
(1482) First printing Euclid's *Elements*
(1489) Johann Widmann: first use of + and – signs
(1492) Pellos: use of decimal point
(1505) Leonardo da Vinci: geometry, art, optics
(1506) Scipione dal Ferro: cubic equations
(1510) Albrecht Dürer: perspective, polyhedra, curves
(1514) Dürer's *Melancholia* contains magic squares
(1525) Stifel: number mysticism; Rudolff: algebra, decimals
(1527) Petrus Apianus; Pascal's triangle
(1530) Copernicus: astronomy, trigonometry
(1540) Gemma Frisius: arithmetic
(1545) Tartaglia: cubic equations, arithmetic
(1545) Ferrari: quartic equations
(1550) Cardano: *Ars Magna*
(1550) Schubel: algebra
(1550) Adam Riese: originator of the radical sign
(1557) Robert Recorde: arithmetic, algebra, first use of = sign
(1564) Galileo Galilei born
(1572) Bombelli: algebra, cubic equations
(1579) Viète: advocated use of decimal notation
(1580) Viète: algebra, geometry, much modern notation
(1583) Clavius: arithmetic, algebra, geometry
(1593) Adrianus Romanus: value of π

In the 1400s the Black Death killed over 70% of the European population. The Turks conquered Constantinople, and many Eastern scholars traveled to Europe, spreading Greek knowledge as they traveled. The period from 1400 to 1600, known as the Renaissance, forever changed the intellectual outlook in Europe and raised up mathematical thinking to new levels. Johann Gutenberg's invention of printing with movable type in 1450 changed the complexion of the world. Linen and cotton paper, which the Europeans learned about from the Chinese through the Arabians, came at precisely the right historical moment. The first printed edition of Euclid's *Elements* in a Latin translation appeared in 1482. Other early printed books were Apollonius' *Conic Sections*, Pappus' works, and Diophantus' *Arithmetica*.

The first breakthrough in mathematics was by artists who discovered mathematical perspective. The theoretical genius in mathematical perspective was Leone Alberti (1404–1472). He was a secretary in the Papal Chancery writing biographies of the saints, but his work *Della Pictura* on the laws of perspective (1435) was a masterpiece. He said, "Nothing pleases me so much as mathematical investigations and demonstrations, especially when I can turn them into some useful practice drawing from mathematics and the principles of painting perspective and some amazing propositions on the moving of weights." He collaborated with Toscanelli, who supplied Columbus with maps for his first voyage. The best mathematician among the Renaissance artists was Albrecht Dürer (1471–1528). The most significant development of the Renaissance was the breakthrough in astronomical theory by Nicolaus Copernicus (1473–1543) and Johannes Kepler (1571–1630). There were no really significant new results in mathematics during this period of history.

It is interesting to tie together some of the previous timelines to trace the history of algebra. It began around 2000 B.C. in Egypt and Babylon. This knowledge was incorporated into the mathematics of Greece between 500 B.C. and A.D. 320, as well as into the Persian civilization and Indian mathematics around A.D. 1000. By the Transition Period, the great ideas of algebra had made their way to Europe, as shown in Figure 4. Additional information can be found on the World Wide Web; check our Web page at **www.mathnature.com.**

Age of Reason 1600 to 1699

From Shakespeare and Galileo to Peter the Great and the great Bernoulli family, this period, also called the Age of Genius, marks the growth of intellectual endeavors; both technology and knowledge grew as never seen before in history. A great deal of the content of this book focuses on discoveries from this period of time, so instead of providing a commentary in this overview, we will simply list the references to this period in world history. Other sources and links are found on our Web page **www.mathnature.com.**

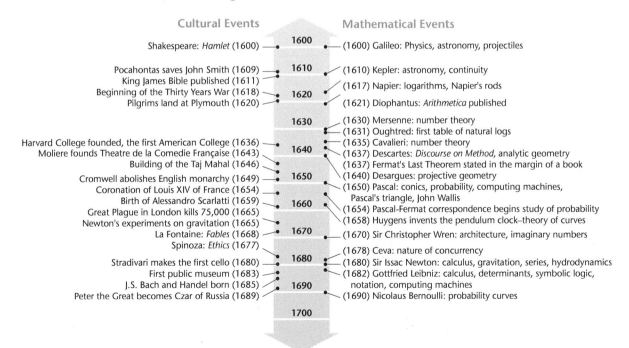

Age of Reason: 1600 to 1699

Cultural Events		Mathematical Events
Shakespeare: *Hamlet* (1600)	**1600**	(1600) Galileo: Physics, astronomy, projectiles
Pocahontas saves John Smith (1609)	**1610**	(1610) Kepler: astronomy, continuity
King James Bible published (1611)		(1617) Napier: logarithms, Napier's rods
Beginning of the Thirty Years War (1618)	**1620**	(1621) Diophantus: *Arithmetica* published
Pilgrims land at Plymouth (1620)		
	1630	(1630) Mersenne: number theory
		(1631) Oughtred: first table of natural logs
Harvard College founded, the first American College (1636)		(1635) Cavalieri: number theory
Moliere founds Theatre de la Comedie Française (1643)	**1640**	(1637) Descartes: *Discourse on Method*, analytic geometry
Building of the Taj Mahal (1646)		(1637) Fermat's Last Theorem stated in the margin of a book
Cromwell abolishes English monarchy (1649)	**1650**	(1640) Desargues: projective geometry
Coronation of Louis XIV of France (1654)		(1650) Pascal: conics, probability, computing machines, Pascal's triangle, John Wallis
Birth of Alessandro Scarlatti (1659)	**1660**	(1654) Pascal-Fermat correspondence begins study of probability
Great Plague in London kills 75,000 (1665)		(1658) Huygens invents the pendulum clock–theory of curves
Newton's experiments on gravitation (1665)		
La Fontaine: *Fables* (1668)	**1670**	(1670) Sir Christopher Wren: architecture, imaginary numbers
Spinoza: *Ethics* (1677)		(1678) Ceva: nature of concurrency
Stradivari makes the first cello (1680)	**1680**	(1680) Sir Issac Newton: calculus, gravitation, series, hydrodynamics
First public museum (1683)		(1682) Gottfried Leibniz: calculus, determinants, symbolic logic, notation, computing machines
J.S. Bach and Handel born (1685)	**1690**	
Peter the Great becomes Czar of Russia (1689)		(1690) Nicolaus Bernoulli: probability curves
	1700	

Early Modern Period: 1700 to 1799

This period marks the dawn of modern mathematics. The Early Modern Period was characterized by experimentation and formalization of the ideas germinated in the previous century. There is so much that we could say about the period from 1700 to 1799. The mathematics that you studied in high school represents, for the most part, the ideas formulated during this period. Take a look at the mathematical events in the following timeline, and you will see an abundance of discoveries, often embodied in the contents of entire books. One of the best sources of information about this period is found at these Web sites:

 **www.mathnature.com and www-history.mcs.st-and.ac.uk/ ~history/Indexes/Full_Chron.html**

There are a multitude of historical references to this period documented throughout the book.

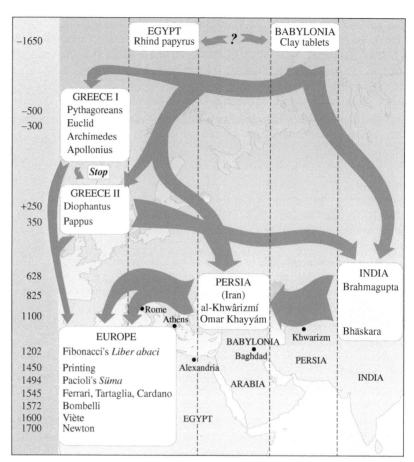

FIGURE 4 Mainstreams in the flow of algebra

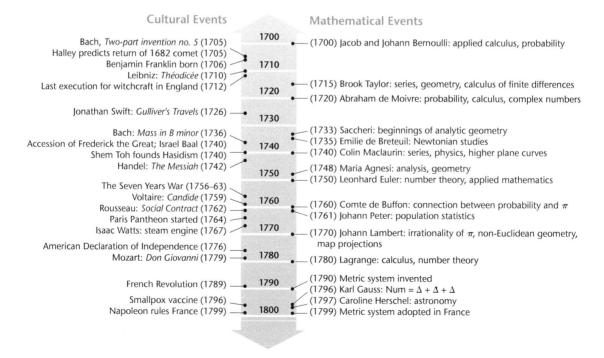

Early Modern Period: 1700 to 1799

Cultural Events

- Bach, *Two-part invention no. 5* (1705)
- Halley predicts return of 1682 comet (1705)
- Benjamin Franklin born (1706)
- Leibniz: *Théodicée* (1710)
- Last execution for witchcraft in England (1712)
- Jonathan Swift: *Gulliver's Travels* (1726)
- Bach: *Mass in B minor* (1736)
- Accession of Frederick the Great; Israel Baal (1740)
- Shem Toh founds Hasidism (1740)
- Handel: *The Messiah* (1742)
- The Seven Years War (1756–63)
- Voltaire: *Candide* (1759)
- Rousseau: *Social Contract* (1762)
- Paris Pantheon started (1764)
- Isaac Watts: steam engine (1767)
- American Declaration of Independence (1776)
- Mozart: *Don Giovanni* (1779)
- French Revolution (1789)
- Smallpox vaccine (1796)
- Napoleon rules France (1799)

1700 / 1710 / 1720 / 1730 / 1740 / 1750 / 1760 / 1770 / 1780 / 1790 / 1800

Mathematical Events

- (1700) Jacob and Johann Bernoulli: applied calculus, probability
- (1715) Brook Taylor: series, geometry, calculus of finite differences
- (1720) Abraham de Moivre: probability, calculus, complex numbers
- (1733) Saccheri: beginnings of analytic geometry
- (1735) Emilie de Breteuil: Newtonian studies
- (1740) Colin Maclaurin: series, physics, higher plane curves
- (1748) Maria Agnesi: analysis, geometry
- (1750) Leonhard Euler: number theory, applied mathematics
- (1760) Comte de Buffon: connection between probability and π
- (1761) Johann Peter: population statistics
- (1770) Johann Lambert: irrationality of π, non-Euclidean geometry, map projections
- (1780) Lagrange: calculus, number theory
- (1790) Metric system invented
- (1796) Karl Gauss: Num $= \Delta + \Delta + \Delta$
- (1797) Caroline Herschel: astronomy
- (1799) Metric system adopted in France

Modern Period: 1800 to Present

What we call the Modern Period includes all of the discoveries of the last two centuries. Students often think that all the important mathematics has been done, and there is nothing new to be discovered, but this is not true. Mathematics is alive and constantly changing. There is no way a short

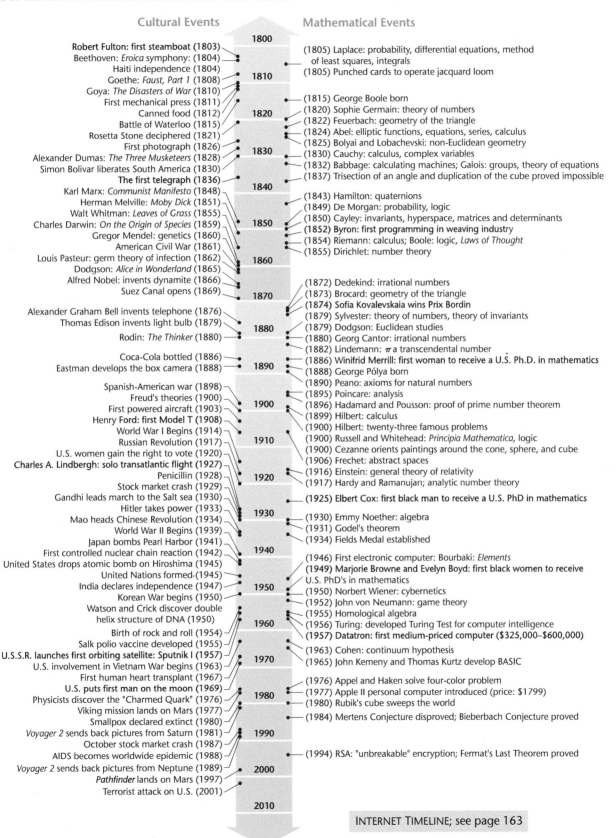

Cultural Events

Robert Fulton: first steamboat (1803)
Beethoven: *Eroica* symphony: (1804)
Haiti independence (1804)
Goethe: *Faust, Part 1* (1808)
Goya: *The Disasters of War* (1810)
First mechanical press (1811)
Canned food (1812)
Battle of Waterloo (1815)
Rosetta Stone deciphered (1821)
First photograph (1826)
Alexander Dumas: *The Three Musketeers* (1828)
Simon Bolivar liberates South America (1830)
The first telegraph (1836)
Karl Marx: *Communist Manifesto* (1848)
Herman Melville: *Moby Dick* (1851)
Walt Whitman: *Leaves of Grass* (1855)
Charles Darwin: *On the Origin of Species* (1859)
Gregor Mendel: genetics (1860)
American Civil War (1861)
Louis Pasteur: germ theory of infection (1862)
Dodgson: *Alice in Wonderland* (1865)
Alfred Nobel: invents dynamite (1866)
Suez Canal opens (1869)
Alexander Graham Bell invents telephone (1876)
Thomas Edison invents light bulb (1879)
Rodin: *The Thinker* (1880)
Coca-Cola bottled (1886)
Eastman develops the box camera (1888)
Spanish-American war (1898)
Freud's theories (1900)
First powered aircraft (1903)
Henry Ford: first Model T (1908)
World War I Begins (1914)
Russian Revolution (1917)
U.S. women gain the right to vote (1920)
Charles A. Lindbergh: solo transatlantic flight (1927)
Penicillin (1928)
Stock market crash (1929)
Gandhi leads march to the Salt sea (1930)
Hitler takes power (1933)
Mao heads Chinese Revolution (1934)
World War II Begins (1939)
Japan bombs Pearl Harbor (1941)
First controlled nuclear chain reaction (1942)
United States drops atomic bomb on Hiroshima (1945)
United Nations formed (1945)
India declares independence (1947)
Korean War begins (1950)
Watson and Crick discover double helix structure of DNA (1950)
Birth of rock and roll (1954)
Salk polio vaccine developed (1955)
U.S.S.R. launches first orbiting satellite: Sputnik I (1957)
U.S. involvement in Vietnam War begins (1963)
First human heart transplant (1967)
U.S. puts first man on the moon (1969)
Physicists discover the "Charmed Quark" (1976)
Viking mission lands on Mars (1977)
Smallpox declared extinct (1980)
Voyager 2 sends back pictures from Saturn (1981)
October stock market crash (1987)
AIDS becomes worldwide epidemic (1988)
Voyager 2 sends back pictures from Neptune (1989)
Pathfinder lands on Mars (1997)
Terrorist attack on U.S. (2001)

1800
1810
1820
1830
1840
1850
1860
1870
1880
1890
1900
1910
1920
1930
1940
1950
1960
1970
1980
1990
2000
2010

Mathematical Events

(1805) Laplace: probability, differential equations, method of least squares, integrals
(1805) Punched cards to operate jacquard loom
(1815) George Boole born
(1820) Sophie Germain: theory of numbers
(1822) Feuerbach: geometry of the triangle
(1824) Abel: elliptic functions, equations, series, calculus
(1825) Bolyai and Lobachevski: non-Euclidean geometry
(1830) Cauchy: calculus, complex variables
(1832) Babbage: calculating machines; Galois: groups, theory of equations
(1837) Trisection of an angle and duplication of the cube proved impossible
(1843) Hamilton: quaternions
(1849) De Morgan: probability, logic
(1850) Cayley: invariants, hyperspace, matrices and determinants
(1852) Byron: first programming in weaving industry
(1854) Riemann: calculus; Boole: logic, *Laws of Thought*
(1855) Dirichlet: number theory
(1872) Dedekind: irrational numbers
(1873) Brocard: geometry of the triangle
(1874) Sofia Kovalevskaia wins Prix Bordin
(1879) Sylvester: theory of numbers, theory of invariants
(1879) Dodgson: Euclidean studies
(1880) Georg Cantor: irrational numbers
(1882) Lindemann: π a transcendental number
(1886) Winifrid Merrill: first woman to receive a U.S. Ph.D. in mathematics
(1888) George Pólya born
(1890) Peano: axioms for natural numbers
(1895) Poincare: analysis
(1896) Hadamard and Pousson: proof of prime number theorem
(1899) Hilbert: calculus
(1900) Hilbert: twenty-three famous problems
(1900) Russell and Whitehead: *Principia Mathematica*, logic
(1900) Cezanne orients paintings around the cone, sphere, and cube
(1906) Frechet: abstract spaces
(1916) Einstein: general theory of relativity
(1917) Hardy and Ramanujan; analytic number theory
(1925) Elbert Cox: first black man to receive a U.S PhD in mathematics
(1930) Emmy Noether: algebra
(1931) Godel's theorem
(1934) Fields Medal established
(1946) First electronic computer: Bourbaki: *Elements*
(1949) Marjorie Browne and Evelyn Boyd: first black women to receive U.S. PhD's in mathematics
(1950) Norbert Wiener: cybernetics
(1952) John von Neumann: game theory
(1955) Homological algebra
(1956) Turing: developed Turing Test for computer intelligence
(1957) Datatron: first medium-priced computer ($325,000–$600,000)
(1963) Cohen: continuum hypothesis
(1965) John Kemeny and Thomas Kurtz develop BASIC
(1976) Appel and Haken solve four-color problem
(1977) Apple II personal computer introduced (price: $1799)
(1980) Rubik's cube sweeps the world
(1984) Mertens Conjecture disproved; Bieberbach Conjecture proved
(1994) RSA: "unbreakable" encryption; Fermat's Last Theorem proved

INTERNET TIMELINE; see page 163

commentary or overview can convey the richness or implications of the mathematical discoveries of this period. As we enter the new millennium, we can only imagine and dream about what is to come!

One of the major themes of this text is problem solving. The following problem set is a potpourri of problems that should give you a foretaste of the variety of ideas and concepts that we will consider in this book. Although none of these problems is to be considered routine, you might wish to attempt to work some of them before you begin, and then return to these problems at the end of your study in this book.

Prologue Problem Set

1. **HISTORICAL QUEST** What are the seven chronological periods into which the prologue divided history? Which period seems the most interesting to you, and why?

2. **HISTORICAL QUEST** Select what you believe to be the most interesting cultural event and the most interesting mathematical event of the Babylonian, Egyptian, and Native American Period.

3. **HISTORICAL QUEST** Select what you believe to be the most interesting cultural event and the most interesting mathematical event of the Greek, Chinese, and Roman Period.

4. **HISTORICAL QUEST** Select what you believe to be the most interesting cultural event and the most interesting mathematical event of the Hindu and Persian Period.

5. **HISTORICAL QUEST** Select what you believe to be the most interesting cultural event and the most interesting mathematical event of the Transition Period.

6. **HISTORICAL QUEST** Select what you believe to be the most interesting cultural event and the most interesting mathematical event of the Age of Reason.

7. **HISTORICAL QUEST** Select what you believe to be the most interesting cultural event and the most interesting mathematical event of the Early Modern Period.

8. **HISTORICAL QUEST** Select what you believe to be the most interesting cultural event and the most interesting mathematical event of the Modern Period.

9. A long, straight fence having a pole every 8 ft is 1,440 ft long. How many fence poles are needed for the fence?

10. How many cards must you draw from a deck of 52 playing cards to be sure that at least two are from the same suit?

11. How many people must be in a room to be sure that at least four of them have the same birthday (not necessarily the same year)?

12. Find the units digit of $3^{2007} - 2^{2007}$.

13. If a year had two consecutive months with a Friday the thirteenth, which months would they have to be?

14. On Saturday evenings, a favorite pastime of the high school students in Santa Rosa, California, is to cruise certain streets. The selected routes are shown in the following illustration. Is it possible to choose a route so that all of the permitted streets are traveled exactly once?

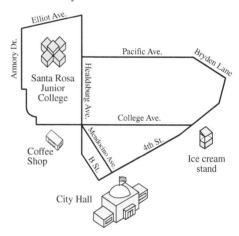

Santa Rosa street problem

15. What is the largest number that is a divisor of both 210 and 330?

16. The News Clip shows a letter printed in the "Ask Marilyn" column of *Parade* magazine (Sept. 27, 1992). How would you answer it?

> **Dear Marilyn,**
>
> I recently purchased a tube of caulking and it says a 1/4-inch bead will yield about 30 feet. But it says a 1/8-inch bead will yield about 96 feet — more than three times as much. I'm not a math genius, but it seems that because 1/8 inch is half of 1/4 inch, the smaller bead should yield only twice as much. Can you explain it?
>
> Norm Bean, St. Louis, Mo.

Hint: We won't give you the answer, but we will quote one line from Marilyn's answer: "So the question should be not why the smaller one yields that much, but why it yields that little."

17. If the population of the world on October 12, 2002 was 6.248 billion, when do you think the world population will reach 7 billion? Calculate the date (to the nearest month) using the information that the world population reached 6 billion on October 12, 1999.

18. The Pacific 12 football conference consists of the following
schools:

Arizona
Arizona State
Cal Berkeley
Colorado
Oregon
Oregon State
Stanford (CA)
UCLA
USC
Utah
Washington
Washington State

   a. Is it possible to visit each of these schools by crossing each
common state border exactly once? If so, show the path.

   b. Is it possible to start the trip in any given state, cross each
common state border exactly once, and end the trip in the
state in which you started?

19. If $(a, b) = a \times b + a + b$, what is the value of $((1, 2), (3, 4))$?

20. If it is known that all Angelenos are Venusians and all Venusians are Los Angeles residents, then what must necessarily
be the conclusion?

21. If 1 is the first odd number, what is the 473rd odd number?

22. If $1 + 2 + 3 + \cdots + n = \frac{n(n + 1)}{2}$, what is the sum of the first
100,000 counting numbers beginning with 1?

23. A four-inch cube is painted red on all sides. It is then cut into
one-inch cubes. What fraction of all the one-inch cubes are
painted on one side only?

24. If slot machines had two arms and people had one arm, then it
is probable that our number system would be based on the
digits 0, 1, 2, 3, and 4 only. How would the number we know
as 18 be written in such a number system?

25. If $M(a, b)$ stands for the larger number in the parentheses, and
$m(a, b)$ stands for the lesser number in the parentheses, what
is the value of $M(m(1, 2), m(2, 3))$?

26. If a group of 50 persons consists of 20 males, 12 children, and
25 women, how many men are in the group?

27. There are only five regular polyhedra, and Figure 5 shows the
patterns that give those polyhedra. Name the polyhedron
obtained from each of the patterns shown.

a.   **b.**   **c.**

d.    **e.**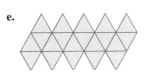

FIGURE 5 Five regular polyhedra patterns

28. Jack and Jill decided to exercise together. Jack walks around
their favorite lake in 16 minutes and Jill jogs around the lake

in 10 minutes. If Jack and Jill start at the same time and at the
same place, and continue to exercise around the lake until
they return to the starting point at the same time, how long
will they be exercising?

29. What is the 1,000th positive integer that is not divisible by 3?

30. A frugal man allows himself a glass of wine before dinner on
every third day, an after-dinner chocolate every fifth day, and
a steak dinner once a week. If it happens that he enjoys all
three luxuries on March 31, what will be the date of the next
steak dinner that is preceded by wine and followed by an
after-dinner chocolate?

31. How many trees must be cut to make a trillion one-dollar
bills? To answer this question you need to make some
assumptions. Assume that a pound of paper is equal to a
pound of wood, and also assume that a dollar bill weighs
about one gram. This implies that a pound of wood yields
about 450 dollar bills. Furthermore, estimate that an average
tree has a height of 50 ft and a diameter of 12 inches. Finally,
assume that wood yields about 50 lb/ft^3.

32. Estimate the volume of beer in the six-pack shown in the
photograph.

33. You are given a square with sides equal to 8 inches, with two
inscribed semicircles of radius 4. What is the area of the
shaded region?

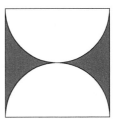

34. Critique the statement given in the News Clip.

> **Smoking ban**
> Judy Green, owner of the White
> Restaurant and an adamant
> opponent of a smoking ban,
> went so far as to survey
> numerous restaurants. She cited
> one restaurant that suffered a
> 75% decline in business after
> the smoking ban was activated.

35. The two small circles have radii of 2 and 3. Find the ratio of the area of the smallest circle to the area of the shaded region.

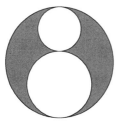

36. A large container filled with water is to be drained, and you would like to drain it as quickly as possible. You can drain the container with either one 1-in. diameter hose or two $\frac{1}{2}$-in.-diameter hoses. Which do you think would be faster (one 1-in. drain or two $\frac{1}{2}$-in. drains), and why?

37. A gambler went to the horse races two days in a row. On the first day, she doubled her money and spent $30. On the second day, she tripled her money and spent $20, after which she had what she started with the first day. How much did she start with?

38. The map shows the percent of children age 19–35 months who are immunized by the state. What conclusions can you draw from this map?

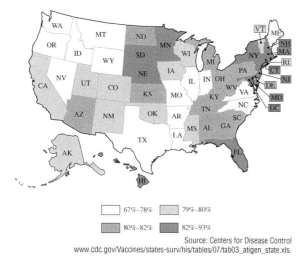

67%–78%   79%–80%
80%–82%   82%–93%

Source: Centers for Disease Control
www.cdc.gov/Vaccines/states-surv/his/tables/07/tab03_atigen_state.xls.

39. A charter flight has signed up 100 travelers. The travelers are told that if they can sign up an additional 25 persons, they can save $78 each. What is the cost per person if 100 persons make the trip?

40. Find $\lim_{n \to \infty} \left(1 + \frac{1}{n}\right)^n$.

41. Suppose that it costs $450 to enroll your child in a 10-week summer recreational program. If this cost is prorated (that is, reduced linearly over the 10-week period), express the cost as a function of the number of weeks that have elapsed since the start of the 10-week session. Draw a graph to show the cost at any time for the duration of the session.

42. Candidates Rameriz (R), Smith (S), and Tillem (T) are running for office. According to public opinion polls, the preferences are (percentages rounded to the nearest percent):

Ranking	38%	29%	24%	10%
1st choice	R	S	T	R
2nd choice	S	R	S	T
3rd choice	T	T	R	S

a. Who will win the plurality vote?
b. Who will win Borda count?
c. Does a strategy exist that the voters in the 24% column could use to vote insincerely to keep Rameriz from winning?

43. Suppose the percentage of alcohol in the blood t hours after consumption is given by

$$C(t) = 0.3e^{-t/2}$$

What is the rate at which the percentage of alcohol is changing with respect to time?

44. If a megamile is one million miles and a kilomile is one thousand miles, how many kilomiles are there in 2.376 megamiles?

45. A map of a small village is shown in Figure 6. To walk from A to B, Sarah obviously must walk at least 7 blocks (all the blocks are the same length). What is the number of shortest paths from A to B?

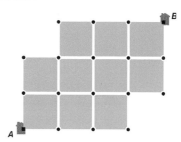

FIGURE 6 A village map

46. A hospital wishes to provide for its patients a diet that has a minimum of 100 g of carbohydrates, 60 g of protein, and 40 g of fats per day. These requirements can be met with two foods:

Food	Carbohydrates	Protein	Fats
A	6 g/oz	3 g/oz	1 g/oz
B	2 g/oz	2 g/oz	2 g/oz

It is also important to minimize costs; food A costs $0.14 per ounce and food B costs $0.06 per ounce. How many ounces of each food should be bought for each patient per day to meet the minimum daily requirements at the lowest cost?

47. On July 24, 2010, the U.S. national debt was $13 trillion and on that date there were 308.1 million people. How long would it take to pay off this debt if *every* person pays $1 per day?

48. Find the smallest number of operations needed to build up to the number 100 if you start at 0 and use only two operations: doubling or increasing by 1. *Challenge*: Answer the same question for the positive integer n.

49. If $\log_2 x + \log_4 x = \log_b x$, what is b?

50. Supply the missing number in the following sequence: 10, 11, 12, 13, 14, 15, 16, 17, 20, 22, 24, _____, 100, 121, 10,000.

51. How many different configurations can you see in Figure 7?

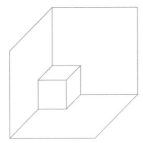

FIGURE 7 Count the cubes

52. Answer the question asked in the News Clip from the "Ask Marilyn" column of *Parade* magazine (July 16, 1995).

> **Dear Marilyn,**
>
> Three safari hunters are captured by a sadistic tribe of natives and forced to participate in a duel to the death. Each is given a pistol and tied to a post the same distance from the other two. They must take turns shooting at each other, one shot per turn. The worst shot of the three hunters (1 in 3 accuracy) must shoot first. The second turn goes to the hunter with 50–50 (1 in 2) accuracy. And (if he's still alive!) the third turn goes to the crack shot (100% accuracy). The rotation continues until only one hunter remains, who is then rewarded with his freedom. Which hunter has the best chance of surviving, and why?

From "Ask Marilyn," by Marilyn vos Savant, *Parade Magazine,* July 16, 1992. Reprinted with permission from Parade, © 1995.

53. Five cards are drawn at random from a pack of cards that have been numbered consecutively from 1 to 104 and have been thoroughly shuffled. What is the probability that the numbers on the cards as drawn are in increasing order of magnitude?

54. What is the sum of the counting numbers from 1 to 104?

55. The Kabbalah is a body of mystical teachings from the Torah. One medieval inscription is shown at the left:

4	9	2
3	5	7
8	1	6

The inscription on the left shows Hebrew characters that can be translated into numbers, as shown at the right. What can you say about this pattern of numbers?

56. What is the maximum number of points of intersection of n distinct lines?

57. The equation $P = 153{,}000e^{0.05t}$ represents the population of a city t years after 2000. What is the population in the year 2000? Show a graph of the city's population for the next 20 years.

58. The Egyptians had an interesting, pictorial numeration system. Here is how you would count using Egyptian numerals:

$$|,\ ||,\ |||,\ ||||,\ |||||,\ ||||||,\ |||||||,\ ||||||||,\ |||||||||,$$
$$\cap,\ \cap|,\ \cap||,\ \cap|||, \ldots$$

Write down your age using Egyptian numerals. The symbol "|" is called a stroke, and the "∩" is called a heel bone. The Egyptians used a scroll for 100, a lotus flower for 1,000, a pointing finger for 10,000, a polliwog for 100,000, and an astonished man for the number 1,000,000. *Without* doing any research, write what you think today's date would look like using Egyptian numerals.

59. If you start with $1 and double your money each day, how much money would you have in 30 days?

60. Consider two experiments and events defined as follows:

Experiment A: Roll one die 4 times and keep a record of how many times you obtain at least one 6. Event $E = \{$obtain at least one 6 in 4 rolls of a single die$\}$

Experiment B: Roll a pair of dice 24 times and keep a record of how many times you obtain at least one 12. Event $F = \{$obtain at least one 12 in 24 rolls of a pair of dice$\}$

Do you think event E or event F is more likely? You might wish to experiment by rolling dice.

1

THE NATURE OF PROBLEM SOLVING

What in the World?

"Hey, Tom, what are you taking this semester?" asked Susan. "I'm taking English, history, and math. I can't believe my math teacher," responded Tom. "The first day we were there, she walked in, wrote her name on the board, and then she asked, 'How much space would you have if you, along with everyone else in the world, moved to California?' What a stupid question ... I would not have enough room to turn around!"

"Oh, I had that math class last semester," said Susan. "It isn't so bad. The whole idea is to give you the ability to solve problems *outside* the class. I want to get a good job when I graduate, and I've read that because of the economy, employers are looking for people with problem-solving skills. I hear that working smarter is more important than working harder."

Overview

There are many reasons for reading a book, but the best reason is because you want to read it. Although you are probably reading this first page because you were required to do so by your instructor, it is my hope that in a short while you will be reading this book because you *want* to read it. It was written for people who think they don't like mathematics, or people who think they can't work math problems, or people who think they are never going to use math. The common thread in this book is *problem solving*—that is, strengthening your ability to solve problems—not in the classroom, but outside the classroom. This first chapter is designed to introduce you to the nature of problem solving. Notice the first thing you see on this page is the question, "What in the world?" Each chapter begins with such a real world question that appears later in the chapter. This first one is considered in Problem 59, page 43.

As you begin your trip through this book, I wish you a BON VOYAGE!

1.1 Problem Solving

The idea that aptitude for mathematics is rarer than aptitude for other subjects is merely an illusion which is caused by belated or neglected beginners.

J.F. HERBART

CHAPTER **CHALLENGE**

At the beginning of each chapter we present a puzzle which represents some pattern. See if you can fill in the question mark.	$A + B = C$ $A + C = D$ $B + C = E$ $F + H = N$ $G + J = \,?$

★ MATH ★ is not a spectator sport

PACIFIC GROVE, CALIFORNIA
BROOKS/COLE PUBLISHING COMPANY

Doug Menuez/Photodisc/Getty Images

A Word of Encouragement

Do you think of mathematics as a difficult, foreboding subject that was invented hundreds of years ago? Do you think that you will never be able (or even want) to use mathematics? If you answered "yes" to either of these questions, then I want you to know that I have written this book for you. I have tried to give you some insight into how mathematics is developed and to introduce you to some of the people behind the mathematics. In this book, I will present some of the great ideas of mathematics, and then we will look at how these ideas can be used in an everyday setting to build your problem-solving abilities. *The most important prerequisite for this course is an openness to try out new ideas—a willingness to experience the suggested activities rather than to sit on the sideline as a spectator.* I have attempted to make this material interesting by putting it together differently from the way you might have had mathematics presented in the past. You will find this book difficult if you wait for the book or the teacher to give you answers—instead, *be willing to guess, experiment, estimate, and manipulate,* and try out problems *without fear of being wrong!*

There is a common belief that mathematics is to be pursued only in a clear-cut logical fashion. This belief is perpetuated by the way mathematics is presented in most textbooks. Often it is reduced to a series of definitions, methods to solve various types of problems, and theorems. These theorems are justified by means of proofs and deductive reasoning. I do not mean to minimize the importance of proof in mathematics, for it is the very thing that gives mathematics its strength. But the power of the imagination is every bit as important as the power of deductive reasoning. As the mathematician Augustus De Morgan once said, "The power of mathematical invention is not reasoning but imagination."

Hints for Success

Mathematics is different from other subjects. One topic builds upon another, and you need to make sure that you understand *each* topic before progressing to the next one.

You must make a commitment to attend each class. Obviously, unforeseen circumstances can come up, but you must plan to attend class regularly. Pay attention to what

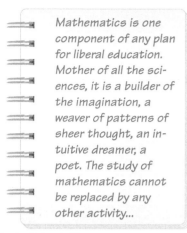

Mathematics is one component of any plan for liberal education. Mother of all the sciences, it is a builder of the imagination, a weaver of patterns of sheer thought, an intuitive dreamer, a poet. The study of mathematics cannot be replaced by any other activity...

American Mathematical Monthly, Volume 56, 1949, p. 19.

your teacher says and does, and take notes. If you must miss class, write an outline of the text corresponding to the missed material, including working out each text example on your notebook paper.

You must make a commitment to daily work. Do not expect to save up and do your mathematics work once or twice a week. It will take a daily commitment on your part, and you will find mathematics difficult if you try to "get it done" in spurts. You could not expect to become proficient in tennis, soccer, or playing the piano by practicing once a week, and the same is true of mathematics. Try to schedule a regular time to study mathematics each day.

Read the text carefully. Many students expect to get through a mathematics course by beginning with the homework problems, then reading some examples, and reading the text only as a desperate attempt to find an answer. This procedure is backward; do your homework only *after* reading the text.

Writing Mathematics

The fundamental objective of education has always been to prepare students for life. A measure of your success with this book is a measure of its usefulness to you in your life. What are the basics for your knowledge "in life"? In this information age with access to a world of knowledge on the Internet, we still would respond by saying that the basics remain "reading, 'riting, and 'rithmetic." As you progress through the material in this book, we will give you opportunities to read mathematics and to consider some of the great ideas in the history of civilization, to develop your problem-solving skills ('rithmetic), and to communicate mathematical ideas to others ('riting). Perhaps you think of mathematics as "working problems" and "getting answers," but it is so much more. Mathematics is a way of thought that includes all three Rs, and to strengthen your skills you will be asked to communicate your knowledge in written form.

Journals

To begin building your skills in writing mathematics, you might keep a journal summarizing each day's work. Keep a record of your feelings and perceptions about what happened in class. Ask yourself, "How long did the homework take?" "What time of the day or night did I spend working and studying mathematics?" "What is the most important idea that I should remember from the day's lesson?" To help you with your journals or writing of mathematics, you will find problems in this text designated **"IN YOUR OWN WORDS."** (For example, look at Problems 1–4 of the problem set at the end of this section.) There are no right answers or wrong answers to this type of problem, but you are encouraged to look at these for ideas of what you might write in your journal.

Journal Ideas

Write in your journal every day.
Include important ideas.
Include new words, ideas, formulas, or concepts.
Include questions that you want to ask later.
If possible, carry your journal with you so you can write in it anytime you get an idea.

Reasons for Keeping a Journal

It will record ideas you might otherwise forget.
It will keep a record of your progress.
If you have trouble later, it may help you diagnose areas for change or improvement.
It will build your writing skills.

Individual Research

At the end of each chapter you will find problems requiring some library research. I hope that as you progress through the course you will find one or more topics that interest you so much that you will want to do additional reading on that topic, even if it is not assigned.

Your instructor may assign one or more of these as term papers. One of the best ways for you to become aware of all the books and periodicals that are available is to log onto the Internet, or visit the library to research specific topics.

Preparing a mathematics paper or project can give you interesting and worthwhile experiences. In preparing a paper or project, you will get experience in using resources to find information, in doing independent work, in organizing your presentation, and in communicating ideas orally, in writing, and in visual demonstrations. You will broaden your background in mathematics and encounter new mathematical topics that you never before knew existed. In setting up an exhibit you will experience the satisfaction of demonstrating what you have accomplished. It may be a way of satisfying your curiosity and your desire to be creative. It is an opportunity for developing originality, craftsmanship, and new mathematical understandings. If you are requested to do some individual research problems, here are some suggestions.

1. *Select a topic that has interest potential.* Do not do a project on a topic that does not interest you. Suggestions are given on the Web at **www.mathnature.com.**

2. *Find as much information about the topic as possible.* Many of the Individual Research problems have one or two references to get you started. In addition, check the following sources:

   Periodicals: *The Mathematics Teacher, Teaching Children Mathematics* (formerly *Arithmetic Teacher),* and *Scientific American;* each of these has its own cumulative index; also check the *Reader's Guide.*

   Source books: *The World of Mathematics* by James R. Newman is a gold mine of ideas. *Mathematics,* a Time-Life book by David Bergamini, may provide you with many ideas. Encyclopedias can be consulted after you have some project ideas; however, I do not have in mind that the term project necessarily be a term paper.

   Internet: Use one or more search engines on the Internet for information on a particular topic. The more specific you can be in describing what you are looking for, the better the engine will be able to find material on your topic. The most widely used search engine is Google, but there are others that you might use. You may also check the Web address for this book to find specific computer links:

 www.mathnature.com

   If you do not have a computer or a modem, then you may need to visit your college or local library for access to this research information.

3. *Prepare and organize your material into a concise, interesting report.* Include drawings in color, pictures, applications, and examples to get the reader's attention and add meaning to your report.

4. *Build an exhibit that will tell the story of your topic.* Remember the science projects in high school? That type of presentation might be appropriate. Use models, applications, and charts that lend variety. Give your paper or exhibit a catchy, descriptive title.

5. *A **term** project cannot be done in one or two evenings.*

Group Research

Working in small groups is typical of most work environments, and being able to work with others to communicate specific ideas is an important skill to learn. At the end of each chapter is a list of suggested group projects, and you are encouraged to work with three or four others to submit a single report.

Guidelines for Problem Solving

We begin this study of **problem solving** by looking at the *process* of problem solving. As a mathematics teacher, I often hear the comment, "I can do mathematics, but I can't solve word problems." There *is* a great fear and avoidance of "real-life" problems because they do not fit into the same mold as the "examples in the book." Few practical problems from everyday life come in the same form as those you study in school.

To compound the difficulty, learning to solve problems takes time. All too often, the mathematics curriculum is so packed with content that the real process of problem solving is slighted and, because of time limitations, becomes an exercise in mimicking the instructor's steps instead of developing into an approach that can be used long after the final examination is over.

Before we build problem-solving skills, it is necessary to build certain prerequisite skills necessary for problem solving. It is my goal to develop your skills in the mechanics of mathematics, in understanding the important concepts, and finally in applying those skills to solve a new type of problem. I have segregated the problems in this book to help you build these different skills:

IN YOUR OWN WORDS	This type of problem asks you to discuss or rephrase main ideas or procedures using your own words.
Level 1 Problems	These are mechanical and drill problems, and are directly related to an example in the book.
Level 2 Problems	These problems require an understanding of the concepts and are loosely related to an example in the book.
Level 3 Problems	These problems are extensions of the examples, but generally do not have corresponding examples.
Problem Solving	These require problem-solving skills or original thinking and generally do not have direct examples in the book. These should be considered Level 3 problems.
Research Problems	These problems require Internet research or library work. Most are intended for individual research but a few are group research projects. You will find these problems for research in the chapter summary and at the Web address for this book:

   www.mathnature.com

The model for problem solving that we will use was first published in 1945 by the great, charismatic mathematician George Pólya. His book *How to Solve It* (Princeton University Press, 1973) has become a classic. In Pólya's book you will find this problem-solving model as well as a treasure trove of strategy, know-how, rules of thumb, good advice, anecdotes, history, and problems at all levels of mathematics. His problem-solving model is as follows.

Guidelines for Problem Solving

Step 1 *Understand the problem.* Ask questions, experiment, or otherwise rephrase the question in your own words.

Step 2 *Devise a plan.* Find the connection between the data and the unknown. Look for patterns, relate to a previously solved problem or a known formula, or simplify the given information to give you an easier problem.

Step 3 *Carry out the plan.* Check the steps as you go.

Step 4 *Look back.* Examine the solution obtained. In other words, check your answer.

Pólya's original statement of this procedure is reprinted in the following box.*

UNDERSTANDING THE PROBLEM

First

You have to understand the problem.

What is the unknown? What are the data? What is the condition? Is it possible to satisfy the condition? Is the condition sufficient to determine the unknown? Or is it insufficient? Or redundant? Or contradictory?

Draw a figure. Introduce a suitable notation.

Separate the various parts of the condition. Can you write them down?

DEVISING A PLAN

Second

Find the connection between the data and the unknown. You may be obliged to consider auxiliary problems if an immediate connection cannot be found.

Have you seen it before? Or have you seen the same problem in a slightly different form?

Do you know a related problem? Do you know a theorem that could be useful?

Look at the unknown! And try to think of a familiar problem having the same or a similar unknown.

Is the problem related to one you have solved before? Could you use it?

Could you use its result? Could you use its method? Should you introduce some auxiliary element in order to make its use possible?

Could you restate the problem? Could you restate it still differently? Go back to definitions.

If you cannot solve the proposed problem try to solve first some related problem. Could you imagine a more accessible related problem? A more general problem? A more special problem? An analogous problem? Could you solve a part of the problem? Keep only a part of the condition, drop the other part; how far is the unknown then determined, how can it vary? Could you derive something useful from the data? Could you think of other data appropriate to determine the unknown? Could you change the unknown or the data, or both if necessary, so that the new unknown and the new data are nearer to each other? Did you use all the data? Did you see the whole condition? Have you taken into account all essential notions involved in the problem?

CARRYING OUT THE PLAN

Third

Carry out your plan.

Carrying out your plan of the solution, *check each step.* Can you see clearly that the step is correct? Can you prove that it is correct?

LOOKING BACK

Fourth

Examine the solution.

Can you *check the result*? Can you check the argument?

Can you derive the result differently? Can you see it at a glance?

Let's apply this procedure for problem solving to the map shown in Figure 1.1; we refer to this problem as the **street problem.** Melissa lives at the YWCA (point *A*) and works at Macy's (point *B*). She usually walks to work. How many different routes can Melissa take?

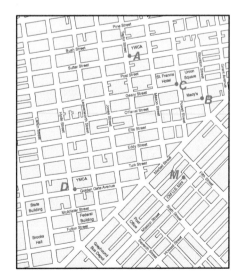

FIGURE 1.1 Portion of a map of San Francisco

*This is taken word for word as it was written by Pólya in 1941. It was printed in *How to Solve It* (Princeton, NJ: Princeton University Press, 1973).

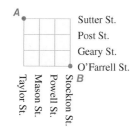

FIGURE 1.2 Simplified portion of Figure 1.1

Where would you begin with this problem?

Step 1   *Understand the Problem.* Can you restate it in your own words? Can you trace out one or two possible paths? What assumptions are reasonable? We assume that Melissa will not do any backtracking—that is, she always travels toward her destination. We also assume that she travels along the city streets—she cannot cut diagonally across a lot or a block.

Step 2   *Devise a Plan.* Simplify the question asked. Consider the simplified drawing shown in Figure 1.2.

Step 3   *Carry Out the Plan.* Count the number of ways it is possible to arrive at each point, or, as it is sometimes called, a *vertex*.

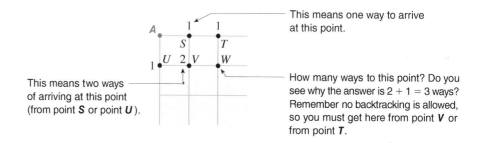

Now fill in all the possibilities on Figure 1.3, as shown by the above procedure.

Step 4   *Look Back.* Does the answer "20 different routes" make sense? Do you think you could fill in all of them?

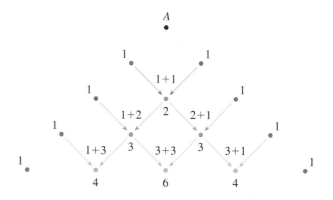

FIGURE 1.3 Map with solution

Example **1**   **Problem solving—from here to there**

In how many different ways could Melissa get from the YWCA (point *A*) to the St. Francis Hotel (point *C* in Figure 1.1), using the method of Figure 1.3?

Solution   Draw a simplified version of Figure 1.3, as shown. There are 6 different paths.

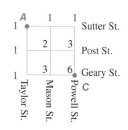

Problem Solving by Patterns

Let's formulate a general solution. Consider a map with a starting point *A*:

Do you see the pattern for building this figure? Each new row is found by adding the two previous numbers, as shown by the arrows. This pattern is known as **Pascal's triangle.** In Figure 1.4 the rows and diagonals are numbered for easy reference.

www.mathnature.com
There is an online interactive version of Pascal's triangle.

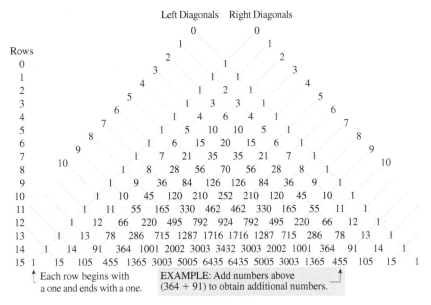

FIGURE 1.4 Pascal's triangle

How does this pattern apply to Melissa's trip from the YWCA to Macy's? It is 3 blocks down and 3 blocks over. Look at Figure 1.4 and count out these blocks, as shown in Figure 1.5.

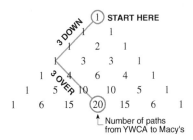

FIGURE 1.5 Using Pascal's triangle to solve the street problem

Historical NOTE

Blaise Pascal (1623–1662)

Described as "the greatest 'might-have-been' in the history of mathematics," Pascal was a person of frail health, and because he needed to conserve his energy, he was forbidden to study mathematics. This aroused his curiosity and forced him to acquire most of his knowledge of the subject by himself. At 18, he had invented one of the first calculating machines. However, at 27, because of his health, he promised God that he would abandon mathematics and spend his time in religious study. Three years later he broke this promise and wrote *Traite du triangle arithmétique*, in which he investigated what we today call Pascal's triangle. The very next year he was almost killed when his runaway horse jumped an embankment. He took this to be a sign of God's displeasure with him and again gave up mathematics—this time permanently.

Example 2   Pascal's triangle to track paths

In how many different ways could Melissa get from the YWCA (point *A* in Figure 1.1) to the YMCA (point *D*)?

Solution   Look at Figure 1.1; from point *A* to point *D* is 7 blocks down and 3 blocks left. Use Figure 1.4 as follows:

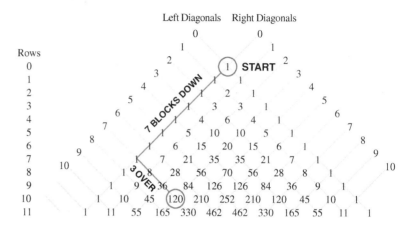

We see that there are 120 paths.

Pascal's triangle applies to the street problem only if the streets are rectangular. If the map shows irregularities (for example, diagonal streets or obstructions), then you must revert back to numbering the vertices.

Example 3   Travel with irregular paths

In how many different ways could Melissa get from the YWCA (point *A*) to the Old U.S. Mint (point *M*)?

Solution   If the streets are irregular or if there are obstructions, you cannot use Pascal's triangle, but you can still count the blocks in the same fashion, as shown in the figure.

There are 52 paths from point *A* to point *M* (if, as usual, we do not allow backtracking).

Historical NOTE

The title page of an arithmetic book by Petrus Apianus in 1527 is reproduced above. It was the first time Pascal's triangle appeared in print.

Problem solving is a difficult task to master, and you are not expected to master it after one section of this book (or even after several chapters of this book). However, you must make building your problem-solving skills an ongoing process. One of the most important aspects of problem solving is to relate new problems to old problems. The problem-solving techniques outlined here should be applied when you are faced with a new problem. When you are faced with a problem similar to one you have already worked, you can apply previously developed techniques (as we did in Examples 1–3). Now, because Example 4 seems to be a new type of problem, we again apply the guidelines for problem solving.

Example 4 Cows and chickens   Pólya's Method

A jokester tells you that he has a group of cows and chickens and that he counted 13 heads and 36 feet. How many cows and chickens does he have?

Solution   Let's use Pólya's problem-solving guidelines.

Understand the Problem. A good way to make sure you understand a problem is to attempt to phrase it in a simpler setting:

one chicken and one cow:	2 heads and 6 feet (chickens have two feet; cows have four)
two chickens and one cow:	3 heads and 8 feet
one chicken and two cows:	3 heads and 10 feet

Devise a Plan. How you organize the material is often important in problem solving. Let's organize the information into a table:

No. of chickens	No. of cows	No. of heads	No. of feet
0	13	13	52

Do you see why we started here? The problem says we must have 13 heads. There are other possible starting places (13 chickens and 0 cows, for example), but an important aspect of problem solving is to start with *some* plan.

No. of chickens	No. of cows	No. of heads	No. of feet
1	12	13	50
2	11	13	48
3	10	13	46
4	9	13	44

Carry Out the Plan. Now, look for patterns. Do you see that as the number of cows decreases by one and the number of chickens increases by one, the number of feet must decrease by two? Does this make sense to you? Remember, step 1 requires that you not just push numbers around, but that you understand what you are doing. Since we need 36 feet for the solution to this problem, we see

$$44 - 36 = 8$$

so the number of chickens must increase by an additional four. The answer is 8 chickens and 5 cows.

Look Back.

No. of chickens	No. of cows	No. of heads	No. of feet
8	5	13	36

Check: 8 chickens have 16 feet and 5 cows have 20 feet, so the total number of heads is $8 + 5 = 13$, and the number of feet is 36.

Example **5**   Number of birth orders

If a family has 5 children, in how many different birth orders could the parents have a 3-boy, 2-girl family?

Solution

Understand the Problem. Part of understanding the problem might involve estimation. For example, if a family has 1 child, there are 2 possible orders (B or G). If a family has 2 children, there are 4 orders (BB, BG, GB, GG); for 3 children, 8 orders; for 4 children, 16 orders; and for 5 children, a total of 32 orders. This means, for example, that an answer of 140 possible orders is an unreasonable answer.

Devise a Plan. You might begin by enumeration:

BBBGG, BBGBG, BBGGB, . . .

This would seem to be too tedious. Instead, rewrite this as a simpler problem and look for a pattern.

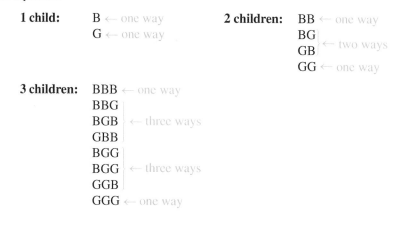

Look at the possibilities:

Look at Pascal's triangle in Figure 1.4; for 5 children, look at row 5.

Carry Out the Plan.

1	5	10	10	5	1
↑	↑	↑	↑	↑	↑
5 boys	4 boys and 1 girl	3 boys and 2 girls	2 boys and 3 girls	1 boy and 4 girls	5 girls

The family could have 3 boys and 2 girls in a total of 10 ways.

Look Back. We predicted that there are a total of 32 ways a family could have 5 children; let's sum the number of possibilities we found in carrying out the plan to see if it totals 32:

1 + 5 + 10 + 10 + 5 + 1 = 32

In this book, we are concerned about the thought process and not just typical "manipulative" mathematics. Using common sense is part of that thought process, and the following example illustrates how you can use common sense to analyze a given situation.

Example 6   Birthday dilemma

Pólya's Method

"I'm nine years old," says Adam.
"I'm ten years old," says Eve.
"My tenth birthday is tomorrow," says Adam.
"My tenth birthday was yesterday," says Eve.
"But I'm older than Eve," says Adam.
How is this possible if both children are telling the truth?

Solution   We use Pólya's problem-solving guidelines for this example.

Understand the Problem. What do we mean by the words of the problem? A birthday is the celebration of the day of one's birth. Is a person's age always the same as the number of birthdays?

Devise a Plan. The only time the number of birthdays is different from the person's age is when we are dealing with a leap year. Let's suppose that the day of this conversation is in a leap year on February 29.

Carry Out the Plan. Eve was born ten years ago (a nonleap year) on February 28 and Adam was born ten years ago on March 1. But if someone is born on March 1 then that person is younger than someone born on February 28, right? Not necessarily! Suppose Adam was born in New York City just after midnight on March 1 and that Eve was born before 9:00 P.M in Los Angeles on February 28.

Look Back. Since Adam was born before 9:00 P.M on February 28, he is older than Eve, even though his birthday is on March 1.

The following example illustrates the necessity of carefully reading the question.

Example 7   Meet for dinner

Pólya's Method

Nick and Marsha are driving from Santa Rosa, CA, to Los Angeles, a distance of 460 miles. They leave at 11:00 A.M. and average 50 mph. On the other hand, Mary and Dan leave at 1:00 P.M in Dan's sports car. Who is closer to Los Angeles when they meet for dinner in San Luis Obispo at 5:00 P.M.?

Solution

Understand the Problem. If they are sitting in the same restaurant, then they are all the same distance from Los Angeles.

The last example of this section illustrates that problem solving may require that you change the conceptual mode.

Example 8   Pascal's triangle—first time in print

If you have been reading the historical notes in the margins, you may have noticed that Blaise Pascal was born in 1623 and died in 1662. You may also have noticed that the first time Pascal's triangle appeared in print was in 1527. How can this be?

Solution   It was a reviewer of this book who brought this apparent discrepancy to my attention. However, the facts are all correct. How could Pascal's triangle have been in print almost 100 years before he was born? The fact is, the number pattern we call Pascal's triangle is *named after* Pascal, but was not *discovered* by Pascal. This number pattern seems to have been discovered several times, by Johann Scheubel in the 16th century and by the Chinese mathematician Nakone Genjun; and recent research has traced the triangle pattern as far back as Omar Khayyám (1048–1122).

"Wait!" you exclaim. "How was I to answer the question in Example 8—I don't know all those facts about the triangle." You are not expected to know these facts, but you are expected to begin to think critically about the information you are given and the assumptions you are making. It was never stated that Blaise Pascal was the first to think of or publish Pascal's triangle!

Problem Set 1.1

Level 1

1. **IN YOUR OWN WORDS**   In the text it was stated that "the most important prerequisite for this course is an openness to try out new ideas—a willingness to experience the suggested activities rather than to sit on the sideline as a spectator." Do you agree or disagree that this is the *most* important prerequisite? Discuss.

2. **IN YOUR OWN WORDS**   What do you thin the primary goal of mathematics education should be? What do you think it is in the United States? Discuss the differences between what it is and what you think it should be.

3. **IN YOUR OWN WORDS**   In the chapter overview (did you read it?), it was pointed out that this book was written for people who think they don't like mathematics, or people who think they can't work math problems, or people who think they are never going to use math. Do any of those descriptions apply to you or to someone you know? Discuss.

4. **IN YOUR OWN WORDS**   At the beginning of this section, three hints for success were listed. Discuss each of these from your perspective. Are there any other hints that you might add to this list?

5. Describe the location of the numbers 1, 2, 3, 4, 5, . . . in Pascal's triangle.

6. Describe the location of the numbers 1, 4, 10, 20, 35, . . . in Pascal's triangle.

7. **IN YOUR OWN WORDS**   In Example 2, the solution was found by going 7 blocks down and 3 blocks over. Could the solution also have been obtained by going 3 blocks over and 7 blocks down? Would this Pascal's triangle solution end up in a different location? Describe a property of Pascal's triangle that is relevant to an answer for this question.

8.

© Tony Freeman/PhotoEdit

  a. If a family has 5 children, in how many ways could the parents have 2 boys and 3 girls?
  b. If a family has 6 children, in how many ways could the parents have 3 boys and 3 girls?

9. **a.** If a family has 7 children, in how many ways could the parents have 4 boys and 3 girls?
  b. If a family has 8 children, in how many ways could the parents have 3 boys and 5 girls?

In Problems 10–13, what is the number of direct routes from point A to point B?

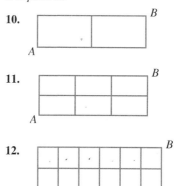

10.

11.

12.

13.

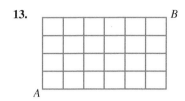

Use the map in Figure 1.6 to determine the number of different paths from point A to the point indicated in Problems 14–17. Remember, no backtracking is allowed.

FIGURE 1.6 Map of a portion of San Francisco

14. *E*   **15.** *F*   **16.** *G*   **17.** *H*

Level 2

18. If an island's only residents are penguins and bears, and if there are 16 heads and 34 feet on the island, how many penguins and how many bears are on the island?

19. Below are listed three problems. Do not solve these problems; simply tell which one you think is most like Problem 18.
 a. A penguin in a tub weighs 8 lb, and a bear in a tub weighs 800 lb. If the penguin and the bear together weigh 802 lb, how much does the tub weigh?
 b. A bottle and a cork cost $1.10, and the bottle is a dollar more than the cork. How much does the cork cost?
 c. Bob has 15 roses and 22 carnations. Carol has twice as many roses and half as many carnations. How many flowers does Carol have?

20. Ten full crates of walnuts weigh 410 pounds, whereas an empty crate weighs 10 pounds. How much do the walnuts alone weigh?

21. There are three separate, equal-size boxes, and inside each box there are two separate small boxes, and inside each of the small boxes there are three even smaller boxes. How many boxes are there all together?

22. Jerry's mother has three children. The oldest is a boy named Harry, who has brown eyes. Everyone says he is a math whiz. The next younger is a girl named Henrietta. Everyone calls her Mary because she hates her name. The youngest child has green eyes and can wiggle his ears. What is his first name?

23. A deaf-mute walks into a stationery store and wants to purchase a pencil sharpener. To communicate this need, the customer pantomimes by sticking a finger in one ear and rotating the other hand around the other ear. The very next customer is a blind person who needs a pair of scissors. How should this customer communicate this idea to the clerk?

24. If you expect to get 50,000 miles on each tire from a set of five tires (four and one spare), how should you rotate the tires so that each tire gets the same amount of wear, and how far can you drive before buying a new set of tires?

25. **a.** What is the sum of the numbers in row 1 of Pascal's triangle?
  b. What is the sum of the numbers in row 2 of Pascal's triangle?
  c. What is the sum of the numbers in row 3 of Pascal's triangle?
  d. What is the sum of the numbers in row 4 of Pascal's triangle?

26. What is the sum of the numbers in row *n* of Pascal's triangle?

Use the map in Figure 1.6 to determine the number of different paths from point A to the point indicated in Problems 27–30. Remember, no backtracking is allowed.

27. *J*   **28.** *I*   **29.** *L*   **30.** *K*

Problems 31–44 are not typical math problems but are problems that require only common sense (and sometimes creative thinking).

31. How many 3-cent stamps are there in a dozen?

32. Which weighs more—a ton of coal or a ton of feathers?

33. If you take 7 cards from a deck of 52 cards, how many cards do you have?

34. Oak Park cemetery in Oak Park, New Jersey, will not bury anyone living west of the Mississippi. Why?

35. If posts are spaced 10 feet apart, how many posts are needed for 100 feet of straight-line fence?

36. At six o'clock the grandfather clock struck 6 times. If it was 30 seconds between the first and last strokes, how long will it take the same clock to strike noon?

37. A person arrives at home just in time to hear one chime from the grandfather clock. A half-hour later it strikes once. Another half-hour later it chimes once. Still another half-hour later it chimes once. What time did the person arrive home?

38. Two girls were born on the same day of the same month of the same year to the same parents, but they are not twins. Explain how this is possible.

39. How many outs are there in a baseball game that lasts the full 9 innings?

40. Two U.S. coins total $0.30, yet one of these coins is not a nickel. What are the coins?

41. Two volumes of Newman's *The World of Mathematics* stand side by side, in order, on a shelf. A bookworm starts at page i of Volume I and bores its way in a straight line to the last page of Volume II. Each cover is 2 mm thick, and the first volume is $\frac{17}{19}$ as thick as the second volume. The first volume is 38 mm thick without its cover. How far does the bookworm travel?

42. A farmer has to get a fox, a goose, and a bag of corn across a river in a boat that is large enough only for him and one of these three items. If he leaves the fox alone with the goose, the fox will eat the goose. If he leaves the goose alone with the corn, the goose will eat the corn. How does he get all the items across the river?

43. Can you place ten lumps of sugar in three empty cups so that there is an odd number of lumps in each cup?

44. Six glasses are standing in a row. The first three are empty, and the last three are full of water. By handling and moving only one glass, it is possible to change this arrangement so that no empty glass is next to another empty one and no full glass is next to another full one. How can this be done?

Level 3

45. **IN YOUR OWN WORDS**   Suppose you have a long list of numbers to add, and you have misplaced your calculator. Discuss the different approaches that could be used for adding this column of numbers.

46. **IN YOUR OWN WORDS**   You are faced with a long division problem, and you have misplaced your calculator. You do not remember how to do long division. Discuss your alternatives to come up with the answer to your problem.

47. **IN YOUR OWN WORDS**   You have 10 items in your grocery cart. Six people are waiting in the express lane (10 items or less); one person is waiting in the first checkout stand and two people are waiting in another checkout stand. The other checkout stands are closed. What additional information do you need in order to decide which lane to enter?

48. **IN YOUR OWN WORDS**   You drive up to your bank and see five cars in front of you waiting for two lanes of the drive-through banking services. What additional information do you need in order to decide whether to drive through or park your car and enter the bank to do your banking?

49. A boy cyclist and a girl cyclist are 10 miles apart and pedaling toward each other. The boy's rate is 6 miles per hour, and the girl's rate is 4 miles per hour. There is also a friendly fly zooming continuously back and forth from one bike to the other. If the fly's rate is 20 miles per hour, by the time the cyclists reach each other, how far does the fly fly?

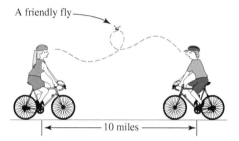

A friendly fly

10 miles

50. Two race cars face each other on a single 30-mile track, and each is moving at 60 mph. A fly on the front of one car flies back and forth on a zigzagging path between the cars until they meet. If the fly travels at 25 mph, how far will it have traveled when the cars collide?

51. Alex, Beverly, and Cal live on the same straight road. Alex lives 10 miles from Beverly and Cal lives 2 miles from Beverly. How far does Alex live from Cal?

52. In a different language, *liro cas* means "red tomato." The meaning of *dum cas dan* is "big red barn" and *xer dan* means "big horse." What are the words for "red barn" in this language?

53. Assume that the first "gh" sound in *ghghgh* is pronounced as in *hiccough,* the second "gh" as in *Edinburgh,* and the third "gh" as in *laugh.* How should the word *ghghgh* be pronounced?

54. Write down a three-digit number. Write the number in reverse order. Subtract the smaller of the two numbers from the larger to obtain a new number. Write down the new number. Reverse the digits again, but add the numbers this time. Complete this process for another three-digit number. Do you notice a pattern, and does your pattern work for all three-digit numbers?

55. Start with a common fraction between 0 and 1. Form a new fraction, using the following rules: *New denominator*: Add the numerator and denominator of the original fraction. *New numerator*: Add the new denominator to the original numerator. Write the new fraction and use a calculator to find a decimal equivalent to four decimal places. Repeat these steps again, this time calling the new fraction the original. Continue the process until a pattern appears about the decimal equivalent. What is the decimal equivalent (correct to two decimal places)?

56. The number 6 has four divisors—namely, 1, 2, 3, and 6. List all numbers less than 20 that have exactly four divisors.

Problem Solving 3

Each section of the book has one or more problems designated by "Problem Solving." These problems may require additional insight, information, or effort to solve. True problem-solving ability comes from solving problems that "are not like the examples" but rather require independent thinking. I hope you will make it a habit to read these problems and attempt to work those that interest you, even though they may not be part of your regular class assignment.

57. Consider the routes from *A* to *B* and notice that there is now a barricade blocking the path. Work out a general solution for the number of paths with a blockade, and then illustrate your general solution by giving the number of paths for each of the following street patterns.

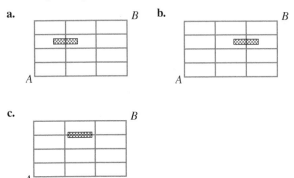

58. HISTORICAL QUEST   Thoth, an ancient Egyptian god of wisdom and learning, has abducted Ahmes, a famous Egyptian scribe, in order to assess his intellectual prowess. Thoth places Ahmes before a large funnel set in the ground (see Figure 1.7). It has a circular opening 1,000 ft in diameter, and its walls are quite slippery. If Ahmes attempts to enter the funnel, he will slip down the wall. At the bottom of the funnel is a sleep-inducing liquid that will instantly put Ahmes to sleep for eight hours if he touches it.* Thoth hands Ahmes two objects: a rope 1,006.28 ft in length and the skull of a chicken. Thoth says to Ahmes, "If you are able to get to the central tower and touch it, we will live in harmony for the next millennium. If not, I will detain you for further testing. Please note that with each passing hour, I will decrease the rope's length by a foot." How can Ahmes reach the central ankh tower and touch it?

*From "The Thoth Maneuver," by Clifford A. Pickover, *Discover*, March 1996, p. 108. Clifford Pickover © 1996. Reprinted with permission of Discover Magazine. Nenad Jakesevic and Sonja Lamut © 1996. Reprinted with permission of Discover Magazine.

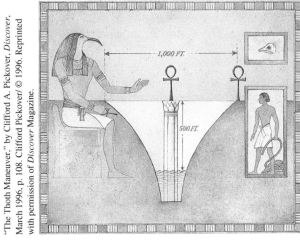

FIGURE 1.7 Ahmes's dilemma. Note that there are two ankh-shaped towers. One stands on a cylindrical platform in the center of the funnel. The platform's surface is at ground level. The distance from the surface to the liquid is 500 ft. The other ankh tower is on land, at the edge of the funnel.

59. A magician divides a deck of cards into two equal piles, counts down from the top of the first pile to the seventh card, and shows it to the audience without looking at it herself. These seven cards are replaced faced down in the same order on top of the first pile. She then picks up the other pile and deals the top three cards up in a row in front of her. If the first card is a six, then she starts counting with "six" and counts to ten, thus placing four more cards on this pile as shown. In turn, the magician does the same for the next two cards. If the card is a ten or a face card, then no additional cards are added. The remainder of this pile is placed on top of the first pile.

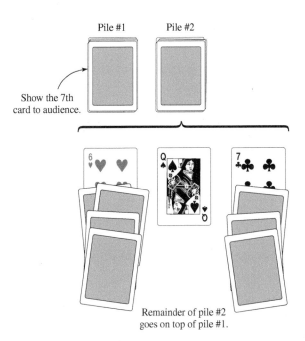

Next, the magician adds the values of the three face-up cards (6 + 10 + 7 for this illustration) and counts down in the first deck this number of cards. That card is the card that was originally shown to the audience. Explain why this trick works.

60. A very magical teacher had a student select a two-digit number between 50 and 100 and write it on the board out of view of the instructor. Next, the student was asked to add 76 to the number, producing a three-digit sum. If the digit in the hundreds place is added to the remaining two-digit number and this result is subtracted from the original number, the answer is 23, which was predicted by the instructor. How did the instructor know the answer would be 23? *Note:* This problem is dedicated to my friend Bill Leonard of Cal State, Fullerton. His favorite number is 23.

1.2 Inductive and Deductive Reasoning

Studying numerical patterns is one frequently used technique of problem solving.

Magic Squares

A magic square is an arrangement of numbers in the shape of a square with the sums of each vertical column, each horizontal row, and each diagonal all equal. One of the most famous ones appeared in a 1514 engraving *Melancholia* by Dürer, as shown in Figure 1.8. (Notice that the date appears in the magic square).

Historical NOTE

Burstein Collection/CORBIS

Melancholia by Albrecht Dürer

Burstein Collection/CORBIS

Detail of Melancholia

IXOHOXI

FIGURE 1.8 Early magic squares

Magic squares can be constructed using the first 9, 16, 25, 36, 49, 64, and 81 consecutive numbers. You may want to try some of them. One with the first 25 numbers is shown here.

23	12	1	20	9
4	18	7	21	15
10	24	13	2	16
11	5	19	8	22
17	6	25	14	3

There are formal methods for finding magic squares, but we will not describe them here. Figure 1.8 shows a rather interesting magic square called IXOHOXI because it is a magic square when it is turned upside down and also when it is reflected in a mirror. You are asked to find another magic square that can be turned upside down and is still a magic square.

Let's consider some other simple patterns.

A Pattern of Nines

A very familiar pattern is found in the ordinary "times tables." By pointing out patterns, teachers can make it easier for children to learn some of their multiplication tables. For example, consider the multiplication table for 9s:

$$1 \times 9 = 9$$
$$2 \times 9 = 18$$
$$3 \times 9 = 27$$
$$4 \times 9 = 36$$
$$5 \times 9 = 45$$
$$6 \times 9 = 54$$
$$7 \times 9 = 63$$
$$8 \times 9 = 72$$
$$9 \times 9 = 81$$
$$10 \times 9 = 90$$

What patterns do you notice? You should be able to see many number relationships by looking at the totals. For example, notice that the sum of the digits to the right of the equality is 9 in all the examples ($1 + 8 = 9, 2 + 7 = 9, 3 + 6 = 9$, and so on). Will this always be the case for multiplication by 9? (Consider $11 \times 9 = 99$. The sum of the digits is 18. However, notice the result if you add the digits of 18.) Do you see any other patterns? Can you explain why they "work"? This pattern of adding after multiplying by 9 generates a sequence of numbers: 9, 9, 9, ... We call this the *nine pattern*. The two number tricks described in the news clip in the margin use this nine pattern.

> Nine is one of the most fascinating of all numbers. Here are two interesting tricks that involve the number nine. You need a calculator for these.
>
> Mix up the serial number on a dollar bill. You now have two numbers, the original serial number and the mixed-up one. Subtract the smaller from the larger. If you add the digits of the answer, you will obtain a 9 or a number larger than 9; if it is larger than 9, add the digits of this answer again. Repeat the process until you obtain a single digit as with the *nine pattern*. That digit will *always* be 9.
>
> Here is another trick. Using a calculator keyboard or push-button phone, choose any three-digit column, row, or diagonal, and arrange these digits in any order. Multiply this number by another row, column, or diagonal. If you repeatedly add the digits the answer will *always* be nine.

Example 1   Eight pattern

Pólya's Method

Find the *eight pattern*.

Solution   We use Pólya's problem-solving guidelines for this example.

Understand the Problem. What do we mean by the *eight pattern?* Do you understand the example for the *nine pattern?*

Devise a Plan. We will carry out the multiplications of successive counting numbers by 8 and if there is more than a single-digit answer, we add the digits.* What we are looking for is a pattern for these single-digit numerals (shown in blue).

Carry Out the Plan.

$$1 \times 8 = 8, \quad 2 \times 8 = \underbrace{16}, \quad 3 \times 8 = \underbrace{24}, \quad 4 \times 8 = \underbrace{32}, \quad 5 \times 8 = \underbrace{40}, \ldots$$
$$\downarrow \qquad\qquad \downarrow \qquad\qquad \downarrow \qquad\qquad \downarrow \qquad\qquad \downarrow$$
$$8 \qquad 1 + 6 = 7 \qquad 2 + 4 = 6 \qquad 3 + 2 = 5 \qquad 4 + 0 = 4$$

Continue with some additional terms:

$$6 \times 8 = 48 \quad \text{and} \quad 4 + 8 = 12 \quad \text{and} \quad 1 + 2 = 3$$
$$7 \times 8 = 56 \quad \text{and} \quad 5 + 6 = 11 \quad \text{and} \quad 1 + 1 = 2$$

---

*Counting numbers are the numbers we use for counting—namely, 1, 2, 3, 4, ... Sometimes they are also called **natural numbers**. The integers are the counting numbers, their opposites, and 0, namely, . . . , −3, −2, −1, 0, 1, 2, 3, ... We assume a knowledge of these numbers.

$$8 \times 8 = 64 \quad \text{and} \quad 6 + 4 = 10 \quad \text{and} \quad 1 + 0 = 1$$
$$9 \times 8 = 72 \quad \text{and} \quad 7 + 2 = 9$$
$$10 \times 8 = 80 \quad \text{and} \quad 8 + 0 = 8$$

We now see the eight pattern: 8, 7, 6, 5, 4, 3, 2, 1, 9, 8, 7, 6, ...

Look Back. Let's do more than check the arithmetic, since this pattern seems clear. The problem seems to be asking whether we understand the concept of a *nine pattern* or an *eight pattern.* Verify that the *seven pattern* is 7, 5, 3, 1, 8, 6, 4, 2, 9, 7, 5, 3, 1, ...

Order of Operations

> Imagination is a
> sort of faint
> perception.
> Aristotle

Complicated arithmetic problems can sometimes be solved by using patterns. Given a difficult problem, a problem solver will often try to *solve a simpler, but similar, problem.*

The second suggestion for solving using Pólya's problem-solving procedure stated, "If you cannot solve the proposed problem, look around for an appropriate related problem (a simpler one, if possible)." For example, suppose we wish to compute the following number:

$$10 + 123,456,789 \times 9$$

Instead of doing a lot of arithmetic, let's study the following pattern:

$$2 + 1 \times 9$$
$$3 + 12 \times 9$$
$$4 + 123 \times 9$$

Do you see the next entry in this pattern? Do you see that if we continue the pattern we will eventually reach the desired expression of $10 + 123,456,789 \times 9$? Using Pólya's strategy, we begin by working these easier problems. Thus, we begin with $2 + 1 \times 9$. There is a possibility of ambiguity in calculating this number:

Left to right	*Multiplication first*
$2 + 1 \times 9 = 3 \times 9 = 27$	$2 + 1 \times 9 = 2 + 9 = 11$

Although either of these might be acceptable in certain situations, it is not acceptable to get two different answers to the same problem. We therefore agree to do a problem like this by multiplying first. If we wish to change this order, we use parentheses, as in $(2 + 1) \times 9 = 27$. We summarize with a procedure known as the **order-of-operations agreement.**

Order of Operations

Step 1 Perform any operations enclosed in parentheses.

Step 2 Perform multiplications and divisions as they occur by working from left to right.

Step 3 Perform additions and subtractions as they occur by working from left to right.

STOP This is important! Take time looking at what this says.

Thus, the correct result for $2 + 1 \times 9$ is 11. Also,

$$3 + 12 \times 9 = 3 + 108 = 111$$
$$4 + 123 \times 9 = 4 + 1,107 = 1,111$$
$$5 + 1,234 \times 9 = 5 + 11,106 = 11,111$$

Do you see a pattern? If so, then make a prediction about the desired result.

If you do not see a pattern, continue with this pattern to see more terms, or go back and try another pattern. For this example, we predict

$$10 + 123{,}456{,}789 \times 9 = 1{,}111{,}111{,}111$$

The most difficult part of this type of problem solving is coming up with a correct pattern. For this example, you might guess that

$$2 + 1 \times 1$$
$$3 + 12 \times 2$$
$$4 + 123 \times 3$$
$$5 + 1{,}234 \times 4$$
$$\vdots$$

leads to $10 + (123{,}456{,}789 \times 9)$. Calculating, we find

$$2 + 1 \times 1 = 2 + 1 = 3$$
$$3 + 12 \times 2 = 3 + 24 = 27$$
$$4 + 123 \times 3 = 4 + 369 = 373$$
$$5 + 1{,}234 \times 4 = 5 + 4{,}936 = 4{,}941$$

If you begin a pattern and it does not lead to a pattern of answers, then you need to remember that part of Pólya's problem-solving procedure is to work both backward and forward. Be willing to give up one pattern and begin another.

We also point out that the patterns you find are not necessarily unique. One last time, we try a pattern for $10 + 123{,}456{,}789 \times 9$:

$$10 + 1 \times 9 = 10 + 9 = 19$$
$$10 + 12 \times 9 = 10 + 108 = 118$$
$$10 + 123 \times 9 = 10 + 1{,}107 = 1{,}117$$
$$10 + 1{,}234 \times 9 = 10 + 11{,}106 = 11{,}116$$
$$\vdots$$

We do see a pattern here (although not quite as easily as the one we found with the first pattern for this example):

$$10 + 123{,}456{,}789 \times 9 = 1{,}111{,}111{,}111$$

Inductive Reasoning

The type of reasoning used here and in the first sections of this book—first observing patterns and then predicting answers for more complicated problems—is called **inductive reasoning.** It is a very important method of thought and is sometimes called the *scientific method.* It involves reasoning from particular facts or individual cases to a general **conjecture**—a statement you think may be true. That is, a generalization is made on the basis of some observed occurrences. The more individual occurrences we observe, the better able we are to make a correct generalization. Peter in the *B.C.* cartoon makes the mistake of generalizing on the basis of a single observation.

| Example | 2 | **Sum of 100 odd numbers** |

What is the sum of the first 100 consecutive odd numbers?

Solution   We use Pólya's problem-solving guidelines for this example.

Understand the Problem. Do you know what the terms mean? Odd numbers are 1, 3, 5, . . . , and *sum* indicates addition:

$$1 + 3 + 5 + \cdots + \; ?$$
↑

The first thing you need to understand is what the last term will be, so you will know when you have reached 100 consecutive odd numbers.

1 + 3 is two terms.
1 + 3 + 5 is three terms.
1 + 3 + 5 + 7 is four terms.

It seems as if the last term is always one less than twice the number of terms. Thus, the sum of the first 100 consecutive odd numbers is

$$1 + 3 + 5 + \cdots + 195 + 197 + 199$$
↑

This is one less than 2(100).

Devise a Plan. The plan we will use is to look for a pattern:

$$1 = 1 \quad \text{One term}$$
$$1 + 3 = 4 \quad \text{Sum of two terms}$$
$$1 + 3 + 5 = 9 \quad \text{Sum of three terms}$$

Do you see a pattern yet? If not, continue:

$$1 + 3 + 5 + 7 = 16$$
$$1 + 3 + 5 + 7 + 9 = 25$$

Carry Out the Plan. It appears that the sum of 2 terms is $2 \cdot 2$; of 3 terms, $3 \cdot 3$; of 4 terms, $4 \cdot 4$; and so on. The sum of the first 100 consecutive odd numbers is therefore $100 \cdot 100$.

Looking Back. Does $100 \cdot 100 = 10,000$ seem correct?

The numbers $2 \cdot 2$, $3 \cdot 3$, $4 \cdot 4$, and $100 \cdot 100$ from Example 2 are usually written as 2^2, 3^2, 4^2, and 100^2. The number b^2 means $b \cdot b$ and is pronounced **b squared,** and the number b^3 means $b \cdot b \cdot b$ and is pronounced **b cubed.** The process of repeated multiplication is called **exponentiation.** Numbers that are multiplied are called **factors,** so we note that b^2 means we have two factors and one multiplication, where as b^3 indicates three factors (two multiplications).

Deductive Reasoning

Another method of reasoning used in mathematics is called **deductive reasoning.** This method of reasoning produces results that are *certain* within the logical system being developed. That is, deductive reasoning involves reaching a conclusion by using a formal structure based on a set of **undefined terms** and a set of accepted unproved **axioms** or **premises.** For example, consider the following argument:

1. If you read the *Times,* then you are well informed.

2. You read the *Times.*

3. Therefore, you are well informed.

Statements 1 and 2 are the *premises* of the argument; statement 3 is called the **conclusion.** If you accept statements 1 and 2 as true, then you *must* accept statement 3 as true. Such reasoning is called *deductive reasoning;* and if the conclusion follows from the premises, the reasoning is said to be **valid.**

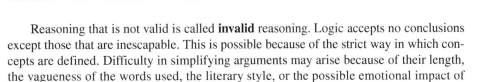

Deductive Reasoning

Deductive reasoning consists of reaching a conclusion by using a formal structure based on a set of *undefined terms* and on a set of accepted unproved *axioms* or *premises*. The conclusions are said to *be proved* and are called **theorems.**

Reasoning that is not valid is called **invalid** reasoning. Logic accepts no conclusions except those that are inescapable. This is possible because of the strict way in which concepts are defined. Difficulty in simplifying arguments may arise because of their length, the vagueness of the words used, the literary style, or the possible emotional impact of the words used.

Consider the following two arguments:

1. If George Washington was assassinated, then he is dead. Therefore, if he is dead, he was assassinated.

2. If you use heroin, then you first used marijuana. Therefore, if you use marijuana, then you will use heroin.

Logically, these two arguments are exactly the same, and both are *invalid* forms of reasoning. Nearly everyone would agree that the first is invalid, but many people see the second as valid. The reason lies in the emotional appeal of the words used.

To avoid these difficulties, we look at the *form* of the arguments and not at the independent truth or falsity of the statements. One type of logic problem is called a **syllogism.** A syllogism has three parts: two *premises,* or hypotheses, and a *conclusion.* The premises give us information from which we form a conclusion. With the syllogism, we are interested in knowing whether the conclusion *necessarily follows* from the premises. If it does, it is called a *valid syllogism*; if not, it is called *invalid.* Consider the following examples:

Valid Forms of Reasoning		*Invalid Forms of Reasoning*
All Chevrolets are automobiles.	*Premise*	Some people are nice.
All automobiles have four wheels.	*Premise*	Some people are broke.
All Chevrolets have four wheels.	*Conclusion*	There are some nice broke people.
All teachers are crazy.	*Premise*	All dodos are extinct.
Karl Smith is a teacher.	*Premise*	No dinosaurs are dodos.
Karl Smith is crazy.	*Conclusion*	Therefore, all dinosaurs are extinct.

To analyze such arguments, we need to have a systematic method of approach. We will use **Euler circles,** named after one of the most famous mathematicians in all of mathematics, Leonhard Euler.

For two sets *p* and *q*, we make the interpretations shown in Figure 1.9.

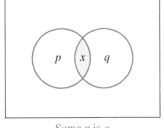

Some *p* is *q*.

(*x* means that intersection is not empty)

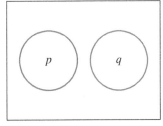

No *p* are *q*.

Disjoint sets

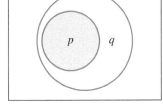

All *p* are *q*.

Subsets

FIGURE 1.9 Euler circles for syllogisms

Historical NOTE

**Leonhard Euler
(1707–1783)**

Euler's name is attached to every branch of mathematics, and we will visit his work many times in this book. His name is pronounced "Oiler" and it is sometimes joked that if you want to give a student a one-word mathematics test, just ask the student to pronounce Leonhard's last name. He was the most prolific writer on the subject of mathematics, and his mathematical textbooks were masterfully written. His writing was not at all slowed down by his total blindness for the last 17 years of his life. He possessed a phenomenal memory, had almost total recall, and could mentally calculate long and complicated problems.

Example 3 Testing for valid arguments

Test the validity of the following arguments.

a. All dictionaries are books.
This is a dictionary.
Therefore, this is a book.
b. If you like potato chips, then you will like Krinkles.
You do not like potato chips.
Therefore, you do not like Krinkles.

Solution

a. Begin by drawing Euler circles showing the first premise:

   All dictionaries are books.

Let p: dictionaries
   q: books

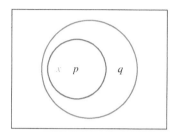

For the second premise, we place x (this object) inside the circle of dictionaries (labeled p). The conclusion, "This object is a book," cannot be avoided (since x *must* be in q), so it is valid.

b. Again, begin by using Euler circles:

   If you like potato chips, then you will like Krinkles.

The first premise is the same as

   All people who like potato chips like Krinkles.

Let p: people who like potato chips
   q: people who like krinkles

For the second premise, you will place the x (you) outside the circle labeled p. Notice that you are not forced to place x into a single region; it could be placed in either of two places—those labeled x_1 and x_2. Since the stated conclusion is not forced, the argument is not valid.

Problem Set 1.2

Level 1

1. **IN YOUR OWN WORDS**   Discuss the nature of *inductive* and *deductive reasoning.*

2. **IN YOUR OWN WORDS**   Explain what is meant by the *seven pattern.*

3. **IN YOUR OWN WORDS**   What do we mean by *order of operations?*

4. **IN YOUR OWN WORDS**   What is the scientific method?

5. **IN YOUR OWN WORDS**   Explain inductive reasoning. Give an original example of an occasion when you have used inductive reasoning or heard it being used.

6. **IN YOUR OWN WORDS**   Explain deductive reasoning. Give an original example of an occasion when you have used deductive reasoning or heard it being used.

Perform the operations in Problems 7–18.

7. **a.** $5 + 2 \times 6$ **b.** $7 + 3 \times 2$

8. **a.** $14 + 6 \times 3$ **b.** $30 \div 5 \times 2$

9. **a.** $3 \times 8 + 3 \times 7$ **b.** $3(8 + 7)$

10. **a.** $(8 + 6) \div 2$ **b.** $8 + 6 \div 2$

11. **a.** $12 + 6/3$ **b.** $(12 + 6)/3$

12. **a.** $450 + 550/10$ **b.** $\dfrac{450 + 550}{10}$

13. **a.** $20/2 \cdot 5$ **b.** $20/(2 \cdot 5)$

14. **a.** $1 + 3 \times 2 + 4 + 3 \times 6$
    b. $3 + 6 \times 2 + 8 + 4 \times 3$

15. **a.** $10 + 5 \times 2 + 6 \times 3$
    b. $4 + 3 \times 8 + 6 + 4 \times 5$

16. a. $8 + 2(3 + 12) - 5 \times 3$
  b. $25 - 4(12 - 2 \times 6) + 3$

17. a. $3 + 9 \div 3 \times 2 + 2 \times 6 \div 3$
  b. $[(3 + 9) \div 3] \times 2 + [(2 \times 6) \div 3]$

18. a. $3 + [(9 \div 3) \times 2] + [(2 \times 6) \div 3]$
  b. $[(3 + 9) \div (3 \times 2)] + [(2 \times 6) \div 3]$

19. Does the B.C. cartoon illustrate inductive or deductive reasoning? Explain your answer.

B.C. reprinted by permission of Johnny Hart and Creators Syndicate.

20. Does the news clip below illustrate inductive or deductive reasoning? Explain your answer.

> The old fellow in charge of the checkroom in a large hotel was noted for his memory. He never used checks or marks of any sort to help him return coats to their rightful owners.
>   Thinking to test him, a frequent hotel guest asked him as he received his coat, "Sam, how did you know this is my coat?"
>   "I don't, sir," was the calm response.
>   "Then why did you give it to me?" asked the guest.
>   "Because," said Sam, "it's the one you gave me, sir."

Lucille J. Goodyear

Problems 21–24 are modeled after Example 1. Find the requested pattern.

21. three pattern

22. four pattern

23. five pattern

24. six pattern

25. a. What is the sum of the first 25 consecutive odd numbers?
  b. What is the sum of the first 250 consecutive odd numbers?

26. a. What is the sum of the first 50 consecutive odd numbers?
  b. What is the sum of the first 1,000 consecutive odd numbers?

27. HISTORICAL QUEST   The first known example of a magic square comes from China. Legend tells us that around the year 200 B.C. the emperor Yu of the Shang dynasty received the following magic square etched on the back of a tortoise's shell:

The incident supposedly took place along the Lo River, so this magic square has come to be known as the Lo-shu magic square. The even numbers are black (female numbers) and the odd numbers are white (male numbers). Translate this magic square into modern symbols.

This same magic square (called *wafq* in Arabic) appears in Islamic literature in the 10th century A.D. and is attributed to Jabir ibn Hayyan.

28. Consider the square shown in Figure 1.10.

10	7	8	11
14	11	12	15
13	10	11	14
15	12	13	16

FIGURE 1.10 Magic square?

a. Is this a magic square?
b. Circle any number; cross out all the numbers in the same row and column. Then circle any remaining number and cross out all the numbers in the same row and column. Circle the remaining number. The sum of the circled numbers is 48. Why?

Level 2

Use Euler circles to check the validity of the arguments in Problems 29–40.

29. All mathematicians are eccentrics.
  All eccentrics are rich.
  Therefore, all mathematicians are rich.

30. All snarks are fribbles.
  All fribbles are ugly.
  Therefore, all snarks are ugly.

31. All cats are animals.
  This is not an animal.
  Therefore, this is not a cat.

32. All bachelors are handsome.
Some bachelors do not drink lemonade.
Therefore, some handsome men do not drink
lemonade.

33. No students are enthusiastic.
You are enthusiastic.
Therefore, you are not a student.

34. No politicians are honest.
Some dishonest people are found out.
Therefore, some politicians are found out.

35. All candy is fattening.
All candy is delicious.
Therefore, all fattening food is delicious.

36. All parallelograms are rectangles.
All rectangles are polygons.
Therefore, all parallelograms are polygons.

37. No professors are ignorant.
All ignorant people are vain.
Therefore, no professors are vain.

38. No monkeys are soldiers.
All monkeys are mischievous.
Therefore, some mischievous creatures are not soldiers.

39. All lions are fierce.
Some lions do not drink coffee.
Therefore, some creatures that drink coffee are not fierce.

40. All red hair is pretty.
No pretty things are valuable.
Therefore, no red hair is valuable.

Level **3**

Problems 41–44 refer to the lyrics of "By the Time I Get to Phoenix." Tell whether each answer you give is arrived at inductively or deductively.

By the Time I Get to Phoenix

By the time I get to Phoenix she'll be risin'.
She'll find the note I left hangin' on her door.
She'll laugh when she reads the part that says I'm leavin',
'Cause I've left that girl so many times before.

By the time I make Albuquerque she'll be workin'.
She'll probably stop at lunch and give me a call.
But she'll just hear that phone keep on ringin'
Off the wall, that's all.

By the time I make Oklahoma she'll be sleepin'.
She'll turn softly and call my name out low.
And she'll cry just to think I'd really leave her,
'tho' time and time I've tried to tell her so,
She just didn't know
I would really go.

Lyrics for "By the Time I get to Phoenix." Words and music by Jimmy Webb. Copyright © 1967 (renewed 1995) EMI Sosaha Music Inc. and Jonathan Three music. All rights reserved. International copyright secured. Used by permission.

41. In what basic direction (north, south, east, or west) is the person traveling?

42. What method of transportation or travel is the person using?

43. What is the probable starting point of this journey?

44. List five facts you know about each person involved.

Problems 45–48 refer to the lyrics of "Ode to Billy Joe." Tell whether each answer you give is arrived at inductively or deductively.

Ode to Billy Joe

It was the third of June, another sleepy, dusty, delta day.
I was choppin' cotton and my brother was balin' hay.
And at dinnertime we stopped and walked back to the house to eat,
And Mama hollered at the back door, "Y'all remember to wipe your feet."
Then she said, "I got some news this mornin' from Choctaw Ridge,
Today Billy Joe McAllister jumped off the Tallahatchee Bridge."

Papa said to Mama, as he passed around the black-eyed peas,
"Well, Billy Joe never had a lick o' sense, pass the biscuits please,
There's five more acres in the lower forty I've got to plow,"
And Mama said it was a shame about Billy Joe anyhow.
Seems like nothin' ever comes to no good up on Choctaw Ridge,
And now Billy Joe McAllister's jumped off the Tallahatchee Bridge.

Brother said he recollected when he and Tom and Billy Joe,
Put a frog down my back at the Carroll County picture show,
And wasn't I talkin' to him after church last Sunday night,
"I'll have another piece of apple pie, you know, it don't seem right,
I saw him at the sawmill yesterday on Choctaw Ridge,
And now you tell me Billy Joe's jumped off the Tallahatchee Bridge."

Mama said to me, "Child, what's happened to your appetite?
I been cookin' all mornin' and you haven't touched a single bite,
That nice young preacher Brother Taylor dropped by today,
Said he'd be pleased to have dinner on Sunday, Oh, by the way,
He said he saw a girl that looked a lot like you up on Choctaw Ridge
And she an' Billy Joe was throwin' somethin' off the Tallahatchee Bridge."

A year has come and gone since we heard the news 'bout Billy Joe,
Brother married Becky Thompson, they bought a store in Tupelo,
There was a virus goin' round, Papa caught it and he died last spring.
And now Mama doesn't seem to want to do much of anything.
And me I spend a lot of time pickin' flowers up on Choctaw Ridge,
And drop them into the muddy water off the Tallahatchee Bridge.

Lyrics for "Ode to Billy Joe" by Bobbie Gentry. © 1967 by Universal Music Corp. on behalf of Northridge Music Co./ASCAP. Used by permission. International copyright secured. All rights reserved.

45. How many people are involved in this story? List them by name and/or description.

46. Who "saw him at the sawmill yesterday"?

47. In which state is the Tallahatchee Bridge located?

48. On what day or days of the week could the death not have taken place?

On what day of the week was the death most probable?

49. Which direction is the bus traveling?*

Did you arrive at your answer using inductive or deductive reasoning?

*"My Favorite Brain Teasers" by Martin Gardner, *Games Magazine*, October 1997, p. 46.

50. Which is larger—the number of all seven-letter English words ending in *ing*, or the number of seven-letter words with "*i*" as the fifth letter?[†] Did you arrive at your answer using inductive or deductive reasoning?

51. Consider the following pattern:

$$9 \times 1 - 1 = 8$$
$$9 \times 21 - 1 = 188$$
$$9 \times 321 - 1 = 2{,}888$$
$$9 \times 4{,}321 - 1 = 38{,}888$$

  a. Use this pattern and inductive reasoning to find the next problem and the next answer in the sequence.

  b. Use this pattern to find

$$9 \times 987{,}654{,}321 - 1$$

  c. Use this pattern to find

$$9 \times 10{,}987{,}654{,}321 - 1$$

52. Consider the following pattern:

$$123{,}456{,}789 \times 9 = 1{,}111{,}111{,}101$$
$$123{,}456{,}789 \times 18 = 2{,}222{,}222{,}202$$
$$123{,}456{,}789 \times 27 = 3{,}333{,}333{,}303$$

  a. Use this pattern and inductive reasoning to find the next problem and the next answer in the sequence.

  b. Use this pattern to find

$$123{,}456{,}789 \times 9{,}000$$

  c. Use this pattern to find

$$123{,}456{,}789 \times 81{,}000$$

53. What is the sum of the digits in

$$333333334^2$$

Did you arrive at your answer using inductive or deductive reasoning?

54. Enter 999999 into your calculator, then divide it by seven. Now toss a die (or randomly pick a number from 1 through 6) and multiply this number by the displayed calculator number. Arrange the digits of the product from lowest to highest (from left to right). What is this six-digit number?

Explain how you arrived at your answer, and discuss whether you arrived at your result empirically, by induction, or by deduction.

Problem Solving **3**

55. How many squares are there in Figure 1.11?

FIGURE 1.11 How many squares?

Hint:

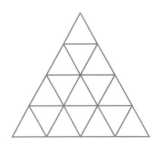

  1 1-by-1 square
    TOTAL: 1
      4 1-by-1 squares
      1 2-by-2 square
    TOTAL: 5 (by addition)
      9 1-by-1 squares
      4 2-by-2 squares
      1 3-by-3 square
    TOTAL: 14 (by addition)

56. How many triangles are there in Figure 1.12?

FIGURE 1.12 How many triangles?

57. You have 9 coins, but you are told that one of the coins is counterfeit and weighs just a little more than an authentic coin. How can you determine the counterfeit with 2 weighings on a two-pan balance scale? (This problem is discussed in Chapter 2).

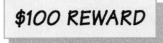

58.

$100 REWARD

In 1987 Martin Gardner (long-time math buff and past editor of the "Mathematical Games" department of *Scientific American*) offered $100 to anyone who could find a 3 × 3 magic square made with consecutive primes. The prize was won by Harry Nelson of Lawrence Livermore Laboratories. He produced the following simplest such square:

1,480,028,201	1,480,028,129	1,480,028,183
1,480,028,153	1,480,028,171	1,480,028,189
1,480,028,159	1,480,028,213	1,480,028,141

Prove this is a magic square.

59.

$100 REWARD (FOR REAL)

Now, a real $100 offer: *Find a 3 × 3 magic square with nine distinct square numbers.* If you find such a magic square, write to me and I will include it in the next edition and pay you a $100 reward . Show that the following magic squares do not win the award.

a.

127^2	46^2	58^2
2^2	113^2	94^2
74^2	82^2	97^2

b.

35^2	3495^2	2958^2
3642^2	2125^2	1785^2
2775^2	2058^2	3005^2

60. Find a 5 × 5 magic square whose magic number is 44. That is, the sum of the rows, columns, and diagonals is 44. Furthermore, the square can be turned upside down without changing this property. *Hint:* The magic number is XLIV, and the entries of the square use Roman numerals.

1.3 | Scientific Notation and Estimation

"How Big Is the Cosmos?" There is a dynamic Web site demonstrating the answer to this question (go to "Powers of Ten" at **www.mathnature.com**). Figure 1.13 illustrates the size of the known cosmos.

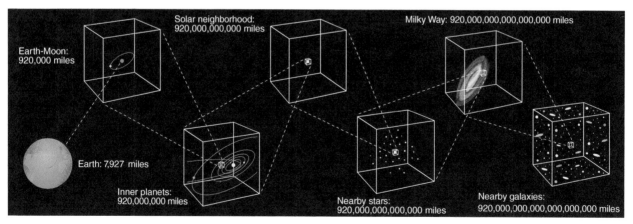

FIGURE 1.13 Size of the universe.* Each successive cube is a thousand times as wide and a billion times as voluminous as the one before it.

How can the human mind comprehend such numbers? Scientists often work with very large numbers. Distances such as those in Figure 1.13 are measured in terms of the distance that light, moving at 186,000 miles per second, travels in a year. In this section, we turn to patterns to see if there is an easy way to deal with very large and very small numbers. We will also discuss estimation as a problem-solving technique.

*Illustration is adapted from *The Universe*, Life Nature Library (1962).

Exponential Notation

We often encounter expressions that comprise multiplication of the same numbers. For example,

$$10 \cdot 10 \cdot 10 \qquad \text{or} \qquad 6 \cdot 6 \cdot 6 \cdot 6 \cdot 6 \cdot 6 \cdot 6 \qquad \text{or}$$
$$15 \cdot 15 \cdot 15 \cdot 15 \cdot 15 \cdot 15 \cdot 15 \cdot 15 \cdot 15 \cdot 15 \cdot 15 \cdot 15 \cdot 15 \cdot 15$$

These numbers can be written more concisely using what is called **exponential notation:**

$$\underbrace{10 \cdot 10 \cdot 10}_{3\ factors} = 10^3 \qquad \underbrace{6 \cdot 6 \cdot 6 \cdot 6 \cdot 6 \cdot 6 \cdot 6}_{7\ factors} = 6^7$$

How would you use exponential notation for the product of the 15s?   *Answer:* 15^{14}.

Exponential Notation

For any nonzero number b and any counting number n,

$$b^n = \underbrace{b \cdot b \cdot b \cdots \cdot b}_{n\ factors}, \qquad b^0 = 1, \qquad b^{-n} = \frac{1}{b^n}$$

The number b is called the **base,** the number n in b^n is called the **exponent,** and the number b^n is called a **power** or **exponential.**

Example 1   Write numbers without exponents

Write without exponents.   **a.** 10^5 **b.** 6^2 **c.** 7^5 **d.** 2^{63} **e.** 3^{-2} **f.** 8.9^0

Solution

a. $10^5 = 10 \cdot 10 \cdot 10 \cdot 10 \cdot 10 = 100{,}000$

b. $6^2 = 6 \cdot 6 = 36$

c. $7^5 = 7 \cdot 7 \cdot 7 \cdot 7 \cdot 7$ or $16{,}807$

d. $2^{63} = \underbrace{2 \cdot 2 \cdot 2 \cdots \cdot 2 \cdot 2}_{63\ factors}$ or $9{,}223{,}372{,}036{,}854{,}775{,}808$

 Note: 10^5 *is not five multiplications, but rather five factors of 10.*

Note: You are not expected to find the form at the right; the factored form is acceptable.

e. $3^{-2} = \dfrac{1}{3^2} = \dfrac{1}{9}$

f. $8.9^0 = 1$ By definition, any nonzero number to the zero power is 1.

Since an exponent indicates a multiplication, the proper procedure is first to simplify the exponent, and then to carry out the multiplication. This leads to an **extended order-of-operations agreement.**

Extended Order of Operations

Step 1   Perform any operations enclosed in parentheses.

Step 2   Perform any operations that involve raising to a power.

Step 3   Perform multiplications and divisions as they occur by working from left to right.

Step 4   Perform additions and subtractions as they occur by working from left to right.

Scientific Notation

There is a similar pattern for multiplications of any number by a power of 10. Consider the following examples, and notice what happens to the decimal point.

$$9.42 \times 10^1 = 94.2 \qquad \text{\textit{We find these answers by direct multiplication.}}$$
$$9.42 \times 10^2 = 942.$$
$$9.42 \times 10^3 = 9,420.$$
$$9.42 \times 10^4 = 94,200.$$

Do you see the pattern? Look at the decimal point (which is included for emphasis). If we multiply 9.42×10^5, how many places to the right will the decimal point be moved?

$$9.42 \times 10^5 = 9\ 42,000.$$

5 places to the right

Using this pattern, can you multiply the following *without direct calculation*?

$$9.42 \times 10^{12} = 9,420,000,000,000$$

This answer is found by observing the pattern, not by direct multiplication.

The pattern also extends to smaller numbers:

$$9.42 \times 10^{-1} = 0.942$$
$$9.42 \times 10^{-2} = 0.0942$$
$$9.42 \times 10^{-3} = 0.00942$$

These numbers are found by direct multiplication. For example,
$9.42 \times 10^{-2} = 9.42 \times \frac{1}{100} = 9.42 \times 0.01 = 0.0942$

Do you see that the same pattern also holds for multiplying by 10 with a negative exponent? Can you multiply the following *without direct calculation*?

$$9.42 \times 10^{-6} = 0.\ 000009\ 42$$

Moved six places to the left

These patterns lead to a useful way for writing large and small numbers, called *scientific notation*.

> ### Scientific Notation
>
> The **scientific notation** for a nonzero number is that number written as a power of 10 times another number x, such that x is between 1 and 10, including 1; that is, $1 \leq x < 10$.

Example **2** Write in scientific notation

Write the given numbers in scientific notation.
a. 123,400   **b.** 0.000035   **c.** 1,000,000,000,000   **d.** 7.35

Solution
a. $123,400 = 1.234 \times 10^5$
b. $0.000035 = 3.5 \times 10^{-5}$
c. $1,000,000,000,000 = 10^{12}$; technically, this is 1×10^{12} with the 1 understood.
d. 7.35 (or 7.35×10^0) is in scientific notation.

NASA/JPL/Caltech/R. Hurt (SSC)

Example 3 **Miles in a light-year**

Assuming that light travels at 186,000 miles per second, what is the distance (in miles) that light travels in 1 year? This is the unit of length known as a *light-year*. Give your answer in scientific notation.

Solution   One year is 365.25 days $= 365.25 \times 24$ hours
$$= 365.25 \times 24 \times 60 \text{ minutes}$$
$$= 365.25 \times 24 \times 60 \times 60 \text{ seconds}$$
$$= 31{,}557{,}600 \text{ seconds}$$

Since light travels 186,000 miles each second and there are 31,557,600 seconds in 1 year, we have

$$186{,}000 \times 31{,}557{,}600 = 5{,}869{,}713{,}600{,}000 \approx 5.87 \times 10^{12}$$

Thus, light travels about 5.87×10^{12} miles in 1 year.

Calculators

Throughout the book we will include calculator comments for those of you who have (or expect to have) a calculator. Calculators are classified according to their ability to perform different types of calculations, as well as by the type of logic they use to do the calculations. The problem of selecting a calculator is further complicated by the multiplicity of brands from which to choose. Therefore, choosing a calculator and learning to use it require some sort of instruction.

For most nonscientific purposes, a four-function calculator with memory is sufficient for everyday use. If you anticipate taking several mathematics and/or science courses, you will find that a scientific calculator is a worthwhile investment. These calculators use essentially three types of logic: *arithmetic, algebraic,* and *RPN.* In the previous section, we discussed the correct order of operations, according to which the correct value for

$$2 + 3 \times 4$$

is 14 (multiply first). An algebraic calculator will "know" this and will give the correct answer, whereas an arithmetic calculator will simply work from left to right and obtain the incorrect answer, 20. Therefore, if you have an arithmetic-logic calculator, you will need to be careful about the order of operations. Some arithmetic-logic calculators provide parentheses, $\boxed{(}\,\boxed{)}$, so that operations can be grouped, as in

$$\boxed{2}\;\boxed{+}\;\boxed{(}\;\boxed{3}\;\boxed{\times}\;\boxed{4}\;\boxed{)}\;\boxed{=}$$

but then you must remember to insert the parentheses.

The last type of logic is RPN. A calculator using this logic is characterized by $\boxed{\text{ENTER}}$ or $\boxed{\text{SAVE}}$ keys and does not have an equal key $\boxed{=}$. With an RPN calculator, the operation symbol is entered after the numbers have been entered. These three types of logic can be illustrated by the problem $2 + 3 \times 4$:

Arithmetic logic: $\boxed{3}\;\boxed{\times}\;\boxed{4}\;\boxed{=}\;\boxed{+}\;\boxed{2}\;\boxed{=}$ *Input to match order of operations.*

Algebraic logic: $\boxed{2}\;\boxed{+}\;\boxed{3}\;\boxed{\times}\;\boxed{4}\;\boxed{=}$ *input is the same as the problem.*

RPN logic: $\boxed{2}\;\boxed{\text{ENTER}}\;\boxed{3}\;\boxed{\text{ENTER}}\;\boxed{4}\;\boxed{\times}\;\boxed{+}$ *Operations input last.*

In this book, we will illustrate the examples using algebraic logic. If you have a calculator with RPN logic, you can use your owner's manual to change the examples to RPN. We do not recommend using an arithmetic logic calculator. We will also indicate the keys to be pushed by drawing boxes around the numerals and operational signs as shown.

Example 4 Calculator addition

Show the calculator steps for 14 + 38.

Solution Be sure to turn your calculator on, or clear the machine if it is already on. A clear button is designated by $\boxed{C}$, and the display will show 0 after the clear button is pushed. You will need to check these steps every time you use your calculator, but after a while it becomes automatic. We will not remind you of this in each example.

Press	Display
$\boxed{1}$	1
$\boxed{4}$	14
$\boxed{+}$	14
$\boxed{38}$	38
$\boxed{=}$	52

Here we show each numeral in a single box, which means you key in one numeral at a time, as shown.
From now on, this will be shown as $\boxed{14}$.
Some calculators display all of keystrokes: 14 + 38

After completing Example 4, you can either continue with the same problem or start a new problem. If the next button pressed is an operation button, the result 52 will be carried over to the new problem. If the next button pressed is a numeral, the 52 will be lost and a new problem started. For this reason, it is not necessary to press $\boxed{C}$ to clear between problems. The button $\boxed{CE}$ is called the *clear entry* key and is used if you make a mistake keying in a number and do not want to start over with the problem. For example, if you want 2 + 3 and accidentally push $\boxed{2}\,\boxed{+}\,\boxed{4}$ you can then push $\boxed{CE}\,\boxed{3}\,\boxed{=}$ to obtain the correct answer. This is especially helpful if you are in the middle of a long calculation. Some models have a $\boxed{\leftarrow}$ key instead of a $\boxed{CE}$ key.

Example 5 Mixed operations using a calculator

Show the calculator steps and display for $4 + 3 \times 5 - 7$.

Solution

Press:	$\boxed{4}$	$\boxed{+}$	$\boxed{3}$	$\boxed{\times}$	$\boxed{5}$	$\boxed{-}$	$\boxed{7}$	$\boxed{=}$ or $\boxed{ENTER}$
Display:	4	4+	4+3	4+3·	4+3·5	4+3·5−	4+3·5−7	12

If you have an algebraic-logic calculator, your machine will perform the correct order of operations. If it is an arithmetic-logic calculator, it will give the incorrect answer 28 unless you input the numbers using the order-of-operations agreement.

Example 6 Calculator multiplication

Everybody Counts, p. 61.

Repeat Example 3 using a calculator; that is, find

$$365.25 \times 24 \times 60 \times 60 \times 186{,}000$$

Solution When you press these calculator keys and then press $\boxed{=}$ the display will probably show something that looks like:

5.86971 12   or   5.86971 + 12   or   5.86971E12

This display is a form of scientific notation. The 12 or +12 at the right (separated by one or two blank spaces) is the exponent on the 10 when the number in the display is written in scientific notation. That is,

5.86971 12   means 5.86971×10^{12}

Suppose you have a particularly large number that you wish to input into a calculator—say, 920,000,000,000,000,000,000 miles divided by 7,927 miles (from Figure 1.13). You can input 7,927, but if you attempt to input the larger number you will be stuck when you fill up the display (9 or 12 digits). Instead, you will need to write

$$920{,}000{,}000{,}000{,}000{,}000{,}000 = 9.2 \times 10^{20}$$

This may be entered by pressing an EE , EEx , or EXP key:

9.2 EE 20 ÷ 7927 =   *Display:* 1.160590387E 17

Do not confuse the scientific notation keys on your calculator with the exponent key. Exponent keys are labeled y^x , $\wedge$ *and key or* 10^x .

This means that the last cube in Figure 1.13 is about 1.2×10^{17} times larger than the earth.

Scientific notation is represented in a slightly different form on many calculators and computers, and this new form is sometimes called **floating-point form.** When representing very large or very small answers, most calculators will automatically output the answers in floating-point notation. The following example compares the different forms for large and small numbers with which you should be familiar.

Example   7   Find scientific and calculator notation

Write each given number in scientific notation and in calculator notation.
a. 745   **b.** 1,230,000,000   **c.** 0.00573   **d.** 0.00000 06239

Solution   The form given in this example is sometimes called **fixed-point form** or **decimal notation** to distinguish it from the other forms.

Fixed-Point	Scientific Notation	Floating-Point
a. 745	7.45×10^2	7.45 02
b. 1,230,000,000	1.23×10^9	1.23 09
c. 0.00573	5.73×10^{-3}	5.73 −03
d. 0.00000 06239	6.239×10^{-7}	6.239 −07

Estimation

The scientist in Figure 1.14 is making an estimate of the velocity of the stream.

Part of problem solving is using common sense about the answers you obtain. This is even more important when using a calculator, because there is a misconception that if a calculator or computer displays an answer, "it must be correct." Reading and understanding the problem are parts of the process of problem solving.

When problem solving, you must ask whether the answer you have found is reasonable. If I ask for the amount of rent you must pay for an apartment, and you do a calculation and arrive at an answer of $16.25, you know that you have made a mistake. Likewise, an answer of $135,000 would not be reasonable. As we progress through this course you will be using a calculator for many of your calculations, and with a calculator you can easily press the wrong button and come up with an outrageous answer. One aspect of *looking back* is using common sense to make sure the answer is reasonable. The ability to recognize the difference between reasonable answers and unreasonable ones is important not only in mathematics, but whenever you are problem solving. This ability is even more important when you use a calculator, because pressing the incorrect key can often cause outrageously unreasonable answers.

Whenever you try to find an answer, you should ask yourself whether the answer is reasonable. How do you decide whether an answer is reasonable? One way is to **estimate** an answer. Webster's *New World Dictionary* tells us that as a verb, to *estimate* means "to form an opinion or a judgment about" or to calculate "approximately."

FIGURE 1.14 Estimating the velocity of a stream

The National Council of Teachers of Mathematics emphases the importance of estimation:

> The broad *mathematical context* for an estimate is usually one of the following types:
>
> A. An exact value is known but for some reason an estimate is used.
> B. An exact value is possible but is not known and an estimate is used.
> C. An exact value is impossible.

We will work on building your estimation skills throughout this book.

Example 8 Estimate annual salary

If your salary is $14.75 per hour, your annual salary is approximately

A. $5,000   B. $10,000   C. $15,000   D. $30,000   E. $45,000

Solution   Problem solving often requires some assumptions about the problem. For this problem, we are not told how many hours per week you work, or how many weeks per year you are paid. We assume a 40-hour work-week, and we also assume that you are paid for 52 weeks per year. *Estimate:* Your hourly salary is about $15 per hour. A 40-hour week gives us $40 \times \$15 = \$600$ per week. For the estimate, we calculate the wages for 50 weeks instead of 52: 50 weeks yields $50 \times \$600 = \$30,000$. The answer is D.

Example 9 Estimate map distance

Use the map in Figure 1.15 to estimate the distance from Orlando International Airport to Disney World.

FIGURE 1.15 Map around Walt Disney World

Solution   Note that the scale is 10 miles to 1 in. Looking at the map, you will note that it is approximately 1.5 in. from the airport to Disney World. This means that we estimate the distance to be 15 miles.

There are two important reasons for estimation: (1) to form a reasonable opinion or (2) to check the reasonableness of an answer. We will consider estimation for measurements in Chapter 9; if reason (1) is our motive, we should not think it necessary to follow an estimation by direct calculation. To do so would defeat the purpose of the estimation. On the other hand, if we are using the estimate for reason (2)—to see whether an answer is reasonable—we might perform the estimate as a check on the calculated answer for Example 3 (the problem about the speed of light):

$$186{,}000 \text{ miles per second} \approx 2 \times 10^5 \text{ miles per second}$$

and

$$\text{one year} \approx 4 \times 10^2 \text{ days}$$
$$\approx \underbrace{4 \times 10^2}_{days} \times \underbrace{2 \times 10}_{hr \ per \ day} \times \underbrace{6 \times 10}_{min \ per \ hr} \times \underbrace{6 \times 10}_{sec \ per \ hr}$$
$$\approx \underbrace{(4 \times 2 \times 6 \times 6) \times 10^5}_{seconds \ per \ year}$$
$$\approx (10 \times 36) \times 10^5$$
$$\approx 3.6 \times 10^7$$

Thus, one light year is about

$$\left(2 \times 10^5 \, \frac{\text{miles}}{\text{second}}\right)\left(3.6 \times 10^7 \, \frac{\text{seconds}}{\text{year}}\right) \approx 7.2 \times 10^{12} \, \frac{\text{miles}}{\text{year}}$$

This estimate seems to confirm the reasonableness of the answer 5.87×10^{12} we obtained in Example 3.

Laws of Exponents

In working out the previous estimation for Example 3, we used some properties of exponents that we can derive by, once again, turning to some patterns. Consider

$$10 \cdot 10 \cdot 10 \cdot 10 \cdot 10 = 10^5$$

and

$$10^2 \cdot 10^3 = (10 \cdot 10) \cdot (10 \cdot 10 \cdot 10) = 10^5$$

When we *multiply powers* of the same base, we *add* exponents. This is called the **addition law of exponents.**

$$2^3 \cdot 2^4 = (2 \cdot 2 \cdot 2) \cdot (2 \cdot 2 \cdot 2 \cdot 2)$$
$$= 2^{3+4}$$
$$= 2^7$$

Suppose we wish to raise a power to a power. We can apply the addition law of exponents. Consider

$$(2^3)^2 = 2^3 \cdot 2^3 = 2^{3+3} = 2^{2 \cdot 3} = 2^6$$
$$(10^2)^3 = 10^2 \cdot 10^2 \cdot 10^2 = 10^{2+2+2} = 10^{3 \cdot 2} = 10^6$$

When we *raise a power to a power*, we *multiply* the exponents. This is called the **multiplication law of exponents.**

A third law is needed to raise products to powers. Consider

$$(2 \cdot 3)^2 = (2 \cdot 3) \cdot (2 \cdot 3)$$
$$= (2 \cdot 2) \cdot (3 \cdot 3)$$
$$= 2^2 \cdot 3^2$$

Thus, $(2 \cdot 3)^2 = 2^2 \cdot 3^2$.

Another result, called the **distributive law of exponents,** says that to *raise a product to a power*, raise each factor to that power and then multiply. For example,

$$(3 \cdot 10^4)^2 = 3^2 \cdot (10^4)^2 = 3^2 \cdot 10^8 = 9 \cdot 10^8$$

Similar patterns can be observed for quotients.

We now summarize the five laws of exponents.*

STOP — Theorems and laws of mathematics are highlighted in a box that looks like this.

Laws of Exponents

Addition law:	$b^m \cdot b^n = b^{m+n}$
Multiplication law:	$(b^n)^m = b^{mn}$
Subtraction law:	$\dfrac{b^m}{b^n} = b^{m-n}$
Distributive laws:	$(ab)^m = a^m b^m \qquad \left(\dfrac{a}{b}\right)^m = \dfrac{a^m}{b^m}$

Example   10   Estimate a speed

Pólya's Method

Under $\frac{3}{4}$ impulse power, the starship *Enterprise* will travel 1 million kilometers (km) in 3 minutes.† Compare full impulse power with the speed of light, which is approximately $1.08 \cdot 10^9$ kilometers per hour (km/hr).

Solution   We use Pólya's problem-solving guidelines for this example.

Understand the Problem. You might say, "I don't know anything about *Star Trek,*" but with most problem solving in the real world, the problems you are asked to solve are often about situations with which you are unfamiliar. Finding the necessary information to understand the question is part of the process. We assume that full impulse is the same as 1 impulse power, so that if we multiply $\frac{3}{4}$ impulse power by $\frac{4}{3}$ we will obtain $\left(\frac{3}{4} \cdot \frac{4}{3} = 1\right)$ full impulse power.

Devise a Plan. We will calculate the distance traveled (in kilometers) in one hour under $\frac{3}{4}$ power, and then will multiply that result by $\frac{4}{3}$ to obtain the distance in kilometers per hour under full impulse power.

Carry Out the Plan.

$$\frac{3}{4} \text{ impulse power} = \frac{1{,}000{,}000 \text{ km}}{3 \text{ min}} \qquad \textit{Given}$$

$$= \frac{10^6 \text{ km}}{3 \text{ min}} \cdot \frac{20}{20} \qquad \textit{Multiply by } 1 = \frac{20}{20} \textit{ to change 3 minutes to 60 minutes.}$$

$$= \frac{10^6 \cdot 2 \cdot 10 \text{ km}}{60 \text{ min}}$$

$$= \frac{2 \cdot 10^7 \text{ km}}{1 \text{ hr}}$$

$$= 2 \cdot 10^7 \text{ km/hr}$$

We now multiply both sides by $\frac{4}{3}$ to find the distance under full impulse.

$$\frac{4}{3}\left(\frac{3}{4} \text{ impulse power}\right) = \frac{4}{3} \cdot 2 \cdot 10^7 \text{ km/hr}$$

$$\text{full impulse power} = \frac{8}{3} \cdot 10^7 \text{ km/hr}$$

$$\approx 2.666666667 \cdot 10^7 \text{ km/hr}$$

*You may be familiar with these laws of exponents from algebra. They hold with certain restrictions; for example, division by zero is excluded. We will discuss different sets of numbers in Chapter 5.

†*Star Trek, The Next Generation* (episode that first aired the week of May 15, 1993).

Comparing this to the speed of light, we see

$$\frac{\text{IMPULSE SPEED}}{\text{SPEED OF LIGHT}} = \frac{2.666666667 \cdot 10^7}{1.08 \cdot 10^9} = \frac{2.666666667}{1.08} \cdot 10^{7-9} \approx 0.025$$

Look Back. We see that full impulse power is about 2.5% of the speed of light.

Comprehending Large Numbers

We began this section by looking at the size of the cosmos. But just how large is large? Most of us are accustomed to hearing about millions, billions (budgets or costs of disasters), or even trillions (the national debt is about $15 trillion), but how do we really understand the magnitude of these numbers?

You may have seen the worldwide show,
Who Wants to Be a Millionaire?

A **million** is a fairly modest number, 10^6. Yet if we were to count one number per second, nonstop, it would take us about 278 hours or approximately $11\frac{1}{2}$ days to count to a million. Not a million days have elapsed since the birth of Christ (a million days is about 2,700 years). A large book of about 700 pages contains about a million letters. How large a room would it take to hold 1,000,000 inflated balloons?

The next big number is a **billion,** which is defined to be 1,000 millions.

However, with the U.S. government bailout in early 2009 we have entered the age of trillions. How large is a **trillion**? How long would it take you to count to a trillion?

Congressional leaders said that as much as $1 trillion will be needed to avoid an imminent meltdown in the U.S. financial system.

Go ahead—make a guess. To get some idea about how large a trillion is, let's compare it to some familiar units:

- If you gave away $1,000,000 *per day*, it would take you more than 2,700 *years* to give away a trillion dollars.
- A stack of a trillion $1 bills would be more than 59,000 miles high.
- At 5% interest, a trillion dollars would earn you $219,178,080 interest *per day*!
- A trillion seconds ago, Neanderthals walked the earth (31,710 years ago).

But a trillion is only 10^{12}, a mere nothing when compared with the real giants. Keep these magnitudes (sizes) in mind. Earlier in this section we noticed that a cube containing our solar neighborhood is 9.2×10^{11} miles on a side. (See Figure 1.13.) This is less than a billion times the size of the earth. (Actually, it is $9.2 \cdot 10^{11} \div 7,927 \approx 1.2 \times 10^8$.)

There is an old story of a king who, being under obligation to one of his subjects, offered to reward him in any way the subject desired. Being of mathematical mind and modest tastes, the subject simply asked for a chessboard with one grain of wheat on the first square, two on the second, four on the third, and so forth. The old king was delighted with this modest request! Alas, the king was soon sorry he granted the request.

Example 11 Estimate a large number

Estimate the magnitude of the grains of wheat on the last square of a chessboard.

Solution   We use Pólya's problem-solving guidelines for this example.*

Understand the Problem. Each square on the chessboard has grains of wheat placed on it. To answer this question you need to know that a chessboard has 64 squares. The first square has $1 = 2^0$ grains, the next has $2 = 2^1$ grains, the next $4 = 2^2$, and so on. Thus, he needed 2^{63} grains of wheat for the last square alone. We showed this number in Example 1d.

Devise a Plan. We know (from Example 1) that $2^{63} \approx 9.22337 \times 10^{18}$. We need to find the size of a grain of wheat, and then convert 2^{63} grains into bushels. Finally, we need to state this answer in terms we can understand.

Carry Out the Plan. I went to a health food store, purchased some raw wheat, and found that there are about 250 grains per cubic inch (in.^{3}). I also went to a dictionary and found that a bushel is 2,150 in.^{3}. Thus, the number of grains of wheat in a bushel is

$$2,150 \times 250 = 537,500 = 5.375 \times 10^5$$

To find the number of bushels in 2^{63} grains, we need to divide:

$$\left(9.922337 \times 10^{18}\right) \div \left(5.375 \times 10^5\right) = \frac{9.22337}{5.375} \times 10^{18-5}$$
$$\approx 1.72 \times 10^{13}$$

Look Back. This answer does not mean a thing without looking back and putting it in terms we can understand. I googled "U.S. wheat production" and found that in 2001 the U.S. wheat production was 2,281,763,000 bushels. To find the number of years it would take the United States to produce the necessary wheat for the last square of the chessboard, we need to divide the production into the amount needed:

$$\frac{1.72 \times 10^{13}}{2.28 \times 10^9} = \frac{1.72}{2.28} \times 10^{13-9} \approx 0.75 \times 10^4 \text{ or } 7.5 \times 10^3$$

This is 7,500 years!

*A chessboard has 64 alternating black and red squares arranged into an 8-by-8 pattern.

What is the name of the largest number you know? Go ahead—answer this question. Recently we have heard about the national debt, which exceeds $15 **trillion.** Table 1.1 shows some large numbers.

TABLE 1.1

Some Large Numbers

Number	Name	Meaning
1	one	1 ← Basic counting unit
2	two	2 ← Number of computer states (on/off)
2^3	byte	8 ← A basic unit on a computer; a string of eight binary digits
10	ten	10 ← Number of fingers on two normal hands
10^2	hundred	100 ← Number of pennies in a dollar
10^3	thousand	1,000 ← About 5,000 of these dots ● would fit 50 per row on this page
2^{10}	kilobyte	1,024 ← Computer term for 1,024 bytes, abbreviated K
10^6	million	1,000,000 ← Number of letters in a large book.
2^{20}	megabyte	1,048,576 ← A unit of computer storage capacity; MB
10^9	billion	1,000,000,000 ← Discussed in text
2^{30}	gigabyte	1,073,741,824 ← Approximately 1,000 MB; abbreviated GB
10^{12}	trillion	1,000,000,000,000 ← National debt is about $15 trillion
10^{15}	quadrillion	1,000,000,000,000,000 ← Number of words ever printed
10^{18}	quintillion	1,000,000,000,000,000,000 ← Estimated number of insects in the world
10^{21}	sextillion	1,000,000,000,000,000,000,000 ← Cups of water in all the oceans
10^{63}	vigintillion	1 followed by 63 zeros ← Chessboard problem; cubic inches in Milky Way
10^{100}	googol	1 followed by 100 zeros ← 10^{128} is the number of neutrons in the universe.
10^{googol}	googolplex	10 to the power of a googol ← This is really too large to comprehend.

Do Things Really Change?

"Students today can't prepare bark to calculate their problems. They depend upon their slates which are more expensive. What will they do when their slate is dropped and it breaks? They will be unable to write!"

Teacher's Conference, 1703

"Students depend upon paper too much. They don't know how to write on slate without chalk dust all over themselves. They can't clean a slate properly. What will they do when they run out of paper?"

Principal's Association, 1815

"Students today depend too much upon ink. They don't know how to use a pen knife to sharpen a pencil. Pen and ink will never replace the pencil."

National Association of Teachers, 1907

"Students today depend upon store bought ink. They don't know how to make their own. When they run out of ink they will be unable to write word or ciphers until their next trip to the settlement. This is a sad commentary on modern education."

The Rural American Teacher, 1929

"Students today depend upon these expensive fountain pens. They can no longer write with a straight pen and nib (not to mention sharpening their own quills). We parents must not allow them to wallow in such luxury to the detriment of learning how to cope in the real business world, which is not so extravagant."

PTA Gazette, 1941

"Ball point pens will be the ruin of education in our country. Students use these devices and then throw them away. The American virtues of thrift and frugality are being discarded. Business and banks will never allow such expensive luxuries."

Federal Teacher, 1950

"Students today depend too much on hand-held calculators."

Anonymous, 1995

Problem Set   **1.3**

1. **IN YOUR OWN WORDS**   What do we mean by *exponent*?

2. **IN YOUR OWN WORDS**   Define *scientific notation* and discuss why it is useful.

3. **IN YOUR OWN WORDS**   Do you plan to use a calculator for working the problems in this book? If so, what type of logic does it use?

4. **IN YOUR OWN WORDS**   Describe the differences in evaluating exponents and using scientific notation on a calculator.

5. **IN YOUR OWN WORDS**   What is the largest number whose name you know? Describe the size of this number.

6. **IN YOUR OWN WORDS**   What is a *trillion*? Do not simply define this number, but discuss its magnitude (size) in terms that are easy to understand.

Write each of the numbers in Problems 7–10 in scientific notation and in floating-point notation (as on a calculator).

7. **a.** 3,200   **b.** 0.0004   **c.** 64,000,000,000

8. **a.** 23.79   **b.** 0.000001   **c.** 35,000,000,000

9. **a.** 5,629   **b.** 630,000   **c.** 0.00000 0034

10. **a.** googol   **b.** 1,200,300   **c.** 0.00000 123

Write each of the numbers in Problems 11–14 in fixed-point notation.

11. **a.** 7^2 **b.** 7.2×10^{10} **c.** $4.56 + 3$

12. **a.** 2^6 **b.** 2.1×10^{-3} **c.** $4.07 + 4$

13. **a.** 6^3 **b.** 4.1×10^{-7} **c.** $4.8 \ -7$

14. **a.** 6^{-2} **b.** 3.217×10^7 **c.** $8.89 -11$

Write each of the numbers in Problems 15–18 in scientific notation

15.

16. The velocity of light in a vacuum is about 30,000,000,000 cm/sec.

17. The distance between Earth and Mars (220,000,000 miles) when drawn to scale is 0.00000 25 in.

18. In 2010, the national debt was approximately $12 trillion. It has been proposed that this number be used to define a new monetary unit, a *light buck*. That is, one light buck is the amount necessary to generate domestic goods and services at the rate of $186,000 per second. What is the national debt in terms of light bucks?

Write each of the numbers in Problems 19–22 in fixed-point notation.

19. A kilowatt-hour is about 3.6×10^6 joules.

20. A ton is about 9.06×10^2 kilograms.

21. The volume of a typical neuron is about 3×10^{-8} cm^3.

22. If the sun were a light bulb, it would be rated at 3.8×10^{25} watts.

23. Estimate the distance from Los Angeles International Airport to Disneyland.

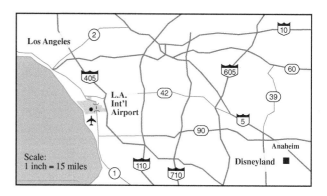

24. Estimate the distance from Fish Camp to Yosemite Village in Yosemite National Park.

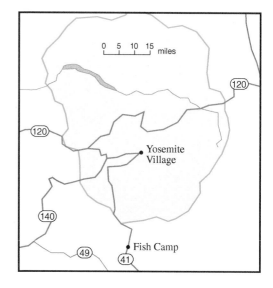

In Problems 25–30, first estimate your answer and then calculate the exact answer.

25. How many pages are necessary to make 1,850 copies of a manuscript that is 487 pages long? (Print on one side only.)

26. If you are paid $16.25 per hour, what is your annual salary?

27. If your car gets 23 miles per gallon, how far can you go on 15 gallons of gas?

28. If your car travels 280 miles and uses 10.2 gallons, how many miles per gallon did you get?

29. In the musical *Rent* there is a song called "Seasons of Love" that uses the number 525,600 minutes. How long is this?

30. It has been estimated that there are 107 billion pieces of mail per year. If the postage rates are raised 2¢, how much extra revenue does that generate?

Level 2

Compute the results in Problems 31–36. Leave your answers in scientific notation.

31. a. $(6 \times 10^5)(2 \times 10^3)$ **b.** $\dfrac{6 \times 10^5}{2 \times 10^3}$

32. a. $\dfrac{(5 \times 10^4)(8 \times 10^5)}{4 \times 10^6}$ **b.** $\dfrac{(6 \times 10^{-3})(7 \times 10^8)}{3 \times 10^7}$

33. a. $\dfrac{(6 \times 10^7)(4.8 \times 10^{-6})}{2.4 \times 10^5}$ **b.** $\dfrac{(2.5 \times 10^3)(6.6 \times 10^8)}{8.25 \times 10^4}$

34. a. $\dfrac{(2xy^{-2})(2^{-1}x^{-1}y^4)}{x^{-2}y^2}$ **b.** $\dfrac{x^2y(2x^3y^{-5})}{2^{-2}x^4y^{-8}}$

35. a. $\dfrac{0.00016 \times 500}{2,000,000}$ **b.** $\dfrac{15,000 \times 0.0000004}{0.005}$

36. a. $\dfrac{4,500,000,000,000 \times 0.00001}{50 \times 0.0003}$

b. $\dfrac{0.0348 \times 0.00000\ 00000\ 00002}{0.000058 \times 0.03}$

Estimate the number of items in each photograph in Problems 37–40.

37.

klenger/iStockphoto.com

38.

Lori Sparkia, 2010/Used under license from Shutterstock.com

39.

Alan Schein Photography/Corbis Edge/Corbis

40.

Robert F. Sisson/National Geographic/Getty Images

In Problems 41–48, you need to make some assumptions before you estimate your answer. State your assumptions and then calculate the exact answer.

41. How many classrooms would be necessary to hold 1,000,000 inflated balloons?

42. Carrie Dashow, the "say hello" woman, is trying to personally greet 1,000,000 people. In her first year, which ended on January 3, 2000, she had greeted 13,688 people. At this rate, how long will it take her to greet one million people?

43. Approximately how high would a stack of 1 million $1 bills be? (Assume there are 233 new $1 bills per inch.)

44. Estimate how many pennies it would take to make a stack 1 in. high. Approximately how high would a stack of 1 million pennies be?

45. If the U.S. annual production of sugar is 30,000,000 tons, estimate the number of grains of sugar produced in a year in the United States. Use scientific notation. (*Note:* There are 2,000 lb per ton; assume there are 2,260,000 grains in a pound of sugar.)

46. The *San Francisco Examiner* (Feb. 6, 2000, Travel Section) reported that David Phillips, a civil engineer at University of California, Davis, was pushing his shopping cart when he noticed a promotion of Healthy Choice®.

He could earn 1,000 airline miles for every 10 bar codes from Healthy Choice products he sent to the company by the end of the month. Frozen entries are about $2 apiece, but with a little work he found individual servings of chocolate pudding for 25 cents each. He was able to accumulate 1,215,000 airline miles. How much did it cost him?

47. A school in Oakland, California, spent $100,000 in changing its mascot sign. If the school had used this amount of money for chalk, estimate the length of the chalk laid end-to-end.

48. "Each year Delta serves 9 million cans of Coke®. Laid end-to-end, they would stretch from Atlanta to Chicago."* Is this a reasonable estimate? What is the actual length of 9 million Coke cans laid end-to-end?

Level 3

49. a. What is the largest number you can represent on your calculator?
b. What is the largest number you can think of using only three digits?
c. Use scientific notation to estimate this number. Your calculator may help, but will probably not give you the answer directly.

50. HISTORICAL QUEST Zerah Colburn (1804–1840) toured America when he was 6 years old to display his calculating ability. He could instantaneously give the square and cube roots of large numbers. It is reported that it took him only a few seconds to find 8^{16}. Use your calculator to *help you* find this number exactly (not in scientific notation).

51. HISTORICAL QUEST Jedidiah Buxion (1707–1772) never learned to write, but given any distance he could tell you the number of inches, and given any length of time he could tell you the number of seconds. If he listened to a speech or a sermon, he could tell the number of words or syllables in it. It reportedly took him only a few moments to mentally calculate the number of cubic inches in a right-angle block of stone

23,451,789 yards long, 5,642,732 yards wide, and 54,465 yards thick. Estimate this answer on your calculator. You will use scientific notation because of the limitations of your calculator, but remember that Jedidiah gave the *exact* answer by working the problem in his head.

52. HISTORICAL QUEST George Bidder (1806–1878) not only possessed exceptional power at calculations but also went on to obtain a good education. He could give immediate answers to problems of compound interest and annuities. One question he was asked was, If the moon is 238,000 miles from the earth and sound travels at the rate of 4 miles per minute, how long would it be before the inhabitants of the moon could hear the Battle of Waterloo? By calculating *mentally,* he gave the answer in less than one minute! First make an estimate, and then use your calculator to give the answer in days, hours, and minutes, to the nearest minute.

53. Estimate the number of bricks required to build a solid wall 100 ft by 10 ft by 1 ft.

54. A sheet of notebook paper is approximately 0.003 in. thick. Tear the sheet in half so that there are 2 sheets. Repeat so that there are 4 sheets. If you repeat again, there will be a pile of 8 sheets. Continue in this fashion until the paper has been halved 50 times. If it were possible to complete the process, how high would you guess the final pile would be? After you have guessed, *compute* the height.

Problem Solving 3

55. If it takes one second to write down each digit, how long will it take to write down all the numbers from 1 to 1,000?

56. If it takes one second to write down each digit, how long will it take to write down all the numbers from 1 to 1,000,000?

57. Imagine that you have written down the numbers from 1 to 1,000. What is the total number of zeros you have recorded?

58. Imagine that you have written down the numbers from 1 to 1,000,000. What is the total number of zeros you have recorded?

59. a. If the entire population of the world moved to California and each person were given an equal amount of area, how much space would you *guess* that each person would have (multiple choice)?
   A. 7 in.^{2}
   B. 7 ft^2
   C. 70 ft^2
   D. 700 ft^2
   E. 1 mi^2
b. If California is 158,600 mi^2 and the world population is 6.3 billion, calculate the answer to part **a.**

60. It is known that a person's body has about one gallon of blood in it, and that a cubic foot will hold about 7.5 gallons of liquid. It is also known that Central Park in New York has an area of 840 acres. If walls were built around the park, how tall would those walls need to be to contain the blood of all 6,300,000,000 people in the world?

1.4 | CHAPTER SUMMARY

Numeracy is the ability to cope confidently with the mathematical demands of adult life.
MATHEMATICS COUNTS

Important Ideas

Guidelines for problem solving [1.1]
Order of operations [1.2]
Extended order of operations [1.3]
Laws of exponents [1.3]
Inductive vs deductive reasoning [1.3]
Euler circles [1.3]

 Take some time getting ready to work the review problems in this section. First review the listed important ideas. Look back at the definition and property boxes in this chapter. If you look online, you will find a list of important terms introduced in this chapter, as well as the types of problems that were introduced in this chapter. You will maximize your understanding of this chapter by working the problems in this section only after you have studied the material.

 You will find some review help online at **www.mathnature.com.** There are links giving general test help in studying for a mathematics examination, as well as specific help for reviewing this chapter.

Chapter 1 Review Questions

1. In your own words, describe Pólya's problem-solving model.

2. In how many ways can a person walk 5 blocks north and 4 blocks west, if the streets are arranged in a standard rectangular arrangement?

3. A chessboard consists of 64 squares, as shown in Figure 1.17. The rook can move one or more squares horizontally or vertically. Suppose a rook is in the upper-left-hand corner of a chessboard. Tell how many ways the rook can reach the point marked "X". Assume that the rook always moves toward its destination.

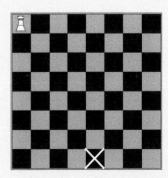

FIGURE 1.17 Chessboard

4. Compute $111,111,111 \times 111,111,111$. Do not use direct multiplication; show all your work.

5. What is meant by "order of operations"?

6. What is scientific notation?

7. Does the story in the news clip illustrate inductive or deductive reasoning?

> Q: What has 18 legs and catches flies?
> A: I don't know, what?
> Q: A baseball team. What has 36 legs and catches flies?
> A: I don't know that, either.
> Q: Two baseball teams. If the United States has 100 senators, and each state has 2 senators, what does...
> A: I know this one!
> Q: Good. What does each state have?
> A: Three baseball teams!

8. Show the calculator keys you would press as well as the calculator display for the result. Also state the brand and model of the calculator you are using.

   a. 2^{63}

   b. $\dfrac{9.22 \times 10^{18}}{6.34 \times 10^{6}}$

9. Assume that there is a $281.9 billion budget "windfall." Which of the following choices would come closest to liquidating this windfall?
   A. Buy the entire U.S. population a steak dinner.
   B. Burn one dollar per second for the next 1,000 years.
   C. Give $80,000 to every resident of San Francisco and use the remainder of the money to buy a $200 iPod for every resident of China.

10. What is wrong, if anything, with the following "Great Tapes" advertisement?

> Instead of reading the 100 greatest books of all time, buy these beautifully transcribed books on tape. If you listen to only one 45-minute tape per day, you will complete the greatest books of all time in only one year.

11. In 1995, it was reported that an iceberg separated from Antarctica. The size of this iceberg was reported equal to to 7×10^{16} ice cubes. Convert this size to meaningful units.

12. The national debt in 2010 soared to $13,800,000,000,000. Write this number in scientific notation. Suppose that in 2010 there were 310,000,000 people in the United States. If the debt is divided equally among these people, how much is each person's share?

13. Rearrange the cards in the formulation shown here so that each horizontal, vertical, and diagonal line of three adds up to 15.

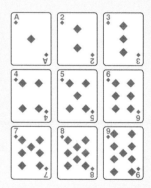

14. Assume that your classroom is 20 ft $\times$ 30 ft $\times$ 10 ft. If you fill this room with dollar bills (assume that a stack of 233 dollar bills is 1 in. tall), how many classrooms would it take to contain the 2010 national debt of $13,800,000,000,000?

Use Euler circles to check the validity of each of the arguments given in Problems 15–18.

15. All birds have wings.
All flies have wings.
Therefore, some flies are birds.

16. No apples are bananas.
All apples are fruit.
Therefore, no bananas are fruit.

17. All artists are creative.
Some musicians are artists.
Therefore, some musicians are creative.

18. All rectangles are polygons.
All squares are rectangles.
Therefore, all squares are polygons.

19. Consider the following pattern:

1 is happy.
10 is happy because $1^2 + 0^2 = 1$, which is happy.
13 is happy because $1^2 + 3^2 = 10$, which is happy.
19 is happy because $1^1 + 9^2 = 82$ and $8^2 + 2^2 = 68$
and $6^2 + 8^2 = 100$ and $1^2 + 0^2 + 0^2 = 1$, which is happy.

On the other hand,

2, 3, 4, 5, 6, 7, 8, and 9 are unhappy.
11 is unhappy because $1^2 + 1^2 = 2$, which is unhappy.
12 is unhappy because $1^2 + 2^2 = 5$, which is unhappy.

Find one unhappy number as well as one happy number.

20. Suppose you could write out 7^{1000}. What is the last digit?

BOOK REPORTS

Write a 500-word report on one of these books:

Mathematical Magic Show, Martin Gardner (New York: Alfred A. Knopf, 1977).

How to Solve It: A New Aspect of Mathematical Method, George Pólya (New Jersey: Princeton University Press, 1945, 1973).

Group RESEARCH PROJECTS

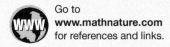

Working in small groups is typical of most work environments, and learning to work with others to communicate specific ideas is an important skill. Work with three or four other students to submit a single report based on each of the following questions.

G1. It is stated in the Prologue that "Mathematics is alive and constantly changing." As we complete the second decade of this century, we stand on the threshold of major changes in the mathematics curriculum in the United States.

Report on some of these recent changes.

REFERENCES Lynn Steen, *Everybody Counts: A Report to the Nation on the Future of Mathematics Education* (Washington, DC: National Academy Press, 1989). See also *Curriculum and Evaluation Standards for School Mathematics* from the National Council of Teachers of Mathematics (Reston, VA: NCTM, 1989). A reassessment of these standards was done by Kenneth A. Ross, *The MAA and the New NCTM Standards* (© 2000 The Mathematical Association of America.)

G2. Do some research on Pascal's triangle, and see how many properties you can discover. You might begin by answering these questions:
  a. What are the successive powers of 11?
  b. Where are the natural numbers found in Pascal's triangle?
  c. What are triangular numbers and how are they found in Pascal's triangle?
  d. What are the tetrahedral numbers and how are they found in Pascal's triangle?
  e. What relationships do the patterns in Figure 1.18 have to Pascal's triangle?

Multiples of 2

Multiples of 3

FIGURE 1.18 Patterns in Pascal's triangle

REFERENCES James N. Boyd, "Pascal's Triangle," *Mathematics Teacher,* November 1983, pp. 559–560.

Dale Seymour, *Visual Patterns in Pascal's Triangle,* (Palo Alto, CA: Dale Seymour Publications, 1986).

Karl J. Smith, "Pascal's Triangle," *Two-Year College Mathematics Journal*, Volume 4, pp. 1–13 (Winter 1973).

Individual RESEARCH PROJECTS

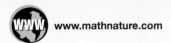
www.mathnature.com

*Learning to use sources outside your classroom and textbook is an important skill, and here are some ideas for extending some of the ideas in this chapter. You can find references to these projects in a library or at **www.mathnature.com**.*

PROJECT 1.1 Find some puzzles, tricks, or magic stunts that are based on mathematics.

PROJECT 1.2 Write a short paper about the construction of magic squares. Figure 1.19 shows a magic square created by Benjamin Franklin.

52	61	4	13	20	29	36	45
14	3	62	51	46	35	30	19
53	60	5	12	21	28	37	44
11	6	59	54	43	38	27	22
55	58	7	10	23	26	39	42
9	8	57	56	41	40	25	24
50	63	2	15	18	31	34	47
16	1	64	49	48	33	32	17

FIGURE 1.19 Benjamin Franklin magic square*

PROJECT 1.3 Design a piece of art based on a magic square.

PROJECT 1.4 An *alphamagic square*, invented by Lee Sallows, is a magic square so that not only do the numbers spelled out in words form a magic square, but the numbers of letters of the words also form a magic square. For example,

five	twenty-two	eighteen
twenty-eight	fifteen	two
twelve	eight	twenty-five

gives rise to two magic squares:

5	22	18
28	15	2
12	8	25

and

4	9	8
11	7	3
6	5	10

The first magic square comes from the numbers represented by the words in the alphamagic square, and the second magic square comes from the numbers of letters in the words of the alphamagic square.

a. Verify that this is an alphamagic square.   **b.** Find another alphamagic square.

PROJECT 1.5 Answer the question posed in Problem 59, Section 1.3 for your own state. If you live in California, then use Florida.

PROJECT 1.6 Read the article "Mathematics at the Turn of the Millennium," by Philip A. Griffiths, *The American Mathematical Monthly,* January 2000, pp. 1–14. Briefly describe each of these famous problems:

a. Fermat's last theorem

b. Kepler's sphere packing conjecture

c. The four-color problem

Which of these problems are discussed later in this text, and where?

The objective of this article was to communicate something about mathematics to a general audience. How well did it succeed with you? Discuss.

*"How Many Squares Are There, Mr. Franklin?" by Maya Mohsin Ahmed, *The Mathematical Monthly,* May 2004, p. 394.

6 THE NATURE OF ALGEBRA

Outline

What in the World?

Will these objects balance?

Hannah, a very small person, is moving into the dorms at her school and she needs to move a very large, heavy chest. She does not know what to do, so she asks her friend, Jane, for help. Jane tells Hannah, "Let's get a big board. I remember from school that you can move a big object with a lever."

"I get it!" Hannah cried loudly. "I have just the right stuff out back. Let's see. . . . Look at how I've put this together."

"What is that you've put on the other end of the lever?" asked Jane.

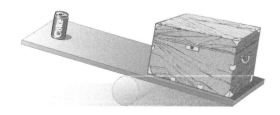

"Well, it's a can of Coke. Will that not work?" asked Hannah.

"That's really silly, Hannah," said Jane sarcastically.

Hannah quickly responded, "Not if the weights of the can of Coke and the trunk are the same. You do not know how much each of these containers weighs, and I'm prepared to show you that they weigh exactly the same!"

Overview

It has been said that algebra is the greatest labor-saving device ever invented. Even though you have probably had algebra sometime in your past, the essential algebraic ideas you will need for the rest of this text are covered or reviewed in this chapter. We begin with the basic building blocks of algebra—namely, polynomials and operations with polynomials. There are four main processes in algebra: **simplify** (Section 6.1), **factor** (Section 6.2), **evaluate** (Section 6.3), and **solve** (Sections 6.4, 6.5, and 6.7). Some applications of these ideas are introduced in the last four sections of this chapter. We look at an application from genetics; take a peek at computer spreadsheets; and solve application problems with numbers, ratios, proportions, percents, distance, and Pythagorean relationships.

6.1 Polynomials

The fact that algebra has its origin in arithmetic, . . . led Sir Isaac Newton to designate it "Universal Arithmetic," a designation which, vague as it is, indicates its character better than any other.

GEORGE E. CHRYSTAL

CHAPTER **CHALLENGE**

See if you can fill in the question mark.   1   2   3   5   ?

Historical NOTE

Algebra and algebraic ideas date back 4,000 years to the Babylonians and the Egyptians; the Hindus and the Greeks also solved algebraic problems. The title of Arab mathematician al-Khwârizmî's text (about A.D. 825), *Hisâb al-jabr w'almugâbalah*, is the origin of the word *algebra*. The book was widely known in Europe through Latin translations. The word *al-jabr or al-ge-bra* became synonymous with equation solving. Interestingly enough, the Arabic word *al-jabr* was also used in connection with medieval barbers. The barber, who also set bones and let blood in those times, was known as an *algebrista*. In the 19th century, there was a significant change in the prevalent attitude toward mathematics: Up to that time, mathematics was expected to have immediate and direct applications, but now mathematicians became concerned with the structure of their subject and with the *validity*, rather than the practicality, of their conclusions. Thus, there was a move toward *pure mathematics* and away from *applied mathematics*.

Many people think of algebra as simply a high school mathematics course in which **variables** (symbols used to represent an unspecified member of some set) are manipulated. This chapter reviews many of these procedures; however, the word **algebra** refers to a structure, or a set of axioms that forms the basis for what is accepted and what is not. For example, in the previous chapter we defined a field, which involves a set, two operations, and 11 specified properties. If you studied Section 5.7, you investigated an algebra with a finite number of elements. As you study the ordinary algebra presented in this chapter, you should remember this is only one of many possible algebras. Additional algebras are often studied in more advanced mathematics courses.

In this chapter we will review much of the algebra you have previously studied. There are four main processes in algebra, which we will review in this chapter: *simplify, factor, evaluate,* and *solve.*

Terminology

Recall that a **term** is a number, a variable, or the product of numbers and variables. Thus, $10x$ is one term, but $10 + x$ is not (because the terms 10 and x are connected by addition and not by multiplication). A fundamental notion in algebra is that of a **polynomial,** which is a term or the sum of terms. We classify polynomials by the number of terms and by degree:

A polynomial with one term is called a **monomial.**

A polynomial with two terms is called a **binomial.**

A polynomial with three terms is called a **trinomial.**

⟨CAUTION⟩ You may think this terminology is not very important, but be careful! It is essential that you know how to use these boldface terms correctly.

There are other words that could be used for polynomials with more than three terms, but this classification is sufficient. To classify by degree, we recall that the **degree of a term** is the number of *variable* factors in that term. Thus, $3x$ is first-degree, $5xy$ is second-degree, 10 is zero-degree, $2x^2$ is second-degree, and $9x^2y^3$ is fifth-degree. The **degree of a polynomial** is the largest degree of any of its terms. A first-degree term is sometimes called **linear,** and a second-degree term is sometimes referred to as **quadratic.** The numerical part of a term, usually written before the variable part, is called the **numerical coefficient.** In $3x$, it is the number 3, in $5xy$ it is the number 5, and in $9x^2y^3$ it is the number 9.

Example **1** **Classify polynomials**

Classify each polynomial by number of terms and by degree. If the expression is not a polynomial, so state.

a. x **b.** $x^2 + 5x - 7$ **c.** $x^3 - \dfrac{2}{x}$ **d.** $x^2 y^3 - xy^2$ **e.** 5

Solution

a. Monomial, degree 1
b. Trinomial, degree 2
c. Not a polynomial because it involves division by a variable. Notice that $x^3 - \frac{x}{2}$ *is a* polynomial because it can be written as $x^3 - \frac{1}{2}x$ and fractional coefficients are permitted.
d. Binomial, degree 5
e. Monomial, degree 0

When writing polynomials, it is customary to arrange the terms from the highest-degree to the lowest-degree term. If terms have the same degree they are usually listed in alphabetical order.

Simplification

When working with polynomials, it is necessary to simplify algebraic expressions. The key ideas of simplification are *similar terms* and the *distributive property*. Terms that differ only in the numerical coefficients are called **like terms** or **similar terms.**

Example **2** **Simplify algebraic expressions**

Simplify the given algebraic expressions.

a. $-12x - (-5)x$ **b.** $-3x - 6x + 2x$ **c.** $2x + 3y + 5x - 2y$
d. $5xy^2 - xy^2 - 4x^2y$ **e.** $(4x - 5) + (5x^2 + 2x - 3)$ **f.** $(4x - 5) - (5x^2 + 2x - 3)$

Solution

a. $-12x - (-5x) = -12x + 5x = -7x$ Add the opposite of ($-5x$).
b. $-3x - 6x + 2x = -7x$
c. $2x + 3y + 5x - 2y = 7x + y$ Note the similar terms.
d. $5xy^2 - xy^2 - 4x^2y = 4xy^2 - 4x^2y$
e. $(4x - 5) + (5x^2 + 2x - 3) = 5x^2 + (4x + 2x) + (-5 - 3)$
$$= 5x^2 + 6x - 8$$
f. Recall that to subtract a polynomial, you subtract *each* term of that polynomial:

$$(4x - 5) - (5x^2 + 2x - 3) = 4x - 5 - 5x^2 - 2x - (-3)$$
$$= -5x^2 + 2x - 2$$

When the algebraic expressions that we are simplifying are polynomials, we specify the form of the simplified expression.

STOP   This is the first of the four main processes of algebra.

Simplify Polynomials

To **simplify** a polynomial means to carry out all operations (according to the order-of-operations agreement) and to write the answer in a form with the highest-degree term first, with the rest of the terms arranged by decreasing degree. If there are two terms of the same degree, arrange those terms alphabetically.

Remember from beginning algebra that $-x = (-1)x$, so to subtract a polynomial you can do it as shown in Example 2f—by subtracting *each* term—or you can think of it as an application of the distributive property:

$$(4x - 5) - (5x^2 + 2x - 3) = 4x - 5 + (-1)(5x^2 + 2x - 3)$$
$$= 4x - 5 + (-1)(5x^2) + (-1)(2x) + (-1)(-3)$$
$$= -5x^2 + 2x - 2$$

The distributive property is also important in multiplying polynomials.

Example 3   Simplify algebraic expressions with parentheses

Simplify the given algebraic expressions.
a. $3x(x^2 - 1)$ **b.** $(2x - 3)(x + 1)$ **c.** $(x + 2)(x^2 + 5x - 2)$ **d.** $(2x + 1)^3$

Solution   In each case, we will distribute the expression on the left: $3x$, $(2x - 3)$, $(x + 2)$, and $(2x + 1)$, respectively. You will find your work easier to read if you work down with the equal signs aligned rather than across your paper. And finally, we use the laws of exponents (Section 1.3, p. 36) to simplify expressions such as $x(x^2) = x^1 x^2 = x^{1+2} = x^3$.

a. $3x(x^2 - 1) = 3x(x^2) + 3x(-1)$ This step is usually done mentally, and is not written down.
$$= 3x^3 - 3x$$

b. $(2x - 3)(x + 1) = (2x - 3)(x) + (2x - 3)(1)$ Mental step
$$= 2x^2 - 3x + 2x - 3 \qquad \text{Distributive property}$$
$$= 2x^2 - x - 3 \qquad \text{Add similar terms.}$$

c. $(x + 2)(x^2 + 5x - 2) = (x + 2)(x^2) + (x + 2)(5x) + (x + 2)(-2)$
$$= x^3 + 2x^2 + 5x^2 + 10x - 2x - 4$$
$$= x^3 + 7x^2 + 8x - 4$$

d. $(2x + 1)^3 = (2x + 1)(2x + 1)(2x + 1)$ Definition of cube
$$= (2x + 1)[(2x + 1)(2x) + (2x + 1)(1)]$$
$$= (2x + 1)[4x^2 + 2x + 2x + 1]$$
$$= (2x + 1)(4x^2 + 4x + 1)$$
$$= (2x + 1)(4x^2) + (2x + 1)(4x) + (2x + 1)(1)$$
$$= 8x^3 + 4x^2 + 8x^2 + 4x + 2x + 1$$
$$= 8x^3 + 12x^2 + 6x + 1$$

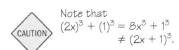

CAUTION Note that
$(2x)^3 + (1)^3 = 8x^3 + 1^3$
$\neq (2x + 1)^3$.

Shortcuts with Products

It is frequently necessary to multiply binomials, and even though we use the distributive property, we want to be able to carry out the process quickly and efficiently in our heads. Consider the following example, which leads us from multiplication using the distributive property to an efficient process that is usually called **FOIL**.

Example 4   Use FOIL to multiply

Simplify: **a.** $(2x + 3)(4x - 5)$ **b.** $(5x - 3)(2x + 3)$ **c.** $(4x - 3)(3x - 2)$

Solution

a. $(2x + 3)(4x - 5) = (2x + 3)(4x) + (2x + 3)(-5)$ Distributive property
$$= \underline{8x^2} \qquad + \qquad \underline{12x + (-10x)} \qquad + \underline{(-15)}$$

↑	↑	↑
Product of first terms	Sum of products of inner terms and outer terms	Product of last terms

$$= 8x^2 + 2x - 15$$

b. $(5x - 3)(2x + 3) = \underbrace{10x^2}_{\uparrow} + \underbrace{(15x - 6x)}_{\uparrow} + \underbrace{(-9)}_{\uparrow}$ Mentally

FIRST terms   OUTER terms and   LAST terms
INNER terms

$$= 10x^2 + 9x - 9$$

c. $(4x - 3)(3x - 2) = 12x^2 - 17x + 6$ Mentally

You are encouraged to carry out the binomial multiplication mentally, as shown in Example 4c. To help you remember the process, we sometimes call this binomial multiplication **FOIL** to remind you.

First terms + **O**uter terms + **I**nner terms + **L**ast terms

Foil Binomial Product

To multiply two binomials, carry out this mental step.

$$(ax + b)(cx + d) = \underbrace{acx^2}_{\uparrow} + \underbrace{(ad + bc)x}_{\uparrow} + \underbrace{bd}_{\uparrow}$$

First terms   **O**uter   **L**ast terms
+
Inner

Example 5 Mentally multiply

Simplify (mentally):
a. $(2x - 3)(x + 3)$ **b.** $(x + 3)(3x - 4)$ **c.** $(5x - 2)(3x + 4)$

Solution

a. $(2x - 3)(x + 3) = \underbrace{2x^2}_{\uparrow \atop \mathbf{F}} + \underbrace{3x}_{\mathbf{O + I}} - \underbrace{9}_{\uparrow \atop \mathbf{L}}$

b. $(x + 3)(3x - 4) = 3x^2 + 5x - 12$
c. $(5x - 2)(3x + 4) = 15x^2 + 14x - 8$

A second shortcut involves raising a binomial to an integral power—for example, $(2x + 1)^3$ or $(a + b)^8$. We look for a pattern with the following example.

Example 6 Expand a binomial   Pólya's Method

Expand (multiply out) the expression $(a + b)^8$.

Solution   We use Pólya's problem-solving guidelines for this example.

Understand the Problem. We could begin by using the definition of 8th power and the distributive property:

$$(a + b)^8 = \underbrace{(a + b)(a + b) \cdots (a + b)}_{8 \text{ factors of } a + b}$$

However, we soon see that this is too lengthy to complete directly.

Devise a Plan. We will consider a pattern of successive powers; that is, consider $(a + b)^n$ for $n = 0, 1, 2, \ldots$.

Carry Out the Plan. We begin by actually doing the multiplications:

$$
\begin{aligned}
n = 0:\ (a + b)^0 &= \qquad\qquad\qquad 1\\
n = 1:\ (a + b)^1 &= \qquad\qquad 1 \cdot a + 1 \cdot b\\
n = 2:\ (a + b)^2 &= \qquad\quad 1 \cdot a^2 + 2 \cdot ab + 1 \cdot b^2\\
n = 3:\ (a + b)^3 &= \quad 1 \cdot a^3 + 3 \cdot a^2 b + 3 \cdot ab^2 + 1 \cdot b^3\\
n = 4:\ (a + b)^4 &= 1 \cdot a^4 + 4 \cdot a^3 b + 6 \cdot a^2 b^2 + 4 \cdot ab^3 + 1 \cdot b^4\\
&\quad\vdots
\end{aligned}
$$

First, ignore the coefficients (shown in color) and focus on the variables:

$$
\begin{aligned}
(a + b)^1:&\quad a \quad b\\
(a + b)^2:&\quad a^2 \quad ab \quad b^2\\
(a + b)^3:&\quad a^3 \quad a^2 b \quad ab^2 \quad b^3\\
(a + b)^4:&\quad a^4 \quad a^3 b \quad a^2 b^2 \quad ab^3 \quad b^4\\
&\quad\vdots
\end{aligned}
$$

Do you see a pattern? As you read from left to right, the powers of a decrease and the powers of b increase. Note that the sum of the exponents for each term is the same as the original exponent:

$$(a + b)^n:\quad a^n b^0 \quad a^{n-1} b^1 \quad a^{n-2} b^2 \quad \cdots \quad a^{n-r} b^r \quad \cdots \quad a^2 b^{n-2} \quad a^1 b^{n-1} \quad a^0 b^n$$

Next, consider the numerical coefficients (shown in color):

$$
\begin{aligned}
(a + b)^0:&\qquad\qquad\qquad 1\\
(a + b)^1:&\qquad\qquad\ 1 \quad 1\\
(a + b)^2:&\qquad\quad 1 \quad 2 \quad 1\\
(a + b)^3:&\qquad 1 \quad 3 \quad 3 \quad 1\\
(a + b)^4:&\quad 1 \quad 4 \quad 6 \quad 4 \quad 1\\
&\quad\vdots
\end{aligned}
$$

Do you see the pattern? Recall Pascal's triangle from Section 1.1 (see Figure 6.1).

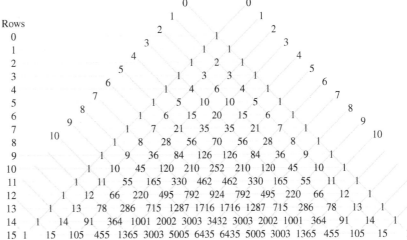

FIGURE 6.1 Pascal's triangle

To find $(a + b)^8$, we look at the 8th row of Pascal's triangle for the coefficients to complete the product:

$$(a + b)^8 = a^8 + 8a^7 b + 28a^6 b^2 + 56a^5 b^3 + 70a^4 b^4 + 56a^3 b^5 + 28a^2 b^6 + 8ab^7 + b^8$$

Look Back. Does this pattern seem correct? We have verified the pattern directly for $n = 0$, 1, 2, 3, and 4. With a great deal of algebraic work, you can verify by direct multiplication that the pattern checks for $(a + b)^8$.

Binomial Theorem

 You should actually FIND these numbers using Figure 6.1. Spend some time studying this theorem. There is a lot of notation here, and you should make sure you understand what it means.

The pattern we discovered for $(a + b)^8$ is a very important theorem in mathematics. It is called the **binomial theorem.** The difficulty in stating this theorem is in relating the coefficients of the expansion to Pascal's triangle. We write $\binom{4}{2}$ to represent the number in row 4, diagonal 2 of Pascal's triangle (see Figure 6.1). We see

$$\binom{4}{2} = 6 \qquad \binom{6}{4} = 15 \qquad \binom{5}{3} = 10 \qquad \binom{15}{7} = 6{,}435$$

We summarize this pattern in the following box.

Binomial Theorem

For any positive integer n,

$$(a + b)^n = \binom{n}{0}a^n + \binom{n}{1}a^{n-1}b + \binom{n}{2}a^{n-2}b^2 + \cdots + \binom{n}{n-1}ab^{n-1} + \binom{n}{n}b^n$$

where $\binom{n}{r}$ is the number in the nth row, rth diagonal of Pascal's triangle.

Pascal's triangle is efficient for finding the numerical coefficients for exponents that are relatively small, as shown in Figure 6.1. However, for larger exponents we will need some additional work, which will be presented in Chapter 12. To **expand** a polynomial is to carry out the operations to simplify the expression.

Example **7** Expand using the binomial theorem

Expand $(x - 2y)^4$.

Solution   In this example, let $a = x$ and $b = -2y$, and look at row 4 of Pascal's triangle for the coefficients.

$(a + b)^4 = a^4 + 4a^3b + 6a^2b^2 + 4ab^3 + b^4$ Binomial theorem; $n = 4$, $a = x$, $b = -2y$

$$\begin{aligned}(x - 2y)^4 &= x^4 + 4x^3(-2y) + 6x^2(-2y)^2 + 4x(-2y)^3 + (-2y)^4 \\ &= x^4 - 8x^3y + 24x^2y^2 - 32xy^3 + 16y^4\end{aligned}$$

Polynomials and Areas

We assume that you know the area formulas for squares and rectangles:

Area of a square: $A = s^2$ \qquad Area of a rectangle: $A = \ell w$

Areas of squares and rectangles are often represented as trinomials. Consider the area represented by the trinomial $x^2 + 3x + 2$. This expression is made up of three terms: x^2, $3x$, and 2. Translate each of these terms into an area:

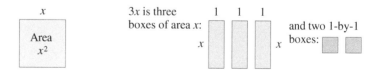

Now you must rearrange these pieces into a rectangle. Think of them as cutouts and move them around. There is only way (not counting order) to fit them into a rectangle:

 This is EASY if you cut out these figures and use them as manipulatives. Rearrangement of strips is hard to show in a book, but if you try it with cutout pieces, you will like it!

 or put together it looks like:

Note: The rectangle with dimensions $x + 2$ by $x + 1$ has the same area as one with dimensions $x + 1$ by $x + 2$.

Thus, $(x + 2)(x + 1) = x^2 + 3x + 2$. These observations provide another way (besides the distributive property) for verifying the shortcut method of FOIL.

Example 8   Binomial product two ways

Find the product $(x + 3)$ $(x + 1)$ both algebraically and geometrically.

Solution

Algebraic: $(x + 3)(x + 1) = x^2 + 4x + 3$

Geometric: Draw a rectangle with sides that measure $x + 3$ and $x + 1$:

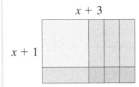

There is one square: x^2
four rectangles: $4x$
three units: 3

Thus, $(x + 3)(x + 1) = x^2 + 4x + 3$.

Problem Set   6.1

Level 1

1. **IN YOUR OWN WORDS**   What is a polynomial?

2. **IN YOUR OWN WORDS**   What is the degree of a polynomial?

3. **IN YOUR OWN WORDS**   Discuss the process for adding and subtracting polynomials.

4. **IN YOUR OWN WORDS**   Discuss the process of multiplying polynomials using the distributive property.

5. **IN YOUR OWN WORDS**   Discuss the process of multiplying binomials using FOIL.

6. **IN YOUR OWN WORDS**   Discuss the process of multiplying binomials using areas.

7. **IN YOUR OWN WORDS**   What is the binomial theorem?

Simplify each expression in Problems 8–22. Classify each answer by number of terms and degree.

8. $(x + 3) + (5x - 7)$

9. $(2x - 4) - (3x + 4)$

10. $(x + y + 2z) + (2x + 5y - 4z)$

11. $(x - y - z) + (2x - 5y - 3z)$

12. $(5x^2 + 2x - 5) + (3x^2 - 5x + 7)$

13. $(2x^2 - 5x + 4) + (3x^2 - 2x - 11)$

14. $(x + 2y - 3z) - (x - 5y + 4z)$

15. $(x^2 + 4x - 3) - (2x^2 + 9x - 6)$

16. $(3x - x^2) - 5(2 - x) - (2x + 3)$

17. $3(x - 5) - 2(x + 8)$

18. $6(x + 1) - 2(x + 1)$

19. $3(2x^2 + 5x - 5) + 2(5x^2 - 3x + 6)$

20. $2(4x^2 - 3x + 2) - 3(x^2 - 5x - 8)$

21. $2(x + 3) - 3(x^2 - 3x + 1) + 4(x - 5)$

22. $3(x - 1) - 2(x^2 + 4x + 5) - 5(x + 8)$

In Problems 23–29, multiply mentally.

23. **a.** $(x + 3)(x + 2)$ **b.** $(y + 1)(y + 5)$
    c. $(z - 2)(z + 6)$ **d.** $(s + 5)(s - 4)$

24. **a.** $(x + 1)(x - 2)$ **b.** $(y - 3)(y + 2)$
    c. $(a - 5)(a - 3)$ **d.** $(b + 3)(b - 4)$

25. **a.** $(c + 1)(c - 7)$ **b.** $(z - 3)(z + 5)$
    c. $(2x + 1)(x - 1)$ **d.** $(2x - 3)(x - 1)$

26. **a.** $(x + 1)(3x + 1)$ **b.** $(x + 1)(3x + 2)$
    c. $(2a + 3)(3a - 2)$ **d.** $(2a + 3)(3a + 2)$

27. **a.** $(x + y)(x + y)$ **b.** $(x - y)(x - y)$
    c. $(x + y)(x - y)$ **d.** $(a + b)(a - b)$

28. **a.** $(5x - 4)(5x + 4)$ **b.** $(3y - 2)(3y + 2)$
    c. $(a + 2)^2$ **d.** $(b - 2)^2$

29. **a.** $(x + 4)^2$ **b.** $(y - 3)^2$
    c. $(s + t)^2$ **d.** $(u - v)^2$

Level 2

Simplify the expressions in Problems 30–37.

30. $(5x + 1)(3x^2 - 5x + 2)$

31. $(2x - 1)(3x^2 + 2x - 5)$

32. $(3x - 1)(x^2 + 3x - 2)$

33. $(5x + 1)(x^3 - 2x^2 + 3x)$

34. $(5x + 1)(3x^2 - 5x + 2) - (x^3 - 4x^2 + x - 4)$

35. $3(3x^2 - 5x + 2) - 4(x^3 - 4x^2 + x - 4)$

36. $(x - 2)(2x - 3) - (x + 1)(x - 5)$

37. $(2x - 3)(3x + 2) + (x + 2)(x + 3)$

Find each product in Problems 38–43 both algebraically and geometrically.

38. $(x + 1)(x + 4)$ **39.** $(x + 2)(x + 4)$

40. $(x + 2)(x + 5)$ **41.** $(x + 3)(x + 4)$

42. $(2x + 1)(2x + 3)$ **43.** $(2x + 3)(3x + 2)$

Use the binomial theorem to expand each binomial given in Problems 44–51.

44. $(x + 1)^3$ **45.** $(x - 1)^3$

46. $(x + y)^5$ **47.** $(x + y)^6$

48. $(x - y)^7$ **49.** $(x - y)^8$

50. $(5x - 2y)^3$ **51.** $(2x - 3y)^4$

Level **3**

52. Write out the first three terms in the expansion $(x + y)^{12}$.

53. Write out the last three terms in the expansion $(x + y)^{14}$.

54. The number of desks in one row is $5d + 2$. How many desks are there in a room of $2d - 1$ rows if they are arranged in a rectangular arrangement?

55. An auditorium has $6x + 2$ seats in each row and $51x - 7$ rows. If the chairs are in a rectangular arrangement, how many seats are there in the auditorium?

56. Each apartment in a building rents for $800 - d$ dollars per month. What is the monthly income from $6d + 12$ units?

57. If a boat is traveling at a rate of $6b + 15$ miles per hour for a time of $10 - 2b$ hours, what is the distance traveled by the boat?

Problem Solving **3**

58. Binomial products can be used to do mental calculations. For example, to multiply a pair of two-digit numbers whose tens digits are the same and whose units digits add up to 10, mentally multiply the units digits and then multiply the tens digit of the first number by one more than the tens digit of the second. For example,

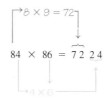

Mentally multiply the given numbers.
a. 62×68 **b.** 57×53
c. 63×67 **d.** 95^2
e. 75^2

59. IN YOUR OWN WORDS Suppose the given numbers for a mental calculation (see Problem 58) are $10x + y$ and $10x + z$. Notice that these two numbers have the same tens digit. Also assume that $y + z = 10$, which says that the units digits of the two numbers sum to 10. Algebraically show why the mental calculation described in Problem 58 "works."

60. IN YOUR OWN WORDS Devise a procedure for mentally multiplying three-digit numbers with the same first two digits and units digits that add up to 10.

6.2 | Factoring

This is the second of the four main processes of algebra.

We have called numbers that are multiplied *factors.* In Section 5.2 we defined *a prime number* and the *prime factorization* of numbers. The same process can be applied to algebraic expressions. To **factor** an expression means to write it in factored form. That is, the word "factor" is sometimes a noun and sometimes a verb.

In this section, we look at the process of *factoring;* we complete our discussion of this topic in Section 6.4 when we use factoring to solve quadratic equations. Factoring is also used extensively in algebra, so to understand some of the algebraic processes, it is necessary to understand factoring.

The approach we take in this section is different from that you will normally see in an algebra course. So often algebra is learned by brute force and memorization or symbol manipulation, but our development uses a geometric visualization that may help in your understanding not only of algebraic processes, but of geometric ones as well.

Using Areas to Factor

In the previous section, we showed how areas can be used to understand multiplication of binomials. We now use areas to factor polynomials.

Example 1   Factor using areas

Factor $2x^2 + 7x + 6$ using areas.

Solution   First draw the areas for the terms:

Rearrange to form a rectangle:

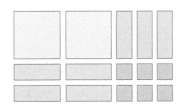

Push these pieces together to form a single rectangle:

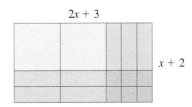

Thus, $2x^2 + 7x + 6 = (2x + 3)(x + 2)$.

The following example shows how to use areas when factoring a polynomial with a subtraction, as well as a polynomial that is not factorable.

Example 2   Factor using areas—advanced types

Factor the following polynomials, if possible, by using areas.
a. $x^2 + 2x - 3$ **b.** $x^2 + 5x + 8$

Solution
a. First draw the rectangles for the terms:

From these rectangles we must subtract three squares; we will indicate these squares to be subtracted by ☐ ☐ ☐.

First arrange the positive pieces and then place the negative pieces (the gray ones) on top of the positive pieces:

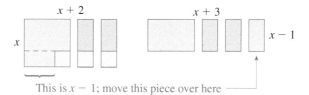

This is $x - 1$; move this piece over here

Thus, $x^2 + 2x - 3 = (x + 3)(x - 1)$.

b.

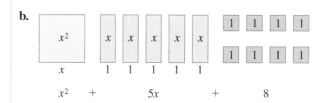

$$x^2 \quad + \quad 5x \quad + \quad 8$$

There is no way of arranging all the pieces to form a rectangle.

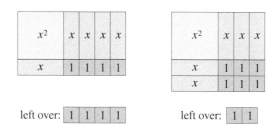

left over: 1 1 1 1   left over: 1 1

We see that this trinomial is not factorable.

Using Algebra to Factor

By thinking through the steps for factoring trinomials by using areas, we can develop a process for algebraic factoring. Consider $x^2 + 3x + 2$ and compare the process below with the discussion at the beginning of this section. We consider the first term and the last term of the given trinomial.

First term: Area of the large square with side x

$$x^2 + 3x + 2 = (x \qquad 2)(x \qquad 1)$$

Last term: Area of two squares with sides of length 1

There may be several ways of rearranging the areas for these first two steps (first term and last term). What you want to do is to rearrange them so that they form a rectangle. By looking at the binomial product and recalling the process we called FOIL, you see that the sum of the outer product and the inner product, which gives the middle term of the trinomial, will be the factorization that gives a rectangular area:

outer product
+
inner product

outer + inner   inner product

$$x^2 + 3x + 2 = (x + 2)(x + 1)$$

This method of factorization is called FOIL.

Example 3 Use FOIL to factor

Factor $2x^2 + 7x + 6$ using FOIL.

Solution   This is the same as Example 1, but now we use FOIL.

First term: $2x^2 + 7x + 6 = (2x\quad)(x\quad)$

Last term: There are several possibilities:

$$(2x + 6)(x + 1)$$
$$(2x + 1)(x + 6)$$
$$(2x + 2)(x + 3)$$
$$(2x + 3)(x + 2)$$

These are equivalent to the different arrangements of "pieces" to form the rectangle in the area method shown in Example 1. Only one will form a rectangle and that is precisely the one that will give the middle term of the trinomial, namely, $7x$:

Middle term: $2x^2 + 7x + 6 = (2x + 3)(x + 2)$

This factorization is unique (except for the order of the factors).

Procedure for Factoring Trinomials

To factor a trinomial:*

Step 1 Find the factors of the second-degree term, and set up the binomials.

Step 2 Find the factors of the constant term, and consider all possible binomials (mentally). Think of the factors that will form a rectangle.

Step 3 Determine the factors that yield the correct middle term. If no pair of factors produces the correct full product, then the trinomial is not factorable using integers.

This factoring approach is called FOIL.

STOP   This is a very common process; make sure you thoroughly understand how to factor trinomials.

Example 4 Factor—advanced types

Factor, if possible.
a. $2x^2 + 11x + 12$ **b.** $x^2 + 3x + 5$

Solution
a. $2x^2 + 11x + 12 = (2x\quad)(x\quad)$ Try (mentally): 1, 12; 12, 1; 2, 6; 6, 2; 3, 4; and 4, 3. Use the pair that gives the middle term, $11x$.

$$2x^2 + 11x + 12 = (2x + 3)(x + 4)$$

b. $x^2 + 3x + 5 = (x\quad)(x\quad)$ Try (mentally): 1, 5; and 5, 1.
Since neither of these gives the middle term, $3x$, we say that the trinomial is not factorable.

---

*In this book, we factor using integers only.

Common Factoring

If several terms share a factor, then that factor is called a **common factor.** For example, the binomial $5x^2 + 10x$ has three common factors: 5, x, and $5x$. To factor this sum of two terms, we must change it to a product, and this can be done several ways:

$$5x^2 + 10x = 5(x^2 + 2x)$$
$$5x^2 + 10x = x(5x + 10)$$
$$5x^2 + 10x = 5x(x + 2)$$

The last of these possibilities has the greatest common factor as a factor, and is said to be **completely factored.**

When combining common factoring with trinomial factoring, the procedure will be easiest if you look for common factors first.

Example   5   Completely factor

Completely factor $6x^3 - 21x^2 - 12x$.

Solution $6x^3 - 21x^2 - 12x = 3x(2x^2 - 7x - 4)$ Common factor first

$\hspace{5.3cm} = 3x(2x \quad)(x \quad)$ Now use FOIL, first terms.

$\hspace{5.3cm} = 3x(2x + 1)(x - 4)$ Last terms

Difference of Squares

The last type of factorization we will consider is called a **difference of squares.** Suppose we start with one square, a^2:

a

a

From this square, we wish to subtract another square, b^2:

This gray square should be smaller than the first ($a^2 > b^2$). Place this square (since it is gray) on top of the larger square:

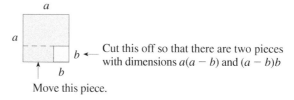

$b \leftarrow$ Cut this off so that there are two pieces with dimensions $a(a - b)$ and $(a - b)b$

Move this piece.

Rearrange these two pieces by moving the smaller one from the bottom and positioning it vertically at the right:

$a \qquad b$

$a - b$ $\leftarrow$ Moved piece

The dimensions of this new arrangement are $(a - b)$ by $(a + b)$. Thus,

$$a^2 - b^2 = (a - b)(a + b)$$

STOP You need to remember this formula.

Difference of Squares

$$a^2 - b^2 = (a - b)(a + b)$$

Example   6   **Completely factor—mixed types**

Completely factor each expression, if possible.
a. $x^2 - 36$ **b.** $8x^2 - 50$ **c.** $6x^4 - 18x^2 - 24$

Solution
a. $x^2 - 36 = (x - 6)(x + 6)$ Difference of squares
b. $8x^2 - 50 = 2(4x^2 - 25)$ Common factor first
        $= 2(2x - 5)(2x + 5)$ Difference of squares
c. $6x^4 - 18x^2 - 24 = 6(x^4 - 3x^2 - 4)$ Common factor
        $= 6(x^2 - 4)(x^2 + 1)$ FOIL
        $= 6(x - 2)(x + 2)(x^2 + 1)$ Difference of squares

Problem Set   6.2

Level 1

1. IN YOUR OWN WORDS   Outline a procedure for factoring.

2. IN YOUR OWN WORDS   What is a difference of squares?

If possible, completely factor the expressions in Problems 3–36.

3. $10xy - 6x$ **4.** $5x + 5$

5. $8xy - 6x$ **6.** $6x - 2$

7. $x^2 - 4x + 3$ **8.** $x^2 - 2x - 3$

9. $x^2 - 5x + 6$ **10.** $x^2 - x - 6$

11. $x^2 - 7x + 12$ **12.** $x^2 - 7x - 8$

13. $x^2 - x - 30$ **14.** $x^2 + 9x + 14$

15. $x^2 - 2x - 35$ **16.** $x^2 - 6x - 16$

17. $3x^2 + 7x - 10$ **18.** $2x^2 + 7x - 15$

19. $2x^2 - 7x + 3$ **20.** $3x^2 - 10x + 3$

21. $3x^2 - 5x - 2$ **22.** $6y^2 - 7y + 1$

23. $2x^2 + 9x + 4$ **24.** $7x^2 + 4x - 3$

25. $3x^2 + x - 2$ **26.** $3x^2 + 7x + 2$

27. $5x^3 + 7x^2 - 6x$ **28.** $8x^3 + 12x^2 + 4x$

29. $7x^4 - 11x^3 - 6x^2$ **30.** $3x^4 + 3x^3 - 36x^2$

31. $x^2 - 64$ **32.** $x^2 - 169$

33. $25x^2 + 50$ **34.** $16x^2 - 25$

35. $x^4 - 1$ **36.** $x^8 - 1$

Level 2

Factor each expression in Problems 37–48 by using areas.

37. $x^2 + 5x + 6$ **38.** $x^2 + 7x + 12$

39. $x^2 + 4x + 3$ **40.** $x^2 + 5x + 4$

41. $x^2 + 6x + 8$ **42.** $x^2 + 2x + 2$

43. $x^2 - 1$ **44.** $x^2 - 4$

45. $x^2 + x - 2$ **46.** $x^2 + x - 6$

47. $x^2 - x - 2$ **48.** $x^2 - x - 6$

Level 3

49. The area of a rectangle is $x^2 - 2x - 143$ square feet. What are the dimensions of the figure?

50. What are the dimensions of a rectangle whose area is $x^2 - 4x - 165$ square feet?

51. What is the time needed to travel a distance of $6x^2 + 5x - 4$ miles if the rate is $3x + 4$ mph?

52. If an auditorium has $x^2 - 50x - 600$ seats arranged in a rectangular fashion, what is the number of rows and how many seats are there in each row?

Factor each expression in Problems 53–58, if possible.

53. $(x + 2)(x + 4) + (5x + 6)(x - 1)$

54. $(2x + 1)(3x + 2) + (3x + 5)(x - 2)$

55. $x^6 - 13x^4 + 36x^2$

56. $x^6 - 26x^4 + 25x^2$

57. $20x^2y^2 + 17x^2yz - 10x^2z^2$

58. $12x^2y^2 + 10x^2yz - 12x^2z^2$

Problem Solving 3

59. IN YOUR OWN WORDS   Pick any three consecutive integers—for example, 4, 5, and 6. The square of the middle term is 1 more than the product of the first and third; for example, 25 is 1 more than 4(6) = 24. Prove this is true for any three consecutive integers.

60. Illustrate the property in Problem 59 geometrically.

6.3 | Evaluation, Applications, and Spreadsheets

If $x = a$, then x and a name the same number; x may then be replaced by a in any expression, and the value of the expression will remain unchanged. When you replace variables by given numerical values and then simplify the resulting numerical expression, the process is called *evaluating an expression*.

Evaluate

 This is the third of the four main processes of algebra.

To **evaluate** an expression means to replace the variable (or variables) with given values, and then to simplify the resulting numerical expression.

Example 1 **Evaluate an expression**

Evaluate $a + cb$, where $a = 2$, $b = 11$, and $c = 3$.

Solution $a + cb$ Remember, *cb* means *c **times** b.*

Step 1 Replace each variable with the corresponding numerical value. You may need additional parentheses to make sure you don't change the order of operations.

$$a + c \cdot b$$
$$\downarrow \downarrow \downarrow \downarrow$$
$$\mathbf{2 + 3(11)}$$ Parentheses are necessary so that the product *cb* is not changed to 311.

Step 2 Simplify: $2 + 3(11) = 2 + 33$ Multiplication before addition
$$= 35$$

Example 2 **Evaluate with exponents; order of operations**

Evaluate the following, where $a = 3$ and $b = 4$.
a. $a^2 + b^2$
b. $(a + b)^2$

Solution
a. $a^2 + b^2 = 3^2 + 4^2$ Remember the order of operations: Multiplication comes first,
$\qquad\quad = 9 + 16$ and $3^2 = 3 \cdot 3$, $4^2 = 4 \cdot 4$, which is multiplication.
$\qquad\quad = 25$
b. $(a + b)^2 = (3 + 4)^2$ Order of operations; parentheses first
$\qquad\qquad = 7^2$
$\qquad\qquad = 49$
Notice that $a^2 + b^2 \neq (a + b)^2$.

Remember that a particular variable is replaced by a single value when an expression is evaluated. You should also be careful to write capital letters differently from lowercase letters, because they often represent different values. This means that you should not assume that $A = 3$ just because $a = 3$. On the other hand, it is possible that other variables *might* have the value 3. For example, just because $a = 3$, do not assume that another variable—say t—cannot also have the value $t = 3$.

Example 3 **Evaluate with mixed operations**

Let $a = 1$, $b = 3$, $c = 2$, and $d = 4$. Find the value of the given capital letters.

a. $G = bc - a$ **b.** $H = 3c + 2d$ **c.** $I = 3a + 2b$ **d.** $R = a^2 + b^2 d$

e. $S = \dfrac{2(b + d)}{2c}$ **f.** $T = \dfrac{3a + bc + b}{c}$

Solution   After you have found the value of a capital letter, write it in the box that corresponds to its numerical value. This exercise will help you check your work.

37	9	5	14	6	

a. $G = bc - a$
$= 3(2) - 1$
$= 6 - 1$
$= 5$

b. $H = 3c + 2d$
$= 3(2) + 2(4)$
$= 6 + 8$
$= 14$

c. $I = 3a + 2b$
$= 3(1) + 2(3)$
$= 3 + 6$
$= 9$

d. $R = a^2 + b^2 d$
$= 1^2 + 3^2(4)$
$= 1 + 9(4)$
$= 37$

e. $S = \dfrac{2(b + d)}{2c}$

$= \dfrac{2(3 + 4)}{2(2)}$

$= \dfrac{2(7)}{4}$

$= \dfrac{7}{2}$

f. $T = \dfrac{3a + bc + b}{c}$

$= \dfrac{3(1) + 3(2) + 3}{2}$

$= \dfrac{3 + 6 + 3}{2}$

$= \dfrac{12}{2}$

$= 6$

After you have filled in the appropriate boxes, the result is

37	9	5	14	6	
R	I	G	H	T	

In algebra, variables are usually represented by either lowercase or capital letters. However, in other disciplines, variables are often represented by other symbols or combinations of letters. For example, I recently took a flight on Delta Air Lines and a formula $VM = \sqrt{A} \times 3.56$ was given as an approximation for the distance you can see from a Delta jet (or presumably any other plane). The article defined VM as the distance you can view in miles when flying at an altitude of A feet. For this example VM is interpreted as a single variable, and not as V *times* M as it normally would be in algebra.

An Application from Genetics

This application is based on the work of Gregor Mendel (1822–1884), an Austrian monk, who formulated the laws of heredity and genetics. Mendel's work was later amplified and explained by a mathematician, G. H. Hardy (1877–1947), and a physician, Wilhelm Weinberg (1862–1937). For years Mendel taught science without any teaching credentials because he had failed the biology portion of the licensing examination! His work, however, laid the foundation for the very important branch of biology known today as genetic science.

Assume that traits are determined by *genes*, which are passed from parents to their offspring. Each parent has a pair of genes, and the basic assumption is that each offspring inherits one gene from each parent to form the offspring's own pair. The genes are selected in a random, independent way. In our examples, we will assume that the researcher is studying a trait that is both easily identifiable (such as color of a rat's fur) and determined by a pair of genes consisting of a *dominant* gene, denoted by A, and a *recessive* gene, denoted by a.

The possible pairings are called *genotypes:*

AA is called *dominant*, or homozygous.

Aa is called *hybrid*, or heterozygous; genetically, the genotype *aA* is the same as *Aa*.

aa is called *recessive*.

The physical appearance is called the *phenotype:*

Genotype *AA* has phenotype *A*.

Genotype *Aa* has phenotype *A* (since *A* is dominant).

Genotype *aA* has phenotype *A*.

Genotype *aa* has phenotype *a*.

In genetics, a square called a *Punnett square* is used to display genotype. For example, suppose two individuals with genotypes *Aa* are mated, as represented by the following Punnett square:

Parent 2

		A	a
	A	AA	Aa
Parent 1	a	aA	aa

We see the result is $AA + Aa + aA + aa = AA + 2Aa + aa$. This reminds us of the binomial product

$$(p + q)^2 = p^2 + 2pq + q^2$$

Let's use binomial multiplication to find the genotypes and phenotypes of a particular example. In population genetics, we are interested in the percent, or relative frequency, of genes of a certain type in the entire population under study. In other words, imagine taking the two genes from each person in the population and putting them into an imaginary pot. This pot is called the *gene pool* for the population. Geneticists study the gene pool to draw conclusions about the population.

Example 4   Find the population percents of phenotypes

Suppose a certain population has two eye color genes: *B* (brown eyes, dominant) and *b* (blue eyes, recessive). Suppose we have an isolated population in which 70% of the genes in the gene pool are dominant *B*, and the other 30% are recessive *b*. What fraction of the population has each genotype? What percent of the population has each phenotype?

Solution   Let $p = 0.7$ and $q = 0.3$. Since p and q give us 100% of all the genes in the gene pool, we see that $p + q = 1$. Since

$$(p + q)^2 = p^2 + 2pq + q^2$$

we can find the percents:

genotype *BB*: $p^2 = (0.7)^2 = 0.49$, so 49% have *BB* genotype

genotype *bB* or *Bb*: $2pq = 2(0.7)(0.3) = 0.42$, so 42% have this genotype

genotype *bb*: $q^2 = (0.3)^2 = 0.09$, so 9% have *bb* genotype

Check genotypes: $0.49 + 0.42 + 0.09 = 1.00$

As for the phenotypes, we look only at outward appearances, and since brown is dominant, *BB*, *bB*, and *Bb* all have brown eyes; this accounts for 91%, leaving 9% with blue eyes.

Spreadsheets

In Section 4.5 we discussed the notion of computer software and mentioned that one of the most important computer applications is in using something called a *spreadsheet*. A **spreadsheet** is a computer program used to manipulate data and carry out calculations or chains of calculations. If you have access to a computer and software such as Excel®, Lotus 1-2-3®, or Quattro-Pro®, you might use that software in conjunction with this section. However, it is not necessary to have this software (or even access to a computer) to be able to study variables and the evaluation of formulas using the ideas of a spreadsheet. In fact, your first inclination when reading this might be to skip over this and say to yourself, "I don't know anything about a spreadsheet, so I will not read this. Besides, my instructor is not requiring this anyway." However, regardless of whether this is assigned, chances are that sooner or later you will be using a spreadsheet.

One of the most interesting, and important, new ways of representing variables is as a **cell,** or a "box."

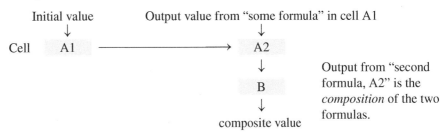

The information in a spreadsheet is stored in a rectangular array of *cells*. The content of each cell can be a number, text, or a formula. The power of a spreadsheet is that a cell's numeric value can be linked to the content of another cell. For example, it is possible to define the content of one cell as the sum of the contents of two other cells. Furthermore, if the value of a cell is changed anywhere in the spreadsheet, all values dependent on it are recalculated and the new values are displayed immediately.

Instead of designating variables as letters (such as x, y, z, . . .) as we do in algebra, a spreadsheet designates variables as cells (such as B2, A5, Z146, . . .). If you type something into a cell, the spreadsheet program will recognize it as text if it begins with a letter, and as a number if it begins with a numeral. It also recognizes the usual mathematical symbols of $+$, $-$, $*$ (for $\times$), $/$ (for $\div$), and $\wedge$ (for raising to a power). Parentheses are used in the usual fashion as grouping symbols. To enter a formula, you must begin with $+$, @, or $=$, depending on the position in the spreadsheet. Compare some algebraic and spreadsheet evaluations:

Algebra	Comment	Spreadsheet	Comment
$3(x + y)$	Variables are x and y.	$+3*(A1 + A2)$	Variables are in contents of cells A1 and A2.
$x^2 + 2x - 5$	Variable is x.	$+B3\wedge2 + 2*B3 - 5$	Variable is the content of cell B3. Begins with "+" to indicate that it is a formula.
$\dfrac{A + B}{2}$	Formula for the average of the variables A and B	$+(A3 + A4)/2$	Variables are the contents of cells A3 and A4.

Example 5 Evaluate using a spreadsheet

Translate each formula into spreadsheet notation.

a. $x + \frac{y}{2}$ **b.** $\dfrac{6x^2 + y}{2x}$ **c.** $-3^2 + (-5)^2 + z^3 + (z + 3)^2$

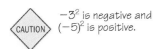

CAUTION -3^2 is negative and $(-5)^2$ is positive.

Solution

a. $+A1 + A2/2$ where the value of x is the content of cell A1 and the value of y is the content of cell A2.

b. $+(6*A1\wedge2 + A2)/(2*A1)$ where the value of x is the content of cell A1 and the value of y is in cell A2.

c. $+(-3\wedge2) + (-5)\wedge2 + A3\wedge3 + (A3 + 3)\wedge2$ where the value of z is the content of cell A3.

For our purposes, we will assume that a spreadsheet program has an almost unlimited number of rows and columns. We will represent a typical spreadsheet as follows:

Spreadsheet Application

	A	B	C	D	E	F	G	H	I	J	K
1											
2											
3											
4											
5											

As an example, we will consider the way in which a spreadsheet program could be used to set up an electronic checkbook. We might fill in the spreadsheet as follows:

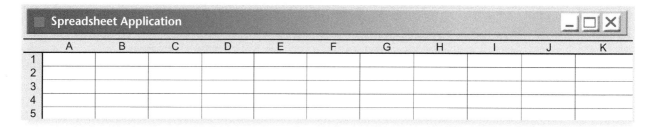

Spreadsheet Application

	A	B	C	D	E	F
1	DESCRIPTION	DEBIT	DEPOSIT	BALANCE		
2	Beginning balance					
3				+D2-B3+C3		
4				+D3-B4+C4		
5				+D4-B5+C5		

After some entries are filled in, the spreadsheet might look like the following:

Spreadsheet Application

	A	B	C	D	E	F
1	DESCRIPTION	DEBIT	DEPOSIT	BALANCE		
2	Beginning balance			1000.00		
3	School bookstore	250.00		750.00		
4	Paper route		100.00	850.00		
5	Ski trip	300.00		550.00		

The power of a spreadsheet derives from the way variables are referenced by cells. For example, if you go back to the spreadsheet and enter a beginning balance of $2,500 in cell D2, *all* the other entries *automatically* change:

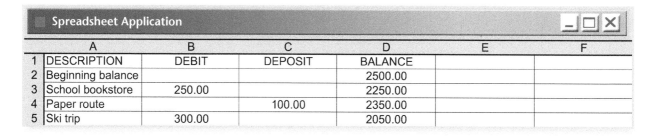

Spreadsheet Application

	A	B	C	D	E	F
1	DESCRIPTION	DEBIT	DEPOSIT	BALANCE		
2	Beginning balance			2500.00		
3	School bookstore	250.00		2250.00		
4	Paper route		100.00	2350.00		
5	Ski trip	300.00		2050.00		

Once the spreadsheet has been set up, the user will enter information in column A and, depending on whether a check has been written or a deposit made, make an entry in either column B or column C. The entries in column D (beginning with cell D3) are automatically calculated by the spreadsheet program. Empty cells are assumed to have the value 0.

It should be clear that each cell from D3 downward needs to contain a different formula. In this example, the column letters and operations of the formula remain unchanged, but each row number is increased by 1 from the cell above. If each of these formulas had to be entered by hand, one by one, it is obvious that setting up a spreadsheet would be very time-consuming. This is not the case, however, and a typical spreadsheet program allows the user to copy the formula from one cell into another cell and at the same time *automatically* change its formula references. Thus, with a single command, each cell in column D is given the correct formula. We will call this command **replicating** a formula or cell. Formulas replicated down a column have their row numbers incremented, and formulas replicated across a row have the column letters incremented.

Example 6   Replicate using a spreadsheet

Consider the following spreadsheet with the indicated formulas.

	A	B	C	D	E	F	G
1	x	y = 10x	x + y	x^2			
2		+10*A2	+A2+B2	+A2^2			
3	+A2+1	+10*A3	+A3+B3	+A3^2			
4							
5							

a. Describe what the spreadsheet would show if cells A3 . . . D3 were replicated in rows 4 and 5.
b. Describe what the spreadsheet would show if column D were replicated in column E.

Solution
a.

	A	B	C	D	E	F	G
1	x	y = 10x	x + y	x^2			
2		+10*A2	+A2+B2	+A2^2			
3	+A2+1	+10*A3	+A3+B3	+A3^2			
4	+A3+1	+10*A4	+A4+B4	+A4^2			
5	+A4+1	+10*A5	+A5+B5	+A5^2			

b.

	A	B	C	D	E	F	G
1	x	y = 10x	x + y	x^2	x^2		
2		+10*A2	+A2+B2	+A2^2	+B2^2		
3	+A2+1	+10*A3	+A3+B3	+A3^2	+B3^2		
4							
5							

Example 7 Find cell value

Given that cell A2 has the value 12, show what the spreadsheet shown in the solution for Example 6a would look like.

Solution

	A	B	C	D	E	F	G
1	x	$y = 10x$	$x + y$	x^2			
2	12	120	132	144			
3	13	130	143	169			
4	14	140	154	196			
5	15	150	165	225			

Spreadsheet Application

We might once again remind you of the power of a computer spreadsheet. Note that the *entire* answer shown in Example 7 would *immediately* be filled in as soon as you fill in the number 12 in cell A2. If you now go back and reenter another number into cell A2, the entire spreadsheet would *immediately* change because every cell is ultimately defined in terms of the content of cell A2 in this example spreadsheet.

Example 8 Find a formula using a spreadsheet

Suppose we look at a spreadsheet and see the entries 1, 1, 2, 3, 5, 8, 13, 21, 34, 55 in successive entries in column A. Suppose that 1 is entered into cell A1 and 1 into cell A2. What is the formula to be placed into cell A3?

	A	B	C
1	1		
2	1		
3	2		
4	3		
5	5		
6	8		
7	13		
8	21		
9	34		
10	55		
11			

Spreadsheet Application

Solution   Cell A3 should contain the formula +A1 +A2. Note that if this formula were replicated down column A through cell A10, the given numbers would be shown.

The real power of a spreadsheet program lies not in its ability to perform calculations, but rather in its ability to answer "what-if" types of questions. For instance, for the set of numbers in Example 8, what if the number in cell A1 is divided by A2, and then the number in cell A2 is divided by A3, and so on for 50 such numbers? In the problem set you are asked to use a spreadsheet to detect a pattern for these quotients.

Example 9 Account value using a spreadsheet

If \$100 is deposited into an account that pays 5% interest compounded yearly, then at the end of the first year, the account will contain 100 + (0.05)*100 = \$105. At the end of two years, the account will contain 105 + (0.05)*105 = \$110.25. Suppose cell A1 contains the value 100. Then what formula must be placed in cell A2 if it is to contain the amount in the account at the end of the first year?

Solution   Cell A2 should contain the formula A1 + (0.05)*A1. Note that if this formula were replicated down column A to cell A11, the column would show the amount in the account at the end of each year through 10 years.

To take advantage of the "what-if power of a spreadsheet, the previous example could be set up to allow for any interest rate. This could be done in the following way:

	A	B	C	D	E
1	Interest rate =				
2	YEAR NUMBER	BALANCE			
3	0				
4	+A3+1	+B3+B1*B3			
5					

Spreadsheet Application

Note that when a number is inserted into cell B1, that number will act as the interest rate, and the number inserted into cell B3 will act as the amount of deposit. Therefore, we see that B1 is the variable representing the interest rate and B3 is the variable representing the beginning balance. If row 4 is *replicated* into rows 5 to 10, we will then obtain the data for the next 7 years. The problem with this replication, however, is that the reference to cell B1 will change as the replication takes place down column B. This difficulty is overcome by using a special character that holds a column or a row constant. The symbol we will use for this purpose is $. (Some spreadsheets use the symbol # for this purpose.) Thus, we would change the formula in cell B4 above to

$+B3+\$B\$1*B3$

to mean that we want not only column B to remain constant, but also we want row 1 to remain unchanged when this entry is replicated. Note that $ applies only to the character directly following its placement. We show the first 7 rows (4 years) of such a spreadsheet for which the rate is 4% and the initial deposit is $1,000.

	A	B	C	D	E
1	Interest rate =	0.04			
2	YEAR NUMBER	BALANCE			
3	0	1000.00			
4	1	1040.00			
5	2	1081.60			
6	3	1124.86			
7	4	1169.86			

Spreadsheet Application

Problem Set 6.3

Level 1

1. IN YOUR OWN WORDS   What is a variable?

2. IN YOUR OWN WORDS   What is a spreadsheet?

3. IN YOUR OWN WORDS   A colleague of mine speculated over lunch a few years ago:

"Someday there will be just one programming language. IBM and Macintosh formats will merge. The trend is just

the same as it is with the languages we speak in the world. Someday the entire world will speak English."

Comment on this statement.

4. **IN YOUR OWN WORDS** Although the terms *program* and *software* can often be interchanged, there is a subtle difference in their usage. Discuss. What is meant when the term *user-friendly* is used to describe software?

In Problems 5–12, write each expression in spreadsheet notation. Let x be in cell A1, y in A2, and z in A3.

5. a. $\frac{2}{3}x^2$ b. $5x^2 - 6y^2$

6. a. $3x^2 - 17$ b. $14y^2 + 12x^2$

7. a. $12(x^2 + 4)$ b. $\frac{15x + 7}{2}$

8. a. $\frac{3x + 1}{12}$ b. $3x + \frac{1}{12}$

9. a. $(5 - x)(x + 3)^2$ b. $6(x + 3)(2x - 7)^2$

10. a. $(x + 1)(2x - 3)(x^2 + 4)$ b. $(2x - 3)(3x^2 + 1)$

11. a. $\frac{1}{4}x^2 - \frac{1}{2}x + 12$ b. $\frac{2}{3}x^2 + \frac{1}{3}x - 17$

12. a. $1 - \frac{x}{yz}$ b. $\frac{1 - x}{yz}$

In Problems 13–18, write each spreadsheet expression in ordinary algebraic notation. Let cell A1 represent the variable x, A2 the variable y, A3 the variable z; B1 is a, B2 is b, and B3 is c.

13. a. $+4*A1+3$
    b. $+5*A1^2 - 3*A1+4$

14. a. $+36*A3^2 - 13*A3+2$
    b. $+13*A2^2+(15/2)$

15. a. $+(5/4)*A1+14^2$
    b. $+(5/4*A1+14)^2$

16. a. $+5*A1^2-3*A2+4$
    b. $+4*(A1^2+5)*(3*A1^2 - 3)^2$

17. a. $+A1/A2*A3$ b. $+A1/(A2*A3)$

18. a. $+B2+B1*\$B\$3$ b. $+A1 + \$B2^2$

In Problems 19–42, let w = 2, x = 1, y = 2, and z = 4. Find the values of the given capital letters.

19. $A = x + z + 8$ 20. $B = 5x + y - z$

21. $C = 10 - w$ 22. $D = 3z$

23. $E = 25 - y^2$ 24. $F = w(y - x + wz)$

25. $G = 5x + 3z + 2$ 26. $H = 3x + 2w$

27. $I = 5y - 2z$ 28. $J = 2w - z$

29. $K = wxy$ 30. $L = x + y^2$

31. $M = (x + y)^2$ 32. $N = x^2 + 2xy + y^2 + 1$

33. $P = y^2 + z^2$ 34. $Q = w(x + y)$

35. $R = z^2 - y^2 - x^2$ 36. $S = (x + y + z)^2$

37. $T = x^2 + y^2z$ 38. $U = \dfrac{w + y}{z}$

39. $V = \dfrac{3wyz}{x}$ 40. $W = \dfrac{3w + 6z}{xy}$

41. $X = (x^2z + x)^2z$ 42. $Y = (wy)^2 + w^2y + 3x$

43. This problem will help you check your work in Problems 19–42. Fill in the capital letters from Problems 19–42 to correspond with their numerical values (the letter O has been filled in for you). Some letters may not appear in the boxes. When you are finished, darken all the blank spaces to separate the words in the secret message. Notice that some of the blank spaces have also been filled in to help you.

17	7	21		18	O	1	11		9	13	2	10
20	11	O	8	21	49	49	21	49			18	
13	5	19	21	3	11	13		13	11	21		
18	13	8	17		11	O	49	,	O	5	48	21	,
49	2	9	20	5	2	18	27	,		13	10	12
21	48	13	5	1	13	17	21	.				

Suppose that a spreadsheet contains the following values:

Spreadsheet Application

	A	B	C	D	E
1	6	-4	2	3	
2					
3					
4					
5					

Determine the value of cell E1 if it contains the formula given in Problems 44–45.

44. a. $+A1 + B1$
    b. $+2*A1 + 3*B1$
    c. $+C1*(A1 + 3*B1)$
    d. $+A1+ \cdots +D1$ or @sum(A1 . . D1)

45. a. $+A1 - B1/C1$
    b. $+(A1 - B1)/C1$
    c. $+A1/C1*D1$
    d. $+(A1+ \cdots +D1)/2$ or @sum(A1 . . D1)/2

Draw a spreadsheet like the one shown and fill in the values of the missing cells assuming that the formula given in Problems 46–47 has been entered in cell C1 and replicated across row 1.

Spreadsheet Application

	A	B	C	D	E
1	1	3			
2					
3					
4					
5					

46. a. +A1 + B1   **b.** +A1 − B1

47. a. +$A$1 + B1   **b.** +$A$1*B1

In Problems 48–49, consider the following spreadsheet, in which the formula for each cell except B1 is displayed. Determine the value of each cell given the value in cell B1.

Spreadsheet Application				_ □ X
	A	**B**	**C**	**D**	**E**
1	+C2+1		+B2+1		
2	+C3+1	+A3+1	+C1+1		
3	+A2+1	+A1+1	+B1+1		
4					
5					

48. a. 1   **b.** −10

49. a. 0   **b.** 100

50. Show how you might use a spreadsheet to calculate the balance at the end of each year if $1,000 is deposited into an account paying 8% compounded yearly.

51. The owner of an auto dealership would like to create a spreadsheet in which sales performance information regarding each salesperson can be tabulated. She would like to use the following format:

Spreadsheet Application				_ □ X
	A	**B**	**C**	**D**	**E**
1	NAME	SALES	COST	PROFIT	COMMISSION
2	John Adams	100,000	80,000	20,000	1,600
3					
4					
5					

Column A is to contain the name of each salesperson; column B, the gross sales; column C, the cost; column D, the profit; and column E, the commission, calculated at 8% of the profit. Construct a spreadsheet for 20 employees.

52. A certain population has two eye color genes: *B* (brown eyes, dominant) and *b* (blue eyes, recessive). Suppose we have an isolated population in which 75% of the genes in the gene pool are dominant *B*, and the other 25% are recessive *b*. What percent of the population has each genotype? What percent of the population has each phenotype?

53. A certain population has two fur color genes: *B* (black, dominant) and *b* (brown, recessive). Suppose we have an isolated population in which 65% of the genes in the gene pool are dominant *B*, and the other 35% are recessive *b*. What percent of the population has each genotype? What percent of the population has each phenotype?

54. A population of self-pollinating pea plants has two genes; *T* (tall, dominant) and *t* (short, recessive). Suppose we have an isolated population in which 50% of the genes in the gene pool are dominant *T*, and the other 50% are recessive *t*. What percent of the population has each genotype? What percent of the population has each phenotype?

55. When flowers known as "four-o'clocks" are crossed, there is an incomplete dominance. A four-o'clock is red if the genotype is *rr* and white if it is *ww*. If *rr* is crossed with *ww*, a hybrid *rw* results. Suppose a population of 20% red four-o'clocks is mixed with a population of 80% white four-o'clocks. What percent of the population has each genotype? What percent of the population has each phenotype?

Problem Solving

56. What do you notice about the nine cells of the spreadsheet given in Problems 48–49?

57. A certain population has two fur color genes: *B* (black, dominant) and *b* (brown, recessive). Suppose you look at a population that is 25% brown and 75% black. Estimate the percentages in the gene pool that are *B* and *b*.

58. A population of self-pollinating pea plants has two genes: *T* (tall, dominant) and *t* (short, recessive). Suppose you look at a population that is 36% short. Estimate the percentages in the gene pool that are *T* and *t*.

59. Earlobes can be characterized as attached or free hanging. Free hanging (*F*) are dominant, and attached (*f*) are recessive. Survey your class to determine the percentage that are attached. Let q^2 be this number between 0 and 1; this represents the *ff* genotype. Estimate the gene pool for your class.

60. There are three genes in the gene pool for blood, *A*, *B*, and *O*. Two of these three are present in a person's blood: *A* and *B* dominate *O*, whereas *A* and *B* are codominant. This gives the following possibilities:

Genotype	Phenotype
AA	type *A* blood
AO	type *A* blood
AB	type *AB* blood
BO	type *B* blood
BB	type *B* blood
OO	type *O* blood

Let *p*, *q*, and *r* represent the relative frequencies of the genes *A*, *B*, and *O*, respectively, in the blood gene pool. Suppose a certain population has 20% type *A*, 30% type *B*, and 50% type *O*. Construct a Punnett square and find $(p + q + r)^2$ to answer the following questions. What percent of the population has each genotype? What percent of the population has each phenotype?

6.4 | Equations

Even though there are many aspects of algebra that are important to the scientist and mathematician, the ability to solve simple equations is important to the layperson and can be used in a variety of everyday applications.

Terminology

STOP Pay attention to the difference between an expression and an equation. Also, note that "to solve" is not the same as "to simplify."

An *equation* is a statement of equality. There are three types of equations: *true, false,* and *open.*

An *open equation* is one with a variable. A *true equation* is an equation without a variable, such as

$$2 + 3 = 5$$

A *false equation* is an equation without a variable, such as

$$2 + 3 = 15$$

STOP This is the fourth (last) of the four main processes of algebra.

Our focus is on *open equations*, those equations with a variable, or unknown.

The values that make an open equation true are said to **satisfy** the equation and are called the **solutions** or **roots** of the equation. To **solve** an open equation is to find all replacements for the variable(s) that make the equation true.

There are three types of open equations. Those that are always true, as in

$$x + 3 = 3 + x$$

are called *identities.* Those that are always false, as in

$$x + 3 = 4 + x$$

are called *contradictions.* Most open equations are true for some replacements of the variable and false for other replacements, as in

$$2 + x = 15$$

Donald Rumsfeld, news briefing on February 12, 2002.

"There are known knowns. There are things we know we know. We also know there are known unknowns. That is to say, we know there are some things we do not know. But there are also unknown unknowns, the ones we don't know we don't know."

These are called *conditional equations.* Generally, when we speak of equations we mean conditional equations. Our concern when solving equations is to find the numbers that satisfy a given equation, so we look for things to do to equations to make the solutions or roots more obvious. Two equations with the same solutions are called **equivalent equations.** An equivalent equation may be easier to solve than the original equation, so we try to get successively simpler equivalent equations until the solution is obvious. There are certain procedures you can use to create equivalent equations. In this section, we will discuss solving the two most common types of equations you will encounter: *linear* and *quadratic.*

Linear equations: $ax + b = 0$ $(a \neq 0)$
Quadratic equations: $ax^2 + bx + c = 0$ $(a \neq 0)$

Linear Equations

To solve a linear equation, you can use one or more of the following **equation properties.**

These properties lead to a procedure for solving equations.

Equation Properties

Addition property	Adding the same number to both sides of an equation results in an equivalent equation.
Subtraction property	Subtracting the same number from both sides of an equation results in an equivalent equation.
Multiplication property	Multiplying both sides of a given equation by the same nonzero number results in an equivalent equation.
Division property	Dividing both sides of a given equation by the same nonzero number results in an equivalent equation.

When these properties are used to obtain equivalent equations, ***the goal is to isolate the variable on one side of the equation,*** as illustrated in Example 1. You can always check the solution to see whether it is correct; substituting the solution into the original equation will verify that it satisfies the equation. Notice how the equation properties are used when solving these equations.

Example 1 Solve simple linear equations; basic operations

Solve the given equations.

a. $x + 15 = 25$ **b.** $x - 36 = 42$ **c.** $3x = 75$ **d.** $\frac{x}{5} = -12$ **e.** $15 - x = 0$

Solution

CAUTION The goal is to isolate the variable on one side of the equal sign.

a.

$x + 15 = 25$ Given equation

$x + 15 - 15 = 25 - 15$ Subtract 15 from both sides.

$x = 10$ Carry out the simplification.

The root (solution) of this simpler equivalent equation is now obvious (it is 10). We often display the answer in the form of this simpler equation, $x = 10$, with the variable isolated on one side.

b.

$x - 36 = 42$ Given equation

$x - 36 + 36 = 42 + 36$ Add 36 to both sides.

$x = 78$ Simplify.

CAUTION Perform the opposite operation to find a simpler equivalent equation.

c. $3x = 75$ Given equation

$\dfrac{3x}{3} = \dfrac{75}{3}$ Divide both sides by 3.

$x = 25$ Simplify.

d. $\dfrac{x}{5} = -12$ Given equation

$5\left(\dfrac{x}{5}\right) = 5(-12)$ Multiply both sides by 5.

$x = -60$ Simplify.

e. $15 - x = 0$ Given equation

$15 - x + x = 0 + x$ Add x to both sides.

$15 = x$ Simplify.

The equation $15 = x$ is the same as $x = 15$. This is a general property of equality called the **symmetric property of equality:** If $a = b$, then $b = a$.

While Example 1 illustrates the basic properties of equations, you will need to solve more complicated linear equations. In the following examples, some of the steps are left for mental calculations.

An equation is like a mystery thriller,
It grips you once you've begun it.
You are the sleuth who stalks the killer,
X represents "whodunit."

I'M SICK OF BEING AN UNKNOWN!

The scene of the crime must first be cleared,
The suspects called into session;
You look for clues to prove your case,
Till you wring from X a confession.

Example **2** **Find the root of a linear equation**

Find the root of the given equations.

a. $5x + 3 - 4x = 6 + 9$ **b.** $6x + 3 - 5x - 7 = 11(-2)$ **c.** $5x + 2 = 4x - 7$
d. $4x + x = 20$ **e.** $3(m + 4) + 5 = 5(m - 1) - 2$

Solution

a.

$5x + 3 - 4x = 6 + 9$	Given equation
$x + 3 = 15$	Simplify.
$x = 12$	Subtract 3 from both sides.

b.

$6x + 3 - 5x - 7 = 11(-2)$	Given equation
$x - 4 = -22$	Simplify.
$x = -18$	Add 4 to both sides.

c.

$5x + 2 = 4x - 7$	Given equation
$x + 2 = -7$	Subtract 4x from both sides.
$x = -9$	Subtract 2 from both sides.

d.

$4x + x = 20$	Given equation
$5x = 20$	Simplify.
$x = 4$	Divide both sides by 5.

e.

$3(m + 4) + 5 = 5(m - 1) - 2$	Given equation
$3m + 12 + 5 = 5m - 5 - 2$	Simplify (distributive property).
$3m + 17 = 5m - 7$	Simplify.
$17 = 2m - 7$	Subtract 3m from both sides.
$24 = 2m$	Add 7 to both sides.
$12 = m$	Divide both sides by 2.

An interesting application of solving equations occurs in changing a decimal fraction to a common fraction. If the decimal is terminating, no equations are necessary because we simply write the decimal as a fraction, for example

$$6.28 = \frac{628}{100}$$
$$= \frac{157}{25}$$

However, if the decimal is repeating, we carry out the procedure outlined in the following box.

Decimal to Fraction

To change a repeating decimal to fractional form:

Step 1 Let n = repeating decimal.

Step 2 Multiply both sides of the equation by 10^k, where k is the number of digits repeating.

Step 3 Subtract the original equation.

Step 4 Solve the resulting equation for n.

Example 3 Changing a repeating decimal to fractional form

Change each decimal to fractional form.
a. $0.\overline{7}$ **b.** 0.123 **c.** $0.\overline{123}$ **d.** $7.5\overline{64}$

Solution

a. Let $n = 0.7777\ldots$ $n = 0.777\ldots$
Multiply both sides of the equation of 10^1. $10n = 7.777\ldots$
Subtract the original equation. $9n = 7.000\ldots$

Solve for n. $n = \dfrac{7}{9}$

Thus, $0.\overline{7} = \dfrac{7}{9}$.

b. This is not a repeating decimal, so we simply write it as a fraction:
$$n = 0.123$$
$$= \frac{123}{1,000}$$

c. Let $n = 0.123123\ldots$ $n = 0.123123\ldots$
Multiply both sides of the equation of 10^3. $1,000n = 123.123\ldots$
Subtract the original equation. $999n = 123.000\ldots$

Solve for n. $n = \dfrac{123}{999} = \dfrac{41}{333}$

Thus, $0.\overline{123} = \dfrac{41}{333}$.

d. Let $n = 7.56464\ldots$ $n = 7.56464\ldots$
Multiply both sides of the equation of 10^2. $100n = 756.4646\ldots$
Subtract the original equation. $99n = 748.9000\ldots$

Solve for n. $n = \dfrac{748.9}{99} \cdot \dfrac{10}{10}$

$$= \frac{7,489}{990}$$

Thus, $7.5\overline{64} = \dfrac{7,489}{990}$.

Quadratic Equations

To solve quadratic equations, you must first use the equation properties to write the equation in the form

$$ax^2 + bx + c = 0$$

There are two commonly used methods for solving quadratic equations. The first uses factoring, and the second uses the quadratic formula. Both of these methods require that you apply the linear equation properties to obtain a 0 on one side. Next, look to see whether the polynomial is factorable. If so, use the **zero-product rule** to set each factor equal to 0, and then solve each of those equations. If the polynomial is not factorable, then use the quadratic formula.

STOP Note that you must first have a zero on one side.

Zero-Product Rule

If $A \cdot B = 0$, then $A = 0$ or $B = 0$, or $A = B = 0$.
If the product of two numbers is 0, then at least one of the factors must be 0.

Example 4 Solve simple quadratic equations

Solve each equation: **a.** $x^2 = x$ **b.** $x(x-8) = 4(x-9)$

Solution

a.
$$x^2 = x \qquad \text{Given equation}$$
$$x^2 - x = 0 \qquad \text{Subtract } x \text{ from both sides.}$$
$$x(x-1) = 0 \qquad \text{Factor, if possible.}$$
$$x = 0, \quad x - 1 = 0 \qquad \text{Zero-product rule; set each factor equal to 0.}$$
$$x = 1 \qquad \text{Solve each of the resulting equations.}$$

⟨CAUTION⟩ First obtain a 0 on one side.

The equation has two roots, $x = 0$ and $x = 1$. Usually you will set each factor equal to 0 and solve mentally.

b.
$$x(x-8) = 4(x-9) \qquad \text{Given equation}$$
$$x^2 - 8x = 4x - 36 \qquad \text{Simplify.}$$
$$x^2 - 12x + 36 = 0 \qquad \text{Subtract } 4x \text{ from both sides and add 36 to both sides.}$$
$$(x-6)(x-6) = 0 \qquad \text{Factor.}$$
$$x = 6 \qquad \text{Set each factor equal to 0 and mentally solve.}$$

Since the factors are the same, there is one root, 6. In such a case we say the root of 6 has **multiplicity** two.

If the quadratic expression is not easily factorable (after you obtain a 0 on one side), then you can use the **quadratic formula,** which is derived in most high school algebra books.

Quadratic Formula

If $ax^2 + bx + c = 0$, $a \neq 0$, then
$$x = \frac{-b \pm \sqrt{b^2 - 4ac}}{2a}$$

Example 5 Use the quadratic formula

Solve the given equations: **a.** $2x^2 + 4x + 1 = 0$ **b.** $x^2 = 6x - 13$

Solution

a. Note that $2x^2 + 4x + 1 = 0$ has a 0 on one side and also that the left-hand side does not easily factor, so we will use the quadratic formula. We begin by (mentally) identifying $a = 2$, $b = 4$, and $c = 1$.

$$2x^2 + 4x + 1 = 0 \qquad \text{Given equation.}$$

$$x = \frac{-(4) \pm \sqrt{4^2 - 4(2)(1)}}{2(2)} \qquad \text{Substitute for } a, b, \text{ and } c \text{ in the quadratic formula.}$$

$$= \frac{-4 \pm \sqrt{8}}{4} \qquad \text{Simplify under the square root.}$$

$$= \frac{-4 \pm 2\sqrt{2}}{4} \qquad \text{Simplify radical.}$$

$$= \frac{2(-2 \pm \sqrt{2})}{4} \qquad \text{Factor a 2 out of the numerator so that we can reduce the fraction. This step is usually done mentally.}$$

$$= \frac{-2 \pm \sqrt{2}}{2} \qquad \text{Reduce the fraction.}$$

Historical NOTE

As early as 2000 B.C., the Babylonians had a well-developed algebra. It did not have the symbolism we associate with modern-day algebra but was written out in words. Even without the symbolism, however, the Babylonians did solve quadratic equations by using a general formula.

STOP This is one of the all time "BIGGIES" in algebra. You should remember it.

b. $\quad\quad\quad\quad x^2 = 6x - 13$ *Given equation*

$x^2 - 6x + 13 = 0$ *Get a 0 on one side.*

$$x = \frac{-(-6) \pm \sqrt{(-6)^2 - 4(1)(13)}}{2(1)}$$ *Substitute for a, b, and c in the quadratic formula.*

$$= \frac{6 \pm \sqrt{-16}}{2}$$ *Simplify.*

The square root of a negative number is not defined in the set of real numbers. Thus, since we are working in the set of real numbers, we say there is no real value.

Historical NOTE

The convention followed in this section of using the last letters of the alphabet for variables and the first letters for constants is credited to René Descartes (1596–1650). Many symbols had been used before his time. In the earliest forms of algebra, statements were written out in words. "A certain number" gave way to the names of colors that were used by some Arabian mathematicians. *Cosa, censo, cubo* were abbreviated by *co, ce, cu*, then by *Q, S, C* before Descartes used x, x^2, and x^3. The quadratic formula, as you see it today, is the result of a slow and tedious evolution of ideas and symbols and is not the work of a single person.

Since most of us have access to a calculator, we often estimate the roots of quadratic equations with radicals as rational (decimal) approximations. We illustrate this with the next calculator example.

Example 6 Approximate roots with the quadratic formula

Solve $5x^2 + 2x - 2 = 0$ and approximate the roots to the nearest hundredth.

Solution   From the quadratic formula, where $a = 5$, $b = 2$, and $c = -2$:

$$x = \frac{-b \pm \sqrt{b^2 - 4ac}}{2a}$$

$$= \frac{-2 \pm \sqrt{2^2 - 4(5)(-2)}}{2(5)}$$

$$= \frac{-2 \pm \sqrt{44}}{2(5)}$$

$$= \frac{-1 \pm \sqrt{11}}{5}$$

$$\approx 0.46, -0.86$$

Example 6 begs the use of a calculator, and for the most part we do not show calculator steps to solve problems because there are many different types of calculators. Although the computational window offers some suggestions, remember to check the owner's manual for the calculator you are using.

COMPUTATIONAL WINDOW

Solve $5x^2 + 2x - 2 = 0$ using an *algebraic calculator.* To approximate these roots:

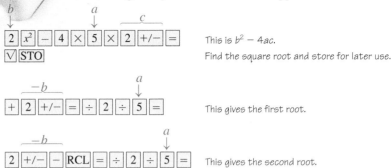

This is $b^2 - 4ac$.
Find the square root and store for later use.

This gives the first root.

This gives the second root.

Some of the steps shown here could be combined because these are simple numbers. These steps give the numerical approximation for a quadratic equation with real roots. For this quadratic equation the roots are (to four decimal places) 0.4633 and -0.8633.

Since you will have occasion to use the quadratic formula over and over again, and since many calculators have programming capabilities, this is a good time to consider writing a simple program to give the real roots for a quadratic equation. First write the equation in the form $ax^2 + bx + c = 0$ and input the a, b, and c values into the calculator as A, B, and C. The program will then output the two real values (if they exist). Each brand of *graphing calculator* is somewhat different, but it is instructive to illustrate the general process. Press the PRGM key. You will then be asked to name the program; we call our program QUAD. Next, input the formula for the two roots (from the quadratic formula). Finally, display the answer:

:$(-B+\sqrt{\ }(B^2 - 4AC))/(2A)$

:Disp Ans

:$(-B-\sqrt{\ }(B^2 - 4AC))/(2A)$

:Disp Ans

Continuing with Example 6, input the A, B, and C values as follows:

5 STO → A 2 STO → B −2 STO → C PRGM QUAD

Then run the program for the DISPLAY: .4633249581
                                          −.8633249581

Finally, today many calculators have a SOLVE key and the only requirement for solving the equation is to check your owner's manual for the correct format. For Example 6, input

solve $(5x^2 + 2x - 2 = 0, x)$

which gives the solution as

$$x = \frac{-(\sqrt{11} + 1)}{5} \quad \text{or} \quad x = \frac{\sqrt{11} - 1}{5}$$

Note that the form here is equivalent to (but not the same as) $x = \dfrac{-1 \pm \sqrt{11}}{5}$ obtained in Example 6.

A newer topic in mathematics is *chaos*, which is featured in the following Guest Essay. The patterns shown in the article are the results of solving a quadratic equation, and they are also related to fractals, which are discussed in Chapter 8.

Guest Essay: CHAOS
Jack Wadhams, Golden West College

An exciting new topic in mathematics and an attempt to bring order to the universe has been labeled **chaos theory**, which provides refreshing insight into how very simple beginnings can yield structures of incredible complexity and of enchanting beauty. Let's trace a chaos path to simple beginnings.

Water flowing through a pipe offers one of the simplest physical models of chaos. Pressure is applied to the end of the pipe and the water flows in straight lines. More pressure increases the speed of the laminar flow until the pressure reaches a critical value, and a radically new situation evolves—turbulence. A simple laminar

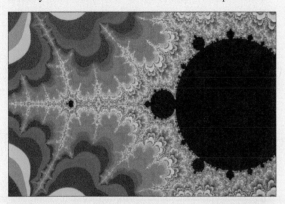

flow suddenly changes to a flow of beautiful complexity consisting of swirls within swirls. Before turbulence, the path of any particle was quite predictable. After a minute change in the pressure, turbulence occurred and predictability was lost. **Chaos** is concerned with systems in which minute changes suddenly transform predictability into unpredictability.

The simple quadratic equation $z_{n+1} = z_n^2 - c$ (where z is a complex number, a number you considered in algebra, but is not in the domain of real numbers we are assuming in this book) offers a fascinating mathematical example of chaos. With this equation and a computer, a graph of unimaginable complexity and surprising beauty can be constructed. To create a graph we plot a grid of points (often more than a million) from a 4×4 square region R centered at the origin of the complex plane. We let $z_0 = 0$ and $c = a + bi$ be a point in the region R. Substitute z_1 and c into the right-hand side of the equation to obtain a second number z_2. After many such iterations, we obtain the sequence of numbers z_0, z_1 ..., z_i, ..., which approaches a fixed value or it does not. If it does approach a fixed value, we paint a black dot on the computer screen at $a + bi$; otherwise, we paint a white dot. This process of selecting a point from region R, done millions of times, produces regions of black and white dots. If the boundary between the convergent and divergent regions is connected, a bumpy curve called the Mandelbrot set is formed. The graph is painted black on the interior of the Mandelbrot set and white on the exterior. We find that points selected far from the Mandelbrot set (the boundary) behave in a very predictable fashion (like the laminar flow in the pipe). However, when we choose points near the Mandelbrot set (the boundary), the behavior is quite unpredictable. We have encountered chaos. Because of the complexity of the Mandelbrot set, it is difficult to determine whether a given point is outside or inside the set.

This path to chaos has led to the Mandelbrot set, the most complicated set in mathematics, and it turns out to be fractal in nature, yet it is generated from a simple quadratic equation. That is, from a very simple quadratic equation, a set of surprising complexity and beauty emerges. Regions of chaotic behavior, under magnification, reveal a self-similar fractal. Our mathematical analogy awakens the possibility that the universe may also originate from a few simple relations that evolve into profoundly complex structures, like our brain, capable of understanding its own origins and still asking about its origins. This chaos path to simple beginnings seems to be fractal.

Problem Set 6.4

Level **1**

1. IN YOUR OWN WORDS   Describe a procedure for solving first-degree equations.

2. IN YOUR OWN WORDS   Describe a procedure for solving second-degree equations.

Solve the equations in Problems 3–5.

3. a. $x - 5 = 10$ **b.** $6 = x - 2$
   c. $8 + x = 4$ **d.** $18 + x = 10$

4. a. $\frac{x}{4} = 8$ **b.** $\frac{x}{-4} = 11$
   c. $4x = 12$ **d.** $-x = 5$

5. a. $13x = 0$ **b.** $-\frac{1}{2}x = 0$
   c. $2x - 5 = 11$ **d.** $8 - 3x = 2$

Express each of the numbers in Problems 6–9 as the quotient of two integers.

6. a. $0.\overline{45}$ **b.** $0.\overline{234}$
7. a. 0.1111 **b.** $0.52\overline{2}$
8. a. $16.\overline{4752}$ **b.** 16.4752
9. a. $0.39\overline{39}$ **b.** $0.6\overline{2}$

Solve the equations in Problems 10–25.

10. a. $A + 13 = 18$ **b.** $5 = 3 + B$
11. a. $-5X = -1$ **b.** $6 = C - 4$
12. a. $2D + 2 = 10$ **b.** $15E - 5 = 0$
13. a. $16F - 5 = 11$ **b.** $6 = 5G - 24$
14. a. $4(H + 1) = 4$ **b.** $5(I - 7) = 0$
15. a. $\frac{J}{5} = 3$ **b.** $\frac{2K}{3} = 6$
16. a. $\frac{3L}{4} = 5$ **b.** $1 = \frac{2M}{3} + 7$
17. a. $7 = \frac{2N}{3} + 11$ **b.** $-5 = \frac{2P + 1}{3}$
18. a. $\frac{2 - 5Q}{3} = 4$ **b.** $\frac{5R - 1}{2} = 5$
19. $5(6S - 81) = -3(15 + 5S)$
20. $3T + 3(T + 2) + (T + 4) + 11 = 0$
21. $3(U - 3) - 2(U - 12) = 18$
22. $6(V - 2) - 4(V + 3) = 10 - 42$
23. $5(W + 3) - 6(W + 5) = 0$
24. $6(Y + 2) = 4 + 5(Y - 4)$
25. $5(Z - 2) - 3(Z + 3) = 9$

Level **2**

26. This problem should help you check your work in Problems 10–25. Fill in the capital letters from Problems 10–25 to correspond with their numerical values (the letter O has been filled in for you). Some letters may not appear in the boxes. When you are finished, darken all the blank spaces to separate the words in the secret message. Notice that one of the blank spaces has also been filled in to help you.

12	−3	0	7	8	−7	−8	$\frac{11}{5}$		2	$\frac{20}{3}$	$\frac{1}{3}$	−9	$\frac{4}{5}$		11
								O							
−15	7	$\frac{20}{3}$	$\frac{20}{3}$	−1	3	−6	4		3	2	−3	$\frac{1}{3}$	4	$\frac{20}{3}$	−28
								O							
−1	5	8	8	7	8	−3	−5	−28		3	$\frac{1}{6}$	$\frac{1}{6}$	7	−6	12
									O						
1	7	−6	4	7	−6	6	$\frac{1}{4}$	$\frac{1}{3}$	$\frac{11}{5}$	$\frac{11}{5}$		$\frac{11}{5}$	8		
											O			!	!

Solve the equations in Problems 27–48.

27. $x^2 = 10x$ **28.** $x^2 = 14x$
29. $5x + 66 = x^2$ **30.** $15x^2 + 4x = 4$
31. $x^3 = 4x$ **32.** $x^3 = x$
33. $4x(x - 9) = 9(1 - 4x)$ **34.** $4(9x - 1) = 9x(4 - x)$
35. $x^2 + 7x + 2 = 0$ **36.** $x^2 - 3x + 1 = 0$
37. $x^2 - 5x - 3 = 0$ **38.** $x^2 - 6x + 9 = 0$
39. $x^2 - 6x + 7 = 0$ **40.** $x^2 - 6x + 6 = 0$
41. $3x^2 + 5x - 4 = 0$ **42.** $2x^2 - x + 3 = 0$
43. $4x^2 + 2x = -5$ **44.** $6x^2 = 13x - 6$
45. $3x^2 = 11x + 4$ **46.** $6x^2 = 17x + 3$
47. $6x^2 = 5x$ **48.** $9x^2 = 2x$

Use a calculator to obtain solutions correct to the nearest hundredth in Problems 49–54.

49. $x^2 + 4 = 3\sqrt{2}\,x$
50. $x^2 - 4\sqrt{3}\,x + 9 = 0$
51. $\sqrt{2}x^2 + 2x - 3 = 0$
52. $4x^2 - 2\sqrt{5}\,x - 2 = 0$
53. $0.02x^2 + 0.831x + 0.0069 = 0$
54. $68.38x^2 - 4.12x - 198.41 = 0$

Level **3**

55. Young's Rule for calculating a child's dosage for medication is

$$\text{CHILD'S DOSE} = \frac{\text{AGE OF CHILD}}{\text{AGE OF CHILD} + 12} \times \text{ADULT DOSE}$$

   a. If an adult's dose of a particular medication is 100 mg, what is the dose for a 10-year-old child?
   b. If a 12-year-old child's dose of a particular medication is 10 mg, what is the adult's dose?

56. Fried's Rule for calculating an infant's dosage for medication is

$$\text{INFANT'S DOSE} = \frac{\text{AGE OF INFANT IN MONTHS}}{150} \times \text{ADULT DOSE}$$

   a. If an adult's dose of a particular medication is 50 mg, what is the dosage for a 10-month-old infant?
   b. If a 15-month-old infant is to receive 7.5 mg of a medication, what is the equivalent adult dose?

Problem Solving **3**

57. Let $a = b = 1$. Consider

$a + b = c$	Given
$(a + b)^2 = c(a + b)$	Multiply both sides by $(a + b)$.
$a^2 + 2ab + b^2 = ac + bc$	Expand by multiplication.
$a^2 + 2ab - ac = bc - b^2$	Subtract ac and b^2 from both sides.
$a^2 + ab - ac = -ab - b^2 + bc$	Subtract ab from both sides.
$a(a + b - c) = -b(a + b - c)$	Common factor.
$a = -b$	Divide both sides by $a + b - c$.

But since $a = b = 1$, we see $a = -1$.
What is wrong here?

58. An approximation for π can be obtained from

$$\frac{\pi^2}{6} = 1 + \frac{1}{2^2} + \frac{1}{3^2} + \frac{1}{4^2} + \ldots$$

   a. Solve for π.
   b. Find an approximation for π using the first 20 terms.
   c. Compare your answer to part **b** with an approximation of π you probably used in grade school, namely, $\frac{22}{7}$.

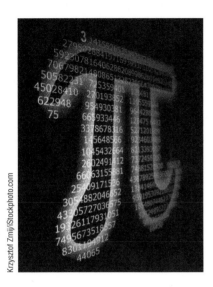

Krzysztof Zmij/iStockphoto.com

59. **HISTORICAL QUEST**   Al-Khwârizmî solved the equation

$$x^2 + 10x = 39$$

   a. Solve this equation.
   b. Here is a translation of his solution:

> . . . *a square and* 10 *roots are equal to* 39 *units. The question therefore in this type of equation is about as follows: What is the square which combined with ten of its roots will give a sum total of* 39? *The manner of solving this type of equation is to take one-half of the roots just mentioned. Now the roots in the problem before us are* 10. *Therefore take* 5, *which multiplied by itself gives* 25, *an amount which you add to* 39 *giving* 64. *Having taken then the square root of this which is* 8, *subtract from it half the roots,* 5, *leaving* 3. *The number three therefore represents one root of this square, which itself, of course is* 9. *Nine therefore gives the square.*

Follow these directions to find a solution. Show each step using modern algebraic notation.

60. **HISTORICAL QUEST**
   a. Consult an algebra textbook and look up the procedure of *completing the square*. Solve Al-Khwârizmî's equation in Problem 59 by completing the square.
   b. Do you think the translation of the solution in Problem 59b better describes what you did in solving the equation in Problem 59a or what you did in solving the equation in part **a**?

6.5 | Inequalities

The techniques of the previous section can also be applied to quantities that are not equal.

Comparison Property

If we are given any two numbers x and y, then obviously either

$$x = y \quad \text{or} \quad x \neq y$$

If $x \neq y$, then either

$$x < y \quad \text{or} \quad x > y$$

This property is called the **comparison property.**[*]

Comparison Property

For any two numbers x and y, exactly one of the following is true:
1. $x = y$ x is equal to (the same as) y
2. $x > y$ x is greater than (larger than) y
3. $x < y$ x is less than (smaller than) y

---

[*]Sometimes this is called the *trichotomy property*.

Solving Linear Inequalities

The comparison property tells us that if two quantities are not exactly equal, we can relate them with a greater-than or a less-than symbol (called an **inequality symbol**). The solution of

$$x < 3$$

has more than one value, and it becomes very impractical to write "The answers are 2, 1, $-110, 0, 2\frac{1}{2}, 2.99, \ldots$." Instead, we relate the answer to a number line, as shown in Figure 6.2. The fact that 3 is not included (3 is not less than 3) in the solution set is indicated by an open circle at the point 3.

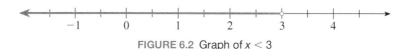

FIGURE 6.2 Graph of $x < 3$

If we want to include the endpoint $x = 3$ with the inequality $x < 3$, we write $x \leq 3$ and say "x is less than or equal to 3." We define two additional inequality symbols:

$x \geq y$ means $x > y$ or $x = y$

$x \leq y$ means $x < y$ or $x = y$

A *statement of order,* called an **inequality,** refers to statements that include one or more of the following relationships:

less than ($<$)   less than or equal to ($\leq$)
greater than ($>$)   greater than or equal to ($\geq$)

Example   **1**   **Solve simple linear inequalities**

Graph the solution sets for the given inequalities.
a. $x \leq 3$ **b.** $x > 5$ **c.** $-2 \leq x$

Solution

a. Notice that in this example the endpoint is included because with $x \leq 3$, it is possible that $x = 3$. This is shown as a solid dot on the number line:

b. $x > 5$

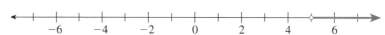

c. $-2 \leq x$

Although you can graph this directly, you will have less chance of making a mistake when working with inequalities if you rewrite them so that the variable is on the left; that is, reverse the inequality to read $x \geq -2$. Notice that the direction of the arrow has been changed, because the symbol requires that the arrow always point to the smaller number. When you change the direction of the arrow, we say that you have *changed the order of the inequality.* For example, if $-2 \leq x$, then $x \geq -2$, and we say the order has been changed. The graph of $x \geq -2$ is shown on the following number line:

On a number line, if $x < y$, then x is to the left of y. Suppose the coordinates x and y are plotted as shown in Figure 6.3.

FIGURE 6.3 Number line showing two coordinates, x and y

If you add 2 to both x and y, you obtain $x + 2$ and $y + 2$. From Figure 6.4, you see that $x + 2 < y + 2$.

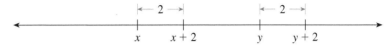

FIGURE 6.4 Number line with 2 added to both x and y

If you add some number c, there are two possibilities.

$c > 0$ ($c > 0$ is read "c is positive")
$c < 0$ ($c < 0$ is read "c is negative")

If $c > 0$, then $x + c$ is still to the left of $y + c$, as shown in Figure 6.5.

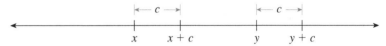

FIGURE 6.5 Adding positive values to x and y

If $c < 0$, then $x + c$ is still to the left of $y + c$. In both cases, $x < y$, which justifies the following property (see Figure 6.6).

FIGURE 6.6 Adding negative values to x and y

Addition Property of Inequality

If $x < y$, then

$x + c < y + c$

Also,   if $x \leq y$, then $x + c \leq y + c$
if $x > y$, then $x + c > y + c$
if $x \geq y$, then $x + c \geq y + c$

Because this **addition property of inequality** is essentially the same as the addition property of equality, you might expect that there is also a multiplication property of inequality. We would hope that we could multiply both sides of an inequality by some number c without upsetting the inequality. Consider some examples.

Let $c = 2$: $5 \cdot 2 < 10 \cdot 2$
$10 < 20$ True

Let $c = 0$: $5 \cdot 0 < 10 \cdot 0$
$0 < 0$ False

Let $c = -2$: $5(-2) < 10(-2)$
$-10 < -20$ False

You can see that you cannot multiply both sides of an inequality by a constant and be sure that the result is still true. However, if you restrict c to a positive value, then you can multiply both sides of an inequality by c. On the other hand, if c is a negative number, then the order of the inequality should be reversed. This is summarized by the **multiplication property of inequality.**

Multiplication Property of Inequality

Positive multiplication $(c > 0)$ **Negative multiplication** $(c < 0)$

If $x < y$, then   If $x < y$, then

$cx < cy$ $cx > cy$

↑   ↑

Order unchanged   *Order reversed*

Also, for $c > 0$,   Also, for $c < 0$,

if $x \leq y$, then $cx \leq cy$ if $x \leq y$, then $cx \geq cy$

if $x > y$, then $cx > cy$ if $x > y$, then $cx < cy$

if $x \geq y$, then $cx \geq cy$ if $x \geq y$, then $cx \leq cy$

The same properties hold for positive and negative division. We can summarize with the following statement, which tells us how to **solve an inequality.**

Solution of Linear Inequalities

The procedure for solving linear inequalities is the same as the procedure for solving linear equations except that if you multiply or divide by a negative number, you reverse the order of the inequality symbol.

In summary, given $x < y$, $x \leq y$, $x > y$, or $x \geq y$:

The **inequality symbols are the *same* if you**

1. Add the same number to both sides.
2. Subtract the same number from both sides.
3. Multiply both sides by a positive number.
4. Divide both sides by a positive number.

} *This works the same as with equations.*

STOP Spend some time with this summary.

The **inequality symbols are *reversed* if you**

1. Multiply both sides by a negative number.
2. Divide both sides by a negative number.
3. Interchange the x and the y.

} *This is where inequalities and equations differ.*

STOP Here is where inequalities differ from equations.

Example 2 Solve linear inequalities

Solve: **a.** $-x \geq 2$ **b.** $\frac{x}{-3} < 1$ **c.** $5x - 3 \geq 7$

Solution

a. $-x \geq 2$

$x \leq -2$ Multiply both sides by -1 and remember to reverse the order of the inequality.

Now, with the variable on the left of the inequality, we graph the solution on a number line:

b. $\dfrac{x}{-3} < 1$

$\quad\quad x > -3$ Multiply both sides by -3 and reverse the order of the inequality.

c. $\quad 5x - 3 \geq 7$

$\quad 5x - 3 + 3 \geq 7 + 3$

$\quad\quad\quad 5x \geq 10$

$\quad\quad\quad \dfrac{5x}{5} \geq \dfrac{10}{5}$

$\quad\quad\quad\quad x \geq 2$

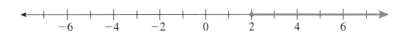

Problem Set

Level 1

1. **IN YOUR OWN WORDS**   What is the comparison property?

2. **IN YOUR OWN WORDS**   Describe a procedure for solving a first-degree inequality.

Graph the solution sets in Problems 3–16.

3. $x < 5$
4. $x \geq 6$
5. $x \geq -3$
6. $x \leq -2$
7. $4 \geq x$
8. $-1 < x$
9. $\frac{x}{2} > 3$
10. $4 < \frac{x}{2}$
11. $-2 > \frac{x}{-4}$
12. $x < 50$
13. $x \geq 100$
14. $x \geq -125$
15. $x \leq -75$
16. $-40 < x$

Solve the inequalities in Problems 17–40.

17. $x + 7 \geq 3$
18. $x - 2 \leq 5$
19. $x - 2 \geq -4$
20. $10 < 5 + y$
21. $-4 < 2 + y$
22. $-3 < 5 + y$
23. $2 > -s$
24. $-t \leq -3$
25. $-m > -5$
26. $5 \leq 4 - y$
27. $3 > 2 - x$
28. $5 \geq 1 - w$
29. $2x + 6 \leq 8$
30. $3y - 6 \geq 9$
31. $3 > s + 9$
32. $2 < 2s + 8$
33. $4 \leq a + 2$
34. $3 > 2b - 13$
35. $3s + 2 > 8$
36. $5t - 7 \geq 8$
37. $7u - 5 \leq 9$
38. $9 - 2v < 5$
39. $5 - 3w > 8$
40. $2 - x \geq 3x + 10$

Level 2

Solve the inequalities in Problems 41–50.

41. $7 - 5A < 2A + 7$
42. $B > 3(1 + B)$
43. $3C > C + 19$
44. $2(D + 7) > 2 - D$
45. $5E - 4 < 3E - 6$
46. $3(3F - 2) > 4F - 3$
47. $4G - 1 > 3(G + 2)$
48. $5(4 + H) < 3(H + 1)$
49. $2 - 3I > 7(1 - I)$
50. $7(J - 2) + 5 \leq 3(2 + J)$

51. Suppose that seven times a number is added to 35 and the result is positive. What are the possible numbers?

52. If the opposite of a number must be greater than twice the number, what are the possible numbers?

53. Suppose that three times a number is added to 12 and the result is negative. What are the possible numbers?

54. If the opposite of a number must be less than 5, what are the possible numbers satisfying this condition?

Problem Solving 3

55. If a number is four more than its opposite, what are the possible numbers?

56. If a number is six less than twice its opposite, what are the possible numbers?

57. If a number is less than four more than its opposite, what are the possible numbers?

58. If a number is less than six minus twice its opposite, what are the possible numbers?

59. Parcel Post services allow that a package can be shipped if its girth plus length (longest side) is no larger than 130 inches. If you have a square package whose length is six times the length of a shorter side, what are the possible lengths for a side of the box?

60. Current postal regulations state that no package may be sent if its combined length, width, and height exceed 72 in. What are the possible dimensions of a box to be mailed with equal height and width if the length is four times the height?

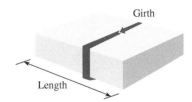

Girth

Length

6.6 | Algebra in Problem Solving

One of the goals of problem solving is to be able to apply techniques that you learn in the classroom to situations outside the classroom. However, a first step is to learn to solve contrived textbook-type word problems to develop the problem-solving skills you will need outside the classroom.

In this section, we will focus on common types of word problems that are found in most textbooks. You might say, "I want to learn how to become a problem solver, and textbook problems are not what I have in mind; I want to do *real* problem solving." But to become a problem solver, you must first learn the basics, and there is good reason why word problems are part of a textbook. We start with these problems *to build a problem-solving* **procedure** *that can be expanded to apply to problem solving in general.*

The most useful axiom in problem solving is the **principle of substitution:** If two quantities are equal, one may be substituted for the other without changing the truth or falsity of this statement.

Substitution Property

If $a = b$, then a may be substituted for b in any mathematical statement without affecting the truth or falsity of the given mathematical statement.

The simplest way to illustrate the substitution property is to use it in evaluating a formula.

Example 1 Find the perimeter

A billiard table is 4 ft by 8 ft. Find the perimeter.

Solution   Use an appropriate formula, $P = 2\ell + 2w$, where $P =$ PERIMETER, $\ell =$ LENGTH, and $w =$ WIDTH. Substitute the known values into the formula:

$$\ell = 8 \quad w = 4$$
$$\downarrow \qquad \downarrow$$
$$P = 2(8) + 2(4) \quad \text{These arrows mean}$$
$$= 16 + 8 \qquad\qquad\; \text{substitution.}$$
$$= 24$$

The perimeter is 24 ft.

"For a minute I thought we had him stymied!"

We will now rephrase Pólya's problem-solving guidelines in a setting that is appropriate to solving word problems. This procedure is summarized in the following box.

Procedure for Problem Solving in Algebra

Step 1   *Understand the Problem.* This means you must read the problem and note what it is about. Focus on processes rather than numbers. You cannot work a problem you do not understand. A sketch may help in understanding the problem.

Step 2   *Devise a Plan.* **Write down a verbal description of the problem using operation signs and an equal or inequality sign.** Note the following common translations.

Symbol	*Verbal Description*
$=$	is equal to; equals; is the same as; is; was; becomes; will be; results in
$+$	plus; the sum of; added to; more than; greater than; increased by; combined; total
$-$	minus; the difference of; the difference between; is subtracted from; less than; smaller than; decreased by; is diminished by
$\times$	times; product; is multiplied by; twice $(2 \times)$; triple $(3 \times)$; of (as in 40% of 300).
$\div$	divided by; quotient of; ratio of; proportional to

Step 3   *Carry out the Plan.* In the context of word problems, we need to proceed deductively by carrying out the following steps.

Choose a variable. If there is a single unknown, choose a variable. If there are several unknowns, you can use the substitution property to reduce the number of unknowns to a single variable. Later we will consider word problems with more than one unknown.

Substitute. Replace the verbal phrase for the unknown with the variable.

Solve the equation. This is generally the easiest step. Translate the symbolic statement (such as $x = 3$) into a verbal statement. Probably no variables were given as part of the word problem, so $x = 3$ is not an answer. Generally, word problems require an answer stated in words. Pay attention to units of measure and other details of the problem.

Step 4   *Look Back.* Be sure your answer makes sense by checking it with the original question in the problem. **Remember to answer the question that was asked.**

Problem solving depends not only on the substitution property, but also on translating statements from English to mathematical symbols, using *variables* as necessary. On a much more advanced level, this process is called *mathematical modeling* (we will consider some mathematical modeling later in this book). However, for now, we will simply call it **translating.** Example 2 reviews some of the terminology introduced in the previous procedure box. These terms include **sum** to indicate the result obtained from addition, **difference** for the result from subtraction, **product** for the result of a multiplication, and **quotient** for the result of a division.

Example 2   Translate word statements

Write the word statement or phrase in symbols. Do not simplify the translated expressions.
a. The sum of seven and a number
b. The difference of a number subtracted from seven
c. The quotient of two numbers
d. The product of two consecutive numbers
e. The difference of the squares of a number and two
f. The square of the difference of two from a number
g. The sum of two times a number and six is equal to two times the sum of a number and three

Solution

a. Since *sum* indicates addition, this can be rewritten as

$$(\text{SEVEN}) + (\text{A NUMBER})$$

Now select some variable—say, $s = $ A NUMBER. The symbolic statement is $7 + s$.

b. First we translate the statement into mathematics symbols: $(\text{SEVEN}) - (\text{A NUMBER})$. Let $d = $ A NUMBER; then the expression is $7 - d$.

c. The quotient of two numbers means $\dfrac{\text{A NUMBER}}{\text{ANOTHER NUMBER}}$. If there is more than one unknown in a problem and no relationship between those unknowns is given, more than one variable may be needed. Let $m = $ A NUMBER and $n = $ ANOTHER NUMBER. Then the expression is $\frac{m}{n}$.

d. The product of two consecutive numbers means $[(\text{A NUMBER})(\text{NEXT CONSECUTIVE NUMBER})]$. If there is more than one unknown in a problem but a given relationship exists between those unknowns, *do not choose more variables than you need* for the problem. In this problem, a consecutive number means one more than the first number:

$$\text{NEXT CONSECUTIVE NUMBER} = \text{A NUMBER} + 1$$

Thus,

$$(\text{A NUMBER})(\text{NEXT CONSECUTIVE NUMBER}) = (\text{A NUMBER})(\text{A NUMBER} + 1)$$

Let $x = $ A NUMBER; then the variable expression is

$$x(x + 1)$$

e. A difference of squares means $(\text{A NUMBER})^2 - 2^2$. Let $x = $ A NUMBER; then

$$x^2 - 2^2$$

Remember, this is called a *difference of squares*.

f. The square of a difference means $(\text{A NUMBER} - 2)^2$; compare with part **e.** Let $x = $ A NUMBER; then

$$(x - 2)^2$$

Remember, this is called a *square of a difference.*

g. If "a number" is referred to more than once in a problem, it is assumed to be the same number.

$$2(\text{A NUMBER}) + 6 = 2(\text{A NUMBER} + 3)$$

Let $n = $ A NUMBER;

$$2n + 6 = 2(n + 3)$$

Number Relationships

The first type of word problem we consider involves number relationships. These are designed to allow you to begin thinking about the *procedure* to use when solving word problems.

Example 3 Formulate an equation

If you add 10 to twice a number, the result is 22. What is the number?

Solution   Read the problem carefully. Make sure you know what is given and what is wanted. Next, write a verbal description (without using variables), using operation signs and an equal sign, but still using the key words. This is called translating the problem.

$$10 + 2(\text{A NUMBER}) = 22$$

When there is a single unknown, choose a variable.

With more complicated problems you will not know at the start what the variable should be.

Let $n = $ A NUMBER. Use the substitution property:

$$10 + 2(\text{A NUMBER}) = 22$$
$$\downarrow$$
$$10 + 2n = 22$$

Solve the equation and check the solution in the original problem to see if it makes sense.

$$10 + 2n = 22$$
$$2n = 12$$
$$n = 6$$

Check: Add 10 to twice 6 and the result is 22. State the solution to a word problem in words: The number is 6.

STOP IMPORTANT: Do not BEGIN by choosing a variable; choose a variable only AFTER you have translated the problem.

The second type of number problem involves **consecutive integers**. If $n = $ AN INTEGER, then

THE SECOND CONSECUTIVE INTEGER $= n + 1$,   and

THE THIRD CONSECUTIVE INTEGER $= n + 2$

Also, if $E = $ AN EVEN INTEGER and if $F = $ AN ODD INTEGER, then

$E + 2 = $ THE NEXT CONSECUTIVE EVEN INTEGER

$F + 2 = $ THE NEXT CONSECUTIVE ODD INTEGER

 CAUTION Notice that you add 2 when you are writing down consecutive evens or consecutive odds.

Example 4 Find consecutive numbers

Find three consecutive integers whose sum is 42.

Solution   Read the problem. Write down a verbal description of the problem, using operation signs and an equal sign:

INTEGER $+$ NEXT INTEGER $+$ THIRD INTEGER $= 42$

This problem has three variables, but they are related. If

$x = $ INTEGER, then
$x + 1 = $ NEXT INTEGER
$x + 2 = $ THIRD INTEGER

Substitute the variables into the verbal equation:

INTEGER $+$ NEXT INTEGER $+$ THIRD INTEGER $= 42$

$$x \quad + \quad x+1 \quad + \quad x+2 \quad = 42$$

Solve the equation.

$$
\begin{aligned}
x + x + 1 + x + 2 &= 42 \\
3x + 3 &= 42 \\
3x &= 39 \\
x &= 13
\end{aligned}
$$

Check: $13 + 14 + 15 = 42$; the integers are 13, 14, and 15.

Distance Relationships

The first example of a problem with several variables that we will consider involves distances. The relationships may seem complicated, but if you draw a figure and remember that the total distance is the sum of the separate parts, you will easily be able to analyze this type of problem.

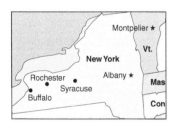

| Example | 5 | **Distance puzzle** | Pólya's Method |

The drive from Buffalo to Albany is 293 miles across northern New York State. On this route, you pass Rochester and then Syracuse before reaching the capital city of Albany. It is 57 miles less from Buffalo to Rochester than from Syracuse to Albany, and 14 miles farther from Rochester to Syracuse than from Buffalo to Rochester. How far is it from Rochester to Syracuse?

Solution   We use Pólya's problem-solving guidelines for this example.

Understand the Problem. First, you should begin by examining the problem. Remember that you cannot solve a problem you do not understand. It must make sense before mathematics can be applied to it. All too often poor problem solvers try to begin solving the problem too soon. Take your time when trying to understand the problem. Start at the beginning of the problem, and make a sketch of the situation, as shown in Figure 6.7. The cities are located in the order sketched on the line.

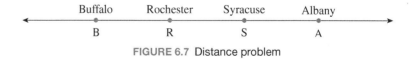

FIGURE 6.7 Distance problem

Devise a Plan. The cities are located in the order sketched in Figure 6.7, but how can that fact give us an equation? To have an equation, you must find an equality. Which quantities are equal? The distances from Buffalo to Rochester, from Rochester to Syracuse, and from Syracuse to Albany must add up to the distance from Buffalo to Albany. That is, the sum of the parts must equal the whole distance—so start there. This is what we mean when we say *translate.*

TRANSLATE.

(DIST. B TO R) $+$ (DIST. R TO S) $+$ (DIST. S TO A) $=$ (DIST. B TO A)

Notice that there appear to be four variables. We now use the substitution property to *evolve.*

EVOLVE. With this step we ask whether we know the value of any quantity in the equation. The first sentence of the problem tells us that the total distance is 293 miles, so

$$(\text{DIST. B TO R}) + (\text{DIST. R TO S}) + (\text{DIST. S TO A}) = (\text{DIST. B TO A})$$

↓ Buffalo to Albany

$$(\text{DIST. B TO R}) + (\text{DIST. R TO S}) + (\text{DIST. S TO A}) = 293$$

Also, part of evolving the equation is to use substitution for the relationships that are given as part of the problem. We now translate the other pieces of given information by adding to the smaller distance in each case.

$$(\text{DIST. B TO R}) + 57 = (\text{DIST. S TO A})$$
$$(\text{DIST. R TO S}) = (\text{DIST. B TO R}) + 14$$

We now use substitution to let the equation evolve into one with a single unknown.

Carry Out the Plan. Pólya's method now tells us to carry out the plan. We use substitution on the above equations:

$$(\text{DIST. B TO R}) + (\text{DIST. R TO S}) + (\text{DIST. S TO A}) = 293$$

↑   ↑

(DIST. B TO R + 14)   (DIST. B TO R) + 57

$$(\text{DIST. B TO R}) + [(\text{DIST. B TO R}) + 14] + [(\text{DIST. B TO R}) + 57] = 293$$

This equation now has a single variable, so we let $d = \text{DIST. B TO R}$ and substitute into the equation:

$$d + [d + 14] + [d + 57] = 293$$

Solve.

$$3d + 71 = 293$$
$$3d = 222$$
$$d = 74$$

The equation is solved. Does that mean that the answer to the problem is "$d = 74$"? No, the question asks for the distance from Rochester to Syracuse, which is $d + 14$. So now interpret the solution and **answer** the question: The distance from Rochester to Syracuse is 88 miles.

Look Back. Notice that the steps we used above can be summarized as **translate, evolve, solve,** and **answer.**

Pólya's procedure requires that we look back. To be certain that the answer makes sense in the original problem, you should always check the solution.

$$74 + 88 + (74 + 57) \overset{?}{=} 293$$
$$293 = 293 \quad ✓$$

Remember this summary.

STOP

Example 6   Zeno's dilemma

Pólya's Method

Once upon a time (about 450 B.C.), a Greek named Zeno made up several word problems that became known as Zeno's paradoxes. This problem is not a paradox, but was inspired by one of Zeno's problems. Consider a race between Achilles and a tortoise. The tortoise has a 100-meter head start. Achilles runs at a rate of 10 meters per second, whereas the tortoise runs 1 meter per second (it is an extraordinarily swift tortoise). How long does it take Achilles to catch up with the tortoise?

Solution   We use Pólya's problem-solving guidelines for this example.

Understand the Problem. Before you begin, make sure you understand the problem. It is often helpful to draw a figure or diagram to help you understand the problem. The situation for this problem is shown in Figure 6.8.

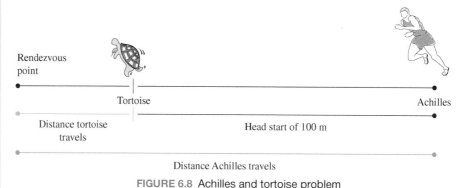

FIGURE 6.8 Achilles and tortoise problem

Devise a Plan. The plan we will use is *translate, evolve, solve,* and *answer.*
Carry Out the Plan.

TRANSLATE.

$$(\text{ACHILLES' DISTANCE TO RENDEZVOUS}) = (\text{TORTOISE'S DISTANCE TO RENDEZVOUS}) + (\text{HEAD START})$$

EVOLVE. The equation we wrote has three unknowns. Our goal is to evolve this equation into one with a single unknown so that we can choose that as our variable. The evolution of the equation requires that we use the substitution property to replace the unknowns with known numbers or with other expressions that, in turn, will lead to an equation with one unknown. We will begin this problem by substituting the known number.

$$(\text{ACHILLES' DISTANCE TO RENDEZVOUS}) = (\text{TORTOISE'S DISTANCE TO RENDEZVOUS}) + (\text{HEAD START})$$
$$\downarrow$$
$$(\text{ACHILLES' DISTANCE TO RENDEZVOUS}) = (\text{TORTOISE'S DISTANCE TO RENDEZVOUS}) + 100$$

There are still two unknowns, which we can change by using the following distance-rate-time formulas:

$$(\text{ACHILLES' DISTANCE TO RENDEZVOUS}) = (\text{ACHILLES' RATE})(\text{TIME TO RENDEZVOUS})$$
$$(\text{TORTOISE'S DISTANCE TO RENDEZVOUS}) = (\text{TORTOISE'S RATE})(\text{TIME TO RENDEZVOUS})$$

These values are now substituted into the equations:

$$(\text{ACHILLES' DISTANCE TO RENDEZVOUS}) = (\text{TORTOISE'S DISTANCE TO RENDEZVOUS}) + 100$$
$$\downarrow \qquad\qquad\qquad\qquad \downarrow$$
$$(\text{ACHILLES' RATE})(\text{TIME TO RENDEZVOUS}) = (\text{TORTOISE'S RATE})(\text{TIME TO RENDEZVOUS}) + 100$$

There are now three unknowns, but the values for two of *these* unknowns are given in the problem.

$$(\text{ACHILLES' RATE})(\text{TIME TO RENDEZVOUS}) = (\text{TORTOISE'S RATE})(\text{TIME TO RENDEZVOUS}) + 100$$
$$\downarrow \qquad\qquad\qquad\qquad\qquad \downarrow$$
$$10 \ (\text{TIME TO RENDEZVOUS}) \qquad = \qquad 1(\text{TIME TO RENDEZVOUS}) + 100$$

The equation now has a single unknown, so let

$$t = \text{TIME TO RENDEZVOUS}$$

The last step in the evolution of this equation is to substitute the variable:

$$10t = t + 100$$

SOLVE.

$$10t = t + 100$$
$$9t = 100$$
$$t = \frac{100}{9}$$

ANSWER. It takes Achilles $11\frac{1}{9}$ seconds to catch up with the tortoise.

Look Back. Does this answer make sense? How long does it take a person to run 100 meters? The problem says Achilles runs at 10 m/sec, so at that rate it would take 10 seconds. The answer seems about right.

Pythagorean Relationships

Many word problems are concerned with relationships involving a right triangle. If two sides of a right triangle are known, the third can be found by using the Pythagorean theorem. Remember, if a right triangle has sides a and b and hypotenuse c, then

$$a^2 + b^2 = c^2$$

Example 7   Use the Pythagorean theorem

If the area of a right triangle is one square unit, and the height is two units longer than the base, find the lengths of the sides of the triangle to the nearest thousandth.

Solution   Draw a picture to help you understand the relationships.

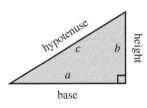

TRANSLATE.

$$\text{AREA} = \frac{1}{2}(\text{BASE})(\text{HEIGHT})$$

EVOLVE. The area is known, so begin by substituting 1 for AREA:

$$\text{AREA} = \frac{1}{2}(\text{BASE})(\text{HEIGHT})$$

$$\downarrow$$

$$1 = \frac{1}{2}(\text{BASE})(\text{HEIGHT})$$

Next, the problem tells us that HEIGHT = BASE + 2. Therefore,

$$1 = \frac{1}{2}(\text{BASE})(\text{HEIGHT})$$

$$\downarrow$$

$$1 = \frac{1}{2}(\text{BASE})(\text{BASE} + 2)$$

SOLVE. There is now a single unknown, so we choose a variable for the unknown. Let $b = \text{BASE}$. Then

$$1 = \frac{1}{2}b(b + 2)$$
$$2 = b(b + 2)$$

Hypatia
(370–415)

The number of important women in the history of mathematics is small when compared to the number of men. One reason for this is that for centuries, women were discouraged from studying mathematics and in most cases were unable to attend standard educational institutions. The first known woman in the history of mathematics is Hypatia. She was a professor of mathematics at the University of Alexandria. She wrote several major works, but her scientific rationalism caused her problems with the Church, and she was considered a heretic. At the age of 45, she was pulled from her carriage, tortured, and murdered for her scientific beliefs.

$$2 = b^2 + 2b$$
$$0 = b^2 + 2b - 2$$
$$b = \frac{-2 \pm \sqrt{2^2 - 4(1)(-2)}}{2(1)} \quad \text{Quadratic formula}$$
$$= \frac{-2 \pm \sqrt{12}}{2}$$
$$= \frac{-2 \pm 2\sqrt{3}}{2}$$
$$= -1 \pm \sqrt{3}$$

Since the base cannot be negative, we have

$$\text{BASE} = -1 + \sqrt{3} \approx 0.7320508$$
$$\text{HEIGHT} = \text{BASE} + 2 = -1 + \sqrt{3} + 2 = 1 + \sqrt{3} \approx 2.7320508$$

The Pythagorean theorem is necessary for finding the third side. When finding the hypotenuse, be sure not to work with the approximate values. **You should round only once in a problem, at the end when you are stating your answer.**

$$(\text{HYPOTENUSE})^2 = (-1 + \sqrt{3})^2 + (1 + \sqrt{3})^2$$
$$= 1 - 2\sqrt{3} + 3 + 1 + 2\sqrt{3} + 3$$
$$= 8$$

It follows that

$$\text{HYPOTENUSE} = \pm\sqrt{8} = 2\sqrt{2} \approx 2.8284271 \quad \text{\small Positive value only, since hypotenuse represents a distance.}$$

ANSWER. State the answer to the specified number of decimal places. The lengths of the sides of the triangle are 0.732, 2.732, and 2.828.

Have you ever wondered why sidewalks, pipes, and tracks have expansion joints every few feet? The next example may help you to understand why; it considers the unlikely situation in which 1-mile sections of pipe are connected together.

Example 8   Pipeline problem

Pólya's Method

A 1-mile-long pipeline connects two pumping stations. Special joints must be used along the line to provide for expansion and contraction due to changes in temperature. However, if the pipeline were actually one continuous length of pipe fixed at each end by the stations, then expansion would cause the pipe to bow. Approximately how high would the middle of the pipe rise if the expansion were just 1 inch over the mile?

Solution   We use Pólya's problem-solving guidelines for this example.

Understand the Problem. First, understand the problem. Draw a picture as shown in Figure 6.9.

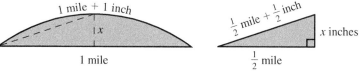

FIGURE 6.9 Pipeline problem

Before beginning the solution to this example, try to guess the answer. Consider the following choices for the rise in pipe:

A. 1 inch   B. 1 foot   C. 1 yard   D. 5 yards   E. 1 mile

Go ahead, choose one of these. This is one problem for which the answer was not intuitive for the author. I guessed incorrectly when I first considered this problem.

Devise a Plan. For purposes of solution, notice from Figure 6.9 that we are assuming that the pipe bows in a circular arc. A triangle would produce a reasonable approximation since the distance x should be quite small compared to the total length. Since a right triangle is used to model this situation, the Pythagorean theorem may be used. The method we will use is to *translate, evolve, solve,* and *answer.*

Carry Out the Plan.   **Translate.**

$$(\text{SIDE})^2 + (\text{HEIGHT})^2 = (\text{HYPOTENUSE})^2$$

EVOLVE. The side is one-half the length of pipe, so it is 0.5 mile. Also, since the expansion is 1 inch, one-half the arc would have length 0.5 mile + 0.5 inch.

$$(\text{SIDE})^2 + (\text{HEIGHT})^2 = (\text{HYPOTENUSE})^2$$
$$\downarrow \qquad\qquad\qquad\qquad \downarrow$$
$$(0.5 \text{ mile})^2 + (\text{HEIGHT})^2 = (0.5 \text{ mile} + 0.5 \text{ in.})^2$$

There is a single unknown, so let $h = $ HEIGHT. Also, notice that there is a mixture of units. Let us convert all measurements to inches. We know that

$$1 \text{ mile} = 5{,}280 \text{ ft} = 5{,}280 \,(12 \text{ in.}) = 63{,}360 \text{ in.}$$
$$\tfrac{1}{2} \text{ mile} = 31{,}680 \text{ in.}$$
$$(0.5 \text{ mile})^2 + (\text{HEIGHT})^2 = (0.5 \text{ mile} + 0.5 \text{ in.})^2$$
$$\downarrow \qquad\qquad\qquad\qquad \downarrow$$
$$(31{,}680)^2 + x^2 \qquad\quad = (31{,}680 + 0.5)^2$$

SOLVE.

$$x^2 = (31{,}680.5)^2 - (31{,}680)^2$$
$$x = \sqrt{(31{,}680.5)^2 - (31{,}680)^2}$$
$$\approx 177.99$$

ANSWER. The pipe rises about 180 in. in the middle.

Look Back. The solution, 177.99 in., is approximately 14.8 ft (choice D). This is an extraordinary result if you consider that the pipe expanded only 1 *inch.* The pipe would bow approximately 14.8 ft at the middle. This answer may not seem correct, but in re-examining the steps, we see that it is! This answer is paradoxical or, at least, counterintuitive.

Problem Set 6.6

Level 1

1. **IN YOUR OWN WORDS**   Outline a procedure for solving word problems in algebra.

2. **IN YOUR OWN WORDS**   Explain what is meant by *translate, evolve,* and *solve.*

Rewrite the word statement or phrase in Problems 3–10, using symbols. Translate and then simplify,

3. **a.** The sum of three and the product of two and four
   b. The product of three and the sum of two and four

4. **a.** The quotient of three divided by the sum of two and four
   b. Ten times the sum of four and three

5. **a.** Eight times nine plus ten
   b. Eight times the sum of nine and ten

6. **a.** The sum of three squared and five squared
   b. The square of the sum of three and five

7. **a.** The square of three increased by the cube of two
   b. The cube of three decreased by the square of two

8. **a.** The square of a number plus five
   b. Six times the cube of a number

9. **a.** The sum of the squares of 4 and 9
   b. The square of the sum of 4 and 9

10. **a.** The sum of the squares of 5 and 8
    b. The square of the sum of 5 and 8

Find the requested number(s) in Problems 11–16. Classify the equation as true, false, or open, and if it is open tell whether it is a conditional, identity, or contradiction.

11. a. Three times the sum of a number and four is equal to sixteen.
   b. Five times the sum of a number and one is equal to the sum of five times the number and five.

12. a. The sum of a number and one is equal to one added to the number.
   b. The difference of the squares of 3 and 4 is one.

13. a. The sum of the squares of 3 and 4 is 25.
   b. The sum of the squares of the first three counting numbers is *n*.

14. a. The square of negative eight is equal to the opposite of eight squared.
   b. Two added to a number is equal to the sum of the number and two.

15. a. The sum of six times a number and twelve is equal to six times the sum of the number and two.
   b. A number times the sum of seven and the number is equal to zero.

16. a. The sum of a number squared and five times the number is equal to six.
   b. The square of a number plus eight times the number is equal to the number times the sum of eight and the number.

In Problems 17–25, write a formula to express the given relation.

17. The area *A* of a parallelogram is the product of the base *b* and the height *h*.

18. The area *A* of a triangle is one-half the product of the base *b* and the height *h*.

19. The area *A* of a rhombus is one-half the product of the diagonals *p* and *q*.

20. The area *A* of a trapezoid is the product of one-half the height *h* and the sum of the bases *a* and *b*.

21. The volume *V* of a cube is the cube of the length *s* of an edge.

22. The volume *V* of a rectangular solid is the product of the length ℓ, the width *w*, and the height *h*.

23. The volume *V* of a cone is one-third the product of pi, the square of the radius *r*, and the height *h*.

24. The volume *V* of a circular cylinder is the product of pi, the square of the radius *r*, and the height *h*.

25. The volume *V* of a sphere is the product of four-thirds pi and the cube of the radius *r*.

Level 2

*Solve Problems 26–48. Because you are practicing a **procedure**, you must show all of your work. Start with a verbal description and end with a sentence answering the question.*

26. If you add seven to twice a number, the result is seventeen. What is the number?

27. If you subtract twelve from twice a number, the result is six. What is the number?

28. If you multiply a number by five and then subtract negative ten, the difference is negative thirty. What is the number?

29. If 6 is subtracted from three times a number, the difference is twice the number. What is the number?

30. Find two consecutive integers whose sum is 117.

31. Find two consecutive even integers whose sum is 94.

32. The sum of three consecutive integers is 105. What are the integers?

33. The sum of four consecutive integers is 74. What are the integers?

34. A house and a lot are appraised at $212,400. If the value of the house is five times the value of the lot, how much is the house worth?

35. A cabinet shop produces two types of custom-made cabinets. If the price of one type of cabinet is four times the price of the other, and the total price for one of each type of cabinet is $4,150, what is price of each cabinet?

36. To stimulate his daughter in the pursuit of problem solving, a math professor offered to pay her $8 for every equation correctly solved and to fine her $5 for every incorrect solution. At the end of the first 26 problems of this problem set, neither owed any money to the other. How many problems did the daughter solve correctly?

37. A professional gambler reported that at the end of the first race at the track he had doubled his money. He bet $30 on the second race and tripled the money he came with. He bet $54 on the third race and quadrupled his original bankroll. He bet $72 on the fourth race and lost it, but still had $48 left. With how much money did he start?

38. A 10-ft pole is to be erected and held in the ground by four guy wires attached at the top. The guy wires are attached to the ground at a distance of 15 ft from the base of the pole. What is the exact length of each guy wire? How much wire should be purchased if it cannot be purchased in fractions of a foot?

39. A diagonal brace is to be placed in the wall of a room. The height of the wall is 8 ft, and the wall is 14 ft long. What is the exact length of the brace, and what is the length of the brace to the nearest foot?

40. In traveling from Jacksonville to Miami, you pass through Orlando and then through Palm Beach. It is 10 miles farther from Orlando to Palm Beach than it is from Jacksonville to Orlando. The distance between Jacksonville and Orlando is 90 miles more than the distance from Palm Beach to Miami. If it is 370 miles from Jacksonville to Miami, how far is it from Jacksonville to Orlando?

41. The drive from New Orleans to Memphis is 90 miles shorter than the drive from Memphis to Cincinnati, but 150 miles farther than the drive from Cincinnati to Detroit. If the total highway distance of a New Orleans–Memphis–Cincinnati–Detroit trip is 1,140 miles, find the length of the Cincinnati–Detroit leg of the trip.

42. Traveling from San Antonio to Dallas, you first pass through Austin and then Waco before reaching Dallas, a total distance of 280 miles. From Austin to Waco is 30 miles farther than from San Antonio to Austin, and also 20 miles farther than from Waco to Dallas. How far is it from Waco to Dallas?

43. Two persons are to run a race, but one can run 10 meters per second, whereas the other can run 6 meters per second. If the slower runner has a 50-meter head start, how long will it be before the faster runner catches the slower runner, if they begin at the same time?

44. If the rangefinder on the *Enterprise* shows a fleeing shuttle-craft 4,500 km away, how long will it take to catch the shuttle if the shuttle travels at 12,000 kph and the *Enterprise* is traveling at 15,000 kph?

Starship *Enterprise*

45. A speeding car is traveling at 80 mph when a police car starts pursuit at 100 mph. How long will it take the police car to catch up to the speeding car? Assume that the speeding car has a 2-mile head start and that the cars travel at constant rates.

46. Two people walk daily for exercise. One is able to maintain 4.0 mph and the other only 3.5 mph. The slower walker has a mile head start when the other begins, yet they finish together. How far did each walk?

47. Two joggers set out at the same time from their homes 21 miles apart. They agree to meet at a point somewhere in between in an hour and a half. If the rate of one is 2 mph faster than the rate of the other, find the rate of each.

48. Two joggers set out at the same time in opposite directions. If they were to maintain their normal rates for four hours, they would be 68 miles apart. If the rate of one is 1.5 mph faster than the rate of the other, find the rate of each.

Level 3

49. The area of a right triangle is 17.5 cm². One leg is 2 cm longer than the other. What is the length of the shortest side?

50. The hypotenuse of a right triangle is 13.0, and one leg is 6.0 units shorter than the other. Find the dimensions of the figure (rounded to the nearest tenth).

51. Find the base and height of a triangle with area 3.0 square feet if its base is 2.0 feet (rounded to the nearest tenth) longer than its height.

52. Find the base and height of a triangle (rounded to the nearest tenth) with area 75.0 in.² if its base is 10.0 in. longer than its height.

53. The annual rate, r, compounded annually, it takes for 1 dollar to grow to A dollars in 2 years is given by the formula $A = (1 + r)^2$. Find the rate necessary for a dollar to double in 2 years.

54. If P dollars is invested at an annual rate r compounded annually, at the end of 2 years it will have grown to an amount A according to the formula $A = P(1 + r)^2$. At what rate will $1,000 grow to $1,500 in 2 years?

Problem Solving 3

55. A 1-mile-long pipeline connects two pumping stations. Special joints must be used along the line to provide for expansion and contraction due to changes in temperature. However, if the pipeline were actually one continuous length of pipe fixed at each end by the stations, then expansion would cause the pipe to bow. Approximately how high would the middle of the pipe rise if the expansion were just one-half inch over the mile?

Historical NOTE

**Henry Wadsworth Longfellow
(1807–1882)**

Well known as a poet, Longfellow was also an accomplished mathematician. He resigned from Harvard University to find time to write, and that writing included some works in mathematics. Problems 56–60 were solved by Longfellow; see an article by Charles E. Mitchell in the May 1989 issue of *The Mathematics Teacher.*

56. HISTORICAL QUEST   (from Bhaskara, ca. A.D. 1120)   "In a lake the bud of a water lily was observed, one cubit above the water, and when moved by the gentle breeze, it sank in the water at two cubits' distance." Find the depth of the water.

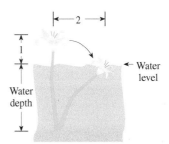

57. HISTORICAL QUEST   (from Bhaskara, ca. A.D. 1120) "One-third of a collection of beautiful water lilies is offered to Mahadev, one-fifth to Huri, one-sixth to the Sun, one-fourth to Devi, and the six which remain are presented to the spiritual teacher." Find the total number of lilies.

58. HISTORICAL QUEST   (from Bhaskara, ca. A.D. 1120) "One-fifth of a hive of bees flew to the Kadamba flower; one-third flew to the Silandhara; three times the difference of these two numbers flew to an arbor, and one bee continued flying about, attracted on each side by the fragrant Keteki and the Malati." Find the number of bees.

59. HISTORICAL QUEST   (from Brahmagupta, ca. A.D. 630) "A tree one hundred cubits high is distant from a well two hundred cubits; from this tree one monkey climbs down the tree and goes to the well, but the other leaps in the air and descends by the hypotenuse from the high point of the leap, and both pass over an equal space." Find the height of the leap.

60. HISTORICAL QUEST   "Ten times the square root of a flock of geese, seeing the clouds collect, flew to the Manus lake; one-eighth of the whole flew from the edge of the water amongst a multitude of water lilies; and three couples were observed playing in the water." Find the number of geese.

6.7 Ratios, Proportions, and Problem Solving

Ratios and proportions are powerful problem-solving tools in algebra. Ratios are a way of comparing two numbers or quantities, whereas a proportion is a statement of equality between two ratios.

Ratios

A *ratio* expresses a size relationship between two sets and is defined as the quotient of two numbers. Some examples include the compression ratio of a car, the gear ratio of a transmission, the pitch of a roof, the steepness of a road, or a player's batting average. It is written using the word *to*, a colon, or a fraction; that is, if the ratio of men to women is 5 **to** 4, this could also be written as $5:4$ or $\frac{5}{4}$.

> **Ratio**
>
> The expression $\frac{a}{b}$ is called the ratio of a to b. The two parts a and b are called its terms.

We will emphasize the idea that a ratio can be written as a fraction (or as a quotient of two numbers). Since a fraction can be reduced, a ratio can also be reduced.

Example 1 Reduce a ratio

Reduce the given ratios to lowest terms.

a. 4 to 52   **b.** 15 to 3   **c.** $1\frac{1}{2}$ to 2   **d.** $1\frac{2}{3}$ to $3\frac{3}{4}$

Solution

a. A ratio of 4 to 52

$$\frac{4}{52} = \frac{1}{13}$$

This is a ratio of 1 to 13.

b. A ratio of 15 to 3

$$\frac{15}{3} = 5$$

Write this as $\frac{5}{1}$ because a ratio compares two numbers. This is a ratio of 5 to 1.

c. A ratio of $1\frac{1}{2}$ to 2

$$\frac{1\frac{1}{2}}{2} = 1\frac{1}{2} \div 2$$

$$= \frac{3}{2} \times \frac{1}{2}$$

$$= \frac{3}{4}$$

This is a ratio of 3 to 4.

d. A ratio of $1\frac{2}{3}$ to $3\frac{3}{4}$

$$\frac{1\frac{2}{3}}{3\frac{3}{4}} = 1\frac{2}{3} \div 3\frac{3}{4}$$

$$= \frac{5}{3} \div \frac{15}{4}$$

$$= \frac{5}{3} \times \frac{4}{15}$$

$$= \frac{4}{9}$$

This is a ratio of 4 to 9.

Proportions

A **proportion** is a statement of equality between ratios. In symbols,

$$\frac{a}{b} = \frac{c}{d}$$
$$\uparrow \quad \uparrow \quad \uparrow$$

"a is to b" **"as"** *"c is to d"*

The notation used in some books is $a : b :: c : d$. Even though we won't use this notation, we will use words associated with this notation to name the terms:

In the more common fractional notation, we have

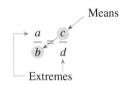

Example 2 Terminology review

Read each proportion, and name the means and the extremes.

a. $\frac{2}{3} = \frac{10}{15}$

b. $\frac{m}{5} = \frac{3}{8}$

Solution

a. $\frac{2}{3} = \frac{10}{15}$ *Read:*   Two is to three as ten is to fifteen.

   Means: 3 and 10   *Extremes:*   2 and 15

b. $\frac{m}{5} = \frac{3}{8}$ *Read:*   *m* is to five as three is to eight.

   Means: 5 and 3   *Extremes:*   *m* and 8

The following property is fundamental to our study of proportions and percents.

Property of Proportions

If the product of the means equals the product of the extremes, then the ratios form a proportion.

   Also, if the ratios form a proportion, then the product of the means equals the product of the extremes. In symbols,

$$\frac{a}{b} = \frac{c}{d}$$

$$\underline{b \times c} = \underline{a \times d}$$
$$\quad\uparrow \qquad\quad \uparrow$$

product of means = product of extremes

Example 3 Form a proportion, if possible

Tell whether each pair of ratios forms a proportion.

a. $\frac{3}{4}, \frac{36}{48}$ b. $\frac{5}{16}, \frac{7}{22}$

Solution

a. *Means*   *Extremes*

4×36 3×48

$144 = 144$

Thus,

$$\frac{3}{4} = \frac{36}{48}$$

They form a proportion.

b. *Means*   *Extremes*

16×7 5×22

$112 \neq 110$

Thus,

$$\frac{5}{16} \neq \frac{7}{22}$$

They do not form a proportion.

You can use the cross-product method not only to see whether two fractions form a proportion, but also to compare the sizes of two fractions. For example, if a and c are whole numbers, and b and d are counting numbers, then the following property can be used to compare the sizes of two fractions:

If $ad = bc$, then $\dfrac{a}{b} = \dfrac{c}{d}$.

If $ad < bc$, then $\dfrac{a}{b} < \dfrac{c}{d}$.

If $ad > bc$, then $\dfrac{a}{b} > \dfrac{c}{d}$.

Example 4 Insert appropriate relation symbol

Insert $=$, $<$, or $>$ as appropriate.

a. $\dfrac{3}{4}\underline{\quad}\dfrac{18}{24}$ b. $\dfrac{1}{2}\underline{\quad}\dfrac{1}{3}$

c. $\dfrac{2}{3}\underline{\quad}\dfrac{7}{8}$ d. $\dfrac{3}{5}\underline{\quad}\dfrac{4}{7}$

Solution

a. $\dfrac{3}{4} \underline{\quad} \dfrac{18}{24}$

$3(24) \underline{\ ?\ } 4(18)$

$72 \underline{\ ?\ } 72$

$\underline{\ =\ }$

b. $\dfrac{1}{2} \underline{\quad} \dfrac{1}{3}$

$1(3) \underline{\ ?\ } 2(1)$

$3 \underline{\ ?\ } 2$

$\underline{\ >\ }$

c. $\dfrac{2}{3} \underline{\quad} \dfrac{7}{8}$

$2(8) \underline{\ ?\ } 3(7)$

$16 \underline{\ ?\ } 21$

$\underline{\ <\ }$

d. $\dfrac{3}{5} \underline{\quad} \dfrac{4}{7}$

$3(7) \underline{\ ?\ } 5(4)$

$21 \underline{\ ?\ } 20$

$\underline{\ >\ }$

Comparing decimal numbers can sometimes be confusing; for example, which is larger,

0.6   or   0.58921?

The larger number is 0.6. To see this, simply write each decimal with the same number of places by affixing trailing zeros, and then compare. That is, write

0.60000
0.58921

Now, it is easy to see that $0.60000 > 0.58921$ because 60,000 hundred thousandths is larger than 58,921 hundred thousandths.

Example 5 | Insert inequality system

Insert $<$ or $>$ as appropriate.

a. 0.28 _____ 0.3   **b.** 0.001 _____ 0.01
c. 0.005 _____ 0.004823   **d.** 3 _____ 0.98712

Solution

a. 0.28 _____ 0.3   **b.** 0.001 _____ 0.01
   0.28 $<$ 0.30   *since 28 < 30*   0.001 $<$ 0.010   *since 1 < 10*

c. 0.005 _____ 0.004823   **d.** 3 _____ 0.98712
   0.005000 $>$ 0.004823   3.00000 $>$ 0.98712

Solving Proportions

The usual setting for a proportion problem is that three of the terms of the proportion are known and one of the terms is unknown. It is always possible to find the missing term by solving an equation. However, when given a proportion, we first use the property of proportions (which is equivalent to multiplying both sides of the equation by the same number).

Example 6 | Find missing term in a proportion

Find the missing term of each proportion.

a. $\frac{3}{4} = \frac{w}{20}$ **b.** $\frac{3}{4} = \frac{27}{y}$ **c.** $\frac{2}{x} = \frac{8}{9}$ **d.** $\frac{t}{15} = \frac{3}{5}$

Solution

a. $\dfrac{3}{4} = \dfrac{w}{20}$ PRODUCT OF MEANS = PRODUCT OF EXTREMES

$$4w = 3(20)$$

$$w = \frac{3(20)}{4}$$ Solve by dividing both sides by 4. Notice that 4 is the number opposite the unknown.

$$w = 15$$

b. $\dfrac{3}{4} = \dfrac{27}{y}$ PRODUCT OF MEANS = PRODUCT OF EXTREMES

$$4(27) = 3y$$

$$\frac{4(27)}{3} = y$$ Divide both sides by 3; Notice that 3 is the number opposite the unknown.

$$36 = y$$

c. $\dfrac{2}{x} = \dfrac{8}{9}$ PRODUCT OF MEANS = PRODUCT OF EXTREMES

$$8x = 2(9)$$
$$x = \dfrac{2(9)}{8}$$ Divide both sides by 8.
Notice that 8 is the number opposite the unknown.
$$x = \dfrac{9}{4}$$

d. $\dfrac{t}{15} = \dfrac{3}{5}$ PRODUCT OF MEANS = PRODUCT OF EXTREMES

$$3(15) = 5t$$
$$\dfrac{3(15)}{5} = t$$ Divide both sides by 5.
Notice that 5 is the number opposite the unknown.
$$9 = t$$

Notice that the unknown term can be in any one of four positions, as illustrated by the four parts of Example 6. But even though you can find the missing term of a proportion (called **solving the proportion**) by the technique used in Example 6, it is easier to think in terms of **the cross-product divided by the number opposite the unknown.** This method is easier than actually solving the equation because it can be done quickly using a calculator, as shown in the following examples.

Procedure for Solving Proportions

Given a proportion:

Step 1   Find the product of the means or the product of the extremes, whichever does not contain the unknown term.

Step 2   Divide this product by the number that is opposite the unknown term.

Example   7   Solve a proportion

Solve the proportion for the unknown term.

a. $\dfrac{5}{6} = \dfrac{55}{y}$ **b.** $\dfrac{5}{b} = \dfrac{3}{4}$ **c.** $\dfrac{2\frac{1}{2}}{5} = \dfrac{a}{8}$

Proportions are quite easy to solve with a calculator. You can multiply the cross-terms and divide by the number opposite the variable all in one calculator sequence.

Notice that your answers don't have to be whole numbers. This means that the correct proportion is $\dfrac{5}{6\frac{2}{3}} = \dfrac{3}{4}$.

Solution

a. $\dfrac{5}{6} = \dfrac{55}{y}$

$$y = \dfrac{6 \times 55}{5}$$ ← Product of the means
← Number opposite the unknown

$$= \dfrac{6 \times 55}{5}$$ You can cancel to simplify many of these problems.

$$= 66$$ $\boxed{6}\,\boxed{\times}\,\boxed{55}\,\boxed{\div}\,\boxed{5}\,\boxed{=}$

b. $\dfrac{5}{b} = \dfrac{3}{4}$

$$b = \dfrac{5 \times 4}{3}$$ ← Product of the extremes
← Number opposite the unknown

$$= \dfrac{20}{3}\ \text{ or } \ 6\frac{2}{3}$$ $\boxed{5}\,\boxed{\times}\,\boxed{4}\,\boxed{\div}\,\boxed{3}\,\boxed{=}$

c. $\dfrac{2\frac{1}{2}}{5} = \dfrac{a}{8}$

$$a = \dfrac{2\frac{1}{2} \times 8}{5} \quad \leftarrow \text{Product of the extremes} \\ \qquad\qquad \leftarrow \text{Number opposite the unknown}$$

$$= \dfrac{\frac{5}{2} \times \frac{8}{1}}{5}$$

$$= \dfrac{20}{5} \qquad \boxed{2.5}\boxed{\times}\boxed{8}\boxed{\div}\boxed{5}\boxed{=}$$

$$= 4$$

Many applied problems can be solved using a proportion. Whenever you are working an applied problem, you should estimate an answer so that you will know whether the result you obtain is reasonable.

When setting up a proportion with units, be sure that like units occupy corresponding positions, as illustrated in Examples 8–11. The proportion is obtained by applying the sentence "*a* is to *b* as *c* is to *d*" to the quantities in the problem.

Example **8** **Cost of a can**

If 4 cans of cola sell for $1.89, how much will 6 cans cost?

Solution   We use Pólya's problem-solving guidelines for this example.

Understand the Problem. We see that 4 cans sell for $1.89 and 8 cans sell for $2(\$1.89) = \$3.78$. We need to find the cost for 6 cans, which must be somewhere between $1.89 and $3.78.

Devise a Plan. There are many possible plans for solving this problem. We will form a proportion.

Carry Out the Plan. Solve "4 cans is to $1.89 as 6 cans is to what?"

$$\dfrac{4 \text{ cans}}{1.89 \text{ dollars}} = \dfrac{6 \text{ cans}}{x \text{ dollars}}$$

$$x = \dfrac{1.89 \times 6}{4}$$

$$= 2.835$$

Look Back. We see that 6 cans will cost $2.84.

Example **9** **Gasoline needed for a trip**

If a 120-mile trip took $8\frac{1}{2}$ gallons of gas, how much gas is needed for a 240-mile trip?

Solution   "120 miles is to $8\frac{1}{2}$ gallons as 240 miles is to how many gallons?"

$$\underset{\underset{\text{gallons}}{\uparrow}}{\overset{\overset{\text{miles}}{\downarrow}}{\dfrac{120}{8\frac{1}{2}}}} = \underset{\underset{\text{gallons}}{\uparrow}}{\overset{\overset{\text{miles}}{\downarrow}}{\dfrac{240}{x}}}$$

$$x = \dfrac{\frac{17}{2} \times 240}{120}$$

$$= 17$$

The trip will require 17 gallons.

Example 10 **Tax on a home**

If the property tax on a $375,000 home is $1,910, what is the tax on a $450,000 home?

Solution   "$375,000 is to $1,910 as $450,000 is to what?"

$$\underset{\underset{\text{tax}}{\uparrow}}{\overset{\overset{\text{value}}{\downarrow}}{\frac{375,000}{1,910}}} = \underset{\underset{\text{tax}}{\uparrow}}{\overset{\overset{\text{value}}{\downarrow}}{\frac{450,000}{x}}}$$

$$x = \frac{1,910 \times 450,000}{375,000} \qquad \text{A calculator is useful here.}$$
$$= 2,292$$

The tax is $2,292.

Example 11 **Formulate a mixture**

In a can of mixed nuts, the ratio of cashews to peanuts is 1 to 6. If a given machine releases 46 cashews into a can, how many peanuts should be released?

Solution   First, understand the problem. This problem is comparing two quantities, cashews and peanuts, so consider writing a proportion.

TRANSLATE.   This is the given ratio.

$$\frac{\text{NUMBER OF CASHEWS}}{\text{NUMBER OF PEANUTS}} = \frac{1}{6}$$

EVOLVE. The NUMBER OF CASHEWS $= 46$, so by substitution

$$\frac{46}{\text{NUMBER OF PEANUTS}} = \frac{1}{6}$$

Let $p =$ NUMBER OF PEANUTS; then the equation is

$$\frac{46}{p} = \frac{1}{6}$$

SOLVE. $6(46) = p$
$\quad\quad\quad 276 = p$

ANSWER. Thus, 276 peanuts should be released.

Problem Set 6.7

Level **1**

1. **IN YOUR OWN WORDS**   What do we mean by ratios and proportions?

2. **IN YOUR OWN WORDS**   How does the property of proportions relate to solving equations?

3. **IN YOUR OWN WORDS**   How does the procedure for solving proportions relate to solving equations?

4. **IN YOUR OWN WORDS**   Describe a process for setting up a proportion, given an applied problem.

Write the ratios given in Problems 5–10 as simplified ratios.

5. A cement mixture calls for 60 pounds of cement for 3 gallons of water. What is the ratio of cement to water?

6. What is the ratio of water to cement in Problem 5?

7. About 106 baby boys are born for every 100 baby girls. Write this as a simplified ratio of males to females.

8. What is the ratio of girls to boys in Problem 7?

9. If you drive 279 miles on $15\frac{1}{2}$ gallons of gas, what is the simplified ratio of miles to gallons?

10. If you drive 151.7 miles on 8.2 gallons of gas, what is the simplified ratio of miles to gallons?

Tell whether each pair of ratios in Problems 11–14 forms a proportion.

11. **a.** $\frac{7}{1}, \frac{21}{3}$ **b.** $\frac{6}{8}, \frac{9}{12}$ **c.** $\frac{3}{6}, \frac{5}{10}$

12. **a.** $\frac{85}{18}, \frac{42}{9}$ **b.** $\frac{403}{341}, \frac{13}{11}$ **c.** $\frac{20}{70}, \frac{4}{14}$

13. **a.** $\frac{3}{4}, \frac{75}{100}$ **b.** $\frac{2}{3}, \frac{67}{100}$ **c.** $\frac{5}{3}, \frac{7\frac{1}{3}}{4}$

14. **a.** $\frac{3}{2}, \frac{5}{3\frac{1}{2}}$ **b.** $\frac{5\frac{1}{5}}{7}, \frac{4}{5}$ **c.** $\frac{1}{3}, \frac{33\frac{1}{3}}{100}$

Insert =, <, or > as appropriate in Problems 15–18.

15. **a.** $\frac{1}{6}$ —— $\frac{1}{8}$ **b.** $\frac{1}{4}$ —— $\frac{1}{3}$ **c.** $\frac{1}{5}$ —— $\frac{1}{8}$

16. **a.** $\frac{25}{5}$ —— $\frac{10}{2}$ **b.** $\frac{14}{15}$ —— $\frac{42}{45}$ **c.** $\frac{11}{16}$ —— $\frac{7}{12}$

17. **a.** 0.8 ____ 0.8001   **b.** 0.8 ____ 0.7999
    c. 2.8 ____ 2.81   **d.** 2.8 ____ 2.88

18. **a.** π ____ 3.1416   **b.** $\sqrt{2}$ ____ 1.4142
    c. $\sqrt{3}$ ____ 1.7320508   **d.** $\sqrt{4}$ ____ 2.0000

Solve each proportion in Problems 19–42 for the item represented by a letter.

19. $\frac{5}{1} = \frac{A}{6}$ 20. $\frac{1}{9} = \frac{4}{B}$ 21. $\frac{C}{2} = \frac{5}{1}$

22. $\frac{7}{D} = \frac{1}{8}$ 23. $\frac{12}{18} = \frac{E}{12}$ 24. $\frac{12}{15} = \frac{20}{F}$

25. $\frac{G}{24} = \frac{14}{16}$ 26. $\frac{4}{H} = \frac{3}{15}$ 27. $\frac{2}{3} = \frac{I}{24}$

28. $\frac{4}{5} = \frac{3}{J}$ 29. $\frac{3}{K} = \frac{2}{5}$ 30. $\frac{L}{18} = \frac{5}{6}$

31. $\frac{7\frac{1}{5}}{9} = \frac{M}{5}$ 32. $\frac{4}{2\frac{2}{3}} = \frac{3}{N}$ 33. $\frac{P}{4} = \frac{4\frac{1}{2}}{6}$

34. $\frac{5}{2} = \frac{Q}{12\frac{3}{5}}$ 35. $\frac{5}{R} = \frac{7}{12\frac{3}{5}}$ 36. $\frac{1\frac{1}{3}}{\frac{1}{9}} = \frac{S}{2\frac{2}{3}}$

37. $\frac{33}{2\frac{1}{5}} = \frac{3\frac{3}{4}}{T}$ 38. $\frac{U}{1\frac{1}{2}} = \frac{\frac{1}{2}}{\frac{3}{4}}$ 39. $\frac{\frac{1}{5}}{\frac{2}{3}} = \frac{\frac{3}{4}}{V}$

40. $\frac{\frac{3}{5}}{\frac{1}{2}} = \frac{X}{\frac{2}{3}}$ 41. $\frac{9}{Y} = \frac{1\frac{1}{2}}{3\frac{2}{3}}$ 42. $\frac{Z}{2\frac{1}{3}} = \frac{1\frac{1}{2}}{4\frac{1}{5}}$

Level **2**

43. If 4 melons sell for $0.52, how much would 7 melons cost?

44. If a 121-mile trip took $5\frac{1}{2}$ gallons of gas, how many miles can be driven with a full tank of 13 gallons?

45. If a family uses $3\frac{1}{2}$ gallons of milk per week, how much milk will this family need for four days?

46. If 2 quarts of paint are needed for 75 ft of fence, how many quarts are needed for 900 ft of fence?

47. If Jack jogs 3 miles in 40 minutes, how long will it take him (to the nearest minute) to jog 2 miles at the same rate?

48. If Jill jogs 2 miles in 15 minutes, how long will it take her (to the nearest minute) to jog 5 miles at the same rate?

49. A moderately active 140-pound person will use 2,100 calories per day to maintain that body weight. How many calories per day are necessary to maintain a moderately active 165-pound person?

50. This problem will help you check your work in Problems 19–42. Fill in the capital letters from Problems 19–42 to correspond with their numerical values in the boxes. For example, if

$$\frac{C}{2} = \frac{5}{1} \quad \text{then} \quad C = \frac{2 \times 5}{1} = 10$$

Now find the box or boxes with number 10 in the corner and fill in the letter C. This has already been done for you. (The letter O has also been filled in for you.) Some letters may not appear in the boxes. When you are finished filling in the letters, darken all the blank spaces to separate the words in the secret message. Notice that one of the blank spaces has also been filled in to help you.

30	15	21	8	36	9	30	6	16	32	10	19
$\frac{1}{4}$	20	8	6	21	9	8	30	$\frac{1}{4}$	8	32	$\frac{1}{4}$
15	30	36	*O*	9	43	32	30	$\frac{5}{2}$	16	2	21
56	8	$\frac{5}{2}$	16	10 *C*	8	43	8	$\frac{5}{2}$	8	9	23
16	2	$\frac{5}{2}$	8	2	$\frac{1}{4}$	8	56				

Level **3**

51. If $\dfrac{V}{T} = \dfrac{V'}{T'}$, find V' when $V = 175$, $T = 300$, and $T' = 273$.

52. If $\dfrac{PV}{T} = \dfrac{P'V'}{T'}$, find V' when $V = 12$, $P = 2$, $T = 300$, $P' = 8$, and $T' = 400$.

53. The *pitch* of a roof is the ratio of the rise to the half-span. If a roof has a rise of 8 feet and a span of 24 feet, what is the pitch?

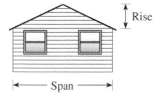

54. What is the pitch of a roof (see Problem 53) with a 3-foot rise and a span of 12 feet?

55. You've probably seen advertisements for posters that can be made from any photograph. If the finished poster will be 2 ft by 3 ft, it's likely that part of your original snapshot will be cut off. Suppose you send in a photo that measures 3 in. by 5 in. If the shorter side of the enlargement will be 2 ft, what size should the longer side of the enlargement be so that the entire snapshot is shown in the poster?

56. Suppose you wish to make a scale drawing of your living room, which measures 18 ft by 25 ft. If the shorter side of

the drawing is 6 in., how long is the longer side of the scale drawing?

57. If the property tax on a $180,000 home is $1,080, what is the tax on a $130,000 home?

Problem Solving **3**

58. To dilute a medication you can use the following formula:

$$\frac{\text{PERCENT OF DILUTED SOLUTION}}{\text{PERCENT OF ORIGINAL SOLUTION}} = \frac{\text{AMOUNT OF STRONG SOLUTION NEEDED}}{\text{AMOUNT OF DILUTED SOLUTION WANTED}}$$

How many units of a 10% solution are needed to prepare 500 units of a 2% solution?

59. At a certain hamburger stand, the owner sold soft drinks out of two 16-gallon barrels. At the end of the first day, she wished to increase her profit, so she filled the soft-drink barrels with water, thus diluting the drink served. She repeated the procedure at the end of the second and third days. At the end of the fourth day, she had 10 gallons remaining in the barrels, but they contained only 1 pint of pure soft drink. How much pure soft drink was served in the four days?

60. Answer the question in the following *Peanuts* cartoon strip.

6.8 | Percents

We frequently use percents, and you have, no doubt, worked with percents in your previous mathematics classes. However, we include this section to review percents and the equivalence of the decimal, fraction, and percent forms.

Percent

We begin with a definition of percent.

> **Percent**
>
> **Percent** is the ratio of a given number to 100. This means that a percent is the numerator of a fraction whose denominator is 100.

The symbol % is used to indicate percent. Since a percent is a ratio, percents can easily be written in fractional form.

Example 1 **Write a percent as a fraction**

Write the following percents as simplified fractions.
a. "Sale 75% OFF"   **b.** "SALARIES UP 6.8%"

Solution

a. 75% means a "ratio of 75 to 100": $\dfrac{75}{100} = \dfrac{3}{4}$

b. 6.8% means a "ratio of 6.8 to 100":

$$6.8 \div 100 = 6\frac{8}{10} \div 100$$

$$= 6\frac{4}{5} \div 100$$

$$= \frac{\overset{17}{\cancel{34}}}{5} \times \frac{1}{\underset{50}{\cancel{100}}}$$

$$= \frac{17}{250}$$

Fractions/Decimals/Percents

Percents can also be written as decimals. Since a percent is a ratio of a number to 100, we can divide by 100 by moving the decimal point.

Procedure for Changing a Percent to a Decimal

To express a percent as a decimal, shift the decimal point two places to the *left* and delete the % symbol. If the percent involves a fraction, write the fraction as a decimal; *then* shift the decimal point.

Example 2 **Write a percent as a decimal**

Write each percent in decimal form.
a. 8 percent   **b.** 6.8%   **c.** $33\frac{1}{3}\%$ **d.** $\frac{1}{2}\%$

Solution

a. 8 %

 If a decimal point is not shown, it is always understood to be at the right of the whole number.

 0. 08 %

 Shift the decimal point two places to the left; add zeros as placeholders, if necessary. Delete percent symbol.

 Answer: 8% = 0.08

b. 6.8%   *Think:*   6. 8%

 Shift two places, add placeholders as necessary, and delete percent symbol.

 Answer: 6.8% = 0.068

c. $33\frac{1}{3}\%$ *Think:* $33\frac{1}{3}\%$

 Decimal point is understood.

 Answer: $33\frac{1}{3}\% = 0.33\frac{1}{3}$ or $0.333\ldots$

d. $\frac{1}{2}\%$

$\frac{1}{2} = 0.5$, so $\frac{1}{2}\% = 0.5\%$ *Think:*   00. 5%

Answer: $0.5\% = 0.005$

Spend some time with this table. In fact, you may want to place a marker on this page for future reference.

As you can see from the examples, every number can be written in three forms: fraction, decimal, and percent. Even though we discussed changing from fraction to decimal form earlier in the text, we'll review the three forms in this section. The procedure for changing from one form to another is given in Table 6.1.

TABLE 6.1

Fraction/Decimal/Percent Conversion Chart

To/From	Fraction	Decimal	Percent
Fraction		Divide the numerator (top) by the denominator (bottom). Write as a terminating or as a repeating decimal (bar notation).	First change the fraction to a decimal by carrying out the division to two decimal places and writing the remainder as a fraction. *Then* move the decimal point two places to the right, and affix a percent symbol.
Terminating decimal	Write the decimal without the decimal point, and multiply by the decimal name of the last digit (rightmost digit).		Shift the decimal point two places to the *right*, and affix a percent symbol.
Percent	Write as a ratio to 100 and reduce the fraction. If the percent involves a decimal, first write the decimal in fractional form, and then multiply by $\frac{1}{100}$. If the percent involves a fraction, delete the percent symbol and multiply by $\frac{1}{100}$.	Shift the decimal point two places to the *left*, and delete the percent symbol. If the percent involves a fraction, first write the fraction as a decimal, and then shift the decimal point.	

Example 3 Write a fraction as a percent

Write each fraction in percent form.
a. $\frac{5}{8}$ **b.** $\frac{5}{6}$

Solution

a. Look under the fraction heading in Table 6.1, and follow the directions for changing a fraction to a percent.

Step 1 $\dfrac{5}{8} = 0.625$

Step 2   0. 62 5 = 62.5%

Two places; add zeros as placeholders as necessary; add percent symbol.

Answer: 62.5%

$$
\begin{array}{r}
0.625 \\
8\overline{)5.000} \\
\underline{48} \\
20 \\
\underline{16} \\
40 \\
\underline{40} \\
0
\end{array}
$$

b. Step 1 $\dfrac{5}{6} = 0.83\dfrac{1}{3}$

Step 2 $0.\,83\dfrac{1}{3} = 83\dfrac{1}{3}\%$

The decimal point is understood.

$$
\begin{array}{r}
0.83 \\
6\overline{)5.000} \\
\underline{48} \\
20 \\
\underline{18} \\
2
\end{array}
$$

Carry out the division two places and save the remainder as a fraction: $\frac{2}{6} = \frac{1}{3}$.

Answer: $83\frac{1}{3}\%$

Example 4   Write a decimal as a percent and as a fraction

Write decimal forms as percents and fractions.
a. 0.85   **b.** 2.485

Solution

a. Step 1 $0.\,85 = 85\,\%$

Two places   Decimal understood

Step 2 85% means $\dfrac{85}{100} = \dfrac{17}{20}$

b. Step 1 $2.485 = 248.5\%$

Step 2 248.5% means $248.5 \times \dfrac{1}{100} = 248\dfrac{1}{2} \times \dfrac{1}{100}$

$$= \dfrac{497}{2} \times \dfrac{1}{100}$$

$$= \dfrac{497}{200} \quad \text{or} \quad 2\dfrac{97}{200}$$

Estimation

Percent problems are very common. We conclude this section with a discussion of estimation and some percent calculations.

The first estimation method is the *unit fraction-conversion method,* which can be used to estimate the common percents of 10%, 25%, $33\frac{1}{3}\%$, and 50%. To estimate the size of a part of a whole quantity, which is sometimes called a **percentage,** rewrite the percent as a fraction and mentally multiply, as shown by the following example.

Unit Fraction Comparison

Percent	Fraction
10%	$\frac{1}{10}$
25%	$\frac{1}{4}$
$33\frac{1}{3}\%$	$\frac{1}{3}$
50%	$\frac{1}{2}$

50% of 800: $\frac{1}{2} \times 800 = 400$ THINK: $800 \div 2 = 400$

25% of 1,200: $\frac{1}{4} \times 1,200 = 300$ THINK: $1,200 \div 4 = 300$

$33\frac{1}{3}\%$ of 600: $\frac{1}{3} \times 600 = 200$ THINK: $600 \div 3 = 200$

10% of 824: $\frac{1}{10} \times 824 = 82.4$ THINK: $824 \div 10 = 82.4$

If the numbers for which you are finding a percentage are not as "nice" as those given here, you can estimate by rounding the number, as shown in Example 5.

Example 5   Estimating percents

Estimate the following percentages:
a. 25% of 312   **b.** 50% of 843   **c.** $33\frac{1}{3}\%$ of 1,856   **d.** 25% of 43,350

Solution

a. Estimate 25% of 312 by rounding 312 so that it is easily divisible by 4:

$\frac{1}{4} \times 320 = 80$ Find $320 \div 4 = 80$.

b. Estimate 50% of 843 by rounding 843 so that it is easily divisible by 2:

$$\tfrac{1}{2} \times 840 = 420 \qquad \text{Find } 840 \div 2 = 420.$$

c. Estimate $33\tfrac{1}{3}\%$ of 1,856 by rounding 1,856 so that it is easily divisible by 3:

$$\tfrac{1}{3} \times 1,800 = 600 \qquad \text{Find } 1,800 \div 3 = 600.$$

d. Estimate 25% of 43,350 by rounding 43,350 so that it is easily divisible by 4:

$$\tfrac{1}{4} \times 44,000 = 11,000$$

A second estimation procedure uses a multiple of a unit fraction. For example,

Think of 75% as $\tfrac{3}{4}$, which is $3 \times \tfrac{1}{4}$.

Think of $66\tfrac{2}{3}\%$ as $\tfrac{2}{3}$, which is $2 \times \tfrac{1}{3}$.

Think of 60% as $\tfrac{6}{10}$, which is $6 \times \tfrac{1}{10}$.

Example 6 Estimate percents

Estimate the following percentages.
a. 75% of 943   **b.** $66\tfrac{2}{3}\%$ of 8,932   **c.** 60% of 954   **d.** 80% of 0.983

Solution

a. 75% of $943 \approx \tfrac{3}{4} \times 1,000 = 3(\tfrac{1}{4} \times 1,000) = 3(250) = 750$

b. $66\tfrac{2}{3}\%$ of $8,932 \approx \tfrac{2}{3} \times 9,000 = 2(\tfrac{1}{3} \times 9,000) = 2(3,000) = 6,000$

c. 60% of $954 \approx \tfrac{6}{10} \times 1,000 = 6(\tfrac{1}{10} \times 1,000) = 6(100) = 600$

d. 80% of $0.983 \approx \tfrac{8}{10} \times 1 = 0.8$

The Percent Problem

Many percentage problems are more difficult than these. The following quotation was found in a recent publication: "An elected official is one who gets 51 percent of the vote cast by 40 percent of the 60 percent of voters who registered." Certainly, most of us will have trouble understanding the percent given in this quotation; but you can't pick up a newspaper without seeing dozens of examples of ideas that require some understanding of percents. A difficult job for most of us is knowing whether to multiply or divide by the given numbers. In this section, I will provide you with a sure-fire method for knowing what to do. The first step is to understand what is meant by **the percent problem.**

Study this percent problem. If you learn this, you get a written guarantee for correctly working percent problems.

The Percent Problem

A	is	$P\%$	of	W
↓		↓		↓
This is the given amount.		The percent is written $\frac{P}{100}$.		This is the whole quantity. It always follows the word "of."

The percent problem won't always be stated in this form, but notice that three quantities are associated with it:

1. The *amount*—sometimes called the **percentage**
2. The *percent*—sometimes called the **rate**
3. The *whole quantity*—sometimes called the **base**

Now, regardless of the form in which you are given the percent problem, follow these steps to write a proportion.

Procedure for Solving the Percent Problem

Step 1 Identify the *percent* first; it will be followed by the symbol % or the word *percent*. Write it as a fraction:

$$\frac{P}{100}$$

Step 2 Identify the *whole quantity* next; it is preceded by the word "of." It is the denominator of the second fraction in the proportion:

$$\frac{P}{100} = \frac{}{W} \ \leftarrow \text{This is the quantity following the word "of."}$$

Step 3 The remaining number is the partial amount; it is the numerator of the second fraction in the proportion:

$$\frac{P}{100} = \frac{A}{W} \ \leftarrow \text{This is the last quantity to be inserted into the problem.}$$

Example 7   Write a percent problem

For each of the following cases, identify the percent, the whole quantity, and the amount (the percentage or part), and then write a proportion.

a. What number is 18% of 200? **b.** 18% of 200 is what number?
c. 150 is 12% of what number? **d.** 63 is what percent of 420?
e. 18% of what number is 72? **f.** 120 is what percent of 60?

Solution

	Percent $P(\%)$	Whole W ("of")	Amount A (part)	Proportion $\frac{P}{100} = \frac{A}{W}$
a. What number is 18% of 200?	18	200	unknown	$\frac{18}{100} = \frac{A}{200}$
b. 18% of 200 is what number?	18	200	unknown	$\frac{18}{100} = \frac{A}{200}$
c. 150 is 12% of what number?	12	unknown	150	$\frac{12}{100} = \frac{150}{W}$
d. 63 is what percent of 420?	unknown	420	63	$\frac{P}{100} = \frac{63}{420}$
e. 18% of what number is 72?	18	unknown	72	$\frac{18}{100} = \frac{72}{W}$
f. 120 is what percent of 60?	unknown	60	120	$\frac{P}{100} = \frac{120}{60}$

Regardless of the arrangement of the question, identify P first.
Second, identify the number following the word "of."
This number is identified last.

Since there are only three letters in the proportion

$$\frac{P}{100} = \frac{A}{W}$$

there are three types of percent problems. These possible types were illustrated in Example 7. To answer a question involving a percent, write a proportion and then solve the proportion. Try solving each proportion in Example 7. The answers are: **a.** $A = 36$; **b.** $A = 36$; **c.** $W = 1{,}250$; **d.** $P = 15$; **e.** $W = 400$; **f.** $P = 200$.

Example **8** **Find the lowest C grade**

In a certain class there are 500 points possible. The lowest C grade is 65% of the possible points. How many points are equal to the lowest C grade?

Solution   What is 65% of 500 points?

$$\frac{65}{100} = \frac{A}{500} \quad \leftarrow \text{The whole amount follows the word "of."}$$

$$A = \frac{65 \times \overset{5}{\cancel{500}}}{\underset{1}{\cancel{100}}}$$

$$= 325$$

Check by estimation: 65% of 500 $\approx 6(\frac{1}{10} \times 500) = 300$.
The lowest C grade is 325 points.

Example **9** **Salary withholding**

If your monthly salary is \$4,500 and 21% is withheld for taxes and Social Security, how much money will be withheld from your check on payday?

Solution   How much is 21% of \$4,500?

$$\frac{21}{100} = \frac{A}{4,500}$$

$$A = \frac{21 \times 4,500}{100}$$

$$= 945$$

Check by estimation: 21% of 4,500 $\approx 2(\frac{1}{10} \times 4,500) = 900$.
The withholding is \$945.

Example **10** **Find the tax rate**

You make a \$25 purchase, and the clerk adds \$2.25 for sales tax. This doesn't seem right to you, so you want to know what percent tax has been charged.

Solution   What percent of \$25 is \$2.25?

$$\frac{P}{100} = \frac{2.25}{25}$$

$$\frac{100 \times 2.25}{25} = P$$

$$9 = P$$

Check by estimation: 9% of 25 $\approx \frac{1}{10} \times 25 = 2.50$.
The tax charged was 9%.

Example **11** **Find total income**

Your neighbors tell you that they paid \$44,370 in taxes last year, and this amounted to 29% of their total income. What was their total income?

Solution   29% of total income is \$44,370.

$$\frac{29}{100} = \frac{44,370}{W}$$

$$\frac{100 \times 44{,}370}{29} = W$$

$$153{,}000 = W$$

Check by estimation: 29% of 153,000 $\approx 3(\frac{1}{10} \times 150{,}000) = 3(15{,}000) = 45{,}000$. Since $45,000 is an estimate for $44,370, we conclude the result is correct. Their total income was $153,000.

Example **12** **Find percent increase**

If 45 is increased to 105, what is the percent increase?

Solution   The amount of increase is $105 - 45 = 60$, so as a percent problem we have "60 is what percent of 45?"

$$\frac{P}{100} = \frac{60}{45}$$

$$P = \frac{100 \times 60}{45}$$

$$\approx 133.3\overline{3}$$

The percent increase is $133 \frac{1}{3}\%$.

WARNING! You must be careful not to add percents. For example, suppose you have $100 and spend 50%. How much have you spent, and how much do you have left?

Amount Spent	*Remainder*
$50	$50

Now, suppose you spend 50% of the remainder. How much have you spent, and how much is left?

New Spending	*Old Spending*	*Remainder*
$25	$50	$25

This means you have spent $75 or 75% of your original bankroll. A common ERROR is to say "50% spending + 50% spending = 100% spending." **Remember, if you add percents, you often obtain incorrect results.**

Example **13** **Critique a percent headline**

A newspaper headline proclaimed:

Teen drug use soars 105%

WASHINGTON —Teen drug use rose 105% between 1995 and 1997.

A national survey showed that between 1995 and 1996 youth drug use rose 30%, but between 1996 and 1997 usage soared 75%.

Over the two-year period, the rise of 105% was attributed to...

What is wrong with the headline?

Solution   We are not given all the relevant numbers, but consider the following possibility: Suppose there are 100 drug users, so a rise of

100 to 130 is a 30% increase

130 to 227 is a 75% increase

100 to 227 is a 127% increase, NOT 105%

Remember, adding percents can give faulty results.

Problem Set 6.8

Level 1

In Problems 1–21, change the given form into the two missing forms.

Fraction	Decimal	Percent
1. _____	0.75	_____
2. _____	0.2	_____
3. _____	_____	40%
4. _____	_____	100%
5. $\frac{1}{3}$	_____	_____
6. $\frac{1}{5}$	_____	_____
7. _____	0.85	_____
8. _____	_____	60%
9. $\frac{3}{8}$	_____	_____
10. _____	_____	45%
11. _____	_____	120%
12. $\frac{2}{3}$	_____	_____
13. _____	0.05	_____
14. _____	_____	$6\frac{1}{2}\%$
15. $\frac{1}{6}$	_____	_____
16. $\frac{5}{6}$	_____	_____
17. _____	_____	$22\frac{2}{9}\%$
18. _____	0.35	_____
19. _____	0.175	_____
20. $\frac{1}{12}$	_____	_____
21. _____	0.0025	_____

Estimate the percentages in Problems 22–28.

22. a. 50% of 2,000   **b.** 25% of 400

23. a. 10% of 95,000   **b.** 10% of 85.6

24. a. 50% of 9,985   **b.** $33\frac{1}{3}\%$ of 3,600

25. a. 25% of 819   **b.** 25% of 790

26. a. 75% of 1,058   **b.** 75% of 94

27. a. 40% of 93   **b.** 90% of 8,741

28. a. $66\frac{2}{3}\%$ of 8,600   **b.** $66\frac{2}{3}\%$ of 35

Write each sentence in Problems 29–46 as a proportion, and then solve to answer the question.

29. What number is 15% of 64?

30. What number is 120% of 16?

31. 14% of what number is 21?

32. 40% of what number is 60?

33. 10 is what percent of 5?

34. What percent of $20 is $1.20?

35. 4 is what percent of 5?

36. 2 is what percent of 5?

37. What percent of 12 is 9?

38. What percent of 5 is 25?

39. 49 is 35% of what number?

40. 3 is 12% of what number?

41. 120% of what number is 16?

42. 21 is $66\frac{2}{3}\%$ of what number?

43. 12 is $33\frac{1}{3}\%$ of what number?

44. What is 8% of $2,425?

45. What is 6% of $8,150?

46. 400% of what number is 150?

Level 2

47. If 11% of the 210 million adult Americans live in poverty, how many adult Americans live in poverty?

48. If 6.2% of the 210 million adult Americans are unemployed, how many adult Americans are unemployed?

49. If the sales tax is 6% and the purchase price is $181, what is the amount of tax?

50. If the sales tax is 5.5% and the purchase price is $680, what is the amount of tax?

51. If you were charged $151 in taxes on a $3,020 purchase, what percent tax were you charged?

52. If 20 is increased to 25, what is the percent increase?

53. If 80 is decreased to 48, what is the percent decrease?

54. Government regulations require that, for certain companies to receive federal grant money, 15% of the total number of employees must meet minority requirements. If a company employs 390 people, how many minority people should be employed to meet the minimum requirements?

55. If Brad's monthly salary is $8,200, and 32% is withheld for taxes and Social Security, how much money is withheld each month?

56. A certain test is worth 125 points. How many points (rounded to the nearest point) are needed to obtain a score of 75%?

57. If Carlos answered 18 out of 20 questions on a test correctly, what was his percentage right?

58. If Wendy answered 15 questions correctly and obtained 75%, how many questions were on the test?

59. Shannon Sovndal received an 8% raise, which amounted to $100 per month. What was his old wage, and what will his new wage be?

60. An advertisement for a steel-belted radial tire states that this tire delivers 15% better gas mileage. If the present gas mileage is 25.5 mpg, what mileage would you expect if you purchased these tires? Round your answer to the nearest tenth of a mile per gallon.

6.9 | Modeling Uncategorized Problems

CAUTION

If you work hard mastering this section, you will have gained an important life skill.

One major criticism of studying the common types of word problems presented in most textbooks is that students can fall into the habit of solving problems by using a template or pattern and be successful in class without ever developing independent problem-solving abilities. Even though problem solving may require algebraic skills, it also requires many other skills; a goal of this book is to help you develop a general problem-solving ability so that when presented with a problem that does not fit a template, you can apply techniques that will lead to a solution.

Most problems that do not come from textbooks are presented with several variables, along with one or more relationships among those variables. In some instances, insufficient information is given; in others there may be superfluous information or inconsistent information. A common mistake when working with these problems is to assume that you know which variable to choose as the unknown in the equation *at the beginning of the problem*. This leads to trying to take too much into your memory at the start, and as a result it is easy to get confused.

Now you are in a better position to practice Polya's problem-solving techniques because you have had some experience in carrying out the second step of the process, which we repeat here for convenience.

Guidelines for Problem Solving

Step 1 *Understand the Problem.* Ask questions, experiment, or otherwise rephrase the question in your own words.

Step 2 *Devise a Plan.* Find the connection between the data and the unknown. Look for patterns, relate to a previously solved problem or a known formula, or simplify the given information to give you an easier problem.

Step 3 *Carry out the Plan.* Check the steps as you go.

Step 4 *Look Back.* Examine the solution obtained.

Remember that the key to becoming a problem solver is to develop the skill to solve problems *that are not like the examples shown in the text*. For this reason, the problems in this section will require that you go beyond copying the techniques developed in the first part of this chapter.

Example 1 School ADA

In California, state funding of education is based on the average daily attendance (ADA). Develop a formula for determining the ADA at your school.

Solution   We use Pólya's problem-solving guidelines for this example.

Most attempts at mathematical modeling come from a real problem that needs to be solved. There is no "answer book" to tell you when you are correct. There is often the need to do additional research to find necessary information, and the need *not* to use certain information that you have to arrive at a solution.

Understand the Problem.   What is meant by ADA? The first step might be a call to your school registrar to find out how ADA is calculated. For example, in California it is based on weekly student contact hours (WSCH), and 1 ADA = 525 WSCH. Thus, you might begin by writing the formula

$$\frac{\text{WSCH}}{525} = \text{TOTAL ADA}$$

 This means that 525 WSCH is 525/525 = 1 ADA or 1050 WSCH is $\frac{1050}{525}$ = 2 ADA. In other words, we divide the WSCH by 525 to find the ADA.

Devise a Plan.   Mathematical modeling requires that we check this formula to see whether it properly models the TOTAL ADA at your school. How is the WSCH determined? In California, the roll sheets are examined at two census dates, and WSCH is calculated as the average of the census numbers. In mathematical modeling, you often need formulas that are not specified as part of the problem. In this case, we need a formula for calculating an average. We use the *mean*:

$$\text{WSCH} = \frac{\text{Census 1} + \text{Census 2}}{2}$$

We now have a second attempt at a formula for TOTAL ADA:

$$\frac{\text{Census 1} + \text{Census 2}}{2} \div 525 = \text{TOTAL ADA}$$

Carry Out the Plan.   Does this properly model the TOTAL ADA? Perhaps, but suppose a taxpayer or congressperson brings up the argument that funding should take into account absent people, because not all classes have 100% attendance each day. You might include an *absence factor* as part of the formula. In California, the agreed absence factor for funding purposes is 0.911. How would we incorporate this into the TOTAL ADA calculation?

$$\frac{\text{Census 1} + \text{Census 2}}{2} \cdot \frac{\text{Absence factor}}{525} = \text{TOTAL ADA}$$

This formula could be simplified to

$$\text{TOTAL ADA} = 0.0008676190476(c_1 + c_2)$$

where c_1 and c_2 are the numbers of students on the roll sheets on the first and second census dates, respectively.

Look Back.   In fact, a Senate bill in California states this formula as

$$\frac{\text{Census 1 WSCH} + \text{Census 2 WSCH}}{2} \cdot \frac{0.911 \text{ Absence factor}}{525} = \text{TOTAL ADA}$$

This is equivalent to the formula we derived.

Example 2 DVR recording

Suppose you wish to record a 30 hours on your DVR and want to obtain the best-quality recording possible. Explain how you could do this. There are two modes for recording on your DVR: HD (high definition will record 20 hours) and SR (standard resolution will record 40 hours). The best-quality recording is on HD.*

Solution   We use Pólya's problem-solving guidelines for this example.

Understand the Problem. We cannot record all 30 hours in HD. If we record in SR we will be able to record the 30 hours but an empty 10 hour space would be left, and we would be sacrificing quality by recording in SR mode. It seems that the solution is to begin in the SR mode and at some "crucial moment" switch to the HD mode with the goal that the 30 hours would just fill the available space.

Devise a Plan. We begin with some assumptions. In reality, the actual space required on different DVRs are not exact. We will assume, however, that the times specified in the problem are exact. That is, a DVR will record for exactly 20 or 40 hours depending on the chosen quality. We also assume a linear relationship between recording time and the amount of tape used.

Let us begin by drawing a picture of our problem:

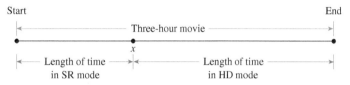

Let x be the length of time that we record in SR mode. Then $30 - x$ is the length of time that we record in HD mode.

How do we represent the fraction that is recorded in the SR mode?

If $x = 30$, then $\frac{3}{4}$ of the DVR capacity is used; remember that 40 hours can be recorded in SR format

If $x = 20$, then $\frac{2}{4}$ of the DVR capacity is used.

If $x = 10$, then $\frac{1}{4}$ of the DVR is used.

Thus, the model seems to be

$$\frac{\text{TIME RECORDING IN THE SR MODE}}{40} = \frac{x}{40}$$

How do we represent the fraction that is recorded in the HD mode? Since the DVR is full in this mode 20 hours, we see that the fraction of the capacity in the HD is

$$\frac{\text{TIME RECORDING IN THE HD MODE}}{20} = \frac{30 - x}{20}$$

Since we want to use the entire 30 hours, both fractions must add up to 1.

$$\frac{x}{40} + \frac{30 - x}{20} = 1$$

Carry Out the Plan. Simplify this equation by multiplying both sides by 40.

$$x + 2(30 - x) = 40$$
$$60 - x = 40$$
$$20 = x$$

The mode should be changed after 20 hours.

Look Back. If we record for 20 hours in SR, we have used up $\frac{1}{2}$ of the tape. We then switch to the HD mode and record for 10 hours, which uses up the other half of the DVR.

---

*The idea for this example is from an article by Gregory N. Fiore in *The Mathematics Teacher*, October 1988.

Example **3** **Time to fill swimming pool**   *Pólya's Method*

An inlet pipe on a swimming pool can be used to fill the pool in 24 hours. The drain pipe can be used to empty the pool in 30 hours. If the pool is half-filled and then the drain pipe is accidentally opened, how long will it take to fill the pool?

Solution   We use Pólya's problem-solving guidelines for this example.

Understand the Problem. Draw a picture, if necessary.

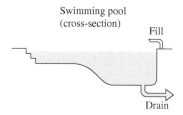

Swimming pool
(cross-section)
Fill
Drain

Water comes into the pool until it is half full. Then water begins draining out of the pool at the same time it is coming in. Is there a solution? What if the drain pipe alone emptied the pool in 20 hours? In that case, the pool would never be more than half full, and instead we could ask when it would be empty. Estimate an answer. Since it takes less time to fill than to drain, the inlet pipe is working faster than the drain, so it will fill. How long? Well, you might guess that it must be longer than 24 hours.

Devise a Plan. Let us denote the amount of water drained as the amount of work done. Then we see

WORK DONE BY INLET PIPE − WORK DONE BY DRAIN = ONE JOB COMPLETED

But wait, is this correct? The drain works only after the pool is half full. One of Pólya's suggestions is to work a simpler problem. How long does it take to fill the first half of the pool? That's easy. Since the pool fills in 24 hours, it must be half full in 12 hours. Now, we can focus on filling the second half of the pool, so we come back to the guide we wrote down above.

Another step we can take when devising a plan is to ask whether there is an appropriate formula. In this case,

WORK
DONE BY = (RATE OF INLET PIPE)(TIME TO FILL)
INLET PIPE

$$= \frac{1}{24}(\text{TIME})$$ $\dfrac{\text{Time}}{\text{to fill}} = \dfrac{\text{time}}{\text{to drain}}$

WORK
DONE BY = (RATE OF DRAIN)(TIME TO DRAIN)
DRAIN

$$= \frac{1}{30}(\text{TIME})$$

Carry Out the Plan. Substitute these formulas into the guide (for the second half of the pool):

WORK DONE BY INLET PIPE − WORK DONE BY DRAIN = ONE-HALF JOB COMPLETED

$$\downarrow \qquad\qquad \downarrow \qquad\qquad \downarrow$$

$$\frac{1}{24}(\text{TIME}) \quad - \quad \frac{1}{30}(\text{TIME}) \quad = \quad \frac{1}{2}$$

Let t = TIME   *Remember that this is the time required to fill the second half of the pool.*

$$\frac{1}{24}t - \frac{1}{30}t = \frac{1}{2}$$

$$(120)\frac{1}{24}t - (120)\frac{1}{30}t = \frac{1}{2}(120) \qquad \text{Multiply both sides by 120.}$$

$$5t - 4t = 60$$

$$t = 60$$

It will take 12 hours to fill the first half of the pool, but it will take 60 more hours to fill the second half. Thus, it will take 72 hours to fill the pool.

Look Back. Does this answer make sense? In 72 hours, $\frac{72}{24} = 3$ swimming pools could be filled. The drain is working for 60 hours, so this is the equivalent of $\frac{60}{30} = 2$ swimming pools drained. Let's see: $3 - 2 = 1$ swimming pool, so it checks.

We have refrained from working so-called age problems because they seem to be a rather useless type of word problem—one that occurs only in algebra books. They do, however, give us a chance to practice our problem-solving skill, so they are worth considering. By the way, the precedent for age problems in algebra books goes back over 2,000 years (see Problem 60 about Diophantus). The age problem given in the next example was found in the first three frames of a *Peanuts* cartoon.

Example 4   Peanuts age problem

Pólya's Method

A man has a daughter and a son. The son is three years older than the daughter. In one year the man will be six times as old as the daughter is now, and in ten years he will be fourteen years older than the combined ages of his children. What is the man's present age?

Solution   We use Pólya's problem-solving guidelines for this example.

Understand the Problem.   There are three people: a man, his daughter, and his son. We are concerned with their ages now, in one year, and in ten years.

Devise a Plan.   Does this look like any of the problems we have solved? We need to distinguish among the persons' ages now and some time in the future. Let us begin by translating the known information:

Ages Now	Ages in One Year	Ages in Ten Years
MAN'S AGE NOW	MAN'S AGE NOW + 1	MAN'S AGE NOW + 10
DAUGHTER'S AGE NOW	DAUGHTER'S AGE NOW + 1	DAUGHTER'S AGE NOW + 10
SON'S AGE NOW	SON'S AGE NOW + 1	SON'S AGE NOW + 10

We are given that

    First equation: SON'S AGE NOW = DAUGHTER'S AGE NOW + 3

and

    MAN'S AGE NOW + 1 = 6(DAUGHTER'S AGE NOW)

This is the same as

    Second equation: MAN'S AGE NOW = 6(DAUGHTER'S AGE NOW) − 1

Finally, we are given that

MAN'S AGE NOW $+ 10 =$ (SON'S AGE NOW $+10$) $+$ (DAUGHTER'S AGE NOW $+ 10$) $+ 14$

$\uparrow$

14 years older

If we simplify this equation we obtain:

Third equation: MAN'S AGE NOW $=$ SON'S AGE NOW $+$ DAUGHTER'S AGE NOW $+ 24$

The plan is to begin with the third equation and evolve it into an equation we can solve.

Carry Out the Plan.

MAN'S AGE NOW $=$ SON'S AGE NOW $+$ DAUGHTER'S AGE NOW $+ 24$ Third equation

$\uparrow$ $\uparrow$

SON'S AGE NOW $=$ DAUGHTER'S AGE NOW $+ 3$ First equation

Second equation

MAN'S AGE NOW $=$ 6(DAUGHTER'S AGE NOW) $- 1$

6(DAUGHTER'S AGE NOW) $- 1 =$ DAUGHTER'S AGE NOW $+ 3 +$ DAUGHTER'S AGE NOW $+ 24$

$$6d - 1 = d + 3 + d + 24 \qquad \text{Let } d = \text{DAUGHTER'S AGE NOW}$$
$$6d - 1 = 2d + 27$$
$$4d = 28$$
$$d = 7$$

DAUGHTER'S AGE NOW $= 7$

MAN'S AGE NOW $= 6$ (DAUGHTER'S AGE NOW) -1

MAN'S AGE NOW $= 6(7) -1 = 41$

The man's present age is 41.

Look Back. From the first equation, SON'S AGE NOW $= 7 + 3 = 10$. In one year the man will be 42, and this is 6 times the daughter's present age. In ten years the man will be 51 and the children will be 20 and 17; the man will be 14 years older than $20 + 17 = 37$.

Example   **5**   **Estimation puzzle**   Pólya's Method

To number the pages of a bulky volume, the printer used 4,001 digits. It was estimated that the volume has 1,000 pages. Is this a good estimate? How many actual pages has the volume?

Solution   We use Pólya's problem-solving guidelines for this example.

Understand the Problem. Page 1 uses one digit; page 49 uses two digits; page 125 uses three digits. Assume that the first page is page 1 and that the pages are numbered consecutively.

Devise a Plan. This does not seem to fit any of the problem types we have considered in this book. Can you reduce this to a simpler problem? If the book has exactly 9 numbered pages, how many digits does the printer use? If the book has exactly 99 numbered pages, how many digits does the printer use? The plan is to count the number of digits on single-digit pages, then those on double-digit pages, then on triple-digit pages.

Carry Out the Plan.

Single-digit pages: 9 digits total

Double-digit pages: $2(90) = 180$ digits total

          Do you see why this is not 2(99)? Remember, you are counting 90 pages (namely, from page 10 to page 99).

Triple-digit pages: $3(900) = 2,700$ digits total

We have now accounted for 2,889 digits. Since we are looking for 4,001 digits and since we can estimate four-digit pages to have $4(9,000) = 36,000$ digits, we need to know how many pages past 999 are necessary. Let x be the total number of pages. Then the number of digits on four-digit pages is

Four-digit pages: $4(x - 999)$

Now we can solve for x by using the following equation:

$$9 + 180 + 2{,}700 + 4(x - 999) = 4{,}001$$
$$4x + 2{,}889 - 3{,}996 = 4{,}001$$
$$4x - 1{,}107 = 4{,}001$$
$$4x = 5{,}108$$
$$x = 1{,}277$$

Look Back. The book has 1,277 pages.

Problem Set 6.9

Level 1

1. **IN YOUR OWN WORDS**   Discuss the difference between solving word problems in textbooks and problem solving outside the classroom.

2. **IN YOUR OWN WORDS**   In the first problem set of this book, we asked you to discuss Pólya's problem-solving model. Now that you have spent some time reading this book, we ask the same question again to see whether your perspective has changed at all. Discuss Pólya's problem-solving model.

Read each of the given problems and then select the best of the given answers in Problems 3–29.

3. The Hidden Valley Summer Camp is taking a field trip to the Exploratorium. There are ten children who are 12 years old or younger, six teens whose ages range from 13 years to 18 years, and three chaperones. The field trip includes transportation and lunch. The costs of the field trip are given:

$150	Bus and driver
$2.50/person	Lunch
$5.00/child	Admission
$6.00/teen	Admission
$7.00/adult	Admission

$25 discount for 25 persons or more

The bus driver will eat lunch, but will not visit the Exploratorium. What is the total cost for the field trip?
A. $307   B. $287   C. $314   D. $157

4. An animal shelter has two purebred Labradors among the 48 dogs available for adoption. It is also known that 7/8 of the dogs are mongrels. How many of the dogs are purebreds?
A. 42   B. 8   C. 4   D. 6

5. Shannon needs to have a term paper printed on a laser printer at Kinko's. The paper is 30 pages long (including a cover page and a bibliography page). Kinko's charges $10.00 for each 30 minutes (with a minimum charge of one hour), plus 10¢/sheet, and a binding fee of $1.25. He will also copy the original at a cost of 7¢/page. If the laser printing takes 45 minutes, what are the total charges?
A. $26.35   B. $21.35   C. $30.00   D. $16.35

6. Hannah is selling snow cones to earn money for a train trip. She sold 23 cones for $1.25 each and spent $4.95 + $0.35 tax. In addition, she received $3.50 in tips. What is the total profit for Hannah's endeavor?
A. $27.00   B. $26.95   C. $32.25   D. $23.45

7. When Melissa went to purchase a purse from a street vendor, she negotiated a purchase price that was 15% less than the $125.00 marked price, plus 7% sales tax on the purchase price. If she has $325.00 in her checking account, how much did she pay for the purse?
A. $113.69   B. $211.31   C. $20.06   D. $304.94

8. Linda finds that her $560 car payment is 28% of her gross monthly income. She knows that $510 is deducted from her paycheck each month, for income tax and Social Security. What is Linda's gross monthly income (rounded to the nearest dollar)?
A. $2,000   B. $157   C. $1,490   D. $930

9. Lou figures that his monthly car insurance payment of $180 is equal to 35% of the amount of her monthly auto loan payment. What is his total combined monthly expense for auto loan payment and insurance (rounded to the nearest dollar)?
A. $577   B. $694   C. $514   D. $63

10. Ben wants to finance the purchase of a guitar that is priced at $1,500. He contacts ABC Finance Company, and they believe the value of the guitar to be worth 10% less than that, and their policy is to lend only 80% of the value of the guitar. What is the down payment?
A. $420   B. $1,320   C. $1,080   D. $1,350

11. Søren's major bills are a variable-rate mortgage, car payments ($325/mo), food ($525/mo), and utilities ($215/mo). Last year his monthly mortgage payment was $2,320. This year, his mortgage payment increased by 3%. How much (rounded to the nearest dollar) will his monthly mortgage payment increase?
A. $3,385   B. $2,390   C. $835   D. $70

12. Theron bought an HDTV for $1,280 retail price and paid 7% state tax. He also received a rebate of 5% of the retail price. What was the total amount that he paid, including tax, for the HDTV?
A. $1,369.60   B. $1,305.60
C. $1,433.60   D. $1,340.20

13. A swimming pool holds 25,500 gallons of water. It will be filled by a pair of 0.5-in.-diameter hoses, each of which supplies 2.50 gallons of water per minute. How many hours will it take for the hoses to fill the pool?
A. 170   B. 83   C. 85   D. 125

14. Cole, a gardener, gives the following estimate for an installation. Each manifold will cost $85 to install, and each one will have three sprinkler heads at a cost of $9.50 each. Overhead adds 10% to the total bill. What is the total cost for this installation, consisting of four manifolds?
A. $113.50   B. $499.40
C. $454.00   D. $103.95

15. A 40-member committee voted on whether to send a certain bill to the governing board. One-fourth voted in favor, 3/5 voted against, and the rest abstained. How many abstained?
A. 6   B. 24   C. 34   D. 7

16. In Karl's math class with 28 students, 1/7 are receiving an A grade, 1/4 are B's, 11 are C's, and the rest are D's or F's. How many are D's or F's?
A. 4   B. 7   C. 6   D. 22

17. Alice paid $350 for her flight from San Francisco to Denver, but Bobbie paid $278 for the same flight. Cal, on the other hand, paid 8% less than Alice. How much was paid for the three seats (rounded to the nearest dollar)?
A. $950   B. $656   C. $1,006   D. $978

18. Doug's monthly salary was $1,250 when he received a 5% raise. Six months later, he received another 2% raise. What is his annual salary, after receiving both raises?
A. $1,337.50   B. $1,338.75
C. $16,050.00   D. $16,065.00

19. Aaron Rodgers (Green Bay Packers) threw 541 passes during the 2009 season. He ran with the ball 25 times. Of the 541 passes, 184 were incomplete, 7 were intercepted, and the rest were completed. What percent of the passes were complete?
A. 64.7%   B. 57.4%   C. 34.0%   D. 35.3%

20. In 2009, Pablo Sandoval (San Francisco Giants) had 633 plate appearances, with 189 hits and 25 home runs. He was paid $401,750. If he played 153 games, approximately how much was he paid for each game he played?
A. $3,000   B. $30,000
C. $300,000   D. $61,000,000

21. An investor has $2,500 at 2.5%, $21,300 at 3.2%, and $8,540 at 3.8%. If this investor is in a 38% tax bracket, how much interest income, after taxes, is realized?
A. $1,068.62   B. $32,340
C. $662.54   D. $406.08

22. An hourly salary of $25 is equivalent to what annual salary? Assume a 40-hour work week.
A. $50,000   B. $52,000   C. $41,600   D. $52,850

23. An annual salary of $83,000 is equivalent to what hourly salary? Assume a 40-hour work week.
A. $38.00   B. $38.90
C. $39.90   D. $41.50

24. How many prime numbers are divisible by 2?
A. 0   B. 1   C. 2   D. 3

25. How many prime numbers are less than 100?
A. 23   B. 24   C. 25   D. 26

26. How far up a wall does a 10-ft ladder reach if the bottom is placed 3 ft from the base of the wall? (Answer to the nearest foot.)
A. 8   B. 9   C. 10   D. 11

27. In order to secure a 10-ft TV antenna, three guy wires are needed. If the guy wires are 12 ft from the base of the antenna, how many feet of wire should be purchased if the packages available are:
A. 20 ft   B. 50 ft   C. 75 ft   D. 100 ft

28. The number of distinct (different) factors of 100 is:
A. 2   B. 4   C. 8   D. 9

29. The number of distinct (different) prime factors of 100 is:
A. 2   B. 4   C. 8   D. 9

30. **IN YOUR OWN WORDS** Look back over your method of solution for any of Problems 3–29. Did you answer any of those by inspection? That is, discuss the role of estimation and common sense in problem solving.

31. **IN YOUR OWN WORDS** In this chapter we have been discussing a problem-solving technique. Look back over your method of solution for any of Problems 3–29 that you have answered. Did you use the method discussed in the text or did you use other procedures? Discuss your own "method of attack" that you *actually* used.

Level 2

32. The product of two consecutive positive even numbers is 440. What are the numbers?

33. The product of two consecutive positive odd numbers is 255. What are the numbers?

34. The sum of an integer and its reciprocal is $\frac{5}{2}$. What is the integer?

35. The sum of a number and twice its reciprocal is 3. What are the numbers?

36. Suppose your monthly salary is $7,415 with the following deductions. (Answers should be the nearest cent.)
a. What is the federal tax (38%)?
b. What is the state tax (6.2%)?
c. What is the retirement deduction (10%)?
d. What are the miscellaneous deductions (4.5%)?
e. What is your take-home salary?

37. Suppose your stock market portfolio was $251,000 at the start of 2000. By the start of 2002, the value was $112,950.
a. What is the percent loss in the two-year period?
b. What is the percent gain necessary for your portfolio to regain its value in the next two years?

38. The top three women in the 2002 WNBA playoffs scored a total of 360 points. The leader, Tamika Whitmore (New York Liberty), scored 13 and 14 more points than the next two scorers. What are the points scored by these three players?

39. The Standard Oil and the Sears buildings have a combined height of 2,590 ft. The Sears Building is 318 ft taller. What is the height of each of these Chicago towers?

40. The combined area of New York and California is 204,192 square miles. The area of California is 108,530 square miles more than that of New York. Find the land area of each state.

Level 3

41. What is the sum of the first 100 consecutive even numbers?

42. A survey of 100 persons at Better Widgets finds that 40 jog, 25 swim, 16 cycle, 15 both swim and jog, 10 swim and cycle, 8 jog and cycle, and 3 persons do all three. How many people at Better Widgets do not take part in any of these three exercise programs?

43. A survey of executives of Fortune 500 companies finds that 520 have MBA degrees, 650 have business degrees, and 450 have both degrees. How many executives with MBAs have nonbusiness degrees?

44. An inlet pipe on a swimming pool can be used to fill the pool in 24 hours. The drain pipe can be used to empty the pool in 30 hours. If the pool is two-thirds filled and then the drain pipe is accidentally opened, how long will it take to fill the pool?

EPA/TIBOR ILLYES/Landov

45. An inlet pipe on a swimming pool can be used to fill the pool in 36 hours. The drain pipe can be used to empty the pool in 40 hours. If the pool is half filled and then the drain pipe is accidentally opened, how much longer will it take to fill the pool?

46. Solve the DVR example for recording a total of ℓ hours where $20 < \ell \leq 40$. (If $\ell \leq 20$, then the solution is obvious; just use the SR mode).

47. Reconsider Problem 0 if you are recording by eliminating the commercials from the recording process. Suppose that recording time is ℓ hours and that there are c minutes of commercials each hour.

48. After paying a real estate agent a commission of 6% on the selling price, $2,525 in other costs, and $65,250 on the mortgage, you receive a cash settlement of $142,785. What was the selling price of your house?

49. An investor has $100,000 to invest and can choose between insured savings at 3.5% interest or annuities paying 6.25%. If the investor wants to earn an annual income of $4,490, how much should be invested in each?

Problem Solving 3

Problems 50–60 do not match the examples in this book, but all the problem-solving techniques necessary to answer these questions have been covered in this book. These problems are designed to test your problem-solving abilities.

50. A swimming pool is 15 ft by 30 ft and an average of 5 ft in depth. It takes 25 minutes longer to fill than to drain the pool. If it can be drained at a rate of 15 ft^3/min faster than it can be filled, what is the drainage rate?

51. The longest rod that will just fit inside a rectangular box, if placed diagonally top to bottom, is 17 inches. The box is 1 inch shorter and 3 inches longer than it is wide. How much must you cut off the rod so that it will lie flat in the bottom of the container? What are the dimensions of the box?

52. A canoeist rows downstream in 1.5 hours and back upstream in 3 hours. What is the rate of the canoe if the distance rowed is 9 miles in each direction?

53. A plane makes a 630-mile flight with the wind in 2.5 hours; the return flight against the wind takes 3 hours. Find the wind speed.

54. A plane makes an 870-mile flight in $3\frac{1}{3}$ hours against a strong head wind, but returns in 50 minutes less with the wind. What is the plane's speed without the wind?

55. A tour agency is booking a tour and has 100 people signed up. The price of a ticket is $2,500 per person. The agency has booked a plane seating 150 people at a cost of $240,500. Additional costs to the agency are incidental fees of $500 per person. For each $5 that the price is lowered, a new person will sign up. How much should be charged for a ticket so that the income and expenses will be the same? The lower price will be charged to all participants, even those already signed up.

56. Imagine that you have written down the numbers from 1 to 1,000,000. What is the total number of zeros you have written down?

57. Suppose you have a large bottle with a canary inside. The bottle is sealed, and it's on a scale. The canary is standing on the bottom of the bottle. Then the canary starts to fly around inside of it. Does the reading on the scale change?

58. An ancient society called a number *sacred* if it could be written as the sum of the squares of two counting numbers.
   a. List five sacred numbers.
   b. Is the product of every two sacred numbers sacred?

59. HISTORICAL QUEST   A army general of the cavalry would always deploy his army in formation, and that formation was in the form of a square. However, when he did this, he saw that he had 284 soldiers left over that would not fit into the square formation. So, he decided to regroup the soldiers into another square formation by increasing each side by one soldier, but this time he was short 25 soldiers. How many soldiers are in this general's army? This question formulated from a problem by the famous mathematician Colin Maclaurin (1698–1746).*

60. HISTORICAL QUEST   Diophantus wrote the following puzzle about himself in *Anthologia Palatina:*

> *Here lies Diophantus. The wonder behold—*
> *Through art algebraic, the stone tells how old:*
> *"God gave him his boyhood one-sixth of this life,*
> *One-twelfth more as youth while whiskers grew rife;*
> *And then yet one-seventh their marriage begun;*
> *In five years there came a bouncing new son.*
> *Alas, the dear child of master and sage*
> *Met fate at just half his dad's final age.*
> *Four years yet his studies gave solace from grief;*
> *Then leaving scenes earthly he, too, found relief."*

What is Diophantus' final age?

*"Colin Maclaurin's Quaint Word Problems" by Bruce Hedman, in *The College Mathematics Journal*, Sept. 2000.

6.10 CHAPTER SUMMARY

Algebra is generous, she often gives more than is asked of her."

D'ALEMBERT

Important Ideas

Binomial product (FOIL) [6.1]
Binomial theorem [6.1]
Procedure for factoring trinomials [6.2]
Difference of squares [6.2]
Evaluate an expression [6.3]
Use a spreadsheet [6.3]
Equation properties [6.4]
Zero product rule [6.4]
Quadratic formula [6.4]
Linear inequalities [6.5]
Addition property of inequality [6.5]
Multiplication property of inequality [6.5]
Procedure for problem solving [6.6]
Property of proportions [6.7]
Procedure for solving proportions [6.7]
Change forms: fraction/decimal/percent [6.8]
Be able to estimate answers to percent problems [6.8]
Solve applied percent problems [6.8]
Guidelines for problem solving [6.9]
Problem-solving examples: genetics [6.3], **linear and quadratic equations** [6.4], **linear inequalities** [6.5], **number relationships** [6.6], **distance relationships** [6.6], **Pythagorean theorem applications** [6.6], **proportion problems** [6.7], **percent problems** [6.8]

Take some time getting ready to work the review problems in this section. First review these important ideas. Look back at the definition and property boxes. If you look online, you will find a list of important terms introduced in this chapter, as well as the types of problems that were introduced. You will maximize your understanding of this chapter by working the problems in this section only after you have studied the material.

You will find some review help online at **www.mathnature.com.** There are links giving general test help in studying for a mathematics examination, as well as specific help for reviewing this chapter.

Chapter 6 Review Questions

1. a. What is algebra?
   b. Briefly name and describe each of the four major processes of algebra.

2. **Simplify** the given expressions.
   a. $(x - 1)(x^2 + 2x + 8)$
   b. $x^2(x^2 - y) - xy(x^2 - 1)$

3. **Evaluate** the given expressions for $x = 2$ and $y = 3$.
   a. $x^3 - y^3$
   b. $(x - y)(x^2 + xy + y^2)$

4. **Factor** the given expressions.
   a. $3x^2 - 27$
   b. $x^2 - 5x - 6$

5. **Solve** the given equations.
   a. $8x - 12 = 0$
   b. $8x - 12 = -2x^2$

6. Factor $x^2 + 5x + 6$ using areas.

Solve the equations and inequalities in Problems 7–15.

7. a. $2x + 5 = 13$ b. $3x + 1 = 7x$

8. a. $\frac{2x}{3} = 6$ b. $2x - 7 = 5x$

9. a. $\frac{P}{100} = \frac{3}{20}$ b. $\frac{25}{W} = \frac{80}{12}$

10. $x^2 = 4x + 5$ 11. $4x^2 + 1 = 6x$

12. $3 < -x$ 13. $2 - x \geq 4$

14. $3x + 2 \leq x + 6$ 15. $14 > 5x - 1$

16. Fill in $=$, $>$, or $<$:
   a. $\frac{2}{3}$ —— $\frac{67}{100}$ b. $\frac{3}{4}$ —— $\frac{75}{100}$ c. $\frac{23}{27}$ —— $\frac{92}{107}$
   d. 0.05 —— 0.1 e. 0.99 —— 0.909

17. In a recipe for bread, flour and water are to be mixed in a ratio of 1 part water to 5 parts flour. If $2\frac{1}{2}$ cups of water is called for, how much flour (to the nearest tenth cup) is needed?

18. The sum of four consecutive even integers is 100. Find the integers.

19. A population of self-pollinating pea plants has two genes: T (tall, dominant) and t (short, recessive). Suppose we have an isolated population in which 52% of the genes in the gene pool are dominant T, and the other 48% are recessive t. What fraction of the population has each genotype? What fraction of the population has each phenotype?

20. The airline distance from Chicago to San Francisco is 1,140 miles farther than the flight from New York to Chicago, and 540 miles shorter than the distance from San Francisco to Honolulu. What is the length of each leg of the 4,980-mile New York–Chicago–San Francisco–Honolulu flight?

BOOK REPORTS

Write a 500-word report on this book:

Hypatia's Heritage, Margaret Alic (Boston: Beacon Press, 1986). This book is a history of women in science from antiquity through the 19th century. Since most of recorded history has been male-dominated, history books reflect this male bias and have ignored the history of women. This book is a rediscovery of women in science.

Group | RESEARCH PROJECTS

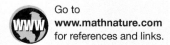

Go to
www.mathnature.com
for references and links.

Working in small groups is typical of most work environments, and learning to work with others to communicate specific ideas is an important skill. Work with three or four other students to submit a single report based on each of the following questions.

G21. Is $\sqrt{2}$ rational or irrational? Give a convincing argument to support your answer.

G22. **Historical Quest**   The Babylonians solved the quadratic equation
$x^2 + px = q$ $(q > 0)$ without the benefit of algebraic notation. Tablet 6967 at Yale University finds a positive solution to this equation to be

$$x = \sqrt{\left(\frac{p}{2}\right)^2 + q} - \frac{p}{2}$$

Using modern algebraic notation, show that this result is correct.

G23. **Historical Quest**   In 1907, the University of Göttingen offered the Wolfskehl Prize of 100,000 marks to anyone who could prove Fermat's last theorem, which seeks any replacements for x, y, and z such that $x^n + y^n = z^n$ (where n is greater than 2 and x, y, and z are counting numbers). In 1937, the mathematician Samuel Drieger announced that 1324, 731, and 1961 solved the equation. He would not reveal n—the power— but said that it was less than 20. That is,

$$1,324^n + 731^n = 1,961^n$$

However, it is easy to show that this cannot be a solution *for any n*. See if you can explain why by investigating some patterns for powers of numbers ending in 4 and 1.

G24. **Historical Quest**   This problem, called "The Ptolematic Riddle," is reported to be an ancient Greek problem, told by the mathematician Colin Maclaurin (1698–1746).*

I am a bronze lion.

Out of my mouth, the sole of my right foot, and my two eyes come four pipes that fill a cistern in different times.

The right eye fills it in two days.

The left eye fills it in three days.

The sole of my foot fills it in four days.

But my mouth takes six days to fill the cistern.

Find how many days all these will fill it together.

G25. **JOURNAL PROBLEM**   (From *Journal of Recreational Mathematics,* Vol. II, No.2) Translate the following message: Wx utgtuz f pbkz tswx wlx xwozm pbkzr, f exbmwo cxlzm xm ts jzszmfi fsv cxlzm lofwzgzm tswx wlx cxlzmr xe woz rfnz uzsxntsfwtxs fkxgz woz rzpxsu tr tncxrrtkiz, fsu T ofgz frrbmzuiv exbsu fs funtmfkiz cmxxe xe wotr kbw woz nfmjts tr wxx sfmmxl wx pxswfts tw. *Ctzmmz uz Ezmnfw*

Individual | RESEARCH PROJECTS

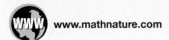

www.mathnature.com

Learning to use sources outside your classroom and textbook is an important skill, and here are some ideas for extending some of the ideas in this chapter. You can find references to these projects in a library or at **www.mathnature.com.**

PROJECT 6.1 Write a paper on the relationship between geometric areas and algebraic expressions.

PROJECT 6.2 Write out a derivation of the quadratic formula.

PROJECT 6.3 Find any replacements for x, y, and z such that $x^n + y^n = z^n$, where n is greater than 2 and where x, y, and z are counting numbers. Write a history of this problem, known as Fermat's Last Theorem.

Historical NOTE

Karl Smith library

**Pierre de Fermat
(1601–1665)**

Pierre de Fermat was a lawyer by profession, but he was an amateur mathematician in his spare time. He became Europe's finest mathematician, and he wrote over 3,000 mathematical papers and notes. However, he published only one, because he did them just for fun. Every theorem that Fermat said he proved has subsequently been verified—with one defying solution until 1993! This problem, known as Fermat's Last Theorem (see the Group Research Project G23), was written by Fermat in the margin of a book:

To divide a cube into two cubes, a fourth power, or in general any power whatever above the second, into powers of the same denomination, is impossible, and I have assuredly found an

admirable proof of this, but the margin is too narrow to contain it.

Many of the prominent mathematicians since his time have tried to prove or disprove this conjecture, and on June 23, 1993, during the third of a series of lectures at a conference held at the Newton Institute in Cambridge, it was reported that British mathematician Andrew Wiles of Princeton had proved a theorem for which Fermat's Last Theorem is a corollary.

Fermat's Last Theorem has been mentioned in literary works ranging from *Sherlock Holmes* to *Star Trek: The Next Generation*. There are many references to this great discovery, and perhaps the best is on DVD as part of the *NOVA* series on the Public Broadcasting System. The title is *The Proof* and it was first aired in 1997.

8 THE NATURE OF NETWORKS AND GRAPH THEORY

What in the World?

"Where do you live, Fritz?" asked Lisel.

"I live at 45 Heimelstraße. I'm looking forward to seeing you on Sunday!" proclaimed Fritz. "I will introduce you to my family and some of my friends on the island. We can take a stroll and I'll buy you a sundae at my favorite shop."

"Take a stroll?!!" screamed Lisel. "You KNOW I don't get it! Everybody thinks they can cross those bridges without doubling back, but I've never been able to do it."

"That's my secret! I can show you if you come on Sunday," said Fritz with a grin.

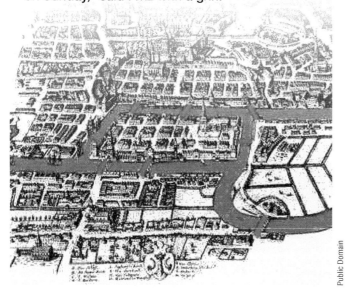

Public Domain

Overview

When we use the word "network" today, we probably think of a computer network, but we use networks every time we make a phone call, send an e-mail or "snail mail," drive on an interstate, or fly in an airplane.

In this chapter we look at mathematical ideas called *circuits, cycles*, and *trees*, which are part of geometry known as *graph theory*. When used in the context of graph theory, the word *graph* means something different from the way we use the term in referring to the coordinate plane or the way we use it to represent statistical data.

Even though these topics sound abstract, they have many interesting and useful applications such as finding the minimum cost of traveling to a number of locations (known as the *traveling salesperson problem*), installing an irrigation system, using a search engine on the Internet, or even coloring maps or making realistic-looking original landscapes in movies.

Many of the applications of this chapter are part of a new branch of mathematics (new in the sense that it began in the late 1930s) and grew out of mathematical problems associated with World War II. This branch of mathematics, called **operations research** (or *operational research*), deals with the application of scientific methods to management decision making, especially for the allocation of resources. Some examples include forecasting water pollution or predicting the scope of the AIDS epidemic.

8.1 | Euler Circuits and Hamiltonian Cycles

There is nothing in the world except empty space. Geometry bent
one way here describes gravitation. Rippled another way
somewhere else it manifests all the qualities of an electromagnetic
wave. Excited at still another plane, the magic material that is
space shows itself as a particle. There is nothing that is foreign or
"physical" immersed in space. Everything that is, is constructed
out of geometry.

JOHN A. WHEELER

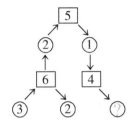

CHAPTER **CHALLENGE**

See if you can fill in the question mark.

We now turn to one of the newer branches of geometry known as *graph theory*, which includes *circuits, cycles,* and *trees.*

Euler Circuits

In the 18th century, in the German town of Königsberg (now the Russian city of Kaliningrad), a popular pastime was to walk along the bank of the Pregel River and cross over some of the seven bridges that connected two islands, as shown in Figure 8.1.

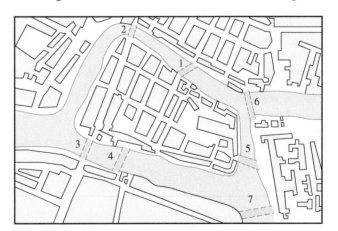

FIGURE 8.1 Königsberg bridges

One day a native asked a neighbor this question, "How can you take a walk so that you cross each of our seven bridges once and only once and end up where you started?" The problem intrigued the neighbor and soon caught the interest of many other people of Königsberg as well. Whenever people tried it, they ended up either not crossing a bridge at all or else crossing one bridge twice. This problem was brought to the attention of the Swiss mathematician Leonhard Euler, who was serving at the court of the Russian empress Catherine the Great in St. Petersburg. The method of solution we discuss here was first developed by Euler, and it led to the development of two major topics in geometry. The first is *networks*, which we discuss in this section, and the second is *topology*, which we discuss in Section 8.3.

We will use Pólya's problem-solving method for the Königsberg bridge problem.

Understand the Problem. To understand the problem, Euler began by drawing a diagram for the problem, as shown in Figure 8.2a.

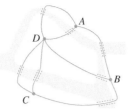

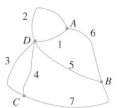

a. Crossing the bridges   **b.** Labeling network

FIGURE 8.2 Königsberg bridge problem

Next, Euler used one of the great problem-solving procedures—namely, to change the conceptual mode. That is, he **let the land area be represented as points (sometimes called *vertices* or *nodes*), and let the bridges be represented by arcs or line segments (sometimes called *edges*) connecting the given points.** As part of understanding the problem, we can do what Euler did—we can begin by tracing a diagram like the one shown in Figure 8.2b.

Devise a Plan. To solve the bridge problem, we need to draw the figure without lifting the pencil from the paper. Figures similar to the one in Figure 8.2b are called **networks** or **graphs.** In a network, the points where the line segments meet (or cross) are called **vertices,** and the lines representing bridges are called **edges** or **arcs.** Each separated part of the plane formed by a network is called a **region.** We say that a graph is **connected** if there is at least one path between each pair of vertices.

Example 1 Count edges, vertices, and regions of a network

Complete the table for each of the given networks.

a.   **b.**   **c.**

d.   **e.**   **f.**

Solution

Graph	Edges (E)	Vertices (V)	Regions (R)	V + R − 2
a.	3	3	2	3
b.	4	3	3	4
c.	5	3	4	5
d.	4	4	2	4
e.	5	4	3	5
f.	6	4	4	6

Note that $V + R - 2 = E$. Do you think this will always be true?

A network is said to be **traversable** if it can be traced in one sweep without lifting the pencil from the paper and without tracing the same edge more than once. Vertices may be passed through more than once. The **degree** of a vertex is the number of edges that meet at that vertex.

Example   **2**   **Test traversablity**

List the number of edges and the degree of each vertex shown in Example 1. Find the sum of the degrees of the vertices, and tell whether each network is traversable.

Solution

Graph	Number of Edges	Degree of Each Vertex	Sum	Traversable
a.	3	2; 2; 2	6	yes
b.	4	3; 2; 3	8	yes
c.	5	4; 3; 3	10	yes
d.	4	2; 2; 2; 2	8	yes
e.	5	2; 3; 2; 3	10	yes
f.	6	3; 3; 3; 3	12	no

Historical   NOTE

Karl Smith library

William Rowan Hamilton (1805–1865)

William Rowan Hamilton has been called the most renowned Irish mathematician. He was a child prodigy who read Greek, Hebrew, and Latin by the time he was five, and by the age of ten he knew over a dozen languages. He was appointed Professor of Astronomy and Royal Astronomer of Ireland at the age of 22. The problem discussed in this section that bears his name was discussed by Leonhard Euler and C. A. Vandermonde in 1771. The problem is named after him because of his invention of a puzzle called "Traveler's Dodecahedron," or "A Voyage 'Round the World." We discuss this problem in the problem set.

First, note that *the sum of the degrees of the vertices in Example 2 equals twice the number of edges.* Do you see why this must always be true? Consider any graph. Each edge must be connected at both ends, so the sum of all of those ends must be twice the number of vertices.

Now, consider a second observation regarding traversability. It is assumed that you worked Example 2 by actually tracing out the networks. However, a more complicated network, such as the Königsberg bridge problem, will require some analysis. The goal is to begin at some vertex, travel on each edge exactly once, and then return to the starting vertex. Such a path is called an **Euler circuit.** We can now rephrase the Königsberg bridge problem: "Does the network in Figure 8.2 have an Euler circuit?"

To answer this question, we will follow Euler's lead and classify vertices. Vertex *A* in Figure 8.2 is degree 3, so the vertex *A* is called an **odd vertex.** In the same way, *D* is an odd vertex, because it is degree 5. A vertex with even degree is called an **even vertex.** Euler discovered that only a certain number of odd vertices can exist in any network if you are to travel it in one journey without retracing any edge. You may start at any vertex and end at any other vertex, as long as you travel the entire network. Also the network must connect each point (this is called a **connected network**).

Let's examine networks more carefully and look for a pattern, as shown in Table 8.1.

TABLE 8.1

	Arrivals and Departures for a Vertex in a Network	
Number of Arcs	**Description**	**Possibilities**
1	1 departure (starting point) 1 arrival (ending point)	
2	1 arrival (arrive then depart) and 1 departure (depart then arrive)	
3	1 arrival, 2 departures 2 arrivals, 1 departure	
4	2 arrivals, 2 departures	
5	2 arrivals, 3 departures (starting point) 3 arrivals, 2 departures (ending point)	

We see that, if the vertex is odd, then it must be a starting point or an ending point. What is the largest number of starting and ending points in any network? [*Answer*: Two—one starting point and one ending point.] This discussion allows us to now formulate the step we have called devise a plan, which we now state without proof.

Count the number of odd vertices:

If there are no odd vertices, the network is traversable and any point may be a starting point. The point selected will also be the ending point.

If there is one odd vertex, the network is not traversable. A network cannot have only one starting or ending point without the other.

If there are two odd vertices, the network is traversable; one odd vertex must be a starting point and the other odd vertex must be the ending point.

If there are more than two odd vertices, the network is not traversable. A network cannot have more than one starting point and one ending point.

Carry Out the Plan. Classify the vertices; there are four odd vertices, so the network is not traversable.

Look Back. We have solved the Königsberg bridge problem, but you should note that saying it cannot be done is not the same thing as saying "I can't do the problem." We can do the problem, and the solution is certain.

We summarize this investigation.

STOP This is the key idea of this section.

Euler's Circuit Theorem

Every vertex on a graph with an Euler circuit has an even degree, and, conversely, if in a connected graph every vertex has an even degree, then the graph has an Euler circuit.

Example 3 Find an Euler circuit

Which of the following networks have an Euler circuit? Do not answer by trial and error, but by analyzing the number of odd vertices.

a.

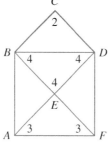

b.

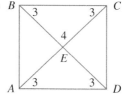

Solution

a. I first saw this network as a child's puzzle in elementary school. It has four even vertices (*B*, *C*, *D*, and *E*) and two odd vertices (*A* and *F*), and it is therefore traversable. To traverse it, you must start at *A* or *F* (that is, at an odd vertex). The path is shown.

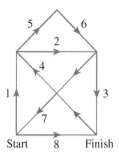

Note that we do not end at the beginning point, so this network does not have an Euler circuit (even though it is traversable).

b. This network has one even vertex and four odd vertices, so it is not traversable and does not have an Euler circuit.

Applications of Euler Circuits

Euler circuits have a wide variety of applications. We will mention a few.

- *Supermarket problem*   Set up the shelves in a market or convenience store so that it is possible to enter the store at the door and travel in each aisle exactly once (once and only once) and leave by the same door.
- *Police patrol problem*   Suppose a police car needs to patrol a gated subdivision and would like to enter the gate, cruise all the streets exactly once, and then leave by the same gate.
- *Floor-plan problem*   Suppose you have a floor plan of a building with a security guard who needs to go through the building and lock each door at the end of the day.
- *Water-pipe problem*   Suppose you have a network of water pipes, and you wish to inspect the pipeline. Can you pass your hand over each pipe exactly once without lifting your hand from a pipe, and without going over some pipe a second time?

We will examine one of these applications and leave the others for the problem set. Let's look at the *floor-plan problem*. This problem, which is related to the Königsberg bridge problem, involves taking a trip through all the rooms and passing through each door only once. There is, however, one important difference between these two problems. The Königsberg bridge problem requires an Euler circuit, but the floor-plan problem does not. In other words, with the bridges we must end up where we started, but the floor plan problem seeks only traversability. Let's draw a floor-plan problem as shown in Figure 8.3a.

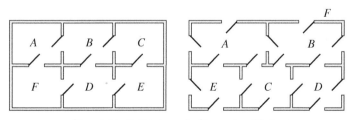

a. Six rooms, 7 doors   **b.** Six rooms, 16 doors

FIGURE 8.3 Floor-plan problem

Label the rooms as *A*, *B*, *C*, *D*, *E*, and *F*. In Figure 8.3a, rooms *A*, *C*, *E*, and *F* have two doors, and rooms *B* and *D* have three doors; in Figure 8.3b, it looks as if there are five rooms, but since there are doors that lead to the "outside," we must count the outside as a room. So this figure also has six rooms labeled *A*, *B*, *C*, *D*, *E*, and *F*. Rooms *A*, *B*, and *C* each have 5 doors, rooms *D* and *E* each have 4 doors, and room *F* has 9 doors.

Make a conjecture about the solution to the floor-plan problem. If there are no rooms with an odd number of doors, then it will be traversable. If there are two rooms with an odd number of doors, then it will be traversable: Start in one of those rooms, and end up in the other.

Example 4 Floor-plan puzzle

Pólya's Method

Solve the floor-plan problems:

a.

b.

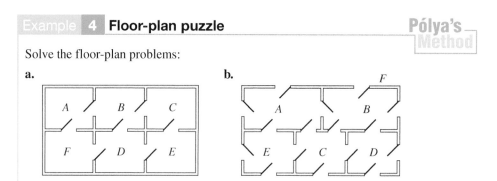

Solution   We use Pólya's problem-solving guidelines for this example.

Understand the Problem. The floor-plan problem asks, "Can we travel into each room and pass through every door once?"

Devise a Plan. Classify each room as even or odd, according to the number of doors in that room. A solution will be possible if there are no rooms with an odd number of doors, or if there are exactly two rooms with an odd number of doors.

Carry Out the Plan.

a. There are six rooms, and rooms *B* and *D* are odd, so this floor plan can be traversed. The solution requires that we begin in either room *B* or room *D*, and finish in the other.

b. There are six rooms, and rooms *A*, *B*, *C,* and *F* are odd (with *D* and *E* even). Since there are more than two odd rooms, this floor plan cannot be traversed. If one of the doors connecting two of the odd rooms is blocked, then the floor plan could be traversed.

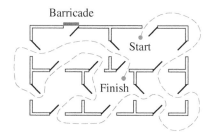

Look Back. We can check our work by actually drawing possible routes, as shown for part **b** above.

Hamiltonian Cycles

One application that cannot be solved using Euler circuits is the so-called **traveling salesperson problem:** A salesperson starts at home and wants to visit several cities without going through any city more than once, and then return to the starting city. This problem is so famous with so many people working on its solution that it is often referred to in the literature as **TSP.** The salesperson would like to do this in the most efficient way (that is, least distance, least time, smallest cost, . . .). To answer this question, we reverse the roles of the vertices and edges of an Euler circuit. Now, we ask whether we can visit each vertex exactly once and end at the original vertex. Such a path is called a **Hamiltonian cycle.**

Example 5 Find a Hamiltonian cycle

Find a Hamiltonian cycle for the network in Figure 8.4.

FIGURE 8.4 Network

Solution Note that this network is the one given in Example 1f. We found in Example 2f, that there was not an Euler circuit for this network. On the other hand, it is easy to find a Hamiltonian cycle:

$$A \rightarrow C \rightarrow B \rightarrow D \rightarrow A$$

Example 6 Identifying cycles

Use Figure 8.5 to decide if the given cycle is Hamiltonian. If it is not, tell why.

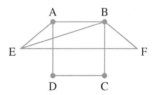

FIGURE 8.5 Network with 6 vertices

a. $A \rightarrow B \rightarrow C \rightarrow D \rightarrow A$ **b.** $C \rightarrow D \rightarrow A \rightarrow B \rightarrow F \rightarrow E \rightarrow A$
c. $D \rightarrow C \rightarrow B \rightarrow A \rightarrow E \rightarrow F$ **d.** $B \rightarrow C \rightarrow D \rightarrow A \rightarrow E \rightarrow F \rightarrow B$

Solution
a. This is not a Hamiltonian cycle because it does not visit each vertex, but repeats the same vertices, which is sometimes called a **loop.**
b. This is not a Hamiltonian cycle because it does not return to the starting point.
c. This is not a Hamiltonian cycle because it does not return to the starting point.
d. This is a Hamiltonian cycle.

It seems as if the problem of deciding whether a network has a Hamiltonian cycle should have a solution similar to that of the Euler circuit problem, but such is not the case. In fact, no solution is known at this time, and it is one of the great unsolved problems of mathematics. In this book, the best we will be able to do is a trial-and-error solution. If you are interested in seeing some of the different attempts at finding a solution to this problem, you can check the web address shown in the margin.

See **www.mathnature. com** for links for solving the TSP.

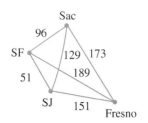

FIGURE 8.6 TSP for four cities

Example   **7**   **Find the shortest trip**   Pólya's Method

A salesman wants to visit four California cities, San Francisco, Sacramento, San Jose, and Fresno. Driving distances are shown in Figure 8.6. What is the shortest trip starting and ending in San Francisco that visits each of these cities?

Solution   Since the best we can do is to offer some possible methods of attack, we will use this example to help build your problem-solving skills. We use Pólya's problem-solving guidelines for this example.

Understand the Problem. Part of understanding the problem is to decide what we mean by the "best" solution. For this problem, let us assume it is the least miles traveled. We also note that, in terms of miles traveled, each route and its reverse are equivalent. That is,

SF → San Jose → Fresno → Sacramento → SF

is the same as

SF → Sacramento → Fresno → San Jose → SF

Devise a Plan. There are several possible methods of attack for this problem: for example *brute force* (listing all possible routes) and *nearest neighbor* (at each city, go to the nearest neighbor that has not been previously visited). Sometimes the nearest-neighbor plan will form a loop without going to some city, so we repair this problem using a method called the *sorted-edge method.* In the sorted-edge method, we sort the choices by selecting the nearest neighbor that does not form a loop.

Carry Out the Plan.
BRUTE FORCE:

$$SF \xrightarrow{96} S \xrightarrow{173} F \xrightarrow{151} SJ \xrightarrow{51} SF \qquad \text{Total: } 471 \text{ miles}$$
$$SF \xrightarrow{96} S \xrightarrow{129} SJ \xrightarrow{151} F \xrightarrow{189} SF \qquad \text{Total: } 565 \text{ miles}$$
$$SF \xrightarrow{51} SJ \xrightarrow{129} S \xrightarrow{173} F \xrightarrow{189} SF \qquad \text{Total: } 542 \text{ miles}$$

Here are the reverse trips (so we don't need to calculate these).

SF → SJ → F → S → SF
SF → F → SJ → S → SF
SF → F → S → SJ → SF

We see that 471 is the minimum number of miles.

NEAREST NEIGHBOR:

$$SF \xrightarrow{51} SJ \xrightarrow{129} S \xrightarrow{96} SF$$ A loop is formed; Fresno is not included because it is never the nearest neighbor if we start in San Francisco.

SORTED EDGE:

For this method, we sort the distances (edges of the graph) from smallest to largest: 51, 96, 129, 151, 173, and 189. This gives the following trip (skipping 96 and 151 because these choices would form a loop):

$$SF \xrightarrow{51} SJ \xrightarrow{129} S \xrightarrow{173} F \xrightarrow{189} SF \qquad \text{Total: } 542 \text{ miles}$$

Look Back. With this simple problem, it is easy to see that the best overall solution is a trip with 471 miles, but as you can imagine, for a larger number of cities the solution may not be at all obvious.

We summarize the **sorted-edge method** for finding an approximate solution to a traveling salesperson problem.

Sorted-Edge Method

Draw a graph showing the cities and the distances; identify the starting vertex.

Step 1   Choose the edge attached to the starting vertex that has the shortest distance or the lowest cost. Travel along this edge to the next vertex.

Step 2   At the second vertex, travel along the edge with the shortest distance or lowest cost. Do not choose a vertex that would lead to a vertex already visited.

Step 3   Continue until all vertices are visited and arriving back at the original vertex.

The sorted-edge method may not produce the optimal solution, so you should also check other methods. Since the brute-force method requires that we check all the routes, it is worthwhile to find a formula that tells us the number of routes we need to check. Note in Example 7 we found three possible routes (along with three reversals). Consider the next example which generalizes the number of routes we found by brute force in Example 7.

Example 8   Find the number of routes

a. How many routes are there for four cities, say, San Francisco, Sacramento, San Jose, and Fresno?

b. How many routes are there for n cities?

Solution

a. If we start in San Francisco, there are 3 cities to which we can travel. Then, by the fundamental counting principle, we have

$$3 \cdot 2 \cdot 1 = 6 \text{ routes}$$

Since half the routes are reversals of the others, we have

$$\frac{3 \cdot 2 \cdot 1}{2} = 3 \text{ routes}$$

b. Following the steps in part **a,** we note that from the first city there are $n - 1$ cities to visit, so (from the fundamental counting principle) there are

$$(n - 1)(n - 2)(n - 3) \cdot \cdots \cdot 3 \cdot 2 \cdot 1 \text{ routes}$$

and if we disregard reversals there are

$$\frac{(n - 1)(n - 2)(n - 3) \cdot \cdots \cdot 3 \cdot 2 \cdot 1}{2} \text{ routes}$$

 This formula will be used later in the text. CAUTION

Problem Set | 8.1

Level 1

1. IN YOUR OWN WORDS   Describe the Königsberg bridge problem.

2. IN YOUR OWN WORDS   Describe the floor-plan problem.

3. IN YOUR OWN WORDS   Describe the solution to the Königsberg bridge problem.

4. IN YOUR OWN WORDS   Describe the traveling salesperson problem.

5. IN YOUR OWN WORDS   Contrast Euler circuits and Hamiltonian cycles.

Which of the networks in Problems 6–11 are Euler circuits?
If a network can be traversed, show how.

6.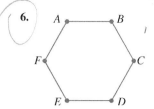

7.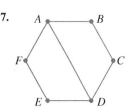

8.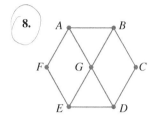

9.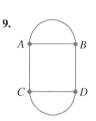

10.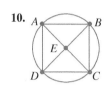

11.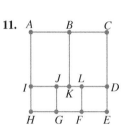

Which of the networks in Problems 12–17 have Hamiltonian
cycles? If a network has one, describe it.

12.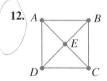

13.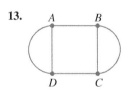

14.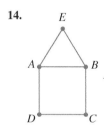

15.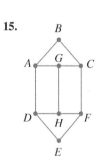

16.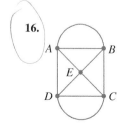

17.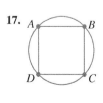

For which of the floor plans in Problems 18–23 can you pass
through all the rooms while going through each door exactly once?
If it is possible, show how it might be done.

18.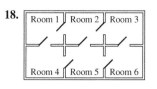

19.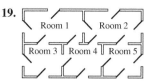

20.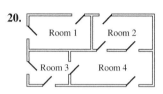

21.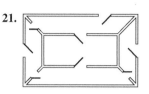

22.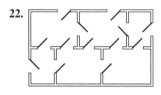

23.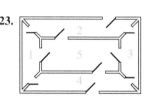

Level **2**

Which of the networks in Problems 24–27 are Euler circuits?
If a network can be traversed, show how. Note these are the same
networks as those given in Problems 28–31.

24.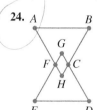

25.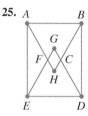

26.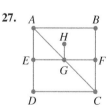

27.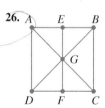

Which of the networks in Problems 28–31 have Hamiltonian
cycles? If a network has one, describe it. Notice these are the same
networks as those given in Problems 24–27.

28.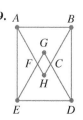

29.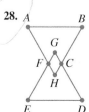

30.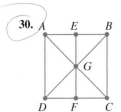

31.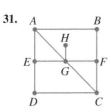

32. After Euler solved the Königsberg bridge problem, an eighth bridge was built as shown in Figure 8.7. Is this network traversable? If so, show how.

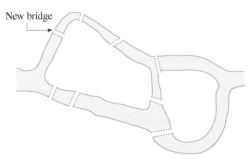

FIGURE 8.7 Königsberg with eight bridges

33. **HISTORICAL QUEST**   **Traveler's Dodecahedron**   This problem was sold in the last half of the 19th century as a puzzle known as the "Traveler's Dodecahedron" or "A Voyage 'Round the World." It consisted of 20 pegs (called *cities*), and the point of the puzzle was to use string to connect each peg only once, arriving back at the same peg you started from. Find a route (starting at Brussels—labeled 1) that visits each of the 20 cities on the dodecahedron shown in Figure 8.8.

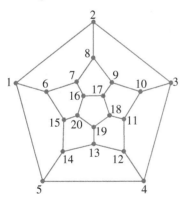

FIGURE 8.8 Hamilton's "traveler's dodecahedron"

34. **HISTORICAL QUEST**   Is there an Euler circuit for the Traveler's Dodecahedron shown in Figure 8.8? If so, show it.

35. Is there an Euler circuit for the graph shown in Figure 8.9?

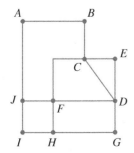

FIGURE 8.9 Network problem

36. Suppose you want to get from point *A* to point *B* in New York City (see Figure 8.10), and also suppose you wish to cross over each of the six bridges exactly once. Is it possible? If so, show one such path.

Bridge 1: George Washington Bridge
Bridge 2: Triborough Bridge
Bridge 3: Queensboro (59th Street) Bridge
Bridge 4: Williamsburg Bridge
Bridge 5: Manhattan Bridge
Bridge 6: Brooklyn Bridge

FIGURE 8.10 New York City

37. A simplified map of New York City, showing the subway connections between Manhattan and The Bronx, Queens, and Brooklyn, is shown in Figure 8.11. Is it possible to travel on the New York subway system and use each subway exactly once? You can visit each borough (The Bronx, Queens, Brooklyn, or Manhattan) as many times as you wish.

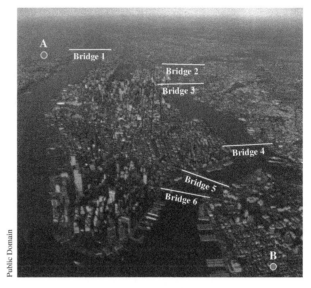

FIGURE 8.11 New York City subways

38. A portion of London's Underground transit system is shown in Figure 8.12. Is it possible to travel the entire system and visit each station while taking each route exactly once?

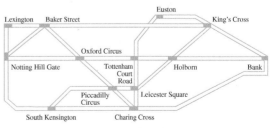

FIGURE 8.12 London Underground

39. In Massachusetts there is a re-creation of an 1830s New England village called Old Sturbridge Village. A map is shown in Figure 8.13. Is it possible to stroll the streets marked in color? Give reasons for your answer.

FIGURE 8.13 Old Sturbridge Village

40. Reconsider the question in Problem 39 if the church across from the Knight Store is opened.

Level 3

41. The edges of a cube form a three-dimensional network. Are the edges of a cube traversable?

42. A saleswoman wants to visit each of the cities New York City, Boston, Cleveland, and Washington, D.C. Driving distances are as shown in Figure 8.14. What is the shortest trip starting in New York that visits each of these cities?

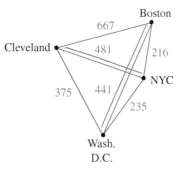

FIGURE 8.14 TSP for four cities

Find a solution using the brute-force method.

43. Repeat Problem 42 using the indicated method.
   a. Find a solution if possible using the nearest-neighbor method.
   b. Find a solution if possible using the sorted-edge method.

44. A salesperson wants to visit each of the cities Denver, St. Louis, Los Angeles, and New Orleans. Driving distances are as shown in Figure 8.15. What is the shortest trip starting in Denver that visits each of these cities?

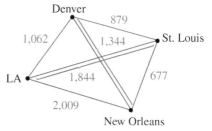

FIGURE 8.15 TSP for four cities

   a. Find a solution if possible using the nearest-neighbor method.
   b. Find a solution if possible using the sorted-edge method.

45. Repeat Problem 44 using the brute-force method.

46. Count the number of vertices, edges (arcs), and regions for each of Problems 6–17. Let V = number of vertices, E = number of edges, and R = number of regions. Compare $V + R$ with E. Make a conjecture relating V, R, and E. This relationship is called *Euler's formula for networks*.

Problem Solving 3

47. The saleswoman in Problem 42 needs to add Atlanta to her itinerary. Driving distances are shown. What is the shortest trip starting in New York that visits each of these cities?

	A	B	C	NYC	D.C.
A	—	1,115	780	887	634
B	1,115	—	667	216	441
C	780	667	—	481	375
NYC	887	216	481	—	235
D.C.	634	441	375	233	—

48. A quality control inspector must visit franchises in Atlanta, Boston, Chicago, Dallas, and Minneapolis. Since this inspection must be monthly, the inspector, who lives in Chicago, would like to find the most efficient route (in terms of distances). Driving distances are shown. What is the most efficient route?

	A	B	C	D	M
A	—	1,115	717	691	1,131
B	1,115	—	1,013	1,845	1,619
C	717	1,013	—	937	420
D	691	1,845	937	—	963
M	1,131	1,619	420	963	—

49. What is the sum of the measures of the angles of a tetrahedron? *Hint:* Consider the sum of the measures of the face angles of a cube. A cube has six square faces, and since each face has four right angles, the sum of the measures of the angles on each face is $360°$; hence, the sum of the measures of the face angles of a cube is $6(360°) = 2,160°$.

50. What is the sum of the measures of the angles of a pentagonal prism? (See Figure 8.16.)

FIGURE 8.16 Pentagonal prism

51. On a planet far, far away, Luke finds himself in a strange building with hexagon-shaped rooms as shown in Figure 8.17.

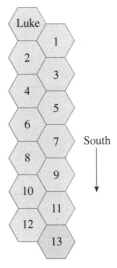

FIGURE 8.17 Strange room arrangement

   In his search for the princess, Luke always moves to an adjacent room and always in a southerly direction.
   a. How many paths are there to room 1?
      to room 2?
      to room 3?
      to room 4?
   b. How many paths are there to room 10?
   c. How many paths are there to room 13?

52. How many paths are there to room *n* in Problem 51?

53. Emil Torday told the story of seeing some African children playing with a pattern in the sand as shown in Figure 8.18.

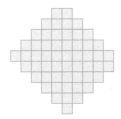

FIGURE 8.18 African sand game

   *The children were drawing, and I was at once asked to perform certain impossible tasks; great was their joy when the white man failed to accomplish them.**

One task was to trace the figure in the sand with one continuous sweep of the finger.

*Quoted by Claudia Zaslavsky in *Africa Counts* (Boston: Prindle, Weber, & Schmidt, 1973) from *On the Trail of the Bushongo* by Emil Torday.

a. What is the children's secret for successfully drawing this pattern?
b. Draw this figure; why is it difficult to do this without knowing something about networks?

54. HISTORICAL QUEST
About a century ago, August Möbius made the discovery that, if you take a strip of paper (see Figure 8.19), give it a single half-twist, and paste the ends together, you will have a piece of paper

FIGURE 8.19 Möbius strip

with only one side! Construct a Möbius strip, and verify that it has only one side. How many edges does it have?

55. Construct a Möbius strip (see Problem 54). Cut the strip in half down the center. Describe the result.

56. Construct a Möbius strip (see Problem 54). Cut the strip in half down the center. Cut it in half again. Describe the result.

57. Construct a Möbius strip (see Problem 54). Cut the strip along a path that is one-third the distance from the edge. Describe the result.

58. Construct a Möbius strip (see Problem 54). Mark a point *A* on the strip. Draw an arc from *A* around the strip until you return to the point *A*. Do you think you could connect *any* two points on the sheet of paper without lifting your pencil?

59. Take a strip of paper 11 in. by 1 in., and give it three half-twists; join the ends together. How many edges and sides does this band have? What happens if you cut down the center of this piece?

60. What is a Klein bottle? Examine the bottle shown in Figure 8.20.

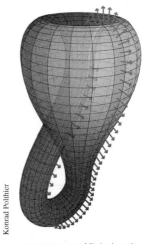

FIGURE 8.20 Klein bottle

Can you build or construct a physical model? You can use the limerick as a hint.

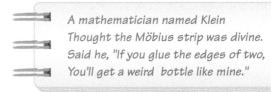

A mathematician named Klein
Thought the Möbius strip was divine.
Said he, "If you glue the edges of two,
You'll get a weird bottle like mine."

8.2 | Trees and Minimum Spanning Trees

 A circuit could be defined as a path/route that begins and ends at the same vertex.

In the last section, we considered graphs with circuits: an Euler circuit (which is a round trip path traveling all the edges) and a Hamiltonian cycle (a path that visits each vertex exactly once). In this section, we consider another kind of graph, called a *tree*, which does not have a circuit.

Trees

Let us begin with an example.

Example 1 | Draw a family tree

Suppose you wish to draw a family tree showing yourself, your parents, and your maternal and paternal grandparents.

Solution One possibility for showing this family tree is shown in Figure 8.21.

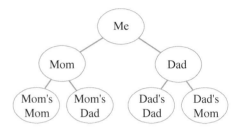

FIGURE 8.21 Personal family tree

Simplified family tree

The family tree shown in Example 1 has two obvious properties. It is a connected graph because there is at least one path between each pair of vertices, and there are no circuits in this family tree. A simplified tree diagram for Example 1 is shown in the margin.

> **Tree**
>
> A *tree* is a graph that is connected and has no circuits.

Example 2 | Determine if a network is a tree

Determine which of the given graphs are trees.

a.    b.    c.

d.   e.

 In a tree, there is always exactly one path from each vertex in the graph to any other vertex in the graph. We illustrate this property of trees with the following example.

Solution
a. This is not a tree because it is not connected.
b. This is a tree.
c. This is a tree.
d. This is not a tree because there is at least one circuit.
e. There is a circuit, so it is not a tree.

Example **3**   **Sprinkler system design**

Ben wishes to install a sprinkler system to water the areas shown in Figure 8.22. Show how this might be done.

FIGURE 8.22 Locations of a faucet and sprinkler heads

Solution   We know there is at least one way to build a tree from each vertex (in this case, the faucet, labeled F). We show one such way in Figure 8.23.

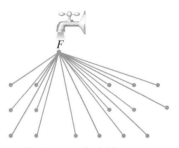

FIGURE 8.23 Sprinkler system

The solution shown for Example 3 may or may not be an efficient solution to the sprinkler system problem. Suppose we connect the vertices in Example 3 without regard to whether the graph is a tree, as shown in Figure 8.24a. Next, we remove edges until the resulting graph is a tree. A tree that is created from another graph by removing edges but keeping a path to each vertex is called a **spanning tree.** Can you form a spanning tree for the graph in Figure 8.24a? If you think about it for a moment, you will see that any connected graph will have a spanning tree, and that if the original graph has at least one circuit, then it will have several different spanning trees. Figure 8.24b shows a spanning tree for the sprinkler problem of Example 3.

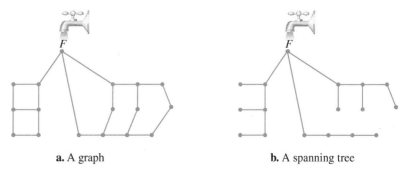

a. A graph   **b.** A spanning tree

FIGURE 8.24 Comparison of a graph and spanning tree for Example 3

Example   **4**   **Find spanning trees**

Find two different spanning trees for each of the given graphs.

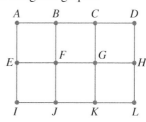

Solution   Since a spanning tree must have a path connecting all vertices, but cannot have any circuits, we remove edges (one at a time) without moving any of the vertices and without creating a disconnected graph. We show two different possibilities for each of the given graphs, while noting that others are possible.

a. This graph has three circuits: $A \to B \to C \to A$, $C \to D \to E \to C$, and $E \to F \to G \to E$. To obtain a spanning tree, we must break up each of these circuits, but at the same time not disconnect the graph. There are many ways we could do this. In the first tree we remove edges $\overline{BC}$, $\overline{CE}$, and $\overline{EF}$. In the second tree, we remove edges $\overline{AB}$, $\overline{CD}$, and $\overline{FG}$, as shown in Figure 8.25.

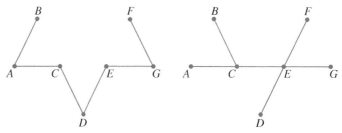

FIGURE 8.25   Spanning tree for graph a

b. There are many circuits and two possible spanning trees, as shown in Figure 8.26.

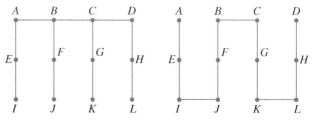

FIGURE 8.26   Spanning tree for graph b

Minimum Spanning Trees

As we can see from Example 4, there may be several spanning trees. Sometimes the length of each edge is associated with a cost or a length, called the edge's **weight.** In such cases we are often interested in minimizing the cost or the distance. If the edges of a graph have weight, then we refer to the graph as a **weighted graph.**

> **Minimum Spanning Tree**
>
> A **minimum spanning tree** is a spanning tree for which the sum of the numbers associated with the edges is a minimum.

Example **5** **Find minimum cost**   *Pólya's Method*

A portion of the Santa Rosa Junior College campus, along with some walkways (lengths shown in feet) connecting the buildings, is shown in Figure 8.27.

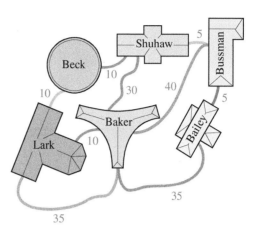

FIGURE 8.27 Portion of campus

Suppose the decision is made to connect each building with a brick walkway, and the only requirement is that there be one brick walkway connecting each of the buildings. We assume that the cost of installing a brick walkway is $100/ft. What is the minimum cost for this project?

Solution   We use Pólya's problem-solving guidelines for this example.

Understand the Problem. To make sure we understand the problem, we consider a simpler problem. Consider the simple graph shown in the margin with costs shown in color. We consider the vertices to be buildings since the only requirement is that there be one brick walkway connecting each of the buildings. To find the best way to construct the walkways, we consider minimum spanning trees. Since this is a circuit, we can break this circuit in one of three ways: eliminate one of the sides, *AB*, *BC*, or *AC*.

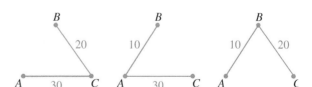

We see that the cost associated with each of these trees is:

$$20 + 30 = 50 \qquad 10 + 30 = 40 \qquad 10 + 20 = 30$$

The minimal cost for this simplified problem is 30.

Devise a Plan. We will carry out the steps for the Santa Rosa campus as follows: Look at Figure 8.27 and find the side with the smallest weight (because we wish to keep the smaller weights). We see there are two sides labeled 5; select either of these. Next, select a side with the smallest remaining weight (it is also 5). Continue by each time selecting the smallest remaining weight until every vertex is connected, but *do not select any edge that creates a circuit.*

Carry Out the Plan. Following this procedure, we select both of the edges labeled 5, as well as the three labeled 10. The resulting pathways are shown in Figure 8.28.

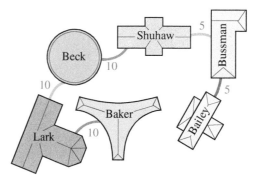

FIGURE 8.28 Minimum spanning tree

We see that the graph in Figure 8.28 is a minimum spanning tree, so the total distance is

$$5 + 5 + 10 + 10 + 10 = 40$$

with a total cost of

$$40 \times \$100 = \$4,000$$

Look Back. We can try other possible routes connecting all of the buildings, but in each case, the cost is more than \$4,000.

The process used in Example 5 illustrates a procedure called **Kruskal's algorithm.**

Pay attention to this procedure (algorithm).

There are many websites that illustrate Kruskal's algorithm. You might wish to explore this idea by checking the links at **www.mathnature.com.**

Kruskal's Algorithm

To construct a minimum spanning tree from a weighted graph, use the following procedure:

Step 1   Select any edge with minimum weight.

Step 2   Select the next edge with minimum weight among those not yet selected.

Step 3   Continue to choose edges of minimum weight from those not yet selected, but make sure not to select any edge that forms a circuit.

Step 4   Repeat the process until the tree connects all the vertices of the original graph.

Example   6   **Find the minimum spanning tree**

Use Kruskal's algorithm to find the minimum spanning tree for the weighted graph in Figure 8.29. The numbers represent hundreds of dollars.

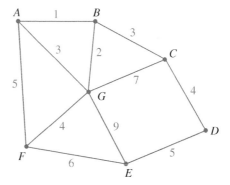

FIGURE 8.29 Find the minimum spanning tree

Solution

Step 1 Choose the side with weight 1 (see Figure 8.30a).

Step 2 Choose the side with weight 2 (Figure 8.30b).

Step 3 Choose the side with weight 3 (Figure 8.30c). Do not connect *AG* because that would form a circuit. Continue with this process to select the two sides with weights of 4 (Figure 8.30c).

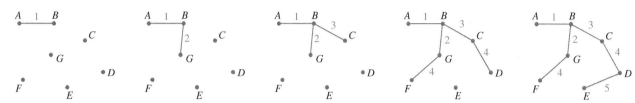

FIGURE 8.30 Steps in finding a minimum spanning tree

Step 4 When we connect the side with the next lowest weight, namely, *ED* with weight 5, we know we are finished because we now have a tree with all of the vertices connected.

We can now calculate the weight of this tree:

$$1 + 2 + 3 + 4 + 4 + 5 = 19$$

Since these weights are in hundreds of dollars, the weight of the minimum spanning tree is $1,900.

The next example is adapted from a standardized test given in the United Kingdom in 1995.

Example 7 Cost of building a pipeline

A company is considering building a gas pipeline network to connect seven wells (*A, B, C, D, E, F, G*) to a processing plant *H*. The possible pipelines that it can construct and their costs (in hundreds of thousands of dollars) are listed in the following table.

Pipeline	AB	AD	AE	BC	BE	BF	CG	DE	DF	EH	FG	FH
Cost	23	19	17	15	30	27	10	14	20	28	11	35

What pipelines do you suggest be built and what is the total cost of your suggested pipeline network?

Solution   Begin by drawing a graph to represent the data. This graph is shown in Figure 8.31.

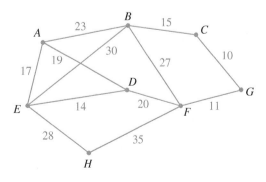

FIGURE 8.31 Building a gas pipeline

We now apply Kruskal's algorithm (in table form).

	Link	*Cost*	*Decision*
Step 1	CG	10	Smallest value: add to tree
Step 2	FG	11	Next smallest value; add to tree
Step 3	DE	14	Add to tree; note that the graph does not need to be connected at this step.
	BC	15	Add to tree
	AE	17	Add to tree
	AD	19	Reject; it forms a circuit *ADE*
	DF	20	Add to tree
	AB	23	Reject; it forms a circuit *ABCGFDE*
	BF	27	Reject; it forms a circuit *BFGC*
Step 4	EH	28	Add to tree; stop because all vertices are now included.

The completed minimal spanning tree is shown in Figure 8.32.

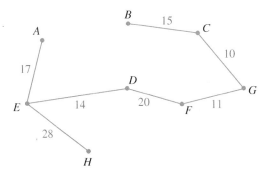

FIGURE 8.32 Minimal spanning tree for pipeline problem

The minimal cost is

$$10 + 11 + 14 + 15 + 17 + 20 + 28 = 115$$

so, the cost of the pipeline is $115,000.

Note in Example 7 that there were eight given vertices, and that there were seven links added to form the minimal spanning tree. This is a general result.

Number-of-vertices-and-edges-in-a-tree theorem

If a graph is a tree with n vertices, then the number of edges is $n - 1$.

In Problem 59, you are asked to explain why this seems plausible. There is another related property that says the converse of this property holds for connected graphs. If the number of edges is one less than the number of vertices in a connected graph, then the graph is a tree.

Problem Set   8.2

1. **IN YOUR OWN WORDS**   What do we mean by a tree?

2. **IN YOUR OWN WORDS**   What do we mean by a spanning tree?

3. **IN YOUR OWN WORDS**   State Kruskal's algorithm. When would you use this algorithm?

Determine whether each of the graphs in Problems 4–11 is a tree. If it is not, explain why.

4.

5.

6.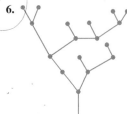

7.

8.

9.

10.

11.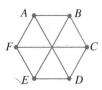

Find two different spanning trees for each graph in Problems 12–19.

12.
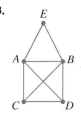

13.
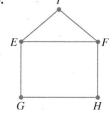

14.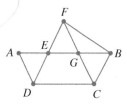

15.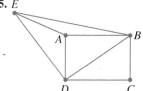

16.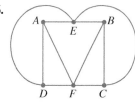

17.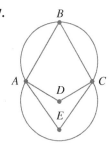

18.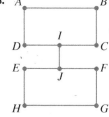

19.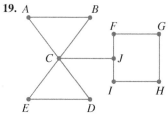

Find all the spanning trees for the graphs in Problems 20–25.

20.

21.

22.

23.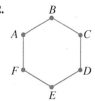

24.

25.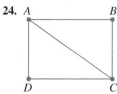

In chemistry, molecules are represented as ball-and-stick models or by bond-line diagrams. For example, the ball-and-stick model for ethane is shown in Figure 8.33a and the bond-line diagram is shown in Figure 8.33b. A corresponding tree diagram is shown in Figure 8.33c.

a. Ball-and-stick model   **b.** Bond-line drawing   **c.** Tree diagram

FIGURE 8.33 Ethane molecule

Draw graphs for each of the molecules in Problems 26–31. If the graph does not form a tree, tell why.

26. Methane

27. Propane

28. Butane

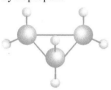

29. Isobutane

30. Cyclopropane

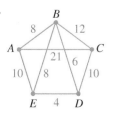

31. Cyclohexane

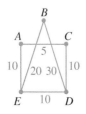

Find the minimum spanning tree for each of the graphs in Problems 32–41.

32.

33.

34.

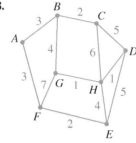

35.

36.

37.

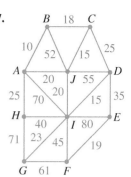

38.

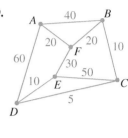

39.

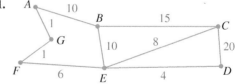

40.

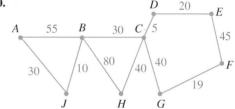

41.

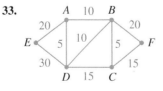

42. A chemist is studying a chemical compound with a treelike structure that contains 39 atoms. How many chemical bonds are there in this molecule?

43. A chemist is studying a chemical compound with a treelike structure that contains 65 atoms. How many chemical bonds are there in this molecule?

44. A website called "The Oracle of Bacon" is hosted by the University of Virginia. (Go to **www.mathnature.com** for a link to this site, if you wish.) It links other actors to Kevin Bacon by the movies in which the actors appeared. For example, I entered the movie star from *Gone with the Wind*, Clark Gable, and the Oracle told me that Clark Gable had a Bacon number of two because Clark Gable was in the 1953 movie *Mogambo* with Donald Siden, and Donald Siden was in the 1995 movie *Balto* with Kevin Bacon. I tried it again with Will Smith, and the Oracle said that he also had a Bacon number of two since he was in the 2000 movie *The Legend of Bagger Vance* with Charlize Theron, who in turn was in the 2002 movie *Trapped* with Kevin Bacon. Robert De Niro has a Bacon number of one because he was in the 1996 movie *Sleepers* with Kevin Bacon. This trivia game was started by Albright College students Craig Fass, Brian Turtle, and Mike Ginelli, who hypothesized that all actors—living or dead—have a Bacon number of 6 or less. If you could draw a diagram of the relationships between Kevin Bacon and other actors, would the result be a tree?

45. Suppose you use the Yahoo search engine to do research for a term paper. You start on the Yahoo page and follow the links. You decide to keep a record of the sites you visit. If you keep the record as a graph, will it form a tree?

46. Use a tree to show the following family tree. You have two children, Shannon and Melissa. Shannon has three children, Søren, Thoren, and Floren. Melissa has two children, Hannah and Banana.

47. Use a tree to show the following management relationships for a college. The positions are a college president; an academic vice president, who reports directly to the president and who supervises six academic deans, each of whom supervises three departments; a vice president for business services, who reports directly to the president and who supervises the personnel office, scholarships and grants, as well as the bookstore and food services; and finally, a vice president of operations, who is in charge of supervising facilities, grounds, and certified staff, and who also reports directly to the president.

48. How many edges are there in a tree with 15 vertices?

49. How many vertices are there in a tree with 48 edges?

50. Suppose you wish to install a drip sprinkler system and need to run a drip water line to five areas, as shown in the given graph. The numbers show the distances in feet. What is the smallest number of feet of drip hose necessary to install?

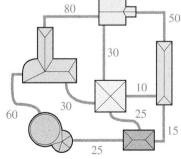

51. Suppose your college is planning to install some covered walkways connecting six buildings as shown in the following map. The plan is to allow a person to walk to any building under cover, and the numbers shown on the map represent distances measured in feet. If the covered walkway costs $350/ft, what is the minimum cost for this project?

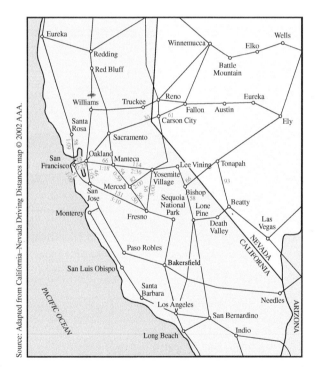

52. A mutual water system obtained estimates for installing water pipes among its respective properties (labeled *A, B, C, D,* and *E*). These amounts (in dollars) are shown in color in Figure 8.34. Which lines should the mutual water system install to minimize the cost?

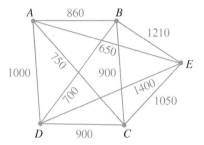

FIGURE 8.34 Water line cost estimates

53. The map in Figure 8.35 shows driving distances and times between California and Nevada cities. Use Kruskal's algorithm to find the minimum spanning tree for the following cities: Santa Rosa, San Francisco, Oakland, Manteca, Yosemite Village, Merced, Fresno, and San Jose.

FIGURE 8.35 California-Nevada driving distances

54. Use the map in Figure 8.35 and Kruskal's algorithm to construct the minimum spanning tree for the cities of Reno, Carson City, Lee Vining, Fallon, Austin, Tonopah, Bishop, Beatty, Death Valley, and Lone Pine.

55. Suppose *XYZ* drilling has four oil wells that must be connected via pipelines to a storage tank. The cost of each pipeline (in millions of dollars) is shown in the following table:

From\To	#1	#2	#3	#4	Tank
#1	—	1	4	2	3
#2	1	—	3	1	2
#3	4	3	—	1	4
#4	2	1	1	—	1
Tank	3	2	4	1	—

a. Represent this information with a weighted graph.
b. Use Kruskal's algorithm to find a minimum spanning tree.
c. What is the minimum cost that links together all of the wells and the tank?

56. Consider the following table showing costs between vertices.

From\To	#1	#2	#3	#4	Tank (#5)
#1	—	3	7	3	2
#2	3	—	6	8	5
#3	7	6	—	10	9
#4	3	8	10	—	4
Tank (#5)	2	5	9	4	—

a. Represent this information with a weighted graph.
b. Use Kruskal's algorithm to find a minimum spanning tree.
c. What is the minimum cost that links together all of the vertices?

57. Suppose a network is to be built connecting the Florida cities of Tallahassee (*T*), Jacksonville (*J*), St. Petersburg *(P)*, Orlando *(O)*, and Miami (*M*). The given numbers show the miles between the cities.

From\To	T	J	P	O	M
T	—	172	249	253	476
J	172	—	219	160	410
P	249	219	—	105	237
O	253	160	105	—	252
M	476	410	237	252	—

a. Represent this information with a weighted graph.
b. Use Kruskal's algorithm to find a minimum spanning tree.
c. What is the minimum cost that links together all of the cities if the cost is \$85/mi?

58. Suppose a network is to be built connecting the cities of Norfolk (*N*), Raleigh (*R*), Charlotte (*C*), Atlanta (*A*), and Savannah (*S*). The given numbers show the miles between cities.

From\To	N	R	C	A	S
N	—	170	333	597	519
R	170	—	175	427	358
C	333	175	—	250	249
A	597	427	250	—	256
S	519	358	249	256	—

a. Represent this information with a weighted graph.
b. Use Kruskal's algorithm to find a minimum spanning tree.
c. What is the minimum cost that links together all of the cities if the cost is \$205/mi?

59. *Number-of-Vertices-and-Edges-in-a-Tree Property*
a. State the number-of-vertices-and-edges-in-a-tree theorem.
b. Consider a tree with one vertex. What is the number of edges? Does the property hold in this case?
c. Consider a tree with two vertices. How many edges can you have and still have a tree? Explain why you cannot have two or more edges.

d. Consider a tree with three vertices. How many edges can you have and still have a tree? Explain why you cannot have three or more edges.

60. **HISTORICAL QUEST**   In 1889, Arthur Cayley proved that a complete graph with *n* vertices has n^{n-2} spanning trees.
a. How many spanning trees are there for a complete graph with 3 vertices, according to Cayley's theorem? Verify this number by drawing a complete graph with 3 vertices and then finding all the spanning trees.
b. How many spanning trees are there for a complete graph with 4 vertices, according to Cayley's theorem? Verify this number by drawing a complete graph with 4 vertices and then finding all the spanning trees.
c. How many spanning trees are there for a complete graph with 5 vertices?
d. How many spanning trees are there for a complete graph with 6 vertices?

8.3 | Topology and Fractals

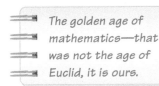

The golden age of mathematics—that was not the age of Euclid, it is ours.

A brief look at the history of geometry illustrates, in a very graphical way, the historical evolution of many mathematical ideas and the nature of changes in mathematical thought. The geometry of the Greeks included very concrete notions of space and geometry. They considered space to be a locus in which objects could move freely about, and their geometry, known as Euclidean geometry, was a geometry of congruence. In this section we investigate two very different branches of geometry that question, or alter, the way we think of space and dimension.

Topology

In the 17th century, space came to be conceptualized as a set of points, and, with the non-Euclidean geometries of the 19th century, mathematicians gave up the notion that geometry had to describe the physical universe. The existence of multiple geometries was accepted, but space was still thought of as a geometry of congruence. The emphasis shifted to sets, and geometry was studied as a mathematical system. Space could be conceived as a set of points together with an abstract set of relations in which these points are involved. The time was right for geometry to be considered as the theory of such a space, and in 1895 Jules-Henri Poincaré published a book using this notion of space and geometry in a systematic development. This book was called *Vorstudien zur Topologie (Introductory Studies in Topology)*. However, topology was not the invention of any one person, and the names of Cantor, Euler, Fréchet, Hausdorff, Möbius, and Riemann are associated with the origins of **topology.** Today it is a broad and fundamental branch of mathematics.

To obtain an idea about the nature of topology, consider a device called a *geoboard,* which you may have used in elementary school. Suppose we stretch one rubber band over the pegs to form a square and another to form a triangle, as shown in Figure 8.36.

Historical NOTE

The set theory of Cantor (see the Historical Note on page 50) provided a basis for topology, which was presented for the first time by Jules-Henri Poincaré (1854–1912) in *Analysis Situs*. A second branch of topology was added in 1914 by Felix Hausdorff (1868–1942) in *Basic Features of Set Theory*. Earlier mathematicians, including Euler, Möbius, and Klein, had touched on some of the ideas we study in topology, but the field was given its major impetus by L. E. J. Brouwer (1882–1966). Today much research is being done in topology, which has practical applications in astronomy, chemistry, economics, and electrical circuitry.

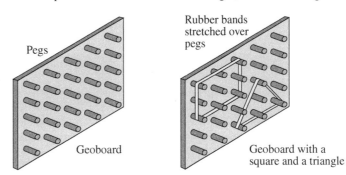

FIGURE 8.36 Creating geometric figures with a geoboard

In high school geometry, the square and the triangle in Figure 8.36 would be seen as different. However, in topology, these figures are viewed as the same object. Topology is concerned with discovering and analyzing the essential similarities and differences between sets and figures. One important idea is called *elastic motion*, which includes bending, stretching, shrinking, or distorting the figure in any way that allows the points to remain distinct. It does not include cutting a figure unless we "sew up" the cut *exactly* as it was before.

> ### Topologically Equivalent Figures
> Two geometric figures are said to be **topologically equivalent** if one figure can be elastically twisted, stretched, bent, shrunk, or straightened into the same shape as the other. One can cut the figure, provided at some point the cut edges are "glued" back together again to be exactly the same as before.

Rubber bands can be stretched into a wide variety of shapes. All forms in Figure 8.37 are topologically equivalent. We say that a curve is **planar** if it lies flat in a plane.

FIGURE 8.37 Topologically equivalent curves

The children and their distorted images are topologically equivalent.

All of the curves in Figure 8.37 are *planar simple closed curves*. A curve is **closed** if it divides the plane into three disjoint subsets: the set of points on the curve itself, the set of points *interior* to the curve, and the set of points *exterior* to the curve. It is said to be **simple** if it has only one interior. Sometimes a simple closed curve is called a **Jordan curve.** Notice that, to pass from a point in the interior to a point in the exterior, it is necessary to cross over the given curve an odd number of times. This property remains the same for any distortion and is therefore called an *invariant* property.

Two-dimensional surfaces in a three-dimensional space are classified according to the number of cuts possible without slicing the object into two pieces. The number of cuts that can be made without cutting the figure into two pieces is called its **genus.** The genus of an object is the number of holes in the object. (See Figure 8.38.)

Genus 0
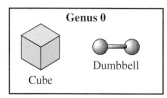
Cube   Dumbbell

Genus 1
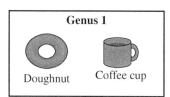
Doughnut   Coffee cup

Genus 2
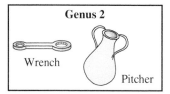
Wrench   Pitcher

Genus 3 or more
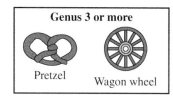
Pretzel   Wagon wheel

FIGURE 8.38 Genus of the surfaces of some everyday objects. Look at the number of holes in the objects.

For example, no cut can be made through a sphere without cutting it into two pieces, so its genus is 0. In three dimensions, you can generally classify the genus of an object by looking at the number of holes the object has. A doughnut, for example, has genus 1 since it has 1 hole. In mathematical terms, we say it has genus 1 since only one closed cut can be made without dividing it into two pieces. All figures with the same genus are topologically equivalent. Figure 8.39 shows that a doughnut and a coffee cup are topologically equivalent, and Figure 8.40 shows objects of genus 0, genus 1, and genus 2.

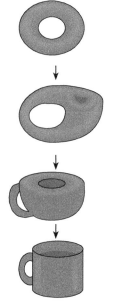

FIGURE 8.39 A doughnut is topologically equivalent to a coffee cup

A sphere has genus 0.

A doughnut has genus 1.

Two holes allow two cuts, so this form has genus 2.

FIGURE 8.40 Genus of a sphere, a doughnut, and a two-holed doughnut

Four-Color Problem

One of the earliest and most famous problems in topology is the **four-color problem.** It was first stated in 1850 by the English mathematician Francis Guthrie. It states that any map on a plane or a sphere can be colored with at most four colors so that any two countries that share a common boundary are colored differently. (See Figure 8.41, for example.)

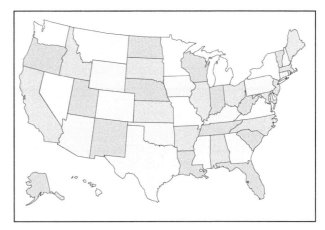

FIGURE 8.41 Every map can be colored with four colors.

All attempts to prove this conjecture had failed until Kenneth Appel and Wolfgang Haken of the University of Illinois announced their proof in 1976. The university honored their discovery using the illustrated postmark.

Since the theorem was first stated, many unsuccessful attempts have been made to prove it. The first published "incorrect proof" is due to Kempe, who enumerated four cases and disposed of each. However, in 1990, an error was found in one of those cases, which it turned out was subcategorized as 1,930 different cases. Appel and Haken reduced the map to a graph as Euler did with the Königsberg bridge problem. They reduced each country to a point and used computers to check every possible arrangement of four colors for each case, requiring more than 1,200 hours of computer time to verify the proof.

Fractal Geometry

One of the newest and most exciting branches of mathematics is called **fractal geometry.** Fractals have been used recently to produce realistic computer images in the movies, and the new supercrisp high-definition television (HDTV) uses fractals to squeeze the HDTV signal into existing broadcast channels. In February 1989, Iterated System, Inc., began marketing a $32,500 software package for creating models of biological systems from fractals. Today you can find hundreds of fractal generators online, most of them free.

Fractals were created to Benoit B. Mandelbrot over 30 years ago, but have become important only in the last few years because of computers. Mandelbrot's first book on fractals appeared in 1975; in it he used computer graphics to illustrate the fractals. The

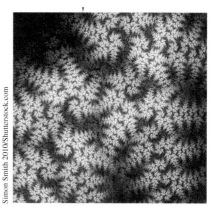

FIGURE 8.42 Fractal images of a mountainscape (generated by Richard Voss) and fern

Historical NOTE

**Benoit Mandelbrot
(1924–2010)**

Professor Mandelbrot first conceived of fractals over 30 years ago, and they became widely appreciated when computers could be used to apply the procedures of fractal geometry. He received his Master's degree at Cal Tech and his Ph.D. from the University of Paris. He was a professor at Yale when he did his formal work with fractals. He died on October 14, 2010.

book inspired Richard Voss, a physicist at IBM, to create stunning landscapes, earthly and otherworldly (see Figure 8.42). "Without computer graphics, this work could have been completely disregarded," Mandelbrot acknowledges.

What exactly is a fractal? We are used to describing the dimension of an object without having a precise definition: A point has 0 dimension; a line, 1 dimension; a plane, 2 dimensions; and the world around us, 3 dimensions. We can even stretch our imagination to believe that Einstein used a four-dimensional model. However, what about a dimension of 1.5? Fractals allow us to define objects with noninteger dimension. For example, a jagged line is given a fractional dimension between 1 and 2, and the exact value is determined by the line's "jaggedness."

We will illustrate this concept by constructing the most famous fractal curve, the so-called "snowflake curve."* Start with a line segment $\overline{AB}$:

A _____ B

Here we say the number of segments is $N = 1$; $r = 1$ is the length of this segment.

Divide this segment into thirds, by marking locations C and D:

A _____ C _____ D _____ B $N = 3$; $r = \frac{1}{3}$ is the length of each segment.

Now construct an equilateral triangle $\triangle CED$ on the middle segment and then remove the middle segment $\overline{CD}$.

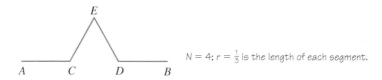

$N = 4$; $r = \frac{1}{3}$ is the length of each segment.

Now, repeat the above steps for each segment:

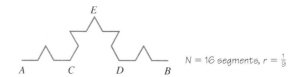

$N = 16$ segments, $r = \frac{1}{9}$

* If you want to investigate the snowflake curve and fractal further, see Group Project G29, p. 423.

Again, repeat the process:

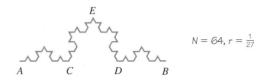

$$N = 64, r = \frac{1}{27}$$

If you repeat this process (until you reach any desired level of complexity), you have a fractal curve with dimension between 1 and 2.

Mandelbrot defined the dimension as follows:

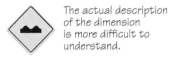

The actual description of the dimension is more difficult to understand.

$$D = \frac{\log N}{\log \frac{1}{r}}$$

where N is any integer and r is the length of each segment.[*] For the illustrations above, we can calculate the dimension:

$$N = 3, \; r = \frac{1}{3}; \; D = 1$$

$$N = 4, \; r = \frac{1}{3}; \; D \approx 1.26$$

$$N = 16, \; r = \frac{1}{9}; \; D \approx 1.26$$

$$N = 64, \; r = \frac{1}{27}; \; D \approx 1.26$$

FIGURE 8.43 Escher print: *Circle Limit III*

Tessellations

The construction of the snowflake curve reminds us of another interesting mathematical construction, called a **tessellation.** By skillfully altering a basic polygon (such as a triangle, rectangle, or hexagon), the artist Escher was able to produce artistic tessellations such as that shown in Figure 8.43.

We can describe a procedure for reproducing a simple tessellation based on the Escher print in Figure 8.43.

Step 1 Start with an equilateral triangle $\triangle ABC$. Mark off the same curve on sides $\overline{AB}$ and $\overline{AC}$, as shown in Figure 8.44. Mark off another curve on side $\overline{BC}$ that is symmetric about the midpoint P. If you choose the curves carefully, as Escher did, an interesting figure suitable for tessellating will be formed.

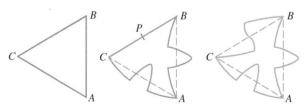

FIGURE 8.44 Tessellation pattern

Step 2 Six of these figures accurately fit together around a point, forming a hexagonal array. If you trace and cut one of these basic figures, you can continue the tessellation over as large an area as you wish, as shown in Figure 8.45.

FIGURE 8.45 Tessellation pattern

[*]Mandelbrot defined r as the ratio L/N, where L is the sum of the lengths of the N line segments. We will discuss logarithms in Chapter 10, but at this point, it is not necessary that you understand this formula.

Guest Essay: WHAT GOOD ARE FRACTALS?

Okay, fractals can make sense out of chaos (see the Guest Essay in Section 6.4), but what can you do with them? It is a question currently being asked by physicists and other scientists at many professional meetings, says Alan Norton, a former associate of Mandelbrot who is now working on computer architectures at IBM. For a young idea still being translated into the dialects of each scientific discipline, the answer, Norton says, is: Quite a bit. The fractal dimension may give scientists a way to describe a complex phenomenon with a single number.

Harold Hastings, professor of mathematics at Hofstra University on Long Island, is enthusiastic about modeling the Okefenokee Swamp in Georgia with fractals. From aerial photographs, he has studied vegetation patterns and found that some key tree groups, such as cypress, are patchier and show a larger fractal dimension than others.

Shaun Lovejoy, a meteorologist who works at Météorologie Nationale, the French national weather service in Paris, confirmed that clouds follow fractal patterns. Again, by analyzing satellite photographs, he found similarities in the shapes of many cloud types that formed over the Indian Ocean. From tiny puff-like clouds to an enormous mass that extended from Central Africa to Southern India, all exhibited the same fractal dimension. Prior to Mandelbrot's discovery of fractals, cloud shapes had not been candidates for mathematical analysis and meteorologists who theorize about the origin of weather ignored them. Lovejoy's work suggests that the atmosphere on a small-scale weather pattern near the Earth's surface resembles that on a large-scale weather pattern extending many miles away, an idea that runs counter to current theories.

The occurrence of earthquakes. The surfaces of metal fractures. The path a computer program takes when it scurries through its memory. The way our own neurons fire when we go searching through *our* memories. The wish list for fractal description grows. Time will tell whether the fractal dimension becomes invaluable to scientists interested in building mathematical models of the world's workings.

Problem Set | 8.3

Level 1

1. **IN YOUR OWN WORDS**   What do we mean by topology?

2. **IN YOUR OWN WORDS**   What is the four-color problem?

3. Group the figures into classes so that all the elements within each class are topologically equivalent, and no elements from different classes are topologically equivalent.

A. 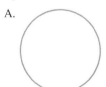   B.

C.   D.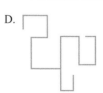

E.   F.

G.   H.

4. Group the figures into classes so that all the elements within each class are topologically equivalent, and no elements from different classes are topologically equivalent.

A.    B.

C. 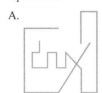   D.

E. 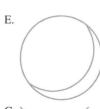   F.

G.    H.

5. Which of the figures in Problem 3 are simple closed curves?

6. Which of the figures in Problem 4 are simple closed curves?

7. Group the letters of the alphabet into classes so that all the elements within each class are topologically equivalent and no elements from different classes are topologically equivalent.

A   B   C   D   E   F   G   H   I   J   K   L   M

N   O   P   Q   R   S   T   U   V   W   X   Y   Z

8. Group the objects into classes so that all the elements within each class are topologically equivalent, and no elements from different classes are topologically equivalent.
A. a glass
B. a bowling ball
C. a sheet of typing paper
D. a sphere
E. a ruler
F. a banana
G. a sheet of two-ring-binder paper

9. Group the objects into classes so that all the elements within each class are topologically equivalent, and no elements from different classes are topologically equivalent.
A. a bolt
B. a straw
C. a horseshoe
D. a sewing needle
E. a brick
F. a pencil
G. a funnel with a handle

Level **2**

In Problems 10–13, determine whether each of the points A, B, and C is inside or outside of the simple closed curve.

10.

11.

12.

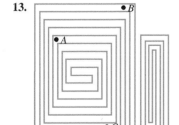

13.

14. a. Let *X* be a point obviously outside the figure given in Problem 10. Draw $\overline{AX}$. How many times does it cross the curve? Repeat for $\overline{BX}$ and $\overline{CX}$.
  b. Repeat part **a** for the figure given in Problem 11.
  c. Repeat part **a** for the figure given in Problem 12.
  d. Repeat part **a** for the figure given in Problem 13.
  e. Make a conjecture based on parts **a–d**. This conjecture involves a theorem called the *Jordan curve theorem.*

15. One of the simplest map-coloring rules of topology involves a map of "countries" with straight lines as boundaries. How many colors would be necessary for the four-corner area on a U.S. map? Note that a common point is not considered a common boundary.

How many colors are needed for the 4-corners area?

16. IN YOUR OWN WORDS   If a map (on a plane or on the surface of a sphere) is partitioned into two or more regions with each vertex of even degree, then the resulting map can be colored with exactly two colors. Draw a map illustrating this fact.

17. IN YOUR OWN WORDS   If a map (on a plane or on the surface of a sphere) is partitioned into regions, each with an even number of edges, and if each vertex is of degree 3, the resulting map can be colored with exactly three colors. Draw a map illustrating this fact.

18. IN YOUR OWN WORDS   If a map (on a plane or on the surface of a sphere) is partitioned into at least five regions, each sharing its borders with exactly three neighboring regions, the resulting map can be colored in three colors. Draw a map illustrating this fact.

19. Color the eight vertices of a cube in two colors (say red and blue) so that any plane containing three points of one color contains one point of the other color.

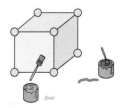

20. Construct a fractal curve by forming squares (rather than triangles as shown in the text). The first step is shown here.

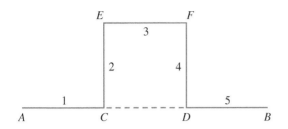

21. Two identical squares joined so that they have a common edge is called a *domino*, as shown in Figure 8.46. Three identical squares can be joined together to form a *tromino*, and they come in two different shapes. *Pentominos*, composed of five squares, come in 12 different shapes.

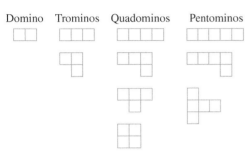

FIGURE 8.46 Mosaic tiles

Complete Figure 8.46 by showing the other 9 pentomino shapes.

Level **3**

22. IN YOUR OWN WORDS   Construct a tessellation using triangles.

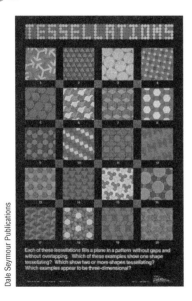

Dale Seymour Publications

23. IN YOUR OWN WORDS   Construct a tessellation using rectangles.

Forming a mosaic pattern using polygons, like those shown in Figure 8.46, is called tiling. A tiling and a tessellation are really the same idea, although the word tessellation is usually used when the pattern is more complicated than a polygon. For example, most classroom floors are tiled with simple squares, a very simple pattern with dominoes. An early example of a tromino pattern is found in an 18th century painting. This pattern is shown in Figure 8.47.

FIGURE 8.47 A tiling pattern for a 6 × 6 square using trominos

Use pentominos to tile a rectangle of the size requested in Problems 24–25.

24. 3 × 20   **25.** 4 × 15

26. IN YOUR OWN WORDS   Design a mosaic using a pentagon.

27. IN YOUR OWN WORDS   Design a mosaic using a hexagon.

28.

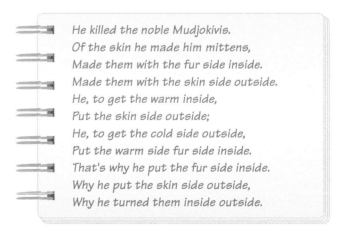

© Kelly M. Houle 1999

This is an example showing a young girl playing on the grass (look at the cylinder). The painting, entitled "Golden Afternoon" (look at the canvas), shows a distorted image that becomes complete when viewed as a reflection; this is called *anamorphosis*. What topological relation does the picture on canvas have with the image in the reflecting glass?

Problem Solving **3**

29. Answer the questions after reading the poem in the News Clip.

> He killed the noble Mudjokivis.
> Of the skin he made him mittens,
> Made them with the fur side inside.
> Made them with the skin side outside.
> He, to get the warm inside,
> Put the skin side outside;
> He, to get the cold side outside,
> Put the warm side fur side inside.
> That's why he put the fur side inside.
> Why he put the skin side outside,
> Why he turned them inside outside.

a. If a right-handed mitten is turned inside out, as is suggested in the poem, will it still fit a right hand?

b. Is a right-handed mitten topologically equivalent to a left-handed mitten?

30. Some mathematicians were reluctant to accept the proof of the four-color problem because of the necessity of computer verification. The proof was not "elegant" in the sense that it required the computer analysis of a large number of cases. Study the map in Figure 8.48 and determine for yourself whether it is the *first five-color map,* providing a counterexample for the computerized "proof."

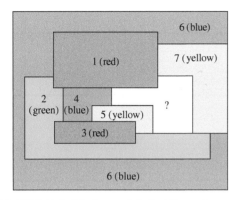

FIGURE 8.48 Is this the world's first five-color map?

What is the color of the white region? Consider the following table:

Region	Blue	Yellow	Green	Red
1	x	x	x	
2	x	x		x
3	x	x	x	
4		x	x	x
5	x		x	x
6		x	x	x
7	x		x	x
?	x	x	x	x

The x's indicate the colors that share a boundary with the given region. As you can see, the white region is bounded by all four colors, so therefore requires a fifth color.

8.4 CHAPTER SUMMARY

Mathematics is an aspect of culture as well as a collection of algorithms.
CARL BOYER

Important Ideas

Königsberg bridge problem [8.1]
Euler's circuit theorem [8.1]
Hamiltonian cycles and the traveling salesperson problem (TSP) [8.1]
Kruskal's algorithm [8.2]
Topologically equivalent figures, four-color problem, and fractals [8.3]

Take some time getting ready to work the review problems in this section. First review these important ideas. Look back at the definition and property boxes. If you look online, you will find a list of important terms introduced in this chapter, as well as the types of problems that were introduced. You will maximize your understanding of this chapter by working the problems in this section only after you have studied the material.

You will find some review help online at **www.mathnature.com.** There are links giving general test help in studying for a mathematics examination, as well as specific help for reviewing this chapter.

Chapter 8 Review Questions

In Problems 1–4, tell whether the network is traversable. If the network is traversable, show how.

1.

2.

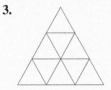

3.

4.

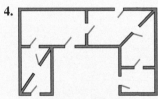

5. Consider the network shown in Figure 8.49.

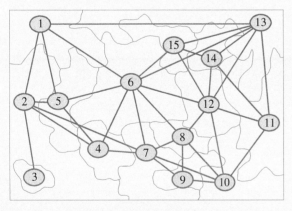

FIGURE 8.49 City network map

  a. Is there a path that is an Euler circuit?
  b. Is there a path that is a Hamiltonian cycle?

6. Draw a map with seven regions such that the indicated number of colors is required so that no two bordering regions have the same color.
  a. Two colors   **b.** Three colors
  c. Four colors   **d.** Five colors

The San Francisco Chronicle *reported that two Stanford graduates, Dave Kaval and Brad Null, set a goal to see a game in every major league baseball stadium. (Note: There are 16 National League and 14 American League teams.) They began in San Francisco and selected the route shown in Figure 8.50. Use this information in Problems 7–10.*

FIGURE 8.50 Tour of major league stadiums (TSP)

7. In how many ways could Kaval and Null start in San Francisco and visit the cities of Minneapolis, Milwaukee, Chicago, St. Louis, Detroit, Cleveland, Cincinnati, and Pittsburgh?

8. If we use the brute-force method for solving the TSP of Kaval and Null, the number of possible routes for the 30 major league cities is the astronomical number 4.4×10^{30}. Use the brute-force method for the simplified problem of finding the best way to begin in San Francisco and visit Los Angeles, San Diego, and Phoenix. The mileage chart is shown below. What is the mileage using the brute-force method?

From\To	SF	LA	SD	P
SF	—	369	502	755
LA	369	—	133	372
SD	502	133	—	353
P	755	372	353	—

9. Use the nearest-neighbor method to approximate the optimal route for the mileage chart shown in Problem 8. What is the mileage when using this route?

10. Show a complete, weighted graph for these cities. Is there a minimum spanning tree? If so, what is the mileage using this method?

11. The Big 10 football conference consists of the following schools:

Ohio State, Penn State, Michigan, Michigan State, Wisconsin, Iowa, Illinois, Northwestern (Ill.), Indiana, Purdue (Indiana), Minnesota

Is it possible to visit each of these schools by crossing each common state border exactly once? If so, find an Euler path.

12. Is it possible to find an Euler circuit for the Big 10 football conference described in Problem 11? That is, is it possible to start the trip in any given state and end the trip in the state in which you started?

In Problems 13–16, consider the graph in Figure 8.51.

FIGURE 8.51 Weighted graph

13. Find the cost of the nearest-neighbor tour, starting at *A*.

14. Find the cost of the nearest-neighbor tour, starting at *M*.

15. How many tours would be necessary to find the most efficient solution by using the brute-force method starting at *K*?

16. Use Kruskal's algorithm to find the cost of the minimum spanning tree.

In Problems 17–19, consider the graph in Figure 8.52.

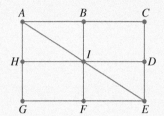

FIGURE 8.52 Graph with 9 vertices

17. Is there an Euler circuit for the graph in Figure 8.52?

18. Find a Hamiltonian circuit for the graph in Figure 8.52.

19. Find a spanning tree for the graph in Figure 8.52.

20. Take a strip of paper 11 in. by 1 in. and give it four half-twists; join the edges together. How many edges and sides does this band have? Cut the band down the center. What is the result?

BOOK REPORTS

Write a 500-word report on one of these books:

The Traveling Salesman Problem: A Guided Tour of Combinatorial Optimization, E. L. Lawler, J. K. Lenstra, A. H. G. Rinnooy Kan, D. B. Shmoys (New York: John Wiley and Sons, 1987).

Graph Theory and Its Applications, Jonathan Gross and Jay Yellen (Boca Raton: CRC Press, LLC, 1998).

Group | RESEARCH PROJECTS

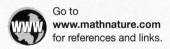

Go to
www.mathnature.com
for references and links.

Working in small groups is typical of most work environments, and learning to work with others to communicate specific ideas is an important skill. Work with three or four other students to submit a single report based on each of the following questions.

G29. Fractals To get you started on your paper, we ask the following question that relates the ideas of series and fractals using the *snowflake curve.* Draw an equilateral triangle with side length a (Figure 8.53a). Next, three equilateral triangles, each of side $\frac{a}{3}$, are cut out and placed in the middle of each side of the first triangle (Figure 8.53b). Repeat this process. As part of the work on this paper, find the perimeter and the area of the snowflake curve formed if you continue this process indefinitely.

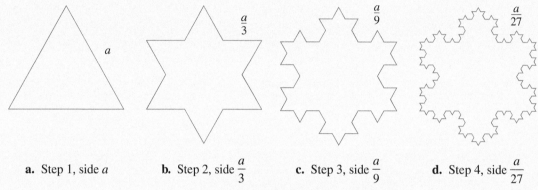

a. Step 1, side a **b.** Step 2, side $\frac{a}{3}$ **c.** Step 3, side $\frac{a}{9}$ **d.** Step 4, side $\frac{a}{27}$

FIGURE 8.53 Construction of a snowflake curve

REFERENCES

Anthony Barcellos, "The Fractal Geometry of Mandelbrot,"
    The College Mathematics Journal, March 1984, pp. 98–114.
"Interview, Benoit B. Mandelbrot," *OMNI*, February 1984, pp. 65–66.
Benoit Mandelbrot, *Fractals: Form, Chance, and Dimension* (San Francisco:
    W. H. Freeman, 1977).
Benoit Mandelbrot, *The Fractal Geometry of Nature* (San Francisco:
    W. H. Freeman, 1982).

G30. Anamorphic Art In Problem 28, Section 8.3 we showed an example of a young girl playing on the grass which was difficult to see on the plane at the bottom, but was easy to see in the cylinder. For example, can you guess what you will see in a reflective cylinder placed in the marked spot in Figure 8.54?

Write a paper about *anamorphic art,* which refers to artwork that is indistinct when viewed from a normal viewpoint, but becomes recognizable when the image is viewed as a reflection. Discuss the two main techniques for creating anamorphic art.

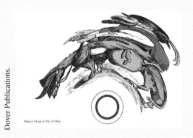

Dover Publications.

FIGURE 8.54 What do you see here?

REFERENCES

Linda Bolton, *Hidden Pictures* (New York: Dial Books, 1993).
"The Secret of Anamorphic Art," Art Johnson and Joan D. Martin, *The Mathematics Teacher, January 1998.*
Ivan Moscovich, *The Magical Cylinder* (Norfork, England: Tarquin Publications, 1988).
Marion Walter, *The Mirror Puzzle* Book, (Norfolk, England: Tarquin Publication, 1985).

Individual RESEARCH PROJECTS

www.mathnature.com

Learning to use sources outside your classroom and textbook is an important skill, and here are some ideas for extending some of the ideas in this chapter. You can find references to these projects in a library or at **www.mathnature.com.**

PROJECT 8.1 Write a report on Ramsey theory.

PROJECT 8.2 Historical Quest   Write a report on the geometry of the Garden Houses of the second-century city of Ostia. See the "What in the World" commentary on page 330.

PROJECT 8.3 Historical Quest   The German artist Albrecht Dürer (1471–1528) was not only a Renaissance artist, but also somewhat of a mathematician. Do some research on the mathematics of Dürer.

PROJECT 8.4 Prepare a classroom demonstration of topology by drawing geometric figures on a piece of rubber inner tube, and illustrate the ways these figures can be distorted.

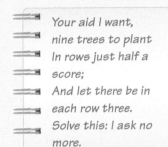
Your aid I want,
nine trees to plant
In rows just half a
score;
And let there be in
each row three.
Solve this: I ask no
more.

PROJECT 8.5 The problem shown in the News Clip was first published by John Jackson in 1821. Without the poetry, the puzzle can be stated as follows: **Arrange nine trees so they occur in ten rows of three trees each.** Find a solution.

PROJECT 8.6 Celebrate the Millennium
   a. Consider the product $1 \cdot 2 \cdot 3 \cdots 1{,}998 \cdot 1{,}999 \cdot 2{,}000$. What is the last digit?
   b. Consider the product $1 \cdot 2 \cdot 3 \cdots 1{,}998 \cdot 1{,}999 \cdot 2{,}000$. From the product, cross out all even factors, as well as all multiples of 5. Now, what is the last digit of the resulting product?

11

THE NATURE OF FINANCIAL MANAGEMENT

Outline

What in the World?

"I think we should pay off our home loan," proclaimed Lorraine. "We have had this loan for almost 20 years and we only owe $20,000. What do you think?"

"I agree. I'd really like to save the $195 per month payment that we are making. Even though it is smaller than most house payments, it would be wonderful to be debt free," said Ron.

"I checked with our bank, and they told me that to pay off the loan, we must pay $20,000 plus a 'prepayment penalty' of 3%!"

"Oh, don't worry about that," chimed Ron. "Most lenders will waive this penalty. I'll call and request them to do this. But I still don't know if it is a wise financial move. Let's think about it . . . " added Lorraine.

Austin MacRae

Overview

The stated goal of this book is to strengthen your ability to solve problems—not the classroom type of problems, but those problems that you may encounter as an employee, a manager, or in everyday living. You can apply your problem-solving ability to your financial life. A goal of this chapter might well be to put some money into your bank account that you would not have had if you had not read this chapter. As a preview to this chapter, consider the question asked in Example 2 of Section 11.5 (page 551):

> Suppose you are 21 years old and will make monthly deposits to a bank account paying 10% annual interest compounded monthly. Which is the better option?
>
> *Option I:* Pay yourself $200 per month for 5 years and then leave the balance in the bank until age 65. (Total amount of deposits is $200 \times 5 \times 12 = \$12,000$.)
>
> *Option II:* Wait until you are 40 years old (the age most of us start thinking seriously about retirement) and then deposit $200 per month until age 65. (Total amount of deposits is $200 \times 25 \times 12 = \$60,000$)
>
> Warning!! The wrong answer to this question could cost you $4,000/mo for the rest of your life!

11.1 | Interest

Finance is the art of passing money from hand to hand until it finally disappears.

ROBERT W. SARNOFF

CHAPTER CHALLENGE
See if you can fill in the question mark.

			?			
		3	8	9		
	7	6	2	4	11	
6	3	4	7	5	2	8

It seems that everyone has money problems . . . . Either we have too much (you've read stories of people who don't know what to do with all their money) or we have too little. Very few people believe that they have "just the right amount of money."

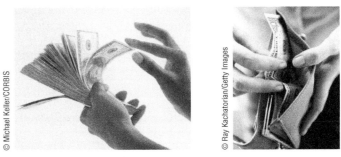

Money . . . too much or too little?

Certain arithmetic skills enable us to make intelligent decisions about how we spend the money we earn.

Amount of Simple Interest

One of the most fundamental mathematical concepts that consumers, as well as business-people, must understand is *interest*. Simply stated, **interest** is money paid for the use of money. We receive interest when we let others use our money (when we deposit money in a savings account, for example), and we pay interest when we use the money of others (for example, when we borrow from a bank).

The amount of the deposit or loan is called the **principal** or **present value,** and the interest is stated as a percent of the principal, called the **interest rate.** The **time** is the length of time for which the money is borrowed or lent. The interest rate is usually an *annual interest rate,* and the time is stated in years unless otherwise given. These variables are related in what is known as the **simple interest formula.**

Remember this fundamental formula.

Simple Interest Formula

$$\text{INTEREST} = \text{PRESENT VALUE} \times \text{RATE} \times \text{TIME}$$

$$I = Prt$$

$I = $ AMOUNT OF INTEREST
$P = $ PRESENT VALUE (or PRINCIPAL)
$r = $ ANNUAL INTEREST RATE
$t = $ TIME (in years)

Suppose you save 20¢ per day, but only for a year. At the end of a year you will have saved $73. If you then put the money into a savings account paying 3.5% interest, how much interest will the bank pay you after one year? The present value (P) is $73, the rate ($r$) is 3.5% = 0.035, and the time (t, in years) is 1. Therefore,

$$I = Prt$$
$$= 73(0.035)(1)$$
$$= 2.555 \qquad \text{You can do this computation on a calculator: } \boxed{73}\boxed{\times}\boxed{.035}\boxed{=}$$

Round money answers to the nearest cent: After one year, the interest is $2.56.

Example 1 | Find the amount of interest

How much interest will you earn in three years with an initial deposit of $73?

Solution $I = Prt = 73(0.035)(3) = 7.665$. After three years, the interest is $7.67.

Future Value

There is a difference between asking for the amount of interest, as illustrated in Example 1, and asking for the **future value.** The future value is the amount you will have after the interest is added to the principal, or present value. Let A = FUTURE VALUE. Then

$$A = P + I$$

Example 2 | Find an amount of interest

Suppose you see a car with a price of $12,436 that is advertised at $290 per month for 5 years. What is the amount of interest paid?

Solution   The present value is $12,436. The future value is the total amount of all the payments:

Monthly payment   Number of years

$$\underbrace{\$290}_{} \qquad \underbrace{\times\ 12}_{\text{Number of payments per year}} \qquad \times\ 5 \qquad = \$17,400$$

Therefore, the amount of interest is

$$I = A - P$$
$$= 17,400 - 12,436$$
$$= 4,964$$

The amount of interest is $4,964.

Interest for Part of a Year

The numbers in Example 2 were constructed to give a "nice" answer, but the length of time for an investment is not always a whole number of years. There are two ways to convert a number of days into a year:

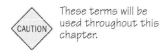

These terms will be used throughout this chapter.

Exact interest: 365 days per year

Ordinary interest: 360 days per year

Most applications and businesses use ordinary interest. So in this book, unless it is otherwise stated, assume ordinary interest; that is, use 360 for the number of days in a year:

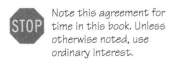

Note this agreement for time in this book. Unless otherwise noted, use ordinary interest.

Time (Ordinary Interest)

$$t = \frac{\text{ACTUAL NUMBER OF DAYS}}{360}$$

Calculating the time using ordinary interest often requires a calculator, as illustrated by Example 3.

Example 3 Time necessary to achieve a financial goal

Suppose you want to save $3,650, and you put $3,000 in the bank at 8% simple interest. How long must you wait?

Solution   Begin by identifying the variables: $P = 3,000$; $r = 0.08$; $I = 3,650 - 3,000 = 650$.

$$I = Prt$$
$$650 = 3,000(0.08)t$$
$$650 = 240t$$
$$\frac{650}{240} = t$$

This is 2 years plus some part of a year. To change the fractional part to days, do not clear your calculator, but subtract 2 (the number of years); then multiply the fractional part by 360:

$\boxed{650}\ \boxed{\div}\ \boxed{240}\ \boxed{-}\ \boxed{2}\ \boxed{=}\ \boxed{\times}\ \boxed{360}\ \boxed{=}$ Display: 255

The time you must wait is 2 years, 255 days.

Example 4 Find the amount to repay a loan

Suppose that you borrow $1,200 on March 25 at 21% simple interest. How much interest accrues by September 15 (174 days later)? What is the total amount that must be repaid?

Solution   We are given $P = 1,200$, $r = 0.21$, and $t = \dfrac{174}{360}$ ← Actual number of days
← Assume ordinary interest.

$$I = Prt \qquad \text{Simple interest formula}$$
$$= 1,200(0.21)\left(\frac{174}{360}\right) \qquad \text{Substitute known values.}$$
$$= 121.8 \qquad \text{Use a calculator to do the arithmetic.}$$

The amount of interest is $121.80. To find the amount that must be repaid, find the future value:

$$A = P + I = 1,200 + 121.80 = 1,321.80$$

The amount that must be repaid is $1,321.80.

It is worthwhile to derive a formula for future value because sometimes we will not calculate the interest separately as we did in Example 4.

$$\text{FUTURE VALUE} = \text{PRESENT VALUE} + \text{INTEREST}$$

$$A = P + I$$
$$= P + Prt \qquad \text{Substitute } I = Prt.$$
$$= P(1 + rt) \qquad \text{Distributive property}$$

STOP This is also known as the present value formula for simple interest when solved for the variable P.

Future Value Formula (Simple Interest)

$$A = P(1 + rt)$$

Example 5   Find a future value

If \$10,000 is deposited in an account earning $5\frac{3}{4}\%$ simple interest, what is the future value in 5 years?

Solution   We identify $P = 10,000$, $r = 0.0575$, and $t = 5$.

$$A = P(1 + rt)$$
$$= 10,000(1 + 0.0575 \times 5)$$
$$= 10,000(1 + 0.2875)$$
$$= 10,000(1.2875)$$
$$= 12,875$$

The future value in 5 years is \$12,875.

Example 6   Find the amount necessary to retire

Suppose you have decided that you will need \$4,000 per month on which to live in retirement. If the rate of interest is 8%, how much must you have in the bank when you retire so that you can live on interest only?

Solution   We are given $I = 4,000$, $r = 0.08$, and $t = \frac{1}{12}$ (one month $= \frac{1}{12}$ year):

$$I = Prt \qquad \text{Simple interest formula}$$
$$4,000 = P(0.08)\left(\frac{1}{12}\right) \qquad \text{Substitute known values.}$$
$$48,000 = 0.08P \qquad \text{Multiply both sides by 12.}$$
$$600,000 = P \qquad \text{Divide both sides by 0.08.}$$

You must have \$600,000 on deposit to earn \$4,000 per month at 8%.

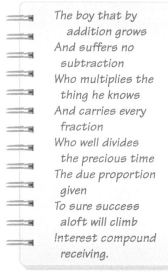

*The boy that by
    addition grows
And suffers no
    subtraction
Who multiplies the
    thing he knows
And carries every
    fraction
Who well divides
    the precious time
The due proportion
    given
To sure success
    aloft will climb
Interest compound
    receiving.*

Compounding Interest

Most banks do not pay interest according to the simple interest formula; instead, after some period of time, they add the interest to the principal and then pay interest on this new, larger amount. When this is done, it is called **compound interest.**

Example 7 Compare simple and compound interest

Compare simple and compound interest for a $1,000 deposit at 8% interest for 3 years.

Solution   Identify the known values: $P = 1,000$, $r = 0.08$, and $t = 3$. Next, calculate the future value using simple interest:

$$A = P(1 + rt)$$
$$= 1,000(1 + 0.08 \times 3)$$
$$= 1,000(1.24)$$
$$= 1,240$$

With simple interest, the future value in 3 years is $1,240.

Next, assume that the interest is **compounded annually.** This means that the interest is added to the principal after 1 year has passed. This new amount then becomes the principal for the following year. Since the time period for each calculation is 1 year, we let $t = 1$ for each calculation.

First year $(t = 1)$: $A = P(1 + r)$
$$= 1,000(1 + 0.08)$$
$$= 1,080$$
$$\downarrow$$

Second year $(t = 1)$: $A = P(1 + r)$ One year's principal is previous year's total.
$$= 1,080(1 + 0.08)$$
$$= 1,166.40$$
$$\downarrow$$

Third year $(t = 1)$: $A = P(1 + r)$
$$= 1,166.40(1 + 0.08)$$
$$= 1,259.71$$

With interest compounded annually, the future value in 3 years is $1,259.71. The earnings from compounding are $19.71 more than from simple interest.

The problem with compound interest relates to the difficulty of calculating it. Notice that, to simplify the calculations in Example 7, the variable representing time t was given the value 1, and the process was repeated three times. Also notice that, after the future value was found, it was used as the principal in the next step. What if we wanted to compound annually for 20 years instead of for 3 years? Look at Example 7 to discover the following pattern:

Simple interest (20 years): $A = P(1 + rt)$
$$= 1,000(1 + 0.08 \times 20)$$
$$= 1,000(1 + 1.6)$$
$$= 1,000(2.6)$$
$$= 2,600$$

Annual compounding (20 years): $A = \underline{P(1 + r \cdot 1)}$ First year
$$\downarrow$$
$$= P(1 + r)(1 + r)$$ Second year; for P use end value from first year.
$$= \underline{P(1 + r)^2}$$ Second year simplified.
$$\downarrow$$
$$= P(1 + r)^2(1 + r)$$ Third year
$$= P(1 + r)^3$$
$$\vdots$$
$$= P(1 + r)^{20}$$ Twentieth year

For a period of 20 years, starting with $1,000 at 8% compounded annually, we have

$$A = 1,000(1.08)^{20}$$

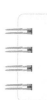

To complete this chapter successfully, you will need to know how to do this on your calculator. Use this as a test problem.

The difficulty lies in calculating this number. For years we relied on extensive tables for obtaining numbers such as this, but the availability of calculators has made such calculations accessible to all. You will need an exponent key. These are labeled in different ways, depending on the brand of calculator. It might be $\boxed{y^x}$ or $\boxed{x^y}$ or $\boxed{\wedge}$. In this book we will show exponents by using $\boxed{\wedge}$, but you should press the appropriate key on your own brand of calculator.

$\boxed{1000}\;\boxed{\times}\;\boxed{1.08}\;\boxed{\wedge}\;\boxed{20}\;\boxed{=}$ Display: 4660.957144

Round money answers to the nearest cent: $4,660.96 is the future value of $1,000 compounded annually at 8% for 20 years. This compounding yields $2,060.96 *more* than simple interest.

Most banks compound interest more frequently than once a year. For instance, a bank may pay interest as follows:

Semiannually: twice a year or every 180 days

Quarterly: 4 times a year or every 90 days

Monthly: 12 times a year or every 30 days

Daily: 360 times a year

If we repeat the same steps for more frequent intervals than annual compounding, we again begin with the simple interest formula $A = P(1 + rt)$.

Semiannually, then $t = \dfrac{1}{2}$: $A = P\left(1 + r \cdot \tfrac{1}{2}\right)$

Quarterly, then $t = \dfrac{1}{4}$: $A = P\left(1 + r \cdot \tfrac{1}{4}\right)$

Monthly, then $t = \dfrac{1}{12}$: $A = P\left(1 + r \cdot \tfrac{1}{12}\right)$

Daily, then $t = \dfrac{1}{360}$: $A = P\left(1 + r \cdot \tfrac{1}{360}\right)$

We now compound for t years and introduce a new variable, n, as follows:

Annual compounding, $n = 1$: $A = P(1 + r)^t$

Semiannual compounding, $n = 2$: $A = P\left(1 + r \cdot \tfrac{1}{2}\right)^{2t}$

Quarterly compounding, $n = 4$: $A = P\left(1 + r \cdot \tfrac{1}{4}\right)^{4t}$

Monthly compounding, $n = 12$: $A = P\left(1 + r \cdot \tfrac{1}{12}\right)^{12t}$

Daily compounding, $n = 360$: $A = P\left(1 + r \cdot \tfrac{1}{360}\right)^{360t}$

We are now ready to state the future value formula for compound interest, which is sometimes called the **compound interest formula.** For these calculations you will need access to a calculator with an exponent key.

Future Value Formula (Compound Interest)

$$A = P\left(1 + \frac{r}{n}\right)^{nt}$$

The variables we use in this formula are presented in a separate box because these variables will be used throughout this chapter. We contrast simple and compound interest in the same summary box.

Contrast Simple and Compound Interest

If interest is withdrawn from the amount in the account, use the *simple interest formula.* If the interest is deposited into the account to accrue future interest, then use the *compound interest formula.*

You will need to know the variables used with the interest formulas in this chapter, so we summarize those in the following definition box.

Interest Variables

$A =$ FUTURE VALUE   This is the principal plus interest.
$P =$ PRESENT VALUE   This is the same as the principal.
$r =$ INTEREST RATE   This is the *annual* interest rate.
$t =$ TIME   This is the time in *years.*
$n =$ NUMBER OF COMPOUNDING PERIODS EACH YEAR
$m =$ PERIODIC PAYMENT   This is usually monthly.

STOP Spend some time here; you will need to remember what these variables represent. These are the variables used in this chapter.

Example 8   Compare compounding methods

Find the future value of $1,000 invested for 10 years at 8% interest
a. compounded annually.
b. compounded semiannually.
c. compounded quarterly.
d. compounded daily.

Solution   Identify the variables: $P = 1,000, r = 0.08, t = 10.$

a. $n = 1$: $A = \$1,000(1 + 0.08)^{10} = \$2,158.92$

b. $n = 2$: $A = \$1,000\left(1 + \frac{0.08}{2}\right)^{2 \cdot 10} = \$2,191.12$

c. $n = 4$: $A = \$1,000\left(1 + \frac{0.08}{4}\right)^{4 \cdot 10} = \$2,208.04$

d. $n = 360$: $A = \$1,000\left(1 + \frac{0.08}{360}\right)^{360 \cdot 10} = \$2,225.34$

Continuous Compounding

A reasonable extension of the current discussion is to ask the effect of more frequent compounding. To model this situation, consider the following contrived example. Suppose $1 is invested at 100% interest for 1 year compounded at different intervals. The compound interest formula for this example is

$$A = \left(1 + \frac{1}{n}\right)^n$$

where n is the number of times of compounding in 1 year. The calculations of this formula for different values of n are shown in the following table.

Number of Periods	Formula	Amount
Annual, $n = 1$	$\left(1 + \frac{1}{1}\right)^1$	$2.00
Semiannual, $n = 2$	$\left(1 + \frac{1}{2}\right)^2$	$2.25
Quarterly, $n = 4$	$\left(1 + \frac{1}{4}\right)^4$	$2.44
Monthly, $n = 12$	$\left(1 + \frac{1}{12}\right)^{12}$	$2.61
Daily, $n = 360$	$\left(1 + \frac{1}{360}\right)^{360}$	$2.71

Looking only at this table, you might (incorrectly) conclude that as the number of times the investment is compounded increases, the amount of the investment increases without bound. Let us continue these calculations for even larger n:

Number of Periods	Amount
$n = 8{,}640$ (compounding every hour)	2.718124536
$n = 518{,}400$ (every minute)	2.718279142
$n = 1{,}000{,}000$	2.718280469
$n = 10{,}000{,}000$	2.718281693
$n = 100{,}000{,}000$	2.718281815

The spreadsheet we are using for these calculations can no longer distinguish the values of $\left(1 + 1/n\right)^n$ for larger n. These values are approaching a particular number. This number, it turns out, is an irrational number, and it does not have a convenient decimal representation. (That is, its decimal representation does not terminate and does not repeat.) Mathematicians, therefore, have agreed to denote this number by using the symbol e. This number is called the **natural base** or **Euler's number.**

> ### The Number e
>
> As n increases without bound, the **number e** is the irrational number that is the limiting value of the formula
>
> $$\left(1 + \frac{1}{n}\right)^n$$

In Section 5.5 we noted that the number e is irrational and consequently does not have a terminating or repeating decimal representation. This same irrational number was used extensively in Chapter 10 as the base number in growth/decay applications as well as in evaluating natural logarithms. Although you must wait until you study the concept of limit in calculus for a formal definition of e, the preceding discussion should be enough to convince you that

Remember this approximate value.

$$e \approx 2.7183$$

Even though you will not find a bank that compounds interest every minute, you will find banks that use this limiting value to compound **continuously.** When using this model, we assume the year has 365 days.

Future Value Formula (Continuous Compounding)

The future value, A, of an investment of P, *compounded continuously* at a rate of r for t years, is found by

$$A = Pe^{rt}$$

It is easy to see how this formula follows from the compound interest formula if we let $\frac{1}{m} = \frac{r}{n}$, so that $n = mr$.

$$A = P\left(1 + \frac{r}{n}\right)^{nt}$$

$$= P\left(1 + \frac{1}{m}\right)^{mrt}$$

$$= P\left[\left(1 + \frac{1}{m}\right)^{m}\right]^{rt}$$

As m gets large, $\left(1 + \dfrac{1}{m}\right)^{m}$ approaches e, so we have

$$A = Pe^{rt}$$

Example 9 Find future value using continuous compounding

Find the future value of $890 invested at 21.3% for 3 years, 240 days, compounded continuously.

Solution We use the formula $A = Pe^{rt}$ where $P = 890$, $r = 0.213$. For continuous compounding, use a 365-day year, so

$$3 \text{ years, } 240 \text{ days} = 3 + \frac{240}{365} = 3.657534247 \text{ years}$$

Remember that t is in years, and also remember to use this calculator value and not a rounded value.

$$A = 890e^{0.213t} \approx 1{,}939.676057$$

The future value is $1,939.68.

Example 10 Compare daily and continuous compounding

Let P dollars be invested at an annual rate of r for t years. Then the future value A depends on the number of times the money is compounded each year. How long will it take for $1,250 to grow to $2,000 if it is invested at
a. 8% compounded daily? Use exact interest.
b. 8% compounded continuously? Give your answer to the nearest day (assume that one year is 365 days).

Solution
a. Use the formula $A = P\left(1 + \frac{r}{365}\right)^{365t}$, and let $n = 365$ (exact interest); $P = \$1{,}250$; $A = \$2{,}000$; and $r = 0.08$; t is the unknown.

$$A = P\left(1 + \frac{r}{365}\right)^{365t} \qquad \text{\textit{Given formula}}$$

$$2{,}000 = 1{,}250\left(1 + \frac{0.08}{365}\right)^{365t} \qquad \text{\textit{Substitute known values.}}$$

$$1.6 = \left(1 + \frac{0.08}{365}\right)^{365t} \qquad \text{\textit{Divide both sides by 1,250.}}$$

$$365t = \log_{(1+0.08/365)} 1.6$$

Definition of logarithm

$$t = \frac{\log_{(1+0.08/365)} 1.6}{365}$$

Divide both sides by 365. Evaluate as $\frac{\log 1.6}{\log(1+0.08/365)} \div 365$.

$$\approx 5.875689182$$

Approximate solution

We see that it is almost 6 years, but we need the answer to the nearest day. The time is 5 years + 0.875689182 year. Multiply 0.875689182 by 365 to find 319.6265516. This means that on the 319th day of the 6th year, we are still a bit short of $2,000, so the time necessary is 5 years, 320 days.

b. For continuous compounding, use the formula $A = Pe^{rt}$.

$$A = Pe^{rt}$$

Given formula

$$2,000 = 1,250e^{0.08t}$$

Substitute known values.

$$1.6 = e^{0.08t}$$

Divide both sides by 1,250.

$$0.08t = \ln 1.6$$

Definition of logarithm

$$t = \frac{\ln 1.6}{0.08}$$

Divide both sides by 0.08. This is the exact solution.

$$\approx 5.875045366$$

Approximate solution

To find the number of days, we once again subtract 5 and multiply by 365 to find that the time necessary is 5 years, 320 days. (*Note:* 319.39 means that on the 319th day, you do not quite have the $2,000. The necessary time is 5 years, 320 days.) Notice that for this example, it does not matter whether we compound daily or continuously.

Inflation

Any discussion of compound interest is incomplete without a discussion of **inflation.** The same procedure we used to calculate compound interest can be used to calculate the effects of inflation. The government releases reports of monthly and annual inflation rates. In 1980 the inflation rate was over 14%, but in 2010 it was less than 1.25%. Keep in mind that inflation rates can vary tremendously and that the best we can do in this section is to assume different constant inflation rates. For our purposes in this book, we will assume continuous compounding when working inflation problems.

Example	**11**	**Find future value due to inflation**

If your salary today is $55,000 per year, what would you expect your salary to be in 20 years (rounded to the nearest thousand dollars) if you assume that inflation will continue at a constant rate of 6% over that time period?

Solution   Inflation is an example of continuous compounding. The problem with estimating inflation is that you must "guess" the value of future inflation, which in reality does not remain constant. However, if you look back 20 years and use an average inflation rate for the past 20 years—say, 6%—you may use this as a reasonable estimate for the next 20 years. Thus, you may use $P = 55,000$, $r = 0.06$, and $t = 20$ to find

$$A = Pe^{rt} = 55,000e^{0.06(20)}$$

Note: Be sure to use parentheses for the exponent:

Display: 182606.430751

The answer means that, if inflation continues at a constant 6% rate, an annual salary of $183,000 (rounded to the nearest thousand dollars) will have about the same purchasing power in 20 years as a salary of $55,000 today.

Present Value

Sometimes we know the future value of an investment and we wish to know its present value. Such a problem is called a *present value problem*. The formula follows directly from the future value formula (by division).

Present Value Formula

$$P = A \div \left(1 + \frac{r}{n}\right)^{nt} = A\left(1 + \frac{r}{n}\right)^{-nt}$$

Example 12   Find a present value for a Tahiti trip

Suppose that you want to take a trip to Tahiti in 5 years and you decide that you will need $5,000. To have that much money set aside in 5 years, how much money should you deposit now into a bank account paying 6% compounded quarterly?

Solution   In this problem, P is unknown and A is given: $A = 5,000$. We also have $r = 0.06$, $t = 5$, and $n = 4$.
Calculate:

$$P = A\left(1 + \frac{r}{n}\right)^{-nt}$$

$$= 5,000\left(1 + \frac{0.06}{4}\right)^{-20}$$

$$= \$3,712.35$$

Example 13   Find the value of an insurance policy

An insurance agent wishes to sell you a policy that will pay you $100,000 in 30 years. What is the value of this policy in today's dollars if we assume a 9% inflation rate, compounded annually?

Solution   This is a present value problem for which $A = 100,000$, $r = 0.09$, $n = 1$, and $t = 30$.
  To find the present value, calculate:

$$P = 100,000(1 + 0.09)^{-30}$$

$$= \$7,537.11$$

This means that the agent is offering you an amount comparable to $7,537.11 in terms of today's dollars.

Example 14   Make your child a millionaire   Pólya's Method

Your first child has just been born. You want to give her 1 million dollars when she retires at age 65. If you invest your money on the day of her birth, how much do you need to invest so that she will have $1,000,000 on her 65th birthday?

Solution   We use Pólya's problem-solving guidelines for this example.

Understand the Problem.   You want to make a single deposit and let it be compounded for 65 years, so that at the end of that time there will be 1 million dollars. Neither the

Monday, March 1, 1982	6-mo. adjustable rate **17.5%**
Tuesday, March 1, 1983	6-mo. adjustable rate **12.5%**
Friday, March 1, 1985	3-mo. adjustable rate **10.5%**
Monday, March 1, 1993	3 mo. adjustable rate **4.5%**
Tuesday, March 1, 1994	3-mo. adjustable rate **3.0%**
Friday, March 1, 1996	3-mo. adjustable rate **4.9%**
Wednesday, March 1, 2000	3-mo. adjustable rate **5.2%**
Saturday, March 1, 2003	6-mo. adjustable rate **1.6%**
Monday, March 1, 2010	3-mo. adjustable rate **0.9%**

rate of return nor the compounding period is specified. We assume daily compounding, a constant rate of return over the time period, and we need to determine whether we can find an investment to meet our goals.

Devise a Plan. With daily compounding, $n = 360$. We will use the present value formula, and experiment with different interest rates:

$$P = 1,000,000\left(1 + \frac{r}{360}\right)^{-(360 \cdot 65)}$$

Carry Out the Plan. We determine the present values based on the different interest rates using a calculator and display the results in tabular form.

Interest Rate	Formula	Value of P
2%	$1,000,000\left(1 + \frac{0.02}{360}\right)^{-(360 \cdot 65)}$	272,541.63
5%	$1,000,000\left(1 + \frac{0.05}{360}\right)^{-(360 \cdot 65)}$	38,782.96
8%	$1,000,000\left(1 + \frac{0.08}{360}\right)^{-(360 \cdot 65)}$	5,519.75
12%	$1,000,000\left(1 + \frac{0.12}{360}\right)^{-(360 \cdot 65)}$	410.27
20%	$1,000,000\left(1 + \frac{0.20}{360}\right)^{-(360 \cdot 65)}$	2.27

Look Back. Look down the list of interest rates and compare the rates with the amount of deposit necessary. Generally, the greater the risk of an investment, the higher the rate. Insured savings accounts may pay lower rates, bonds may pay higher rates for long-term investments, and other investments in stamps, coins, or real estate may pay the highest rates. The amount of the investment necessary to build an estate of 1 million dollars is dramatic!

Problem Set 11.1

Level 1

1. **IN YOUR OWN WORDS**   What is interest?

2. **IN YOUR OWN WORDS**   Contrast amount of interest and interest rate.

3. **IN YOUR OWN WORDS**   Compare and contrast simple and compound interest.

4. **IN YOUR OWN WORDS**   Compare and contrast present value and future value.

5. **IN YOUR OWN WORDS**   What is the subject of Example 14? Discuss the real life application of this example in your own life.

Use estimation to select the best response in Problems 6–15. Do not calculate.

6. If you deposit $100 in a bank account for a year, then the amount of interest is likely to be
   A. $2   B. $5
   C. $102   D. impossible to estimate

7. If you deposit $100 in a bank account for a year, then the future value is likely to be
   A. $2   B. $5
   C. $102   D. impossible to estimate

8. If you purchase a new automobile and finance it for four years, the amount of interest you might pay is
   A. $400   B. $100
   C. $4,000   D. impossible to estimate

9. What is a reasonable monthly income when you retire?
   A. $300   B. $10,000
   C. $500,000 D. impossible to estimate

10. In order to retire and live on the interest only, what is a reasonable amount to have in the bank?
    A. $300   B. $10,000
    C. $500,000 D. impossible to estimate

11. If $I = Prt$ and $P = \$49,236.45$, $r = 10.5\%$, and $t = 2$ years, estimate I.
    A. $10,000   B. $600
    C. $50,000   D. $120,000

12. If $I = Prt$ and $I = \$398.90$, $r = 9.85\%$, and $t = 1$ year, estimate P.
   A. $400   B. $40
   C. $40,000   D. $4,000

13. If $t = 3.52895$, then the time is about 3 years and how many days?
   A. 30   B. 300
   C. 52   D. 200

14. If a loan is held for 450 days, then t is about
   A. 450   B. 3
   C. $1\frac{1}{4}$ D. 5

15. If a loan is held for 180 days, then t is about
   A. 180   B. $\frac{1}{2}$
   C. $\frac{1}{4}$ D. 3

In Problems 16–19, calculate the amount of simple interest earned.

16. $1,000 at 8% for 5 years

17. $5,000 at 10% for 3 years

18. $2,000 at 12% for 5 years

19. $1,000 at 14% for 30 years

In Problems 20–25, find the future value, using the future value formula and a calculator.

20. $350 at $4\frac{3}{4}\%$ simple interest for 2 years

21. $835 at 3.5% compounded semiannually for 6 years

22. $575 at 5.5% compounded quarterly for 5 years

23. $9,730.50 at 7.6% compounded monthly for 7 years

24. $45.67 at 3.5% compounded daily for 3 years

25. $119,400 at 7.5% compounded continuously for 30 years

In Problems 26–30, find the present value, using the present value formula and a calculator.

26. Achieve $5,000 in three years at 3.5% simple interest.

27. Achieve $2,500 in five years at 8.2% interest compounded monthly.

28. Achieve $420,000 in 30 years at 6% interest compounded monthly.

29. Achieve a million dollars in 30 years at 6% interest compounded continuously.

30. Achieve $225,500 at 8.65% compounded continuously for 8 years, 135 days.

31. If $12,000 is invested at 4.5% for 20 years, find the future value if the interest is compounded:
   a. annually
   b. semiannually
   c. quarterly
   d. monthly
   e. daily
   f. every minute ($N = 525,600$)
   g. continuously
   h. simple (not compounded)

32. If $34,500 is invested at 6.9% for 30 years, find the future value if the interest is compounded:
   a. annually
   b. semiannually
   c. quarterly
   d. monthly
   e. daily
   f. every minute ($N = 525,600$)
   g. continuously
   h. simple (not compounded)

Level 2

Find the total amount that must be repaid on the notes described in Problems 33–34.

33. $1,500 borrowed at 21% simple interest. What is the total amount to be repaid 55 days later?

34. $8,553 borrowed at 16.5% simple interest. What is the total amount to be repaid 3 years, 125 days later?

35. Find the cost of each item in 5 years, assuming an inflation rate of 9%.
   a. cup of coffee, $1.75
   b. Sunday paper, $1.25
   c. Big Mac, $1.95
   d. gallon of gas, $2.95
   e. HDTV set, $1,600
   f. small car, $19,000
   g. car, $28,000
   h. tuition, $16,000

36. Find the cost of each item in 10 years, assuming an inflation rate of 5%.
   a. movie admission, $7.00
   b. CD, $14.95
   c. textbook, $90.00
   d. electric bill, $105
   e. phone bill, $45
   f. pair of shoes, $85
   g. new suit, $570
   h. monthly rent, $800

37. How much would you have in 5 years if you purchased a $1,000 5-year savings certificate that paid 4% compounded quarterly?

38. What is the interest on $2,400 for 5 years at 12% compounded continuously?

39. What is the future value after 15 years if you deposit $1,000 for your child's education and the interest is guaranteed at 16% compounded continuously?

40. Suppose you see a car with an advertised price of $18,490 at $480 per month for 5 years. What is the amount of interest paid?

41. Suppose you see a car with an advertised price of $14,500 at $410.83 per month for 4 years. What is the amount of interest paid?

42. Suppose you buy a home and finance $285,000 at $2,293.17 per month for 30 years. What is the amount of interest paid?

43. Suppose you buy a home and finance $170,000 at $1,247.40 per month for 30 years. What is the amount of interest paid?

44. Find the cost of a home in 30 years, assuming an annual inflation rate of 10%, if the present value of the house is $125,000.

45. Find the cost of the monthly rent for a two-bedroom apartment in 30 years, assuming an annual inflation rate of 10%, if the current rent is $850.

46. Suppose that an insurance agent offers you a policy that will provide you with a yearly income of $50,000 in 30 years. What is the comparable salary today, assuming an inflation rate of 6% compounded annually?

47. If a friend tells you she earned $5,075 interest for the year on a 5-year certificate of deposit paying 5% simple interest, what is the amount of the deposit?

48. If Rita receives $45.33 interest for a deposit earning 3% simple interest for 240 days, what is the amount of her deposit?

49. If John wants to retire with $10,000 per month, how much principal is necessary to generate this amount of monthly income if the interest rate is 15%?*

50. If Melissa wants to retire with $50,000 per month, how much principal is necessary to generate this amount of monthly income if the interest rate is 12%?*

51. If Jack wants to retire with $1,000 per month, how much principal is necessary to generate this amount of monthly income if the interest rate is 6%?

Level 3

52. In 2009, the U.S. national soared to 11.0 trillion dollars.
   a. If this debt is shared equally by the 300 million U.S. citizens, how much would it cost each of us (rounded to the nearest thousand dollars)?
   b. If the interest rate is 6%, what is the interest on the national debt *each second?* Assume a 365-day year.

 You can check on the current national debt at **www.brillig.com/debt_clock/** This link, as usual, can be accessed through **www .mathnature.com**

In Problems 53–56, calculate the time necessary to achieve an investment goal. Give your answer to the nearest day. Use a 365-day year.†

53. $1,000 at 8% simple interest; deposit $750

54. $3,500 at 6% simple interest; deposit $3,000

55. $5,000 at 5% daily interest; deposit $3,500

---

*You might think these are exorbitant monthly incomes, but if you assume 10% average inflation for 40 years, a monthly income of $220 today will be equivalent to about $10,000 per month in 40 years.
†Problems 53–58 require Chapter 10 (on solving exponential equations)

56. $5,000 at 4.5% compounded continuously; deposit $3,500

57. Suppose that $1,000 is invested at 7% interest compounded monthly. Use the formula

$$A = P\left(1 + \frac{r}{n}\right)^{nt}$$

   a. How long (to the nearest month) before the value is $1,250?
   b. How long (to the nearest month) before the money doubles?
   c. What is the interest rate (compounded monthly and rounded to the nearest percent) if the money doubles in 5 years?

58. Suppose that $1,000 is invested at 5% interest compounded continuously. Use the formula

$$A = Pe^{rt}$$

   a. How long (to the nearest day) before the value is $1,250?
   b. How long (to the nearest day) before the money doubles?
   c. What is the interest rate (compounded continuously and rounded to the nearest tenth of a percent) if the money doubles in 5 years?

Problem Solving 3

59. The News Clip below is typical of what you will see in a newspaper.

NEW, HIGHEST INTEREST RATE EVER ON INSURED SAVINGS

8.33% annual yield on
8% interest compounded daily
Annual yield based on daily compounding when funds and interest remain on deposit a year. Note: Federal regulations require a substantial interest penalty for early withdrawal of principal from Certificate Accounts.

The Clip gives two rates, the *annual yield* or *effective rate* (8.33%) and a *nominal rate* (8%). Since banks pay interest compounded for different periods (quarterly, monthly, daily, for example), they calculate a rate for which annual compounding would yield the same amount at the end of 1 year. That is, for an 8% rate:

Nominal Rate	Effective Rate
8%, annual compounding	8%
8%, semiannual compounding	8.16%
8%, quarterly compounding	8.24%
8%, monthly compounding	8.30%
8%, daily compounding	8.33%

To find a formula for effective rate, we recall that the compound interest formula is

$$A = P\left(1 + \frac{r}{n}\right)^{nt}$$

and the future value formula for simple interest is

$$A = P(1 + Yt)$$

The effective rate, Y, is a rate such that, at the end of one year ($t = 1$), the future value for the simple interest is equal to the future value for the compound interest rate r with n compounding periods. That is,

$$P\left(1 + \frac{r}{n}\right)^n = P(1 + Y)$$

Find a formula for effective (annual) rate, Y, for which the future value for compound interest is equal to the future value for simple interest at the end of 1 year.

60. Find the effective yield for the following investments (see Problem 59). Round to the nearest hundredth of a percent.
  a. 6%, compounded quarterly
  b. 6%, compounded monthly
  c. 4%, compounded semiannually
  d. 4%, compounded daily

11.2 Installment Buying

Two types of consumer credit allow you to make installment purchases. The first, called **closed-end,** is the traditional installment loan. An **installment loan** is an agreement to pay off a loan or a purchase by making equal payments at regular intervals for some specific period of time. In this book, it is assumed that all installment payments are made monthly.

There are two common ways of calculating installment interest. The first uses simple interest and is called *add-on interest*, and the second uses compound interest and is called *amortization*. We discuss the simple interest application in this section, and the compound interest application in Section 11.6.

In addition to closed-end credit, it is common to obtain a type of consumer credit called **open-end, revolving credit,** or, more commonly, a **credit card** loan. MasterCard, VISA, and Discover cards, as well as those from department stores and oil companies, are examples of open-end loans. This type of loan allows for purchases or cash advances up to a specified maximum **line of credit** and has a flexible repayment schedule.

Add-On Interest

The most common method for calculating interest on installment loans is by a method known as **add-on interest.** It is nothing more than an application of the simple interest formula. It is called *add-on interest* because the interest is *added to* the amount borrowed so that both interest and the amount borrowed are paid for over the length of the loan. You should be familiar with the following variables:

P = AMOUNT TO BE FINANCED (present value)

r = ADD-ON INTEREST RATE

t = TIME (in years) TO REPAY THE LOAN

I = AMOUNT OF INTEREST

A = AMOUNT TO BE REPAID (future value)

m = AMOUNT OF THE MONTHLY PAYMENT

N = NUMBER OF PAYMENTS

MasterCard is a registered trademark of MasterCard International, Inc.

STOP Do you see why this is called add-on interest? Do these formulas make sense to you?

Installment Loan Formulas

AMOUNT OF INTEREST:	$I = Prt$
AMOUNT REPAID:	$A = P + I$ or $A = P(1 + rt)$
NUMBER OF PAYMENTS:	$N = 12t$
AMOUNT OF EACH PAYMENT:	$m = \frac{A}{N}$

Example 1 Find a monthly payment

You want to purchase a computer that has a price of $1,399, and you decide to pay for it with installments over 3 years. The store tells you that the interest rate is 15%. What is the amount of each monthly payment?

Solution   You ask the clerk how the interest is calculated, and you are told that the store uses add-on interest. Thus, $P = 1,399$, $r = 0.15$, $t = 3$, and $N = 36$.

Two-step solution

$$I = Prt$$
$$= 1,399(0.15)(3)$$
$$= 629.55$$
$$A = P + I$$
$$= 1,399 + 629.55$$
$$= 2,028.55$$

One-step solution

$$A = P(1 + rt)$$
$$= 1,399(1 + 0.15 \cdot 3)$$
$$= 2,028.55$$

$$m = \frac{2,028.55}{36}$$
$$\approx 56.35$$

The amount of each monthly payment is $56.35.

The most common applications of installment loans are for the purchase of a car or a home. Interest for purchasing a car is determined by the add-on method, but interest for purchasing a home is not. We will, therefore, delay our discussion of home loans until after we have discussed periodic payments with compound interest. The next example shows a calculation for a car loan.

Example 2 Find a monthly payment

Pólya's Method

Suppose that you have decided to purchase a Toyota Prius and want to determine the monthly payment if you pay for the car in 4 years. The value of your trade-in is $4,100.

Solution   We use Póylya's problem-solving guidelines for this example.

Understand the Problem. Not enough information is given, so you need to ask some questions of the car dealer:

Sticker price of the car (as posted on the window): $22,720

Dealer's preparation charges (as posted on the window): $350.00

Total asking (sticker) price: $23,070

Tax rate (determined by the state):   8%

Add-on interest rate: 6%

You need to make an offer.

Devise a Plan. The plan is to offer the dealer 2% over dealer's cost. Assuming that the dealer accepts that offer, then we will calculate the monthly payment.

Carry Out the Plan. If you are serious about getting the best price, find out the **dealer's cost**—the price the dealer paid for the car you want to buy. In this book, we will tell you the dealer's cost, but in the real world you will need to do some homework to find it (consult an April issue of *Consumer Reports*). Assume that the dealer's cost for this car is $19,993.45. You decide to offer the dealer 2% *over* this cost. We will call this a 2% **offer:**

$$\$19,993.45(1 + 0.02) = \$20,393.32$$

You will notice that we ignored the sticker price and the dealer's preparation charges. Our offer is based only on the *dealer's cost*. Most car dealers will accept an offer that is between 5% and 10% over what they actually paid for the car. For this example, we will assume that the dealer accepted a price of $20,400. We also assume that we have a trade-in with a value of $4,100. Here is a list of calculations shown on the sales contract:

Sale price of Prius:	$20,394.00
Destination charges:	200.00
Subtotal:	20,594.00
Tax (8% rate)	1,647.52
Less trade-in	4,100.00
Amount to be financed:	18,141.52

We now calculate several key amounts:

Interest: $I = Prt = 18{,}141.52(0.06)(4) = 4{,}353.96$

Amount to be repaid: $A = P + I = 18{,}141.52 + 4{,}353.96 = 22{,}495.48$

Monthly payment: $m = \dfrac{22{,}495.48}{48} \approx 468.66$

Look Back. The monthly payment for the car is $468.66.

Annual Percentage Rate (APR)

An important aspect of add-on interest is that the actual rate you pay exceeds the quoted add-on interest rate. The reason for this is that you do not keep the entire amount borrowed for the entire time. For the car payments calculated in Example 2, the principal used was $14,090, but you do not *owe* this entire amount for 4 years. After the first payment, you will owe *less* than this amount. In fact, after you make 47 payments, you owe only $293.32; but the calculation shown in Example 2 assumes that the principal remains constant for 4 years. To see this a little more clearly, consider a simpler example.

Suppose you borrow $2,000 for 2 years with 10% add on-interest. The amount of interest is

$$\$2{,}000 \times 0.10 \times 2 = \$400$$

Now if you pay back $2,000 + $400 at the end of two years, the annual interest rate is 10%. However, if you make a partial payment of $1,200 at the end of the first year and $1,200 at the end of the second year, your total paid back is still the same ($2,400), but you have now paid a higher annual interest rate. Why? Take a look at Figure 11.1.

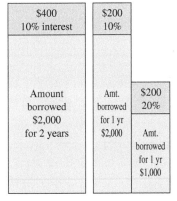

FIGURE 11.1 Interest on a $2,000 two-year loan

On the left we see that the interest on $2,000 is $400. But if you make a partial payment (figure on the right), we see that $200 for the first year is the correct interest, but the remaining $200 interest piled on the remaining balance of $1,000 is 20% interest (not the stated 10%). Note that since you did not owe $2,000 for 2 years, the interest rate, r, necessary to give $400 interest can be calculated using $I = Prt$:

$$(2{,}000)r(1) + (1{,}000)r(1) = 400$$
$$3{,}000r = 400$$
$$r = \frac{400}{3{,}000}$$
$$\approx 0.13333 \quad \text{or} \quad 13.3\%$$

This number, 13.3%, is called the *annual percentage rate.* This number is too difficult to calculate, as we have just done here, if the number of months is very large. We will, instead, give an approximation formula.

APR Formula

The **annual percentage rate,** or **APR,** is the rate paid on a loan when that rate is based on the actual amount owed for the length of time that it is owed. It can be approximated for an add-on interest rate, r, with N payments by using the formula

$$APR \approx \frac{2Nr}{N + 1}$$

We can verify this formula for the example illustrated in Figure 11.1:

$$APR \approx \frac{2(2)(0.10)}{2 + 1} \approx 0.1333$$

In 1968, a Truth-in-Lending Act was passed by Congress; it requires all lenders to state the true annual interest rate, which is called the *annual percentage rate* (APR) and is based on the actual amount owed. Regardless of the rate quoted, when you ask a salesperson what the APR is, the law requires that you be told this rate. This regulation enables you to compare interest rates *before* you sign a contract, which must state the APR even if you haven't asked for it.

Example **3**   **Find an APR for a installment purchase**

In Example 1, we considered the purchase of a computer with a price of $1,399, paid for in installments over 3 years at an add-on rate of 15%. Use the given APR formula (rounded to the nearest tenth of a percent) to approximate the APR.

Solution   Knowing the amount of the purchase is not necessary when finding the APR. We need to know only N and r. Since N is the number of payments, we have $N = 12(3) = 36$, and r is given as 0.15:

$$APR \approx \frac{2(36)(0.15)}{36 + 1} \approx 0.292$$

The APR is approximately 29.2%.

Example **4**   **Find an APR for a car**

Consider a Blazer with a price of $18,436 that is advertised at a monthly payment of $384.00 for 60 months. What is the APR (to the nearest tenth of a percent)?

Solution   We are given $P = 18,436$, $m = 384$, and $N = 60$. The APR formula requires that we know the rate r. The future value is the total amount to be repaid $(A = P + I)$ and the amount of interest is $I = Prt$. Now, $A = 384(60) = 23,040$, so $I = A - P = 23,040 - 18,436 = 4,604$. Since $N = 12t$, we see that $t = 5$ when $N = 60$.

$$
\begin{array}{ll}
I = Prt & \text{Simple interest formula} \\
4,604 = 18,436(r)(5) & \text{Substitute known values.} \\
920.8 = 18,436r & \text{Divide both sides by 5.} \\
0.0499457583 \approx r & \text{Divide both sides by 18,436.}
\end{array}
$$

Finally, from the APR formula, $APR \approx \frac{2Nr}{N+1}$,

$$APR \approx \frac{2(60)(0.0499457583)}{61} \approx 0.098$$

Don't round until the last step. You will really need a calculator for a problem like this one, so we will show you the appropriate steps:

Find A.

Find I.   Find r.   Find APR.

Display: .0982539508   The APR is approximately 9.8%.

Many automobiles are being offered at 0% interest! Good deal? It seems so, but buyer beware! Consider the following example.

Example 5   Compare APR and add-on rate

A local car dealer offered a 2002 Dodge 3/4 ton 4 × 4 pick-up truck with a manufacturer's suggested retail price (MSRP) of $33,29, less factory and dealer rebates of $5,489, for an "out-the-door no-haggle price of $27,801." The advertisement also offered "0% APR for 60 months" and in smaller print "In lieu of rebate." Suppose you can get a 2.5% add-on rate from the credit union. Should you choose the 0% APR or the 2.5% add-on rate? What is the credit union's APR rate?

Solution   The 0% APR would finance $33,290 for 60 months; the monthly payment would be

$$\frac{\$33,290}{60} = \$554.83/\text{mo}$$

The credit union rate is 2.5% for 60 months, so

$$I = Prt = \$27,801(0.025)(5) = \$3,475.13$$
$$A = P + I = \$31,276.13$$

The monthly payment would be

$$\frac{\$31,276.13}{60} = \$521.27$$

If we convert the 2.5% credit union add-on rate to an APR, we find

$$APR \approx \frac{2(0.025)(60)}{61} \approx 4.9\%$$

Note that the 0% APR financing is more costly than the credit union's 4.9% APR.

Open-End Credit

The most common type of open-end credit used today involves credit cards issued by VISA, MasterCard, Discover, American Express, department stores, and oil companies. Because you don't have to apply for credit each time you want to charge an item, this type of credit is very convenient.

When comparing the interest rates on loans, you should use the APR. Earlier, we introduced a formula for add-on interest; but for credit cards, the stated interest rate *is* the APR. However, the APR on credit cards is often stated as a daily or a monthly rate. For credit cards, we use a 365-day year rather than a 360-day year.

Don't forget: credit cards use a 365-day year (exact interest).

Example 6 Find APR from a given rate

Convert the given credit card rate to APR (rounded to the nearest tenth of a percent).

a. $1\frac{1}{2}\%$ per month

b. Daily rate of 0.05753%

Solution

a. Since there are 12 months per year, multiply a monthly rate by 12 to get the APR:

$$1\frac{1}{2}\% \times 12 = 18\% \text{ APR}$$

b. Multiply the daily rate by 365 to obtain the APR:

$$0.05753\% \times 365 = 20.99845\%$$

Rounded to the nearest tenth, this is equivalent to 21.0% APR.

Many credit cards charge an annual fee; some charge $1 every billing period the card is used, whereas others are free. These charges affect the APR differently, depending on how much the credit card is used during the year and on the monthly balance. If you always pay your credit card bill in full as soon as you receive it, the card with no yearly fee would obviously be the best for you. On the other hand, if you use your credit card to stretch out your payments, the APR is more important than the flat fee. For our purposes, we won't use the yearly fee in our calculations of APR on credit cards. Like annual fees, the interest rates or APRs for credit cards vary greatly. Because VISA and MasterCard are issued by many different banks, the terms can vary greatly even in one locality.

Credit Card Interest

An interest charge added to a consumer account is often called a **finance charge.** The finance charges can vary greatly even on credit cards that show the *same* APR, depending on the way the interest is calculated. There are three generally accepted methods for calculating these charges: *previous balance, adjusted balance,* and *average daily balance.*

Procedures for Calculating Credit Card Interest

For credit card interest, use the simple interest formula, $I = Prt$.

Previous balance method   Interest is calculated on the previous month's balance. With this method, P = previous balance, r = annual rate, and $t = \frac{1}{12}$.

Adjusted balance method   Interest is calculated on the previous month's balance *less* credits and payments. With this method, P = adjusted balance, r = annual rate, and $t = \frac{1}{12}$.

Average daily balance method   Add the outstanding balances for *each day* in the billing period, and then divide by the number of days in the billing period to find what is called the *average daily balance*. With this method, P = average daily balance, r = annual rate, and t = number of days in the billing period divided by 365.

In Example 7 we compare the finance charges on a $1,000 credit card purchase, using these three different methods.

Example 7 Contrast methods for calculating credit card interest

Calculate the interest on a $1,000 credit card bill that shows an 18% APR, assuming that $50 is sent on January 3 and is recorded on January 10. Contrast the three methods for calculating the interest.

Solution The three methods are the *previous balance method*, *adjusted balance method*, and *average daily balance method*. All three methods use the formula $I = Prt$.

Method

	Previous Balance	Adjusted Balance	Average Daily Balance
P:	$1,000	$1,000 − $50 = $950	Balance is $1,000 for 10 days of the 31-day month; balance is $950 for 21 days of the 31-day month: $$\frac{10 \times \$1,000 + 21 \times \$950}{31} = \$966.13$$
r:	0.18	0.18	0.18
t:	$\dfrac{1}{12}$	$\dfrac{1}{12}$	$\dfrac{31}{365}$
$I = Prt$	$\$1,000(0.18)\left(\dfrac{1}{12}\right)$	$\$950(0.18)\left(\dfrac{1}{12}\right)$	$\$966.13(0.18)\left(\dfrac{31}{365}\right)$
	= $15.00	= $14.25	= $14.77

You can sometimes make good use of credit cards by taking advantage of the period during which no finance charges are levied. Many credit cards charge no interest if you pay in full within a certain period of time (usually 20 or 30 days). This is called the **grace period.** On the other hand, if you borrow cash on your credit card, you should know that many credit cards have an additional charge for cash advances—and these can be as high as 4%. This 4% is *in addition* to the normal finance charges.

Problem Set 11.2

Level 1

1. **IN YOUR OWN WORDS** What is add-on interest?

2. **IN YOUR OWN WORDS** What is APR?

3. **IN YOUR OWN WORDS** Compare and contrast open-end and closed-end credit.

4. **IN YOUR OWN WORDS** Discuss the methods of calculating credit card interest.

5. **IN YOUR OWN WORDS** If you have a credit card, describe the method of calculating interest on your card. Name the bank issuing the credit card. If you do not have a credit card, contact a bank and obtain an application to answer this question. Name the bank.

6. **IN YOUR OWN WORDS** Describe a good procedure for saving money with the purchase of an automobile.

Use estimation to select the best response in Problems 7–24. Do not calculate.

7. If you purchase a $2,400 item and pay for it with monthly installments for 2 years, the monthly payment is
   A. $100 per month
   B. more than $100 per month
   C. less than $100 per month

8. If you purchase a $595.95 item and pay for it with monthly installments for 1 year, the monthly payment is
   A. about $50
   B. more than $50
   C. less than $50

9. If I do not pay off my credit card each month, the most important cost factor is
   A. the annual fee   B. the APR   C. the grace period

10. If I pay off my credit card balance each month, the most important cost factor is
A. the annual fee
B. the APR
C. the grace period

11. The method of calculation most advantageous to the consumer is the
A. previous balance method
B. adjusted balance method
C. average daily balance method

12. If you purchase an item for $1,295 at an interest rate of 9.8%, and you finance it for 1 year, then the amount of add-on interest is about
A. $13.00   B. $500   C. $130

13. If you purchase an item for $1,295 at an interest rate of 9.8%, and you finance it for 4 years, then the amount of add-on interest is about
A. $13.00   B. $500   C. $130

14. If you purchase a new car for $10,000 and finance it for 4 years, the amount of interest you would expect to pay is about
A. $4,000   B. $400   C. $24,000

15. A reasonable APR to pay for a 3-year installment loan is
A. 1%   B. 12%   C. 32%

16. A reasonable APR to pay for a 3-year automobile loan is
A. 6%   B. 40%   C. $2,000

17. If you wish to purchase a car with a sticker price of $10,000, a reasonable offer to make to the dealer is:
A. $10,000   B. $9,000   C. $11,000

18. A reasonable APR for a credit card is
A. 1%   B. 30%   C. 12%

19. In an application of the average daily balance method for the month of August, t is
A. $\frac{1}{12}$ B. $\frac{30}{365}$ C. $\frac{31}{365}$

20. When using the average daily balance method for the month of September, t is
A. $\frac{1}{12}$ B. $\frac{30}{365}$ C. $\frac{31}{365}$

21. If your credit card balance is $650 and the interest rate is 12% APR, then the credit card interest charge is
A. $6.50   B. $65   C. $8.25

22. If your credit card balance is $952, you make a $50 payment, the APR is 12%, and the interest is calculated according to the previous balance method, then the finance charge is
A. $9.52   B. $9.02   C. $9.06

23. If your credit card balance is $952, you make a $50 payment, the APR is 12%, and the interest is calculated according to the adjusted balance method, then the finance charge is
A. $9.52   B. $9.02   C. $9.06

24. If your credit card balance is $952, you make a $50 payment, the APR is 12%, and the interest is calculated according to the average daily balance method, then the finance charge is
A. $9.52   B. $9.02   C. $9.06

Convert each credit card rate in Problems 25–30 to the APR.*

25. Oregon, $1\frac{1}{4}$% per month

26. Arizona, $1\frac{1}{3}$% per month

27. New York, $1\frac{1}{2}$% per month

28. Tennessee, 0.02740% daily rate

29. Ohio, 0.02192% daily rate

30. Nebraska, 0.03014% daily rate

Calculate the monthly finance charge for each credit card transaction in Problems 31–34. Assume that it takes 10 days for a payment to be received and recorded, and that the month is 30 days long.

31. $300 balance, 18%, $50 payment
  a. previous balance method
  b. adjusted balance method
  c. average daily balance method

32. $300 balance, 18%, $250 payment
  a. previous balance method
  b. adjusted balance method
  c. average daily balance method

33. $3,000 balance, 15%, $50 payment
  a. previous balance method
  b. adjusted balance method
  c. average daily balance method

34. $3,000 balance, 15%, $2,500 payment
  a. previous balance method
  b. adjusted balance method
  c. average daily balance method

Round your answers in Problems 35–38 to the nearest dollar.

35. Make a 6% offer on a Chevrolet Corsica that has a sticker price of $14,385 and a dealer cost of $13,378.

36. Make a 5% offer on a Ford Escort that has a sticker price of $13,205 and a dealer cost of $12,412.70.

37. Make a 10% offer on a Saturn that has a sticker price of $19,895 and a dealer cost of $17,250.

38. Make a 10% offer on a Nissan Pathfinder that has a sticker price of $32,129 and a dealer cost of $28,916.

Level 2

Find the APR (rounded to the nearest tenth of a percent) for each of the loans described in Problems 39–42.

39. Purchase a living room set for 3,600 at 12% add-on interest for 3 years.

40. Purchase a stereo for $2,500 at 13% add-on interest for 2 years.

41. Purchase an oven for $650 at 11% add-on interest for 2 years.

42. Purchase a refrigerator for $2,100 at 14% add-on interest for 3 years.

*These rates were the listed finance charges on purchases of less than $500 on a Citibank VISA statement.

Assume the cars in Problems 43–46 can be purchased for 0% down for 60 months (in lieu of rebate).

a. *Find the monthly payment if financed for 60 months at 0% APR.*
b. *Find the monthly payment if financed at 2.5% add-on interest for 60 months.*
c. *Use the APR approximation formula for part* **b.**
d. *State whether the 0% APR or the 2.5% add-on rate should be preferred.*

43. A Dodge Ram that has a sticker price of $20,650 with factory and dealer rebates of $2,000

44. A BMW that has a sticker price of $62,490 with factory and dealer rebates of $6,000

45. A car with a sticker price of $42,700 with factory and dealer rebates of $5,100

46. A car with a sticker price of $36,500 with factory and dealer rebates of $4,200

Level 3

For each of the car loans described in Problems 47–52, give the following information.

a. *Amount to be paid*
b. *Amount of interest*
c. *Interest rate*
d. *APR (rounded to the nearest tenth percent)*

47. A newspaper advertisement offers a $9,000 car for nothing down and 36 easy monthly payments of $317.50.

48. A newspaper advertisement offers a $4,000 used car for nothing down and 36 easy monthly payments of $141.62.

49. A newspaper advertisement offers a $14,350 car for nothing down and 48 easy monthly payments of $488.40.

50. A car dealer will sell you the $16,450 car of your dreams for $3,290 down and payments of $339.97 per month for 48 months.

51. A car dealer will sell you a used car for $6,798 with $798 down and payments of $168.51 per month for 48 months.

52. A car dealer will sell you the $30,450 car of your dreams for $6,000 down and payments of $662.06 per month for 60 months.

53. A car dealer carries out the following calculations:

List price	$5,368.00
Options	$1,625.00
Destination charges	$ 200.00
Subtotal	$7,193.00
Tax	$ 431.58
Less trade-in	$2,932.00
Amount to be financed	$4,692.58
8% interest for 48 months	$1,501.63
Total	$6,194.21
MONTHLY PAYMENT	$ 129.05

What is the annual percentage rate?

54. A car dealer carries out the following calculations:

List price	$15,428.00
Options	$ 3,625.00
Destination charges	$ 350.00
Subtotal	$19,403.00
Tax	$ 1,164.18
Less trade-in	$ 7,950.00
Amount to be financed	$12,617.18
5% interest for 48 months	$ 2,523.44
Total	$15,140.62
MONTHLY PAYMENT	$ 315.43

What is the annual percentage rate?

55. A car dealer carries out the following calculations:

List price	$ 9,450.00
Options	$ 1,125.00
Destination charges	$ 300.00
Subtotal	$10,875.00
Tax	$ 652.50
Less trade-in	$ .00
Amount to be financed	$11,527.50
11% interest for 48 months	$ 5,072.10
Total	$16,599.60
MONTHLY PAYMENT	$ 345.83

What is the annual percentage rate?

Problem Solving 3

56. The finance charge statement on a Sears Revolving Charge Card statement is shown here. Why do you suppose that the limitation on the 50¢ finance charge is for amounts less than $28.50?

> **SEARS ROEBUCK AND CO.**
> **SEARSCHARGE SECURITY AGREEMENT**
>
> 4. FINANCE CHARGE. If I do not pay the entire New Balance within 30 days (28 days for February statements) of the monthly billing date, a FINANCE CHARGE will be added to the account for the current monthly billing period. **THE FINANCE CHARGE** will be either a minimum of $0.50 if the Average Daily Balance is $28.50 or less, or a periodic rate of 1.75% per month (**ANNUAL PERCENTAGE RATE** of 21%) on the Average Daily Balance.

57. Marsha needs to have a surgical procedure done and does not have the $3,000 cash necessary for the operation. Upon talking to an administrator at the hospital, she finds that it will accept MasterCard, VISA, and Discover credit cards. All of these credit cards have an APR of 18%, so she figures that it does not matter which card she uses, even though she plans to take a year to pay off the loan. Assume that Marsha makes a payment of $300 and then receives a bill. Show the interest from credit cards of 18% APR according to the previous balance, adjusted balance, and average daily balance methods. Assume that the month has 31 days and that it takes 14 days for Marsha's payment to be mailed and recorded.

58. Karen and Wayne need to buy a refrigerator because theirs just broke. Unfortunately, their savings account is depleted, and they will need to borrow money in order to buy a new one. The bank offers them a personal loan at 21% (APR), and Sears offers them an installment loan at 15% (add-on rate). Suppose that the refrigerator at Sears costs $1,598 plus 5% sales tax, and Karen and Wayne plan to pay for the refrigerator for 3 years. Should they finance it with the bank or with Sears?

59. Karen and Wayne need to buy a refrigerator because theirs just broke. Unfortunately, their savings account is depleted, and they will need to borrow money in order to buy a new one. Sears offers them an installment loan at 15% (add-on rate). If the refrigerator at Sears costs $1,598 plus 5% sales tax, and Karen and Wayne plan to pay for the refrigerator for 3 years, what is the monthly payment?

60. **Rule of 78** With a typical installment loan, you are asked to sign a contract stating the terms of repayment. If you pay off the loan early, you are entitled to an interest rebate. For example, if you finance $500 and are charged $90 interest (APR 8.46%), the total to be repaid is $590 with 24 monthly payments of $24.59. After 1 year, you decide to pay off the loan, so you figure that the rebate should be $45 (half of the interest for 2 years), but instead you are told the interest rebate is only $23.40. What happened? Look at the fine print on the contract. It says interest will be refunded according to the Rule of 78. The formula for the rebate is as follows:

$$\text{INTEREST REBATE} = \frac{k(k+1)}{n(n+1)} \times \text{FINANCE CHARGE}$$

where k is the number of payments remaining and n is the total number of payments. Determine the interest rebate on the following:
   a. $1,026 interest on an 18-month loan; pay off loan after 12 months.
   b. $350 interest on a 2-year loan with 10 payments remaining.
   c. $10,200 borrowed at 11% on a 4-year loan with 36 months remaining.
   d. $51,000 borrowed at 10% on a 5-year loan with 18 payments remaining.

11.3 Sequences

In the previous sections we considered financial applications dealing with a lump sum, or with applications based on simple or compound interest. However, many financial problems in real life deal with periodic payments in which the interest is calculated on a month-by-month basis. In order to consider such financial applications, it is necessary to understand two important mathematical concepts. The first, sequences, is considered in this section, and the second, series, is considered in the next.

Sequences or Progressions

Patterns are sometimes used as part of an IQ test. It used to be thought that an IQ test measured "innate intelligence" and that a person's IQ score was fairly constant. Today, it is known that this is not the case. IQ test scores can be significantly changed by studying the types of questions asked. Even if you have never taken an IQ test, you have taken (or will take) tests that ask pattern-type questions.

An example of an IQ test is shown below. It is a so-called "quickie" test, but it illustrates a few mathematical patterns (see Problems 1–6 on this IQ test). The purpose of this section is to look at some simple patterns to become more proficient in recognizing them, and then to apply them to develop some important financial formulas.

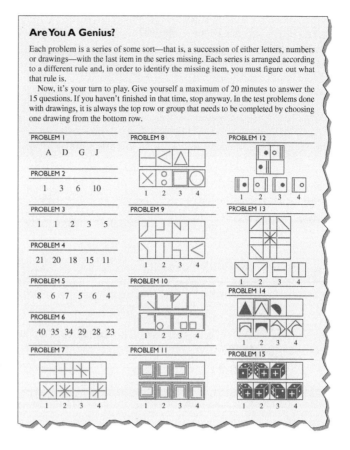

Arithmetic Sequences

Perhaps the simplest pattern is the counting numbers themselves: 1, 2, 3, 4, 5, 6, ... A list of numbers having a first number, a second number, a third number, and so on is called a **sequence.**

Arithmetic growth is linear.

The numbers in a sequence are called the **terms** of the sequence. The sequence of counting numbers is formed by adding 1 to each term to obtain the next term. Your math assignments may well have been identified by some sequence: "Do the multiples of 3 from 3 to 30," that is, 3, 6, 9, . . . , 27, 30. This sequence is formed by adding 3 to each term. Sequences obtained by adding the same number to each term to obtain the next term are called *arithmetic sequences* or *arithmetic progressions*.

Arithmetic Sequence

An **arithmetic sequence** is a sequence whose consecutive terms differ by the same real number, called the **common difference.**

Example 1 Find the missing term of an arithmetic sequence

Show that each sequence is arithmetic, and find the missing term.
a. 1, 4, 7, 10, 13, _____, . . .
b. 20, 14, 8, 2, −4, −10, _____, . . .
c. $a_1, a_1 + d, a_1 + 2d, a_1 + 3d, a_1 + 4d,$ _____, . . .

Solution

a. Look for a common difference by subtracting each term from the succeeding term:

$$4 - 1 = 3, \quad 7 - 4 = 3, \quad 10 - 7 = 3, \quad 13 - 10 = 3$$

 Do not check only the first difference. All the differences must be the same.

If the difference between each pair of consecutive terms of the sequence is the same number, then that number is the common difference; in this case it is 3. To find the missing term, simply add the common difference. The next term is

$$13 + 3 = 16$$

b. The common difference is −6. The next term is found by adding the common difference:

$$-10 + (-6) = -16$$

c. The common difference is d, so the next term is

$$(a_1 + 4d) + d = a_1 + 5d$$

Example 1c leads us to a formula for arithmetic sequences:

a_1 is the first term of an arithmetic sequence.

a_2 is the second term of an arithmetic sequence, and

$$a_2 = a_1 + d$$

a_3 is the third term of an arithmetic sequence, and

$$a_3 = a_2 + d = (a_1 + d) + d = a_1 + 2d$$

a_4 is the fourth term of an arithmetic sequence, and

$$a_4 = a_3 + d = (a_1 + 2d) + d = a_1 + 3d$$

a_{43} is the 43rd term of an arithmetic sequence, and

$$a_{43} = a_1 + \underline{42}d$$
One less than the term number
$$\vdots$$

This pattern leads to the following formula.

General Term of an Arithmetic Sequence

The *general term* of an arithmetic sequence $a_1, a_2, a_3, \ldots, a_n$, with common difference d is

$$a_n = a_1 + (n - 1)d$$

Example 2 Find a sequence given a general term

If $a_n = 26 - 6n$, list the sequence.

Solution

$$a_1 = 26 - 6(1) = 20 \qquad a_1 \text{ means evaluate } 26 - 6n \text{ for } n = 1.$$
$$a_2 = 26 - 6(2) = 14$$

$$a_3 = 26 - 6(3) = 8$$
$$a_4 = 26 - 6(4) = 2$$

The sequence is 20, 14, 8, 2, ...

Geometric Sequences

A second type of sequence is the *geometric sequence* or *geometric progression*. If each term is *multiplied* by the same number (instead of *added* to the same number) to obtain successive terms, a geometric sequence is formed.

1   2   4   8   16

Geometric growth is exponential.

Geometric Sequence

A **geometric sequence** is a sequence whose consecutive terms have the same quotient, called the **common ratio.**

If the sequence is geometric, the number obtained by dividing any term into the following term of that sequence will be the same nonzero number. No term of a geometric sequence may be zero.

Example 3 Find the common ratio of a geometric sequence

Show that each sequence is geometric, and find the common ratio.
a. 2, 4, 8, 16, 32, ———, . . .   **b.** 10, 5, $\frac{5}{2}, \frac{5}{4}, \frac{5}{8}$, ———, . . .
c. $g_1, g_1 r, g_1 r^2, g_1 r^3, g_1 r^4$, ———, . . .

Solution
a. First, verify that there is a common ratio:

$$\frac{4}{2} = 2, \quad \frac{8}{4} = 2, \quad \frac{16}{8} = 2, \quad \frac{32}{16} = 2$$

The common ratio is 2, so to find the next term, multiply the common ratio by the preceding term. The next term is

$$32(2) = 64$$

b. The common ratio is $\frac{1}{2}$ (be sure to check *each* ratio). The next term is found by multiplication:

$$\frac{5}{8}\left(\frac{1}{2}\right) = \frac{5}{16}$$

c. The common ratio is r, and the next term is

$$g_1 r^4(r) = g_1 r^5$$

As with arithmetic sequences, we denote the terms of a geometric sequence by using a special notation. Let $g_1, g_2, g_3, \ldots, g_n, \ldots$ be the terms of a *geometric* sequence. Example 3c leads us to a formula for geometric sequences.

$$g_2 = rg_1$$
$$g_3 = rg_2 = r(rg_1) = r^2 g_1$$
$$g_4 = rg_3 = r(rg_2) = r(r^2 g_1) = r^3 g_1$$
$$g_5 = rg_4 = r(r^3 g_1) = r^4 g_1$$
$$\vdots$$

one less than the term number
$$g_{92} = r^{\overline{91}} g_1$$

Look for patterns to find the following formula.

General Term Geometric Sequence

For a geometric sequence $g_1, g_2, g_3, \ldots, g_n, \ldots$, with common ratio r, the *general term* is

$$g_n = g_1 r^{n-1}$$

Example 4   Find the terms of a geometric sequence

List the sequence generated by $g_n = 50(2)^{n-1}$.

Solution

$$g_1 = 50(2)^{1-1} = 50$$
$$g_2 = 50(2)^{2-1} = 100$$
$$g_3 = 50(2)^{3-1} = 200$$
$$g_4 = 50(2)^{4-1} = 400$$

The sequence is $50, 100, 200, 400, \ldots$.

Fibonacci-Type Sequences

Even though our attention is focused on arithmetic and geometric sequences, it is important to realize that there can be other types of sequences.

The next type of sequence came about, oddly enough, by looking at the birth patterns of rabbits. In the 13th century, Leonardo Fibonacci wrote a book, *Liber Abaci*, in which he discussed the advantages of the Hindu-Arabic numerals over Roman numerals. In this

Leonardo Fibonacci (ca. 1175–1250)

Fibonacci, also known as Leonardo da Pisa, visited a number of Eastern and Arabic cities, where he became interested in the Hindu-Arabic numeration system we use today. He wrote *Liber Abaci,* in which he strongly advocated the use of the Hindu-Arabic numeration system. Howard Eves, in his book *In Mathematical Circles,* states: "Fibonacci sometimes signed his work with the name *Leonardo Bigollo.* Now *bigollo* has more than one meaning; it means both 'traveler' and 'blockhead.' In signing his work as he did, Fibonacci may have meant that he was a great traveler, for so he was. But a story has circulated that he took pleasure in using this signature because many of his contemporaries considered him a blockhead (for his interest in the new numbers), and it pleased him to show these critics what a blockhead could accomplish."

Historical NOTE

book, one problem was to find the number of rabbits alive after a given number of generations. Let us consider what he did with this problem.

Kerstin Jönsson/epa/Corbis

Example **5** **Find the number of rabbits**

Pólya's Method

Suppose a pair of rabbits will produce a new pair of rabbits in their second month, and thereafter will produce a new pair every month. The new rabbits will do exactly the same. Start with one pair. How many pairs will there be in 10 months?

Solution   We use Pólya's problem-solving guidelines for this example.

Understand the Problem. We can begin to understand the problem by looking at the following chart:

Number of Months	Number of Pairs	Pairs of Rabbits (the pairs shown in color are ready to reproduce in the next month)
Start	1	
1	1	
2	2	
3	3	
4	5	
5	8	
⋮	⋮	Same pair (rabbits never die)

Devise a Plan. We look for a pattern with the sequence 1, 1, 2, 3, 5, 8, . . . ; it is not arithmetic and it is not geometric. It looks as if (after the first two months) each new number can be found by adding the two previous terms.

Carry Out the Plan. $1 + 1 = 2$

$$1 + 2 = 3$$
$$2 + 3 = 5$$
$$3 + 5 = 8$$
$$5 + 8$$

Do you see the pattern? The sequence is 1, 1, 2, 3, 5, 8, 13, 21, 34, 55, 89, . . .

Look Back. Using this pattern, Fibonacci was able to compute the number of pairs of rabbits alive after 10 months (it is the tenth term after the first 1): 89. He could also compute the number of pairs of rabbits after the first year or any other interval. Without a pattern, the problem would indeed be a difficult one.

Fibonacci Sequence

A **Fibonacci-type sequence** is a sequence in which any two numbers form the first and second terms, and subsequent terms are found by adding the previous two terms. The **Fibonacci sequence** is that sequence for which the first two terms are both 1.

If we state this definition symbolically with first term s_1, second term s_2, and general term s_n, we have a formula for the general term.

General Term of a Fibonacci Sequence

For a Fibonacci sequence $s_1, s_2, s_3, \ldots, s_n, \ldots$, the general term is given by

$$s_n = s_{n-1} + s_{n-2}$$

for $n \geq 3$.

Example 6   Find the terms of a Fibonacci-type sequence

a. If $s_1 = 5$ and $s_2 = 2$, list the first five terms of this Fibonacci-type sequence.
b. If s_1 and s_2 represent any first numbers, list the first eight terms of this Fibonacci-type sequence.

Solution

a. 5, 2, 7, 9, 16

with $2+7$, $5+2$, $7+9$

b. s_1 and s_2 are given.

$$s_3 = s_2 + s_1$$
$$s_4 = s_3 + s_2 = (s_1 + s_2) + s_2 = s_1 + 2s_2$$
$$s_5 = s_4 + s_3 = (s_1 + 2s_2) + (s_1 + s_2) = 2s_1 + 3s_2$$
$$s_6 = s_5 + s_4 = (2s_1 + 3s_2) + (s_1 + 2s_2) = 3s_1 + 5s_2$$
$$s_7 = s_6 + s_5 = (3s_1 + 5s_2) + (2s_1 + 3s_2) = 5s_1 + 8s_2$$
$$s_8 = s_7 + s_6 = (5s_1 + 8s_2) + (3s_1 + 5s_2) = 8s_1 + 13s_2$$

Look at the coefficients in the algebraic simplification and notice that the Fibonacci sequence 1, 1, 2, 3, 5, 8, . . . is part of the construction of any Fibonacci-type sequence regardless of the terms s_1 and s_2.

Historically, there has been much interest in the Fibonacci sequence. It is used in botany, zoology, business, economics, statistics, operations research, archeology, architecture, education, and sociology. There is even an official Fibonacci Association.

An example of Fibonacci numbers occurring in nature is illustrated by a sunflower. The seeds are arranged in spiral curves as shown in Figure 11.2.

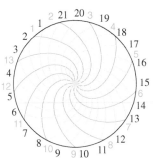

FIGURE 11.2 The arrangement of the pods (phyllotaxy) of a sunflower illustrates a Fibonacci sequence.

If we count the number of counterclockwise spirals (13 and 21 in this example), they are successive terms in the Fibonacci sequence. This is true of all sunflowers and, indeed, of the seed head of any composite flower such as the daisy or aster.

Example 7 Classify sequences

Classify the given sequences as arithmetic, geometric, Fibonacci-type, or none of the above. Find the next term for each sequence and give its general term if it is arithmetic, geometric, or Fibonacci-type.

a. $15, 30, 60, 120, \ldots$ **b.** $15, 30, 45, 60, \ldots$ **c.** $15, 30, 45, 75, \ldots$
d. $15, 20, 26, 33, \ldots$ **e.** $3, 3, 3, 3, \ldots$ **f.** $15, 30, 90, 360, \ldots$

Solution

a. $15, 30, 60, 120, \ldots$ does not have a common difference, but a common ratio of 2, so this is a geometric sequence. The next term is $120(2) = 240$. The general term is $g_n = 15(2)^{n-1}$.

b. $15, 30, 45, 60, \ldots$ has a common difference of 15, so this is an arithmetic sequence. The next term of the sequence is $60 + 15 = 75$. The general term is $a_n = 15 + (n - 1)15 = 15 + 15n - 15 = 15n$.

c. $15, 30, 45, 75, \ldots$ does not have a common difference or a common ratio. Next, we check for a Fibonacci-type sequence by adding successive terms: $15 + 30 = 45$; $30 + 45 = 75$, so this is a Fibonacci-type sequence. The next term is $45 + 75 = 120$. The general term is $s_n = s_{n-1} + s_{n-2}$ where $s_1 = 15$ and $s_2 = 30$.

d. $15, 20, 26, 33, \ldots$ does not have a common difference or a common ratio. Since $15 + 20 \neq 26$, we see it is not a Fibonacci-type sequence. We do see a pattern, however, when looking at the differences:

$$20 - 15 = 5; \quad 26 - 20 = 6; \quad 33 - 26 = 7$$

The next difference is 8. Thus, the next term is $33 + 8 = 41$.

e. 3, 3, 3, 3, ... has a common difference of 0 and the common ratio is 1, so it is both arithmetic and geometric. The next term is 3. The general term is $a_n = 3 + (n - 1)0 = 3$ or $g_n = 3(1)^{n-1} = 3$.

f. 15, 30, 90, 360, ... does not have a common difference or a common ratio. We see a pattern when looking at the ratios:

$$\frac{30}{15} = 2; \quad \frac{90}{30} = 3; \quad \frac{360}{90} = 4$$

The next ratio is 5. Thus, the next term is $360(5) = 1,800$.

General terms can be given for sequences that are not arithmetic, geometric, or Fibonacci-type. Consider the following example.

Example 8 Find the terms of a given sequence

Find the first four terms for the sequences with the given general terms. If the general term defines an arithmetic, geometric, or Fibonacci-type sequence, so state.

a. $s_n = n^2$ **b.** $s_n = (-1)^n - 5n$ **c.** $s_n = s_{n-1} + s_{n-2}$, where $s_1 = -4$ and $s_2 = 6$
d. $s_n = 2n$ **e.** $s_n = 2n + (n - 1)(n - 2)(n - 3)(n - 4)$

Solution

a. Since $s_n = n^2$, we find $s_1 = (1)^2 = 1$; $s_2 = (2)^2 = 4$, $s_3 = (3)^2, \ldots$.
The sequence is $1, 4, 9, 16, \ldots$.

b. Since $s_n = (-1)^n - 5n$, we find

$$s_1 = (-1)^1 - 5(1) = -6$$
$$s_2 = (-1)^2 - 5(2) = -9$$
$$s_3 = (-1)^3 - 5(3) = -16$$
$$s_4 = (-1)^4 - 5(4) = -19$$

The sequence is $-6, -9, -16, -19, \ldots$.

c. $s_n = s_{n-1} + s_{n-2}$ is the form of a Fibonacci-type sequence. Using the two given terms, we find:

$$s_1 = -4 \quad \text{Given}$$
$$s_2 = 6 \quad \text{Given}$$
$$s_3 = s_2 + s_1 = 6 + (-4) = 2$$
$$s_4 = s_3 + s_2 = 2 + 6 = 8$$

The sequence is $-4, 6, 2, 8, \ldots$.

d. $s_n = 2n$; $s_1 = 2(1) = 2$; $s_2 = 2(2) = 4$; $s_3 = 2(3) = 6$; ....
The sequence is $2, 4, 6, 8, \ldots$; this is an arithmetic sequence.

e. $s_n = 2n + (n - 1)(n - 2)(n - 3)(n - 4)$

$$s_1 = 2(1) + (1 - 1)(1 - 2)(1 - 3)(1 - 4) = 2$$
$$s_2 = 2(2) + (2 - 1)(2 - 2)(2 - 3)(2 - 4) = 4$$
$$s_3 = 2(3) + (3 - 1)(3 - 2)(3 - 3)(3 - 4) = 6$$
$$s_4 = 2(4) + (4 - 1)(4 - 2)(4 - 3)(4 - 4) = 8$$

The sequence is $2, 4, 6, 8, \ldots$.

Examples 8d and 8e show that if only a finite number of successive terms is known and no general term is given, then a *unique* general term cannot be given. That is, if we are given the sequence

2, 4, 6, 8, . . .

the next term is probably 10 (if we are thinking of the general term of Example 8d), but it *may* be something different. In Example 8e,

$$s_5 = 2(5) + (5 - 1)(5 - 2)(5 - 3)(5 - 4) = 34$$

This gives the unlikely sequence 2, 4, 6, 8, 34, ... In general, you are looking for the simplest general term; nevertheless, you must remember that answers are not unique *unless the general term is given.*

COMPUTATIONAL WINDOW

If you have access to a spreadsheet program, it is easy to generate the terms of a sequence. The spreadsheet below shows the first 19 terms for the sequences given in Example 8.

Spreadsheet Application

	A	B	C	D	E	F	G
1	Term	a	b	c	d	e	
2	1	1	-6	-4	2	2	
3	2	4	-9	6	4	4	
4	3	9	-16	2	6	6	
5	4	16	-19	8	8	8	
6	5	25	-26	10	10	34	
7	6	36	-29	18	12	132	
8	7	49	-36	28	14	374	
9	8	64	-39	46	16	856	
10	9	81	-46	74	18	1698	
11	10	100	-49	120	20	3044	
12	11	121	-56	194	22	5062	
13	12	144	-59	314	24	7944	
14	13	169	-66	508	26	11906	
15	14	196	-69	822	28	17188	
16	15	225	-76	1330	30	24054	
17	16	256	-79	2152	32	32792	
18	17	289	-86	3482	34	43714	
19	18	324	-89	5634	36	57156	
20	19	361	-96	9116	38	73478	

The formulas for the cells correspond to the formulas in Example 8.
Term: 1; +A2+1; replicate

a: +A2^2; +A3^2; replicate

b: +(−1)^A2 − 5*A2; +(−1)^A3 − 5*A3; replicate

c: −4; 6; +D2+D3; replicate

d: +2*A2; +2*A3; replicate

e: +2*A2+(A2 − 1)*(A2 − 2)*(A2 − 3)*(A2 − 4); replicate

We conclude this section by summarizing the procedure for classifying sequences.

Procedure for Classifying Sequences

To classify the sequence $s_1, s_2, s_3, \ldots, s_n$:

Step 1   Check to see if it is *arithmetic*. Find the successive differences:

$$s_2 - s_1 = d_1$$
$$s_3 - s_2 = d_2$$
$$s_4 - s_3 = d_3$$
$$\vdots$$

If all these differences

$$d_1 = d_2 = d_3 = \ldots$$

are the same, then it is an arithmetic sequence.

Step 2   Check to see if it is *geometric*. Find successive ratios

$$\frac{s_2}{s_1} = r_1; \quad \frac{s_3}{s_2} = r_2; \quad \frac{s_4}{s_3} = r_3, \ldots$$

If all these ratios

$$r_1 = r_2 = r_3 = \ldots$$

are the same, then it is a geometric sequence.

Step 3   Check to see if it is *Fibonacci-type*. Check to see if

$$s_3 = s_2 + s_1$$
$$s_4 = s_3 + s_2$$
$$\vdots$$

If these sums check, then it is a Fibonacci-type sequence.

Step 4   If the sequence is not arithmetic, geometric, Fibonacci, or Fibonacci-type, then we classify it by saying it is none of the above.

Problem Set 11.3

Level 1

1. IN YOUR OWN WORDS   What is a sequence?

2. IN YOUR OWN WORDS   What do we mean by a general term?

3. IN YOUR OWN WORDS   What is an arithmetic sequence?

4. IN YOUR OWN WORDS   What is a geometric sequence?

5. IN YOUR OWN WORDS   What is a Fibonacci sequence?

In Problems 6–31,
a. *Classify the sequences as arithmetic, geometric, Fibonacci, or none of these.*
b. *If arithmetic, give d; if geometric, give r; if Fibonacci, give the first two terms; and if none of these, state a pattern using your own words.*
c. *Supply the next term.*

6. 2, 4, 6, 8, _____, . . .

7. 2, 4, 8, 16, _____, . . .

8. 2, 4, 6, 10, _____, . . .

9. 5, 15, 25, _____, . . .

10. 5, 15, 45, _____, . . .

11. 5, 15, 20, _____, . . .

12. 1, 5, 25, _____, . . .

13. 25, 5, 1, _____, . . .

14. 9, 3, 1, _____, . . .

15. 1, 3, 9, _____, . . .

16. 21, 20, 18, 15, 11, _____, . . .

17. 8, 6, 7, 5, 6, 4, _____, . . .

18. 2, 5, 8, 11, 14, _____, . . .

19. 3, 6, 12, 24, 48, _____, . . .

20. 5, −15, 45, −135, 405, _____, . . .

21. 10, 10, 10, _____, . . .

22. 2, 5, 7, 12, _____, . . .

23. $3, 6, 9, 15,$ _____, ...

24. $1, 8, 27, 64, 125,$ _____, ...

25. $8, 12, 18, 27,$ _____, ...

26. $3^2, 3^5, 3^8, 3^{11},$ _____, ...

27. $4^5, 4^4, 4^3, 4^2,$ _____, ...

28. $\frac{1}{2}, \frac{1}{3}, \frac{2}{3}, \frac{1}{4}, \frac{3}{4}, \frac{1}{5}, \frac{2}{5}, \frac{3}{5}, \frac{4}{5}, \frac{1}{6},$ _____, ...

29. $\frac{1}{10}, \frac{1}{5}, \frac{3}{10}, \frac{2}{5}, \frac{1}{2},$ _____, ...

30. $\frac{4}{3}, 2, 3, 4\frac{1}{2},$ _____, ...

31. $\frac{7}{12}, \frac{2}{3}, \frac{3}{4}, \frac{5}{6},$ _____, ...

Level 2

In Problems 32–47,
  a. *Find the first three terms of the sequences whose nth terms are given.*
  b. *Classify the sequence as arithmetic (give d), geometric (give r), both, or neither.*

32. $s_n = 4n - 3$

33. $s_n = -3 + 3n$

34. $s_n = 10n$

35. $s_n = 2 - n$

36. $s_n = 7 - 3n$

37. $s_n = 10 - 10n$

38. $s_n = \frac{2}{n}$

39. $s_n = 1 - \frac{1}{n}$

40. $s_n = \frac{n-1}{n+1}$

41. $s_n = \frac{1}{2}n(n+1)$

42. $s_n = \frac{1}{4}n^2(n+1)^2$

43. $s_n = (-1)^n$

44. $s_n = -5$

45. $s_n = \frac{2}{3}$

46. $s_n = (-1)^{n+1}$

47. $s_n = (-1)^n(n+1)$

Find the requested terms in Problems 48–55.

48. Find the 15th term of the sequence $s_n = 4n - 3$

49. Find the 69th term of the sequence $s_n = 7 - 3n$

50. Find the 20th term of the sequence $s_n = (-1)^n(n+1)$

51. Find the 3rd term of the sequence $s_n = (-1)^{n+1}5^{n+1}$

52. Find the first five terms of the sequence where
$$s_1 = 2 \text{ and } s_n = 3s_{n-1}, n \geq 2$$

53. Find the first five terms of the sequence where
$$s_1 = 3 \text{ and } s_n = \frac{1}{3}s_{n-1}, n \geq 2$$

54. Find the first five terms of the sequence where
$$s_1 = 1, s_2 = 1, \text{ and } s_n = s_{n-1} + s_{n-2}, n \geq 3$$

55. Find the first five terms of the sequence where
$$s_1 = 1, s_2 = 2, \text{ and } s_n = s_{n-1} + s_{n-2}, n \geq 3$$

Problem Solving 3

56. Is the following sequence a Fibonacci sequence? a_n is one more than the nth term of the Fibonacci sequence.

57. Is the following sequence a Fibonacci sequence?

$1, 1, 2, 3, 5, 8, \ldots, a_n$, where a_n is the integer nearest to

$$\frac{1}{\sqrt{5}}\left[\frac{1+\sqrt{5}}{2}\right]^n$$

58. Apartment blocks of n floors are to be painted blue and yellow, with the rule that no two adjacent floors can be blue. (They can, however, be yellow.) Let a_n be the number of ways to paint a block with n floors.*

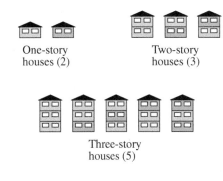

One-story houses (2)   Two-story houses (3)

Three-story houses (5)

Four-story houses (8)

Does the sequence $a_1, a_2, a_3, \ldots$ form a Fibonacci sequence?

59. Consider the following magic trick. The magician asks the audience for any two numbers (you can limit it to the counting numbers between 1 and 10 to keep the arithmetic manageable). Add these two numbers to obtain a third number. Add the second and third numbers to obtain a fourth. Continue until ten numbers are obtained. Then ask the audience to add the ten numbers, while the magician instantly gives the sum.

Consider the example shown here:

First number:	5
Second number:	9
(3) Add:	14
(4)	23
(5)	37
(6)	60
(7)	97
(8)	157
(9)	254
(10)	411
Add column:	1,067

*From "Fibonacci Forgeries" by Ian Stewart, *Scientific American*, May 1995, p. 104. Illustration by Johnny Johnson. © 1995 by Scientific American, Inc. All rights reserved.

The trick depends on the magician's ability to multiply quickly and mentally by 11. Consider the following pattern of multiplication by 11:

$11 \times 10 = 110$
$11 \times 11 = 121$
$11 \times 12 = 132$

Sum of the two digits
↓
$11 \times 13 = 14\,3$
↑ ↑
Original two digits

$11 \times 52 = 57\,2$

Sum of the two digits may be a two-digit number.
↓
$11 \times 74 = 7\,\boxed{11}\,4$
$= 814$

Do the usual carry.

Consider 11 times the 7th number in the example in the pattern:

$$11 \times 97 = 9\,\boxed{16}\,7 = 1,067$$

Note that this is the sum of the ten numbers. Explain why this magician's trick works, and why it is called *Fibonacci's magic trick*.

60. Fill in the blanks so that

$$\text{\_\_\_}, 8, \text{\_\_\_}, \text{\_\_\_}, 27, \text{\_\_\_}, \ldots$$

is

a. an arithmetic sequence.
b. a geometric sequence.
c. a sequence that is neither arithmetic nor geometric, for which you are able to write a general term.

11.4 | Series

In the last section we looked at a list of numbers having a first number, a second number, a third number, and so on. We called it a sequence, and in this section we look at the sum of terms of a sequence. If the terms of a sequence are added, the expression is called a **series**. We first consider a finite sequence along with its associated sum. Note that a capital letter is used to indicate the sum.

CAUTION Write a lowercase s on your paper; now write a capital S. Do they look different? You need to distinguish between the lowercase s and capital S in your own written work.

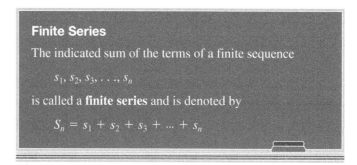

Finite Series

The indicated sum of the terms of a finite sequence

$$s_1, s_2, s_3, \ldots, s_n$$

is called a **finite series** and is denoted by

$$S_n = s_1 + s_2 + s_3 + \ldots + s_n$$

Example 1 Find the sum of terms of a sequence

a. Find S_4, where $s_n = 26 - 6n$.
b. Find S_3, where $s_n = (-1)^n n^2$.

Solution

a. $S_4 = s_1 + s_2 + s_3 + s_4$

$$= \overbrace{[26 - 6(1)]}^{s_1} + \overbrace{[26 - 6(2)]}^{s_2} + \overbrace{[26 - 6(3)]}^{s_3} + \overbrace{[26 - 6(4)]}^{s_4}$$

$$= 20 + 14 + 8 + 2$$

$$= 44$$

b. $S_3 = s_1 + s_2 + s_3$

$$= \overbrace{[(-1)^1(1)^2]}^{s_1} + \overbrace{[(-1)^2(2)^2]}^{s_2} + \overbrace{[(-1)^3(3)^2]}^{s_3}$$

$$= -1 + 4 + (-9)$$

$$= -6$$

The terms of the sequence in Example 1b alternate in sign: $-1, 4, -9, 16, \ldots$. A factor of $(-1)^n$ or $(-1)^{n+1}$ in the general term will cause the sign of the terms to alternate, creating a series called an **alternating series.**

Summation Notation

Before we continue to discuss finding the sum of the terms of a sequence, we need a handy notation, called **summation notation.** In Example 1a we wrote

$$S_4 = s_1 + s_2 + s_3 + s_4$$

Using summation notation (or, as it is sometimes called, **sigma notation**), we could write this sum using the Greek letter Σ:

$$S_4 = \sum_{k=1}^{4} s_k = s_1 + s_2 + s_3 + s_4$$

The sigma notation evaluates the expression (s_k) immediately following the sigma (Σ) sign, first for $k = 1$, then for $k = 2$, then for $k = 3$, and finally for $k = 4$, and then adds these numbers. That is, the expression is evaluated for *consecutive counting numbers* starting with the value of k listed at the bottom of the sigma $(k = 1)$ and ending with the value of k listed at the top of the sigma $(k = 4)$. For example, consider $s_k = 2k$ with $k = 1, 2, 3, 4, 5, 6, 7, 8, 9, 10$. Then

This is the last natural number in the domain. It is called the upper limit.
$\downarrow$

$$\sum_{k=1}^{10} 2k \} \quad \leftarrow \text{This is the function being evaluated. It is called the general term.}$$

$\uparrow$
This is the first natural number in the domain. It is called the lower limit.

Thus, $\displaystyle\sum_{k=1}^{10} 2k = 2(1) + 2(2) + 2(3) + 2(4) + 2(5) + 2(6) + 2(7) + 2(8) + 2(9) + 2(10)$

$$= 110.$$

The words **evaluate** and **expand** are both used to mean "write out an expression in summation notation, and then sum the resulting terms, if possible."

Example 2   Evaluate a summation

a. Evaluate: $\displaystyle\sum_{k=3}^{6} (2k + 1)$

b. Expand: $\displaystyle\sum_{k=3}^{n} \frac{1}{2^k}$

Solution

a. $\displaystyle\sum_{k=3}^{6}(2k+1) = \underbrace{(2\cdot\mathbf{3}+1)}_{} + \overbrace{(2\cdot\mathbf{4}+1)}^{k=4} + \underbrace{(2\cdot\mathbf{5}+1)}_{} + \underbrace{(2\cdot\mathbf{6}+1)}_{}$

　　Evaluate the expression 2k + 1 for k = 3　　　　k = 5　　　　k = 6

$= 7 + 9 + 11 + 13$

$= 40$

b. $\displaystyle\sum_{k=3}^{n}\frac{1}{2^k} = \frac{1}{2^3} + \frac{1}{2^4} + \frac{1}{2^5} + \frac{1}{2^6} + \cdots + \frac{1}{2^{n-1}} + \frac{1}{2^n}$

Arithmetic Series

An **arithmetic series** is the sum of the terms of an arithmetic sequence. Let us consider a rather simple-minded example. How many blocks are shown in the stack in Figure 11.3? We can answer this question by simply counting the blocks: There are 34 blocks. Somehow it does not seem like this is what we have in mind with this question. Suppose we ask a better question: How many blocks are in a similar building with n rows?

Row 1:
Row 2:
Row 3:
Row 4:

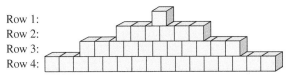

FIGURE 11.3 How many blocks?

We notice that the number of blocks (counting from the top) in each row forms an arithmetic series:

$$1 + 6 + 11 + 16 + \cdots$$

Look for a pattern:

Denote one row by $A_1 = 1$ block.

Two rows: $A_2 = 1 + 6 = 7$

Three rows: $A_3 = 1 + 6 + 11 = 18$

Four rows: $A_4 = 1 + 6 + 11 + 16 = 34$ (shown in Figure 11.3)

$$\vdots$$

What about 10 rows?

$$A_{10} = 1 + 6 + 11 + 16 + 21 + 26 + 31 + 36 + 41 + 46$$

Instead of adding all these numbers directly, let us try an easier way. Write down A_{10} twice, once counting from the top and once counting from the bottom:

$$A_{10} = \ 1 \ + \ 6 \ + 11 + 16 + 21 + 26 + 31 + 36 + 41 + 46$$
$$\updownarrow \ \ \updownarrow \ \ \updownarrow \ \ \updownarrow \ \ \updownarrow \ \ \updownarrow \ \ \updownarrow \ \ \updownarrow \ \ \updownarrow \ \ \updownarrow$$
$$A_{10} = 46 + 41 + 36 + 31 + 26 + 21 + 16 + 11 + \ 6 \ + \ 1$$

Add these equations:

$$2A_{10} = 47 + 47 + 47 + 47 + 47 + 47 + 47 + 47 + 47 + 47$$

　　　　　Number of terms

$$2A_{10} = \overbrace{10}(47) = 470$$

　　　　Repeated term

$$A_{10} = 10\left(\tfrac{47}{2}\right) = 235 \qquad \text{Divide both sides by 2.}$$

　　Average of 1st and last terms

This pattern leads us to a formula for n terms. We note that the number of blocks is an arithmetic sequence with $a_1 = 1$, $d = 5$; thus since $a_n = a_1 + (n - 1)d$, we have for the blocks in Figure 11.3 a stack starting with 1 and ending (in the nth row) with

$$a_n = 1 + (n - 1)5 = 1 + 5n - 5 = 5n - 4$$

Thus,   Number of blocks in n rows   number of rows

$$A_n = n\left[\frac{1 + (5n - 4)}{2}\right]$$

Average of 1st and last terms

$$= n\left[\frac{5n - 3}{2}\right]$$

$$= \frac{1}{2}(5n^2 - 3n)$$

This formula can be used for the number of blocks for any number of rows. Looking back, we see

$$n = 1:\quad A_1 = \frac{1}{2}[5(1)^2 - 3(1)] = 1$$

$$n = 4:\quad A_4 = \frac{1}{2}[5(4)^2 - 3(4)] = 34 \text{ (Figure 11.3)}$$

$$n = 10:\quad A_{10} = \frac{1}{2}[5(10)^2 - 3(10)] = 235$$

If we carry out these same steps for A_n where $a_n = a_1 + (n - 1)d$, we derive the following formula for the sum of the terms of an arithmetic sequence.

YIELD These formulas are not as difficult as they look. The first formula tells us that the sum of n terms of an arithmetic sequence is n times the average of the first and last terms.

Arithmetic Series Formula

The sum of the terms of an arithmetic sequence $a_1, a_2, a_3, \ldots, a_n$ with common difference d is

$$A_n = \sum_{k=1}^{n} a_k = n\left(\frac{a_1 + a_n}{2}\right) \text{ or } A_n = \frac{n}{2}[2a_1 + (n - 1)d]$$

The last part of the formula for A_n is used when the last term is not explicitly stated or known. To derive this formula, we know $a_n = a_1 + (n - 1)d$ so

$$A_n = n\left(\frac{a_1 + a_n}{2}\right)$$

$$= n\left(\frac{a_1 + [a_1 + (n - 1)d]}{2}\right)$$

$$= \frac{n}{2}[a_1 + a_1 + (n - 1)d]$$

$$= \frac{n}{2}[2a_1 + (n - 1)d]$$

Example 3 **Find the sum of the numbers of a sequence**

In a classroom of 35 students, each student "counts off" by threes (i.e., 3, 6, 9, 12, ...). What is the sum of the students' numbers?

Solution   We recognize the sequence 3, 6, 9, 12, ... as an arithmetic sequence with the first term $a_1 = 3$ and the common difference $d = 3$. The sum of these numbers is denoted by A_{35} since there are 35 students "counting off":

$$A_{35} = \frac{35}{2}[2(3) + (35 - 1)3] = 1{,}890$$

Peanuts: © 2010 Peanuts Worldwide LLC., dist by UFS, Inc.

Geometric Series

A **geometric series** is the sum of the terms of a geometric sequence. To motivate a formula for a geometric series, we once again consider an example. Suppose Charlie Brown receives a chain letter, and he is to copy this letter and send it to six of his friends.

You may have heard that chain letters "do not work." Why not? Consider the number of people who could become involved with this chain letter if we assume that everyone carries out their task and does not break the chain. The first mailing would consist of six letters. The second mailing involves 42 letters since the second mailing of 36 letters is added to the total: $6 + 36 = 42$.

1st mailing:

2nd mailing:

The number of letters in each successive mailing is a number in the geometric sequence

$$6, 36, 216, 1296, \ldots \quad \text{or} \quad 6, 6^2, 6^3, 6^4, \ldots$$

How many people receive letters with 11 mailings, assuming that no person receives a letter more than once? To answer this question, consider the series associated with a geometric sequence. We begin with a pattern:

Denote one mailing by	$G_1 = 6$
Two mailings:	$G_2 = 6 + 6^2$
Three mailings:	$G_3 = 6 + 6^2 + 6^3$
	$\vdots$
Eleven mailings:	$G_{11} = 6 + 6^2 + \cdots + 6^{11}$

We could probably use a calculator to find this sum, but we are looking for a formula, so we try something different. In fact, this time we will work out the general formula. Let

$$G_n = g_1 + g_2 + g_3 + \cdots + g^n$$
$$G_n = g_1 + g_1 r + g_1 r^2 + \cdots + g_1 r^{n-1}$$

Multiply both sides of the latter equation by r:

$$rG_n = g_1 r + g_1 r^2 + g_1 r^3 + \cdots + g_1 r^n$$

Notice that, except for the first and last terms, all the terms in the expansions for G_n and rG_n are the same, so that if we subtract one equation from the other, we have

$$G_n - rG_n = g_1 - g_1 r^n$$
$$(1 - r)G_n = g_1(1 - r^n) \qquad \text{We solve for } G_n.$$
$$G_n = \frac{g_1(1 - r^n)}{1 - r} \qquad \text{if } r \neq 1$$

For Charlie Brown's chain letter problem, $g_1 = 6$, $n = 11$, and $r = 6$, so we find

$$G_{11} = \frac{6(1 - 6^{11})}{1 - 6} = \frac{6}{5}(6^{11} - 1) = 435{,}356{,}466$$

This is more than the number of people in the United States! The number of letters in only two more mailings would exceed the number of men, women, and children in the whole world.

Geometric Series Formula

The sum of the terms of a geometric sequence $g_1, g_2, g_3, \ldots, g_n$ with common ratio r (**where** $r \neq 1$) **is**

$$G_n = \frac{g_1(1 - r^n)}{1 - r}$$

Example 4   Make a financial decision

Suppose some eccentric millionaire offered to hire you for a month (say, 31 days) and offered you the following salary choice. She will pay you \$500,000 per day or else will pay you 1¢ for the first day, 2¢ for the second day, 4¢ for the third day, and so on for the 31 days. Which salary should you accept?

Solution   If you are paid \$500,000 per day, your salary for the 31 days is

$$\$500,000(31) = \$15,500,000$$

Now, if you are paid using the doubling scheme, your salary is (in cents)

$$1 + 2 + 4 + 8 + \cdots + \overbrace{\text{last day}}^{\text{31st day}} \quad \text{or} \quad 2^0 + 2^1 + 2^2 + 2^3 + \cdots + 2^{30}$$

We see that this is the sum of the geometric sequence where $g_1 = 1$ and $r = 2$. We are looking for G_{31}:

$$G_{31} = \frac{1(1 - 2^{31})}{1 - 2} = -(1 - 2^{31}) = 2^{31} - 1$$

Using a calculator, we find this to be 2,147,483,647 cents or \$21,474,836.47. You should certainly accept the doubling scheme (starting with 1¢, but do not ask for any days off).

Example 5   Find the number of games   Pólya's Method

The NCAA men's basketball tournament has 64 teams. How many games are necessary to determine a champion?

Solution   We use Pólya's problem-solving guidelines for this example.

Understand the Problem. Most tournaments are formed by drawing an elimination schedule similar to the one shown in Figure 11.4. This is sometimes called a *two-team elimination tournament.*

Devise a Plan. We could obtain the answer to the question by direct counting, but instead we will find a general solution, working backward. We know there will be 1 championship game and 2 semifinal games; continuing to work backward, there are 4 quarter-final games, . . . :

$$1 + 2 + 2^2 + 2^3 + \cdots$$

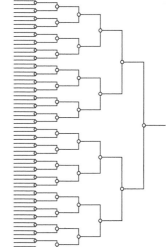

FIGURE 11.4 NCAA playoffs

We recognize this as a geometric series. We note that since there are 64 teams, the first round has $64/2 = 32$ games. Also, we know that $2^5 = 32$, so we must find

$$1 + 2 + 2^2 + 2^3 + 2^4 + 2^5$$

Carry Out the Plan. We note that $g_1 = 1$, $r = 2$, and $n = 6$:

$$G_6 = \frac{1(1 - 2^6)}{1 - 2} = 2^6 - 1 = 63$$

Thus, the NCAA playoffs will require 63 games.

Look Back. We see not only that the NCAA tournament has 63 games for a playoff tournament, but, in general, that if there are 2^n teams in a tournament, there will be $2^n - 1$ games. However, do not forget to check by estimation or by using common sense. Each game eliminates one team, and so 63 teams must be eliminated to crown a champion.

Infinite Geometric Series

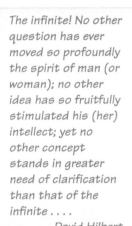

The infinite! No other question has ever moved so profoundly the spirit of man (or woman); no other idea has so fruitfully stimulated his (her) intellect; yet no other concept stands in greater need of clarification than that of the infinite . . . .

David Hilbert

We have just found a formula for the sum of the first n terms of a geometric sequence. Sometimes it is also possible to find the sum of an entire infinite geometric series. Suppose an infinite geometric series

$$g_1 + g_2 + g_3 + g_4 + \cdots$$

is denoted by G. This is an **infinite series.**

The **partial sums** are defined by

$$G_1 = g_1; \quad G_2 = g_1 + g_2; \quad G_3 = g_1 + g_2 + g_3; \ldots$$

Consider the partial sums for an infinite geometric series with $g_1 = \frac{1}{2}$ and $r = \frac{1}{2}$. The geometric sequence is $\frac{1}{2}, \frac{1}{4}, \frac{1}{8}, \frac{1}{16}, \ldots$. The first few partial sums can be found as follows:

$$G_1 = \frac{1}{2}; \quad G_2 = \frac{1}{2} + \frac{1}{4} = \frac{3}{4}; \quad G_3 = \frac{1}{2} + \frac{1}{4} + \frac{1}{8} = \frac{7}{8}$$

Does this series have a sum if you add *all* its terms? It does seem that as you take more terms of the series, the sum is closer and closer to 1. Analytically, we can check the partial sums on a calculator or spreadsheet (see below). Geometrically, you can see (Figure 11.5) that if the terms are laid end-to-end as lengths on a number line, each term is half the remaining distance to 1.

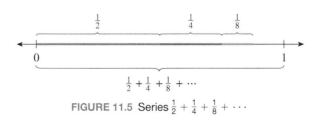

FIGURE 11.5 Series $\frac{1}{2} + \frac{1}{4} + \frac{1}{8} + \cdots$

It appears that the partial sums are getting closer to 1 as n becomes larger. We *can* find the sum of an infinite geometric sequence.

COMPUTATIONAL WINDOW

It is easy to use a spreadsheet (review Section 6.3) to look at the partial sums of a sequence. For the sequence $\frac{1}{2}, \frac{1}{4}, \frac{1}{8}, \ldots$, define the cells as shown:

Replicate subsequent rows. The output is:

				Spreadsheet Application
n	Term	Partial sum		

Spreadsheet Application

	A	B	C
1	n	term	partial sum
2	1	0.5	+B2
3	+A2+1	+B2*.5	+C2+B3
4	+A3+1	+B3*.5	+C3+B4

n	Term	Partial sum
1	.5	.5
2	.25	.75
3	.125	.875
4	.0625	.9375
5	.03125	.96875
6	.015625	.984375
7	.0078125	.9921875
8	.00390625	.99609375
9	.00195313	.99804688
10	.00097656	.99902344
⋮	⋮	⋮
20	.00000095	.99999905

Consider

$$G_n = \frac{g_1(1 - r^n)}{1 - r} = \frac{g_1 - g_1 r^n}{1 - r} = \frac{g_1}{1 - r} - \frac{g_1}{1 - r}r^n$$

Now, g_1, r, and $1 - r$ are fixed numbers. If $|r| < 1$, then r^n approaches 0 as n grows, and thus G_n approaches $\frac{g_1}{1 - r}$.

Infinite Geometric Series Formula

If $g_1, g_2, g_3, \ldots, g_n, \ldots$ is an infinite geometric sequence with a common ratio r such that $|r| < 1$, then its sum is denoted by G and is found by

$$G = \frac{g_1}{1 - r}$$

If $|r| \geq 1$, the infinite geometric series has no sum.

Example 6 Find the distance a pendulum travels

The path of each swing of a pendulum is 0.85 as long as the path of the previous swing (after the first). If the path of the tip of the first swing is 36 in. long, how far does the tip of the pendulum travel before it eventually comes to rest?

Solution

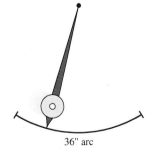

36" arc

$$\begin{aligned} \text{TOTAL DISTANCE} \quad &= 36 + 36(0.85) + 36(0.85)^2 + \cdots \\ &= \frac{36}{1 - 0.85} \\ &= 240 \end{aligned}$$

Infinite geometric series; $g_1 = 36$; $r = 0.85$

The tip of the pendulum travels 240 in.

Summary of Sequence and Series Formulas

We conclude this section by repeating the important formulas related to sequences and series. Given a sequence of numbers, a *series* arises by considering the *sum* of the terms of the sequence. The formulas for the *general term of a sequence* and for the *sum* (of terms of the sequence; that is, a *series*) are given in Table 11.1.

Distinguishing a Series from a Sequence

Type	Definition	Notation	Formula
Sequences	A list of numbers having a first term, a second term, . . .	s_n	
Arithmetic	A sequence with a common difference, d	a_n	$a_n = a_1 + (n-1)d$
Geometric	A sequence with a common ratio, r	g_n	$g_n = g_1 r^{n-1}$
Fibonacci	A sequence with first two terms given, and subsequent terms the sum of the two previous terms		$s_n = s_{n-1} + s_{n-2}, n \geq 3$
Series	The indicated sum of terms of a sequence	S_n	
Arithmetic	Sum of the terms of an arithmetic sequence: $$A_n = \sum_{k=1}^{n} a_k = a_1 + a_2 + a_3 + \ldots + a_n$$	A_n	$A_n = n\left(\dfrac{a_1 + a_n}{2}\right)$ or $A_n = \dfrac{n}{2}[2a_1 + (n-1)d]$
Geometric	Sum of the terms of a geometric sequence: $$G_n = \sum_{k=1}^{n} g_k = g_1 + g_2 + g_3 + \ldots + g_n$$	G_n	$G_n = \dfrac{g_1(1 - r^n)}{1 - r}, r \neq 1$
	Sum of the terms of an infinite geometric sequence: $$G = g_1 + g_2 + g_3 + \cdots$$	G	$G = \dfrac{g_1}{1 - r}, |r| < 1$

Problem Set   11.4

Level 1

1. **IN YOUR OWN WORDS**   Distinguish a sequence from a series.

2. **IN YOUR OWN WORDS**   Explain summation notation.

3. **IN YOUR OWN WORDS**   What is a partial sum?

4. **IN YOUR OWN WORDS**   Distinguish a geometric series and an infinite geometric series.

Find the requested values in Problems 5–10.

5. S_5 when $s_n = 15 - 3n$

6. S_8 when $s_n = 5n$

7. S_4 when $s_n = 5 \cdot 2^n$

8. S_6 when $s_n = (-1)^n$

9. S_7 when $s_n = (-1)^n$

10. S_3 when $s_n = 8 \cdot 5^n$

Evaluate the expressions in Problems 11–18.

11. $\displaystyle\sum_{k=3}^{5} k$

12. $\displaystyle\sum_{k=1}^{4} k^2$

13. $\displaystyle\sum_{k=2}^{6} k^2$

14. $\displaystyle\sum_{k=2}^{5} (100 - 5k)$

15. $\sum_{k=1}^{10} [1^k + (-1)^k]$ **16.** $\sum_{k=1}^{5} (-2)^{k-1}$

17. $\sum_{k=0}^{4} 3(-2)^k$ **18.** $\sum_{k=1}^{3} (-1)^k(k^2 + 1)$

Level 2

If possible, find the sum of the infinite geometric series in Problems 19–24.

19. $1 + \frac{1}{2} + \frac{1}{4} + \cdots$

20. $1 + \frac{3}{2} + \frac{9}{4} + \cdots$

21. $1 + \frac{1}{3} + \frac{1}{9} + \cdots$

22. $100 + 50 + 25 + \cdots$

23. $-20 + 10 - 5 + \cdots$

24. $-100 + 50 - 25 + \cdots$

25. Find the sum of the first 5 odd positive integers.

26. Find the sum of the first 5 even positive integers.

27. Find the sum of the first 5 positive integers.

28. Find the sum of the first 10 odd positive integers.

29. Find the sum of the first 10 even positive integers.

30. Find the sum of the first 10 positive integers.

31. Find the sum of the first 100 odd positive integers.

32. Find the sum of the first 100 even positive integers.

33. Find the sum of the first 100 positive integers.

34. Find the sum of the first n odd positive integers.

35. Find the sum of the first n even positive integers.

36. Find the sum of the first n positive integers.

37. Find the sum of the first 20 terms of the arithmetic sequence whose first term is 100 and whose common difference is 50.

38. Find the sum of the first 50 terms of the arithmetic sequence whose first term is -15 and whose common difference is 5.

39. Find the sum of the even integers between 41 and 99.

40. Find the sum of the odd integers between 48 and 136.

The game of pool uses 15 balls numbered from 1 to 15 (see Figure 11.6). In the game of rotation, a player attempts to "sink" a ball in a pocket of the table and receives the number of points on the ball. Answer the questions in Problems 41–44.

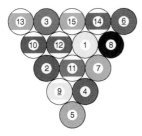

FIGURE 11.6 Pool balls

41. How many points would a player who "runs the table" receive? (To "run the table" means to sink all the balls.)

42. Suppose Missy sinks balls 1 through 8, and Shannon sinks balls 9 through 15. What are their respective scores?

43. Suppose Missy sinks the even-numbered balls and Shannon sinks the odd-numbered balls. What are their respective scores?

44. Suppose we consider a game of "super pool," which has 30 consecutively numbered balls on the table. How many points would a player receive to "run the table"?

45. The *Peanuts* cartoon (p. 549) expresses a common feeling regarding chain letters. Consider the total number of letters sent after a particular mailing:

1st mailing:	6
2nd mailing:	$6 + 36 = 42$
3rd mailing:	$6 + 36 + 216 = 258$

Determine the total number of letters sent in five mailings of the chain letter.

46. How many blocks would be needed to build a stack like the one shown in Figure 11.7 if the bottom row has 28 blocks?

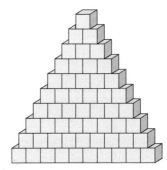

FIGURE 11.7 How many blocks?

47. Repeat Problem 46 if the bottom row has 87 blocks.

48. Repeat Problem 46 if the bottom row has 100 blocks.

49. A pendulum is swung 20 cm and allowed to swing freely until it eventually comes to rest. Each subsequent swing of the bob of the pendulum is 90% as far as the preceding swing. How far will the bob travel before coming to rest?

50. The initial swing of the tip of a pendulum is 25 cm. If each swing of the tip is 75% of the preceding swing, how far does the tip travel before eventually coming to rest?

51. A flywheel is brought to a speed of 375 revolutions per minute (rpm) and allowed to slow and eventually come to rest. If, in slowing, it rotates three-fourths as fast each subsequent minute, how many revolutions will the wheel make before returning to rest?

52. A rotating flywheel is allowed to slow to a stop from a speed of 500 rpm. While slowing, each minute it rotates two-thirds as many times as in the preceding minute. How many revolutions will the wheel make before coming to rest?

53. Advertisements say that a new type of superball will rebound to 9/10 of its original height. If it is dropped from a height of 10 ft, how far, based on the advertisements, will the ball travel before coming to rest?

David S. Baker/Shutterstock.com

54. A tennis ball is dropped from a height of 10 ft. If the ball rebounds 2/3 of its height on each bounce, how far will the ball travel before coming to rest?

Level **3**

55. A culture of bacteria increases by 100% every 24 hours. If the original culture contains 1 million bacteria ($a_0 = 1$ million), find the number of bacteria present after 10 days.

56. Use Problem 55 to find a formula for the number of bacteria present after d days.

57. How many games are necessary for a two-team elimination tournament with 32 teams?

58. Games like "*Wheel of Fortune*" and "*Jeopardy*" have one winner and two losers. A three-team game tournament is illustrated by Figure 11.8. If "Jeopardy" has a Tournament of Champions consisting of 27 players, what is the necessary number of games?

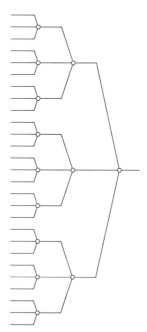

FIGURE 11.8 A three-team tournament

59. How many games are necessary for a three-team elimination tournament with 729 teams?

Problem Solving **3**

60. a. How many blocks are there in the solid figure shown in Figure 11.9?

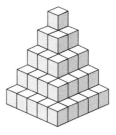

FIGURE 11.9 How many blocks?

b. How many blocks are there in a similar figure with 50 layers?

11.5 Annuities

Sir Isaac Newton, one of the greatest mathematicians of all time, worked at the mint, but apparently did not like to apply mathematics to money. In a book by Rev. J. Spence published 1858, Spence writes, "Sir Isaac Newton, though so deep in algebra and fluxions, could not readily make up a common account: and, when he was Master of the Mint, used to get somebody else to make up his accounts for him." There is an important lesson here.

If you do not like to work with money, hire someone to help you. When Albert Einstein was asked what was the most amazing formula he knew, you might think he would have given his famous formula $E = mc^2$, but he did not. He thought the most amazing formula was the compound interest formula.

Ordinary Annuities

One of the most fundamental mathematical concepts for businesspeople and consumers is the idea of interest. We have considered present- and future-value problems involving a fixed amount, so we refer to such problems as **lump-sum problems.** On the other hand, it is far more common to encounter financial problems based on monthly or other periodic payments, so we refer to such problems as **periodic-payment problems.** Consider the situation in which the *monthly payment* is known and the future value is to be determined. A sequence of payments into or out of an interest-bearing account is called an **annuity.** If the payments are made into an interest-bearing account at the end of each time period, and if the frequency of payments is the same as the frequency of compounding, the annuity is called an *ordinary annuity.* The amount of an annuity is the sum of all payments made plus all accumulated interest. In this book we will assume that all annuities are ordinary annuities.

The best way to understand what we mean by an annuity is to consider an example. Suppose you decide to give up smoking and save the $2 per day you spend on cigarettes. How much will you save in 5 years? (Assume that each year has 360 days.) If you save the money without earning any interest, you will have

$$\$2 \times 360 \times 5 = \$3,600$$

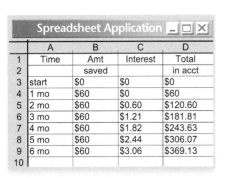

	A	B	C	D
	Time	Amt	Interest	Total
1		saved		in acct
2				
3	start	$0	$0	$0
4	1 mo	$60	$0	$60
5	2 mo	$60	$0.60	$120.60
6	3 mo	$60	$1.21	$181.81
7	4 mo	$60	$1.82	$243.63
8	5 mo	$60	$2.44	$306.07
9	6 mo	$60	$3.06	$369.13
10				

However, let us assume that you save $2 per day, and at the end of each month you deposit the $60 (assume that all months are 30 days; that is, assume ordinary interest) into an account earning 12% interest compounded monthly. Now, how much will you have in 5 years? This is an example of an annuity. We could solve the problem using a spreadsheet to simulate our bank statement. Part of such a spreadsheet is shown in the margin.

Notice that even though the interest on $60 for one month is $0.60, the total monthly increase in interest is not linear, because the interest is compounded.

To derive a formula for annuities, let us consider this problem for a period of 6 months, and calculate the amounts plus interest for *each* deposit separately. We need a new variable to represent the amount of periodic deposit. Since this is usually a monthly payment, we let m = periodic payment. The **monthly payment** is a periodic payment that is made monthly.

We are given $m = 60$, $r = 0.12$, and $n = 12$ ("monthly deposit" means "monthly compounding" for an ordinary annuity). Let $i = r/n$. For this example, $i = 0.12/12 = 0.01$. The time, t, varies for each deposit. Remember that the deposit comes at the *end* of the month.

First deposit will earn 5 months' interest:	$60(1 + 0.01)^5 = 63.06$
Second deposit will earn 4 months' interest:	$60(1 + 0.01)^4 = 62.44$
Third deposit will earn 3 months' interest:	$60(1 + 0.01)^3 = 61.82$
Fourth deposit will earn 2 months' interest:	$60(1 + 0.01)^2 = 61.21$
Fifth deposit will earn 1 month's interest:	$60(1 + 0.01)^1 = 60.60$
Sixth deposit will earn no interest:	60.00
TOTAL IN THE ACCOUNT	369.13

This leads us to the following pattern (using variables). The total after 6 months is:

$$A = m + m(1 + i)^1 + m(1 + i)^2 + m(1 + i)^3 + m(1 + i)^4 + m(1 + i)^5$$

$$= \sum_{k=1}^{6} m(1 + i)^{k-1}$$

We are using the following formula for the sum of the terms of a geometric sequence: That is, it is the sum of the terms of a geometric sequence with $g_1 = m$ and common ratio $(1 + i)$. The sum, G_n, is the future value A. Thus (from the formula for the sum of a geometric sequence), we have

$$A = \frac{m[1 - (1 + i)^{nt}]}{1 - (1 + i)}$$

$$= \frac{m[1 - (1 + i)^{nt}]}{-i}$$

$$= \frac{m[(1 + i)^{nt} - 1]}{-i}$$

For the total after nt periods, we recognize this as a geometric series with first term m and common ratio 1 + i.

 This is one of the most useful formulas for you to use in your personal financial planning.

Ordinary Annuity Formula

The future value, A, of an annuity is found with the formula

$$A = m\left[\frac{\left(1 + \frac{r}{n}\right)^{nt} - 1}{\frac{r}{n}}\right]$$

where r is the annual rate, m the periodic payment, t the time (in years), and n is the number of payments per year.

Example 1   Find the value of an ordinary annuity

How much do you save in 5 years if you deposit \$60 at the end of each month into an account paying 12% compounded monthly?

Solution   Begin by identifying the problem type as well as the variables: *annuity; $t = 5$, $m = \$60$, $r = 0.12$, and $n = 12$.* Next, evaluate the formula:

$$A = m\left[\frac{\left(1 + \frac{r}{n}\right)^{nt} - 1}{\frac{r}{n}}\right]$$

$$= 60\left[\frac{(1 + 0.01)^{60} - 1}{0.01}\right]$$

$$\approx 4,900.180191$$

The future value is \$4,900.18. A graph is shown in Figure 11.10.

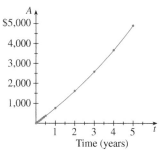

FIGURE 11.10 Growth of an account with a \$60 monthly deposit. The graph shows both deposits and interest compounded monthly at 12% annual rate.

**Isaac Newton
(1642–1727)**

Newton was one of the greatest mathematicians of all time. He was a genius of the highest order but was often absent-minded. One story about Newton is that, when he was a boy, he was sent to cut a hole in the bottom of the barn door for the cats to go in and out. He cut two holes—a large one for the cat and a small one for the kittens. Newton's influence on mathematics was so great that the field is sometimes divided into pre-Newtonian mathematics and post-Newtonian mathematics. Post-Newtonian mathematics is characterized by the changing and the infinite rather than by the static and the finite. As an example of his tremendous ability, when Newton was 74 years old the mathematician Leibniz (see the Historical Note on p. 85) posed a challenge problem to all the mathematicians in Europe. Newton received the problem after a day's work at the mint (remember he was 74!) and solved the problem that evening. His intellect was monumental.

The following example is called the Financial Independence Example. It answers the question, "Why should I take math?"

Financial Independence

Example 2 Retirement calculation

Pólya's Method

Suppose you are 21 years old and will make monthly deposits to a bank account paying 10% annual interest compounded monthly.

Option I: Pay yourself $200 per month for 5 years and then leave the balance in the bank until age 65. (Total amount of deposits is $200 \times 5 \times 12 = \$12{,}000$.)

Option II: Wait until you are 40 years old (the age most of us start thinking seriously about retirement) and then deposit $200 per month until age 65. (Total amount of deposits is $200 \times 25 \times 12 = \$60{,}000$.)

Compare the amounts you would have from each of these options.

Solution   We use Pólya's problem-solving guidelines for this example.

Understand the Problem. When most of us are 21 years old, we do not think about retirement. However, if we do, the results can be dramatic. With this example, we investigate the differences if we save early (for 5 years) or later (for 25 years).

Devise a Plan. We calculate the value of the annuity for the 5 years of the first option, and then calculate the effect of leaving the value at the end of 5 years (the annuity) in a savings account until retirement. This part of the problem is a future value problem because it becomes a lump sum problem when deposits are no longer made (after 5 years). For the second option, we calculate the value of the annuity for 25 years.

Carry Out the Plan. *Option I:* $200 per month for 5 years at 10% annual interest is an annuity with $m = 200$, $r = 0.10$, $t = 5$, and $n = 12$; this is an *annuity*.

$$A = 200\left[\frac{\left(1 + \frac{0.1}{12}\right)^{12(5)} - 1}{\frac{0.1}{12}}\right] \approx 15{,}487.41443$$

At the end of 5 years the amount in the account is $15,487.41. This money is left in the account, so it is now a future value problem for 39 years (ages 26 to 65); this part of the problem is a **future value problem** with $P = 15{,}487.41$, $r = 0.1$, $t = 39$, and $n = 12$, so that

$$A = P\left(1 + \frac{r}{n}\right)^{nt} = 15{,}487.41\left(1 + \frac{0.1}{12}\right)^{12(39)} \approx 752{,}850.86$$

(It is 752,851.08 if you use the calculator value for A from the first part of the problem.) The amount you would have at age 65 from 5 years of payments to yourself starting at age 21 is $752,850.86.

Option II: If you wait until you are 40 years old, this is an *annuity* problem with $m = 200$, $r = 0.10$, $t = 25$, and $n = 12$:

$$A = 200\left[\frac{\left(1 + \frac{0.1}{12}\right)^{12(25)} - 1}{\frac{0.1}{12}}\right]$$

$$\approx 265{,}366.6806$$

The amount you would have at age 65 from 25 years of payments to yourself starting at age 40 is $265,366.68.

Look Back. Retirement Options I and II are compared graphically in Figure 11.11.

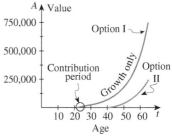

FIGURE 11.11 Comparison of Options I and II

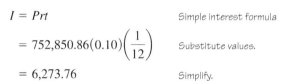

Example 3 Why study math? For real!

The previous example gave you a choice:

Option I: Pay yourself $200 per month for 5 years beginning when you are 21 years old (this is comparable to the car payments you might make).

Option II: Wait until age 40, then make payments of $200 per month to yourself for the next 25 years. If you were to select one of these options, what effect would it have on your retirement monthly income, assuming you decide to live on the interest only and that the interest rate is 10%?

 Would you rather have $6,274/mo or $2,211/mo, or "How would you like to have $4,000/mo—free money from your math class!"

Solution   Option I gives you a retirement fund of $752,850.86. This will provide a monthly income as determined by the simple interest formula (because the interest is not left to accumulate):

$$I = Prt \qquad \text{Simple interest formula}$$

$$= 752{,}850.86(0.10)\left(\frac{1}{12}\right) \qquad \text{Substitute values.}$$

$$= 6{,}273.76 \qquad \text{Simplify.}$$

Option II gives you a retirement fund of $265,366.68. This will provide a monthly income found as follows:

$$I = Prt \qquad \text{Repeat the steps from Option I.}$$

$$= 265{,}366.68(0.10)\left(\frac{1}{12}\right) \qquad \text{Substitute values.}$$

$$= 2{,}211.39 \qquad \text{Simplify.}$$

The better choice (Option I) would mean that you would have about $4,000 *more* each and every month that you live beyond age 65. Did you ever ask the question "Why should I take math?"

Sinking Funds

Sinking Fund

We now consider the situation in which we need (or want) to have a lump sum of money (a future value) in a certain period of time. The present value formula will tell us how much we need to have today, but we frequently do not have that amount available. Suppose your goal is $10,000 in 5 years. You can obtain 8% compounded monthly, so the present value formula yields

$$P = A\left(1 + \frac{r}{n}\right)^{-nt} = \$10{,}000\left(1 + \frac{0.08}{12}\right)^{-5(12)} \approx \$6{,}712.10$$

However, this is more than you can afford to put into the bank now. The next choice is to make a series of small equal investments to accumulate at 8% compounded monthly, so that the end result is the same—namely, $10,000 in 5 years. The account you set up to receive those investments is called a **sinking fund.**

To find a formula for a sinking fund, we begin with the formula for an ordinary annuity, and solve for *m* (which is the unknown for a sinking fund). Once again, we let $i = r/n$:

$$A = m\left[\frac{(1 + i)^{nt} - 1}{i}\right] \qquad \text{Annuity formula}$$

$$Ai = m\left[(1 + i)^{nt} - 1\right] \qquad \text{Multiply both sides by } i.$$

$$\frac{Ai}{(1 + i)^{nt} - 1} = m \qquad \text{Divide both sides by } [(1 + i)^{nt} - 1].$$

Sinking Fund Formula

If the future value (A) is known, and you wish to find the amount of the periodic payment (m), use the *sinking fund formula*

$$m = \frac{A\left(\frac{r}{n}\right)}{\left(1 + \frac{r}{n}\right)^{nt} - 1}$$

where r is the annual rate, t is the time (in years), and n is the number of times per year the payments are made.

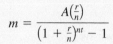 **4 Find the monthly payment to save a given amount**

Suppose you want to have $10,000 in 5 years and decide to make monthly payments into an account paying 8% compounded monthly. What is the amount of each monthly payment?

Solution You might begin by estimation. If you are paid *no* interest, then since you are making 60 equal deposits, the amount of each deposit would be

$$\frac{10,000}{60} \approx \$166.67$$

Therefore, since you are paid interest, you would expect the amount of each deposit to be somewhat less than this estimation. This is a **sinking fund problem.** We identify the known values: $A = \$10,000$ (future value), $r = 0.08$, $t = 5$, and $n = 12$. Finally, use the appropriate formula:

$$m = \frac{A\left(\frac{r}{n}\right)}{\left(1 + \frac{r}{n}\right)^{nt} - 1} = \frac{10,000\left(\frac{0.08}{12}\right)}{\left(1 + \frac{0.08}{12}\right)^{12(5)} - 1} \approx 136.0972762$$

The necessary monthly payment to the account is $136.10.

CAUTION

Spend a few minutes with this idea; in your own words, can you explain when you would use this formula?

"Sure it was your idea, Bob, but I don't like naming it 'The Sinking Fund.'"

Harley Schwardron © Tribune Media Services. Used with permission.

Variable	Input to Storage
P	STO P
A	STO A
m	STO M
r	STO R
n	STO N

COMPUTATIONAL WINDOW

Most graphing calculators have the ability to accept programs. Modern calculators require no special ability to write a program. We input the values of the variables into the memory locations as shown in the margin:

When using a calculator, generally the only difficulty is the proper use of parentheses:

Type	Formula	Calculator Notation
Future value	$A = P\left(1 + \dfrac{r}{n}\right)^{nt}$	P*(1+R/N)^(N*T)
Present value	$P = A\left(1 + \dfrac{r}{n}\right)^{-nt}$	A*(1+R/N)^(−N*T)
Annuity	$A = m\left[\dfrac{\left(1 + \frac{r}{n}\right)^{nt} - 1}{\frac{r}{n}}\right]$	M*(((1+R/N)^(N*T)−1)/(R/N))
Sinking fund	$m = \dfrac{A\left(\frac{r}{n}\right)}{\left(1 + \frac{r}{n}\right)^{nt} - 1}$	(A*R/N)/((1+R/N)^(N*T)−1)

To write a program, press the PRGM key and then input the formula. Most calculator programs also require some statement that forces the output of an answer. Check with your owner's manual, but this is usually a one-step process. To use your calculator for one of these formulas, you simply need to identify the type of financial problem, input the values for the appropriate variables, and then run the program containing the formula you wish to evaluate.

Problem Set 11.5

Level 1

1. **IN YOUR OWN WORDS** What do we mean by a lump-sum problem?

2. **IN YOUR OWN WORDS** Why should we call an annuity a periodic payment problem?

3. **IN YOUR OWN WORDS** What is an annuity?

4. **IN YOUR OWN WORDS** What is a sinking fund?

5. **IN YOUR OWN WORDS** Distinguish an annuity from a sinking fund.

6. **IN YOUR OWN WORDS** Describe Example 3 and comment on its possible relevance.

*Use a calculator to evaluate an **ordinary annuity formula***

$$A = m\left[\frac{\left(1 + \frac{r}{n}\right)^{nt} - 1}{\frac{r}{n}}\right]$$

for m, r, and t (respectively) given in Problems 7–22. Assume monthly payments.

7. $50; 5%; 3 yr	8. $50; 6%; 3 yr
9. $50; 8%; 3 yr	10. $50; 12%; 3 yr
11. $50; 5%; 30 yr	12. $50; 6%; 30 yr
13. $50; 8%; 30 yr	14. $50; 12%; 30 yr

15. $100; 5%; 10 yr

16. $100; 6%; 10 yr

17. $100; 8%; 10 yr

18. $100; 12%; 10 yr

19. $150; 5%; 35 yr

20. $150; 6%; 35 yr

21. $650; 5%; 30 yr

22. $650; 6%; 30 yr

In Problems 23–34, find the value of each annuity at the end of the indicated number of years. Assume that the interest is compounded with the same frequency as the deposits.

Amount of Deposit m	Frequency n	Rate r	Time t
23. $500	annually	8%	30 yr
24. $500	annually	6%	30 yr
25. $250	semiannually	8%	30 yr
26. $600	semiannually	2%	10 yr
27. $300	quarterly	6%	30 yr
28. $100	monthly	4%	5 yr
29. $200	quarterly	8%	20 yr
30. $400	quarterly	11%	20 yr
31. $30	monthly	8%	5 yr
32. $5,000	annually	4%	10 yr
33. $2,500	semiannually	8.5%	20 yr
34. $1,250	quarterly	3%	20 yr

Find the amount of periodic payment necessary for each deposit to a sinking fund in Problems 35–46.

Amount Needed A	Frequency n	Rate r	Time t
35. $7,000	annually	8%	5 yr
36. $25,000	annually	11%	5 yr
37. $25,000	semiannually	12%	5 yr
38. $50,000	semiannually	14%	10 yr
39. $165,000	semiannually	2%	10 yr
40. $3,000,000	semiannually	3%	20 yr
41. $500,000	quarterly	8%	10 yr
42. $55,000	quarterly	10%	5 yr
43. $100,000	quarterly	8%	8 yr
44. $35,000	quarterly	8%	12 yr
45. $45,000	monthly	7%	30 yr
46. $120,000	quarterly	7%	30 yr

Level 2

47. Self-employed persons can make contributions for their retirement into a special tax-deferred account called a *Keogh account.* Suppose you are able to contribute $20,000 into this account at the end of each year. How much will you have at the end of 20 years if the account pays 8% annual interest?

48. The owner of Sebastopol Tree Farm deposits $650 at the end of each quarter into an account paying 8% compounded quarterly. What is the value of the account at the end of 5 years?

49. The owner of Oak Hill Squirrel Farm deposits $1,000 at the end of each quarter into an account paying 8% compounded quarterly. What is the value at the end of 5 years, 6 months?

50. Clearlake Optical has a $50,000 note that comes due in 4 years. The owners wish to create a sinking fund to pay this note. If the fund earns 8% compounded semiannually, how much must each semiannual deposit be?

51. A business must raise $70,000 in 5 years. What should be the size of the owners' quarterly payment to a sinking fund paying 8% compounded quarterly?

52. A lottery offers a $1,000,000 prize to be paid in 20 equal installments of $50,000 at the end of each year. What is the future value of this annuity if the current annual rate is 5%?

© AP/Wide World Photos

Level 3

53. A lottery offers a $1,000,000 prize to be paid in 29 equal annual installments of $20,000 with a 30th final payment of $420,000. What is the total value of this annuity if the current annual rate is 5%?

54. John and Rosamond want to retire in 5 years and can save $150 every three months. They plan to deposit the money at the end of each quarter into an account paying 6.72% compounded quarterly. How much will they have at the end of 5 years?

55. In 2005 the maximum Social Security deposit by an individual was $6,885. Suppose you are 25 and make a deposit of this

amount into an account at the end of each year. How much would you have (to the nearest dollar) when you retire if the account pays 5% compounded annually and you retire at age 65?

56. You want to retire at age 65. You decide to make a deposit to yourself at the end of each year into an account paying 13%, compounded annually. Assuming you are now 25 and can spare $1,200 per year, how much will you have when you retire at age 65?

57. Repeat Problem 56 using your own age.

58. Repeat Problem 55 using your own age.

Problem Solving 3

59. Clearlake Optical has developed a new lens. The owners plan to issue a $4,000,000 30-year bond with a contract rate of 5.5% paid annually to raise capital to market this new lens. This means that Clearlake will be required to pay 5.5% interest each year for 30 years. To pay off the debt, Clearlake will also set up a sinking fund paying 8% interest compounded annually. What size annual payment is necessary for interest and sinking fund combined?

60. The owners of Bardoza Greeting Cards wish to introduce a new line of cards but need to raise $200,000 to do it. They decide to issue 10-year bonds with a contract rate of 6% paid semiannually. This means Bardoza must make interest payments to the bondholders each 6 months for 10 years. They also set up a sinking fund paying 8% interest compounded semiannually. How much money will they need to make the semiannual interest payments as well as payments to the sinking fund?

11.6 | Amortization

In the previous sections we considered the lump-sum formulas for present value and for future value. We also considered the periodic payment formula, which provided the future value of periodic payments into an interest-bearing account. With the annuity formula, we assumed that we knew the amount of the periodic payment.

Present Value of an Annuity

In the real world, if you need or want to purchase an item and you do not have the entire amount necessary, you can generally save for the item, or purchase the item and pay for it with monthly payments. Let us consider an example. Suppose you can afford $275 per month for an automobile. One possibility is to put the $275 per month into a bank account until you have enough money to buy a car. To find the future value of this monthly payment, you would need to know the interest rate (say, 5.2%) and the length of time you will make these deposits (say, 48 months or monthly payments for 4 years). The future value in the account is found using the annuity formula:

$$A = m\left[\frac{\left(1 + \frac{r}{n}\right)^{nt} - 1}{\frac{r}{n}}\right] = 275\left[\frac{\left(1 + \frac{0.052}{12}\right)^{48} - 1}{\frac{0.052}{12}}\right] \approx 14{,}638.04004$$

This means that if you make these payments to yourself, in 4 years you will have saved $275 \times 48 = \$13,200$, but because of the interest paid on this account, the total amount in the account is $14,638.04.

However, it is more common to purchase a car and agree to make monthly payments to pay for it. Given the annuity calculation above, can we conclude that we can look for a car that costs $14,638? No, because if we borrow to purchase the car we need to *pay* interest charges rather than *receive* the interest as we did with the annuity. Well, then, how much can we borrow when we assume that we know the monthly payment, the interest rate, and the length of time we will pay? This type of financial problem is called the **present value of an annuity.**

Continuing with this car payment example, we need to ask, "What is the present value of 14,638.04004?" This is found using the formula $P = A\left(1 + \frac{r}{n}\right)^{-nt}$:

$$P = 14{,}638.04004\left(1 + \frac{0.052}{12}\right)^{-48} \approx 11{,}894.46293$$

This means we could finance a loan in the amount of $11,894.46 and pay it off in 48 months with payments of $275, provided the interest rate is 5.2% compounded monthly.

We will now derive a formula for the present value of an annuity. For convenience, we let $i = r/n$. Since $A = P(1 + i)^{nt}$ and $A = m\left[\frac{(1 + i)^{nt} - 1}{i}\right]$, we see

$$P(1 + i)^{nt} = m\left[\frac{(1 + i)^{nt} - 1}{i}\right] \qquad \text{Both the left and right sides are equal to } A.$$

$$P = \frac{m}{i}\left[\frac{(1 + i)^{nt} - 1}{(1 + i)^{nt}}\right] \qquad \text{Divide both sides by } (1 + i)^{nt}.$$

$$= \frac{m}{i}\left[1 - \frac{1}{(1 + i)^{nt}}\right]$$

$$= \frac{m}{i}\left[1 - (1 + i)^{-nt}\right]$$

CAUTION The financial problem called the present value of an annuity is not the same as a present value financial problem, and it is also not the same as an annuity.

COMPUTATIONAL WINDOW

A formula for the present value of an annuity would be input into a calculator program as follows:
M*((1 − (1 + R/N)^(−N*T))/(R/N))

Present Value of an Annuity

If the periodic payment is known (m) and you wish to find the *present value of those periodic payments*, use the *present value of an annuity* formula:

$$P = m\left[\frac{1 - \left(1 + \frac{r}{n}\right)^{-nt}}{\frac{r}{n}}\right]$$

where P is the present value of the annuity, r is the annual interest rate, and n is the number of payments per year.

Example 1   Find the amount you can afford for a car

You look at your budget and decide that you can afford $250 per month for a car. What is the *maximum loan* you can afford if the interest rate is 13% and you want to repay the loan in 4 years?

Solution   This requires the *present value of an annuity* formula. First, determine the given variables: $m = 250$, $r = 0.13$, $t = 4$, $n = 12$; thus,

$$P = m\left[\frac{1 - \left(1 + \frac{r}{n}\right)^{-nt}}{\frac{r}{n}}\right] = 250\left[\frac{1 - \left(1 + \frac{0.13}{12}\right)^{-12(4)}}{\frac{0.13}{12}}\right] \approx 9{,}318.797438$$

This means that you can afford to finance about $9,319. To keep the payments at $250 (or less), a down payment should be made, if necessary, to lower the price of the car to the finance amount.

Example 2 Find the home you can afford Pólya's Method

Suppose your budget (or your banker) tells you that you can afford $1,575 per month for a house payment. If the current interest rate for a home loan is 10.5% and you will finance the home for 30 years, what is the expected price of the home you can afford? Assume that you have saved the money to make the required 20% down payment.

Solution We use Pólya's problem-solving guidelines for this example.

Understand the Problem. Most textbook problems give you a price for a home and ask for the monthly payment. This problem takes the real-life situation in which you know the monthly payment and wish to know the price of the house you can afford.

Devise a Plan. We first find the amount of the loan, and then find the down payment by subtracting the amount of the loan from the price of the home we wish to purchase.

Carry Out the Plan. We first find the amount of the loan; this is the **present value of an annuity.** We know $m = 1,575$, $r = 0.105$, $t = 30$, $n = 12$; thus,

$$P = m\left[\frac{1 - \left(1 + \frac{r}{n}\right)^{-nt}}{i}\right] = 1,575\left[\frac{1 - \left(1 + \frac{0.105}{12}\right)^{-12(30)}}{\frac{0.105}{12}}\right] \approx 172{,}180.2058$$

The loan that you can afford is about $172,180.

What about the down payment? If there is a 20% down payment, then the amount of the loan is 80% of the price of the home. We know the amount of the loan, so the problem is now to determine the home price such that 80% of the price is equal to the amount of the loan. In symbols,

$$0.80x = 172{,}180.2058$$

which means that you simply divide the calculator output for the amount of the loan by 0.8 to find 215,225.2573.

Look Back. Given the conditions of the problem, we can look back to check our work (rounded to the nearest dollar for the check):

Purchase price of home:	$215,225
Less 20% down payment:	$ 43,045
Amount of loan:	$172,180

Example 3

Theresa's Social Security benefit is $450 per month if she retires at age 62 instead of age 65. What is the present value of an annuity that would pay $450 per month for 3 years if the current interest rate is 10% compounded monthly?

Solution Here, $m = 450$, $r = 0.10$, $t = 3$, and $n = 12$; then,

$$P = m\left[\frac{1 - (1 + i)^{-N}}{i}\right] = 450\left[\frac{1 - \left(1 + \frac{0.10}{12}\right)^{-36}}{\frac{0.10}{12}}\right] \approx 13{,}946.05601$$

The present value of this decision is $13,946.06. This represents the value of the additional 3 years of Social Security payments.

Monthly Payments

The process of paying off a debt by systematically making partial payments until the debt (principal) and the interest are repaid is called **amortization.** If the loan is paid off in regular equal installments, then we use the formula for the present value of an annuity to find the monthly payments by algebraically solving for m, where we let $i = r/n$:

$$P = m\left[\frac{1 - (1 + i)^{-nt}}{i}\right]$$ *Present value of an annuity formula*

$$Pi = m\left[1 - (1 + i)^{-nt}\right]$$ *Multiply both sides by i.*

$$\frac{Pi}{1 - (1 + i)^{-nt}} = m$$ *Divide both sides by $1 - (1 + i)^{-nt}$.*

COMPUTATIONAL
WINDOW

To program the amortization formula into a calculator input it as

(P*R/N)/(1 − (1+R/N)^
(−N*T))

Amortization Formula

If the amount of the loan is known (P), and you wish to find the amount of the periodic payment (m), use the formula

$$m = \frac{P\left(\frac{r}{n}\right)}{1 - \left(1 + \frac{r}{n}\right)^{-nt}}$$

where r is the annual rate, t is the time (in years), and n is the number of payments per year.

Example   4   Find the monthly payment for a house

In 2010, the average price of a new home was $291,000 and the interest rate was 6%. If this amount is financed for 30 years at 6% interest, what is the monthly payment?

Solution   This is an *amortization* problem with $P = 291{,}000$, $r = 0.06$, $t = 30$, and $n = 12$; then

$$m = \frac{P\left(\frac{r}{n}\right)}{1 - \left(1 + \frac{r}{n}\right)^{-nt}} = \frac{291{,}000\left(\frac{0.06}{12}\right)}{1 - \left(1 + \frac{0.06}{12}\right)^{-12(30)}} \approx 1{,}744.69202819$$

The monthly payment is $1,744.69. This is the payment for interest and principal to pay off a 30-year 6% loan of $291,000.

It is noteworthy to see how much interest is paid for the home loan of Example 4. There are 360 payments of $1,744.69, so the total amount repaid is

$$360(1{,}744.69) = 628{,}088.40$$

Since the loan was for $291,000, the interest is

$$\$628{,}088.40 - \$291{,}000 = \$337{,}088.40$$

The interest is more than the amount of the loan!

The amount of interest paid can be reduced by making a larger down payment. For Example 4, if a 20% down payment (which is fairly standard) was made, then $291,000(0.80) = $232,800 is the amount to be financed. If this amount is amortized over 20 years (instead of 30), the monthly payments are $1,667.85. The total amount paid on *this* loan is

Amount of each payment

$$240(\overbrace{1{,}667.85}) + \underbrace{58{,}200} = 458{,}484$$
$\uparrow$
Number of payments   Down payment

The savings yielded over the term of the loan by making a 20% down payment for 20 years rather than financing the entire amount for 30 years is $628,088.40 − $458,484 = $169,604.40.

It is interesting to see how much a difference in rates will affect the costs in Example 4. Suppose the interest rate rises by $\frac{1}{2}$%. If $P = \$291{,}000$, $r = 0.065$, $t = 30$, and $n = 12$, then (using the amortization formula)

$$m = \frac{P\left(\frac{r}{n}\right)}{1 - \left(1 + \frac{r}{n}\right)^{-nt}} = \frac{291{,}000\left(\frac{0.065}{12}\right)}{1 - \left(1 + \frac{0.065}{12}\right)^{-12(30)}} \approx 1{,}839.32$$

The interest on the 30-year 6% loan in Example 4 was $337,088.40; now at 6.5% interest for 30 years the total interest is

$$360(\$1{,}839.32) - \$291{,}000 = \$371{,}155.20$$

an additional cost of almost $34,100 ($371,155.20 − $337,088.40 = $34,066.80).

Most of the time when you obtain a home loan, you will need to make a choice about which loan offer is best for your particular situation, and a difference of $\frac{1}{2}$% between different choices is common.

Example 5 Make the better home loan choice

Suppose you are considering a $400,000 30-year home loan and are considering two possibilities:

Loan A: 7.25% + 0 pts   Loan B: 6.875% + 2.375 pts

Which is the better loan if the home is sold in 10 years?

Solution You might think that the lower rate is always the better choice, but you need to take into consideration the loan fees. One point on a loan is 1% of the amount of the loan. This means that 2.375 points represents a loan charge of

$$0.02375(\$400{,}000) = \$9{,}500$$

First, use the amortization formula for each loan:

$$\text{Loan A:} \quad m = \frac{\$400{,}000\left(\frac{0.0725}{12}\right)}{1 - \left(1 + \frac{0.0725}{12}\right)^{-12(30)}} \approx \$2{,}728.71$$

$$\text{Loan B:} \quad m = \frac{\$400{,}000\left(\frac{0.06875}{12}\right)}{1 - \left(1 + \frac{0.06875}{12}\right)^{-12(30)}} \approx \$2{,}627.72$$

The difference in payments is $100.99/mo. Now, find the present value of an annuity with $m = \$100.99$ using the 6.875% rate for 10 years:

$$A = \$100.99\left[\frac{1 - \left(1 + \frac{0.06875}{12}\right)^{-12(10)}}{\frac{0.06875}{12}}\right]$$

$$\approx \$8{,}746.35$$

Since the fees ($9,500) are greater than the present value of this annuity, the better choice is Loan A, even though it has the higher rate.

We should note that even though both amortization and add-on interest calculate the monthly (or periodic) payment, you should pay attention to which procedure or formula to use.

Distinguish Add-On Simple Interest and Amortization

To calculate the monthly (or periodic) payment, consider one of the following methods:

Simple interest   Use this with installment loans or loans that use the words "add-on interest." To calculate the payment:

Step 1 Calculate the interest using $I = Prt$.

Step 2 Add the interest to the amount of the loan using $A = P + I$.

Step 3 Divide this result by the number of payments (N):

$$m = \frac{A}{N}$$

The interest rate, r, used for the add-on rate is not the same as the annual interest rate (APR).

Compound interest   Use this with long-term loans, such as when purchasing real estate. Those loans are *amortized,* which means the interest rate, r, is the same as the annual interest rate, and the payments pay off both the principal and the interest.

Step 1 Identify the variables P, r, n, and t.

Step 2 Use the *amortization formula*:

$$m = \frac{P\left(\frac{r}{n}\right)}{1 - \left(1 + \frac{r}{n}\right)^{-nt}}$$

Problem Set **11.6**

Level **1**

1. **IN YOUR OWN WORDS**   What does amortization mean?

2. **IN YOUR OWN WORDS**   Describe when you would use the present value of an annuity formula.

3. The variables m, n, r, t, A, and P are used in the various financial formulas. Tell what each of these variables represents.

*Use a calculator to evaluate the **present value of an annuity** formula*

$$P = m\left[\frac{1 - \left(1 + \frac{r}{n}\right)^{-nt}}{\frac{r}{n}}\right]$$

for the values of the variables m, r, and t (respectively) given in Problems 4–11. Assume $n = 12$.

4. $50; 5%; 5 yr

5. $50; 6%; 5 yr

6. $50; 8%; 5 yr

7. $150; 5%; 30 yr

8. $150; 6%; 30 yr

9. $150; 8%; 30 yr

10. $1,050; 5%; 30 yr

11. $1,050; 6%; 30 yr

*Use a calculator to evaluate the **amortization** formula*

$$m = \frac{P\left(\frac{r}{n}\right)}{1 - \left(1 + \frac{r}{n}\right)^{-nt}}$$

for the values of the variables P, r, and t (respectively) given in Problems 12–19. Assume $n = 12$.

12. $14,000; 5%; 5 yr

13. $14,000; 10%; 5 yr

14. $14,000; 19%; 5 yr

15. $150,000; 8%; 30 yr

16. $150,000; 9%; 30 yr

17. $150,000; 10%; 30 yr

18. $260,000; 12%; 30 yr

19. $260,000; 9%; 30 yr

Find the present value of the ordinary annuities in Problems 20–31.

	Amount of Deposit m	Frequency n	Rate r	Time t
20.	$500	annually	8%	30 yr
21.	$500	annually	6%	30 yr
22.	$250	semiannually	8%	30 yr

	Amount of Deposit m	Frequency n	Rate r	Time t
23.	$600	semiannually	2%	10 yr
24.	$300	quarterly	6%	30 yr
25.	$100	monthly	4%	5 yr
26.	$200	quarterly	8%	20 yr
27.	$400	quarterly	11%	20 yr
28.	$ 30	monthly	8%	5 yr
29.	$ 75	monthly	4%	10 yr
30.	$ 50	monthly	8.5%	20 yr
31.	$100	quarterly	3%	20 yr

Level 2

Find the monthly payment for the loans in Problems 32–45.

32. $500 loan for 12 months at 12%

33. $100 loan for 18 months at 18%

34. $4,560 loan for 20 months at 21%

35. $3,520 loan for 30 months at 19%

36. Used-car financing of $2,300 for 24 months at 15%

37. New-car financing of 2.9% on a 30-month $12,450 loan

38. Furniture financed at $3,456 for 36 months at 23%

39. A refrigerator financed for $985 at 17% for 15 months

40. A $112,000 home bought with a 20% down payment and the balance financed for 30 years at 11.5%

41. A $108,000 condominium bought with a 30% down payment and the balance financed for 30 years at 12.05%

42. Finance $450,000 for a warehouse with a 12.5% 30-year loan

43. Finance $859,000 for an apartment complex with a 13.2% 20-year loan

44. How much interest (to the nearest dollar) would be saved in Problem 40 if the home were financed for 15 rather than 30 years?

45. How much interest (to the nearest dollar) would be saved in Problem 41 if the condominium were financed for 15 rather than 30 years?

46. Melissa agrees to contribute $500 to the alumni fund at the end of each year for the next 5 years. Shannon wants to match Melissa's gift, but he wants to make a lump-sum contribution. If the current interest rate is 12.5% compounded annually, how much should Shannon contribute to equal Melissa's gift?

47. A $1,000,000 lottery prize pays $50,000 per year for the next 20 years. If the current rate of return is 12.25%, what is the present value of this prize?

48. You look at your budget and decide that you can afford $250 per month for a car. What is the maximum loan you can afford if the interest rate is 13% and you want to repay the loan in 4 years?

Level 3

49. Suppose you have an annuity from an insurance policy and you have the option of being paid $250 per month for 20 years or having a lump-sum payment of $25,000. Which has more value if the current rate of return is 10%, compounded monthly?

50. An insurance policy offers you the option of being paid $750 per month for 20 years or a lump sum of $50,000. Which has more value if the current rate of return is 9%, compounded monthly, and you expect to live for 20 years?

51. I recently found a real-life advertisement in the newspaper:

(Only the phone number has been changed.) Suppose that you have won a $20,000,000 lottery, paid in 20 annual installments. How much would be a fair price to be paid today for the assignment of this prize? Assume the interest rate is 5%.

52. The bottom notice (not circled) states that $6,000 is needed for 90 days, and that the advertiser is willing to pay 20% interest. How much would you expect to receive in 90 days if you lent this party the $6,000?

53. Suppose your gross monthly income is $5,500 and your current monthly payments are $625. If the bank will allow you to pay up to 36% of your gross monthly income (less current monthly payments) for a monthly house payment, what is the maximum loan you can obtain if the rate for a 30-year mortgage is 9.65%?

Problem Solving 3

54. As the interest rate increases, determine whether each of the given amounts increases or decreases. Assume that all other variables remain constant.
    a. future value
    b. present value
    c. annuity

55. As the interest rate increases, determine whether each of the given amounts increases or decreases. Assume that all other variables remain constant.
    a. monthly value for a sinking fund
    b. monthly value for amortization
    c. present value of an annuity

56. Suppose your gross monthly income is $4,550 and your spouse's gross monthly salary is $3,980. Your monthly bills are $1,235. The home you wish to purchase costs $355,000 and the loan is an 11.85% 30-year loan. How much down payment (rounded to the nearest hundred dollars) is necessary to be able to afford this home? This down payment is what percent of the cost of the home? Assume the bank will allow you to pay up to 36% of your gross monthly income (less current monthly payments) for house payments.

57. Suppose you want to purchase a home for $225,000 with a 30-year mortgage at 10.24% interest. Suppose also that you can put down 25%. What are the monthly payments? What is

the total amount paid for principal and interest? What is the amount saved if this home is financed for 15 years instead of for 30 years?

58. The McBertys have $30,000 in savings to use as a down payment on a new home. They also have determined that they can afford between $1,500 and $1,800 per month for mortgage payments. If the mortgage rates are 11% per year compounded monthly, what is the price range for houses they should consider for a 30-year loan?

59. Rework Problem 58 for a 20-year loan instead of a 30-year loan.

60. Rework Problem 58 if interest rates go down to 10.2%.

11.7 Summary of Financial Formulas

Definitions of variables:

P = present value (principal)
A = future value
I = amount of interest
r = annual interest rate
t = number of years
n = periods; number of times compounded each year

For many students, the most difficult part of working with finances (other than the problem of lack of funds) is in determining *which* formula to use. If we wish to free ourselves from the problem of lack of funds, we must use our knowledge in a variety of situations that occur outside the classroom.

We will now outline a procedure for using the financial formulas we have introduced in this chapter that you can use to unlock your financial security. First, review the meaning of the variables, as shown in the margin. Next, study the following procedure for working financial problems.

Classification of Financial Problems

When classifying financial formulas:

Step 1 Is the interest compounded?

If the interest is *removed*, use the **simple interest formula.**
If the interest is *added* to the account, use the **compound interest formula.**

Step 2 Is it a lump sum problem? What is the unknown?

If the future value is unknown, then it is a **future value problem.**
If the present value is unknown, then it is a **present value problem.**

Step 3 Is it a periodic payment problem with the periodic payment known?

If the future value is desired, then it is an **ordinary annuity.**
If the present value is desired, then it is a **present value of an annuity.**

Step 4 Is it a periodic payment problem with the periodic payment unknown?

If the future value is known, then it is a **sinking fund.**
If the present value is known, then it is an **amortization** problem.

The rest of this section discusses this procedure box with a bit more detail.

Is the interest compounded?

If the interest is *removed* from the account, then use the *simple interest formula.*

$$I = Prt$$

Use this for amount of interest; any one of the variables *I*, *P*, *r*, or *t*, may be unknown.

Examples: amount of interest; add-on interest; car payments; using the r from the simple interest formula when calculating the APR; finding the APR when given the purchase price and the monthly payment; credit card interest

If the interest is *added* to the account, then use a *compound interest formula.* In such a case there are two remaining questions to ask when classifying a compound interest problem.

Is it a lump-sum problem? If it is, then what is the unknown?

If FUTURE VALUE is the unknown, then it is a *future value* problem.

$$A = P\left(1 + \frac{r}{n}\right)^{nt} \quad \text{or} \quad A = Pe^{rt}$$

Examples: future value; inflation; retirement planning

If PRESENT VALUE is the unknown, then it is a *present value* problem.

$$P = A\left(1 + \frac{r}{n}\right)^{-nt}$$

Examples: present value; retirement planning

Is it a periodic payment problem? If it is, then is the periodic payment known?

PERIODIC PAYMENT KNOWN and you want to find the future value, then it is an *ordinary annuity* problem.

$$A = m\left[\frac{\left(1 + \frac{r}{n}\right)^{nt} - 1}{\frac{r}{n}}\right]$$

Examples: future value of periodic payments made to an interest-bearing account; retirement planning

PERIODIC PAYMENT KNOWN and you want to find the present value, then it is a *present value of an annuity* problem.

$$P = m\left[\frac{1 - \left(1 + \frac{r}{n}\right)^{-nt}}{\frac{r}{n}}\right]$$

Examples: if the monthly payment, time, and rate are known, how much loan is possible? the current value of a known annuity (as in selling off the proceeds from an insurance policy or winning the lottery)

PERIODIC PAYMENT UNKNOWN and you know the future value, then it is a *sinking fund* problem.

$$m = \frac{A\left(\frac{r}{n}\right)}{\left(1 + \frac{r}{n}\right)^{nt} - 1}$$

Example: the periodic payment necessary to make to an interest-bearing account in order to reach some known financial goal

PERIODIC PAYMENT UNKNOWN and you know the present value, then it is an *amortization* problem.

$$m = \frac{P\left(\frac{r}{n}\right)}{1 - \left(1 + \frac{r}{n}\right)^{-nt}}$$

Example 1 Monthly payment for an amortized loan

Figure 11.12 reproduces part of an advertisement to refinance a loan.

Here is an example of how some of my clients are using this new program:

Bills	Current Debt	Current Pmt.	New Loan
Mortgage	$378,000	$2,389	
Home Equity Loan	$36,000	$345	**$434,200**
Visa	$8,000	$190	
Master Card	$5,000	$150	**New Payment**
Sears	$3,500	$105	
Department Store	$3,700	$145	**$1,397**
Total	**$434,200**	**$3,324**	

FIGURE 11.12 Super duper brand new mortgage program

Assume a 6.5% annual mortgage rate. Find the monthly payment for both the old mortgage and for the new loan.

Solution   The present value is known, and we see the monthly payment, so this is an amortization problem. Here are the variable values:

Mortgage	P	r	n	t	$m = \dfrac{P\left(\frac{r}{n}\right)}{1 - \left(1 + \frac{r}{n}\right)^{-nt}}$
Old	$378,000	0.065	12	30	$m = \$2,389.21$
New	$434,200	0.065	12	30	$m = \$2,744.43$

Wait a minute! The advertisement shows a new monthly payment of $1,397. The new loan is at a new "teaser" rate. These loans were particularly responsible for the financial melt-down of 2009. The person who did not read the fine print and do some math calculations became trapped when the teaser rate increased to an unaffordable rate.

Example 2 Classifying financial problems

Classify each formula as a financial problem type, and give one possible example which would use the given formula.
a. $y = 500(1.07)^{20}$ **b.** $y = 280,000\left(1 + \frac{0.04}{4}\right)^{-60}$ **c.** $y = 80(0.05)(20)$

d. $y = 480\left[\dfrac{\left(1 + \frac{0.04}{12}\right)^{120} - 1}{\frac{0.04}{12}}\right]$

Solution
a. Future value problem; specifically the future value of $500 invested at 7% interest for 20 years.
b. Present value problem; how much would need to be invested today to yield $280,000 in 15 years if the money is invested at 4%?
c. Simple interest formula; what is the future value of $80 invested at 5% for 20 years?
d. Ordinary annuity; what is the future value of $480 monthly payment invested at 4% for 10 years?

Problem Set 11.7

Level 1

1. **IN YOUR OWN WORDS** What are a reasonable down payment and monthly payment for a home in your area?

2. **IN YOUR OWN WORDS** What are a reasonable down payment and monthly payment for a new automobile?

3. **IN YOUR OWN WORDS** Outline a procedure for identifying the type of financial formula for a given applied problem.

4. What is the formula for the present value of an annuity? What is the unknown?

5. What is the amortization formula? What is the unknown?

Classify the type of financial formula for the information given in Problems 6–11.

Lump-sum Problems

	P	*A*
6.	known	unknown
7.	unknown	known

Periodic Payment Problems

	P	*A*	*m*
8.	unknown		known
9.		unknown	known
10.		known	unknown
11.	known		unknown

In Problems 12–15, match each formula in Column A with the type of financial problem in Column B.

Column A   Column B

12. $A = m\left[\dfrac{\left(1 + \frac{r}{n}\right)^{nt} - 1}{\frac{r}{n}}\right]$ Annuity

13. $P = m\left[\dfrac{1 - \left(1 + \frac{r}{n}\right)^{-nt}}{\frac{r}{n}}\right]$ Amortization

14. $m = \dfrac{A\left(\frac{r}{n}\right)}{\left(1 + \frac{r}{n}\right)^{nt} - 1}$ Present value of an annuity

15. $m = \dfrac{P\left(\frac{r}{n}\right)}{1 - \left(1 + \frac{r}{n}\right)^{-nt}}$ Sinking fund

Classify the financial problems in Problems 16–19, and then answer each question by assuming a 12% interest rate compounded annually.

16. Find the value of a $1,000 certificate in 3 years.

17. Deposit $300 at the end of each year. What is the total in the account in 10 years?

18. An insurance policy pays $10,000 in 5 years. What lump-sum deposit today will yield $10,000 in 5 years?

19. What annual deposit is necessary to give $10,000 in 5 years?

Level 2

In Problems 20–52: **a.** *State the type; and* **b.** *Answer the question.*

20. Find the value of a $1,000 certificate in $2\frac{1}{2}$ years if the interest rate is 12% compounded monthly.

21. You deposit $300 at the end of each year into an account paying 12% compounded annually. How much is in the account in 10 years?

22. A 5-year term insurance policy has an annual premium of $300, and at the end of 5 years, all payments and interest are refunded. What lump-sum deposit is necessary to equal this amount if you assume an interest rate of 10% compounded annually?

23. What annual deposit is necessary to have $10,000 in 5 years if all the money is deposited at 9% interest compounded annually?

24. A $5,000,000 apartment complex loan is to be paid off in 10 years by making 10 equal annual payments. How much is each payment if the interest rate is 14% compounded annually?

25. The price of automobiles has increased at 6.25% per year. How much would you expect a $20,000 automobile to cost in 5 years if you assume annual compounding?

26. The amount to be financed on a new car is $9,500. The terms are 7% for 4 years. What is the monthly payment?

27. What deposit today is equal to 33 annual deposits of $500 into an account paying 8% compounded annually?

28. If you can afford $875 for your house payments, what is the loan you can afford if the interest rate is 6.5% and the monthly payments are made for 30 years?

29. What is the monthly payment for a home costing $125,000 with a 20% down payment and the balance financed for 30 years at 12%?

30. Ricon Bowling Alley will need $80,000 in 4 years to resurface the lanes. What lump sum would be necessary today if the owner of the business can deposit it in an account that pays 9% compounded semiannually?

31. Rita wants to save for a trip to Tahiti, so she puts $2.00 per day into a jar. After 1 year she has saved $730 and puts the money into a bank account paying 10% compounded annually. She continues to save in this manner and makes her annual $730 deposit for 15 years. How much does she have at the end of that time period?

32. Karen receives a $12,500 inheritance that she wants to save until she retires in 20 years. If she deposits the money in a fixed 11% account, compounded daily ($n = 365$), how much will she have when she retires?

33. You want to give your child a million dollars when he retires at age 65. How much money do you need to deposit into an account paying 9% compounded monthly if your child is now 10 years old?

34. An accounting firm agrees to purchase a computer for $150,000 (cash on delivery) and the delivery date is in 270 days. How much do the owners need to deposit in an account paying 18% compounded quarterly so that they will have $150,000 in 270 days?

35. For 5 years, Thompson Cleaners deposits $900 at the end of each quarter into an account paying 8% compounded quarterly. What is the value of the account at the end of 5 years?

36. What is the necessary amount of monthly payments to an account paying 18% compounded monthly in order to have $100,000 in $8\frac{1}{3}$ years if the deposits are made at the end of each month?

37. Mark's Grocery Store is going to be remodeled in 5 years, and the remodeling will cost $300,000. How much should be deposited now in order to pay for this remodeling if the account pays 12% compounded monthly?

38. If an apartment complex will need painting in $3\frac{1}{2}$ years and the job will cost $45,000, what amount needs to be deposited into an account now in order to have the necessary funds? The account pays 12% interest compounded semiannually.

39. Teal and Associates needs to borrow $45,000. The best loan they can find is one at 12% that must be repaid in monthly installments over the next $3\frac{1}{2}$ years. How much are the monthly payments?

40. Certain Concrete Company deposits $4,000 at the end of each quarter into an account paying 10% interest compounded quarterly. What is the value of the account at the end of $7\frac{1}{2}$ years?

41. Major Magic Corporation deposits $1,000 at the end of each month into an account paying 18% interest compounded monthly. What is the value of the account at the end of $8\frac{1}{3}$ years?

42. What is the future value of $112,000 invested for 5 years at 14% compounded monthly?

43. What is the future value of $800 invested for 1 year at 10% compounded daily?

44. What is the future value of $9,000 invested for 4 years at 20% compounded monthly?

45. If $5,000 is compounded annually at 5.5% for 12 years, what is the future value?

46. If $10,000 is compounded annually at 8% for 18 years, what is the future value?

47. You owe $5,000 due in 3 years, but you would like to pay the debt today. If the present interest rate is compounded annually at 11%, how much should you pay today so that the present value is equivalent to the $5,000 payment in 3 years?

48. Sebastopol Movie Theater will need $20,000 in 5 years to replace the seats. What deposit should be made today in an account that pays 9% compounded semiannually?

49. The Fair View Market must be remodeled in 3 years. It is estimated that remodeling will cost $200,000. How much should be deposited now (to the nearest dollar) to pay for this remodeling if the account pays 10% compounded monthly?

50. A laundromat will need seven new washing machines in $2\frac{1}{2}$ years for a total cost of $2,900. How much money (to the nearest dollar) should be deposited now to pay for these machines? The interest rate is 11% compounded semiannually.

51. A computerized checkout system is planned for Able's Grocery Store. The system will be delivered in 18 months at a cost of $560,000. How much should be deposited today (to the nearest dollar) into an account paying 7.5% compounded daily?

52. A lottery offers you a choice of $1,000,000 per year for 5 years or a lump-sum payment. What lump-sum payment (rounded to the nearest dollar) would equal the annual payments if the current interest rate is 14% compounded annually?

Level 3

Problems 53–55 are based on a 30-year fixed-rate home loan of $185,500 with an interest rate of 7.75%.

53. What is the monthly payment?

54. What is the total amouht of interest paid?

55. Suppose you reduce the term to 20 years. What is the total amount of interest paid, and what is the savings over the 30-year loan?

Problems 56–58 are based on a 30-year fixed-rate home loan of $418,500 with an interest rate of 8.375%.

56. What is the monthly payment?

57. What is the total amount of interest paid?

58. Suppose you reduce the term to 22 years. What is the total amount of interest paid, and what is the savings over the 30-year loan?

Problem Solving 3

59. A contest offers the winner $50,000 now or $10,000 now and $45,000 in one year. Which is the better choice if the current interest rate is 10% compounded monthly and the winner does not intend to use any of the money for one year?

60. In 1982 the inflation rate hit 16%. Suppose that the average cost of a textbook in 1982 was $15. What is the expected cost in the year 2012 if we project this rate of inflation on the cost? (Assume continuous compounding.) If the average cost of a textbook in 2010 was $120, what is the actual inflation rate (rounded to the nearest tenth percent)?

---

*This problem requires Chapter 10 (solving exponential equations).

11.8 CHAPTER SUMMARY

To get money is difficult, to keep it is more difficult, but to spend it wisely is most difficult of all.

ANONYMOUS

Important Ideas

Simple interest formula and the future value formula for compound interest [11.1]
Ordinary and exact interest [11.1]
Interest formula variables [11.1]
Credit card interest [11.2]
Arithmetic, geometric, and Fibonacci sequences [11.3]
Distinguish between sequences and series [11.3, 11.4]
Retirement decisions [11.5]
Add-on interest vs. amortization [11.2; 11.6]
Distinguish financial problems [11.7]

 Take some time getting ready to work the review problems in this section. First review these important ideas. Look back at the definition and property boxes. If you look online, you will find a list of important terms introduced in this chapter, as well as the types of problems that were introduced. You will maximize your understanding of this chapter by working the problems in this section only after you have studied the material.

 You will find some review help online at **www.mathnature.com**. There are links giving general test help in studying for a mathematics examination, as well as specific help for reviewing this chapter.

Chapter 11 Review Questions

1. **IN YOUR OWN WORDS**   Explain the difference between a sequence and a series. Include in your discussion how to distinguish arithmetic, geometric, and Fibonacci-type sequences, and give the formulas for their general terms. What are the relevant formulas for arithmetic and geometric series?

2. **IN YOUR OWN WORDS**   Outline a procedure for identifying financial formulas. Include in your discussion future value, present value, ordinary annuity, present value of an annuity, amortization, and sinking fund classifications.

3. Classify each sequence as arithmetic, geometric, Fibonacci-type, or none of these. Find an expression for the general term if it is one of these types; otherwise, give the next two terms.
   a. 5, 10, 15, 20, . . .
   b. 5, 10, 20, 40, . . .
   c. 5, 10, 15, 25, . . .
   d. 5, 10, 20, 35, . . .
   e. 5, 50, 500, 5,000, . . .
   f. 5, 50, 5, 50, . . .

4. a. Evaluate: $\sum_{k=1}^{3}(k^2 - 2k + 1)$
   b. Expand: $\sum_{k=1}^{4}\dfrac{k-1}{k+1}$

5. Suppose someone tells you she has traced her family tree back 10 generations. What is the minimum number of people on her family tree if there were no intermarriages?

6. A certain bacterium divides into two bacteria every 20 minutes. If there are 1,024 bacteria in the culture now, how many will there be in 24 hours, assuming that no bacteria die? Leave your answer in exponential form.

7. Suppose that the car you wish to purchase has a sticker price of $22,730 with a dealer cost of $18,579. Make a 5% offer for this car (rounded to the nearest hundred dollars).

8. Suppose that the amount to be financed for a car purchase is $13,500 at an add-on interest rate of 2.9% for 2 years.
   a. What are the monthly installment and the amount of interest that you will pay?
   b. Use the APR formula for this loan.

9. If a car with a cash price of $11,450 is offered for nothing down with 48 monthly payments of $353.04, what is the APR?

10. From the consumer's point of view, which method of calculating interest on a credit card is most advantageous? Illustrate the three types of calculating interest for a purchase of $525 with 9% APR for a 31-day month in which it takes 7 days for your $100 payment to be received and recorded.

11. Suppose that you want to have $1,000,000 in 50 years. To achieve this goal, how much do you need to deposit today if you can earn 9% interest compounded monthly?

12. **a.** What is the monthly payment for a home loan of $154,000 if the rate is 8% and the time is 20 years?

    b. If you paid a 20% down payment, what is the price of the home?

    c. What would you expect this home to be worth in 30 years if you assume an inflation rate of 4%?

13. Suppose that you expect to receive a $100,000 inheritance when you reach 21 in three years and four months. What is the present value of your inheritance if the current interest rate is 6.4% compounded monthly?

Use the advertisement shown in Figure 11.13 *as a basis for answering Problems 14–20. Assume the current interest rate is 5%.*

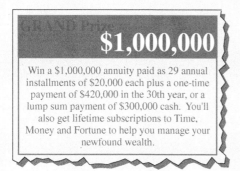

FIGURE 11.13 Contest prize notice

14. What is the present value of the $420,000 payment to be received in 30 years?

15. What is the actual value of the annuity portion of the prize?

16. What is the present value of the annuity?

17. Suppose you take the $300,000 cash payment and still want to have $420,000 in 30 years. How much of the $300,000 do you need to set aside now to have $420,000 in 30 years?

18. Suppose you take the $300,000 cash payment and set aside $100,000 for savings. You plan on using the interest on the remaining $200,000. What are your annual earnings from interest?

19. Which option should you take and why?

20. If the current interest rate is 10%, which option should you take and why?

BOOK REPORTS

Write a 500-word report on this book:

What Are Numbers? (Glenview, IL: Scott, Foresman and Company, 1969) by Louis Auslander. Here is a problem from this book (p. 112): "Suppose a ball has the property that whenever it is dropped, it bounces up 1/2 the distance that it fell. For instance, if we drop it from 6 feet, it bounces up 3 feet. Let us hold the ball 6 feet off the ground and drop it. How far will the ball go before coming to rest?" Include the solution of this problem as part of your report.

Group RESEARCH PROJECTS

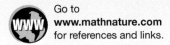

Go to
www.mathnature.com
for references and links.

Working in small groups is typical of most work environments, and learning to work with others to communicate specific ideas is an important skill. Work with three or four other students to submit a single report based on each of the following questions.

G37. Suppose you have just inherited $30,000 and need to decide what to do with the money. Write a paper discussing your options and the financial implications of those options. The paper you turn in should offer several alternatives and then the members of your group should reach a consensus of the best course of action.

G38. Suppose you were hired for a job paying $21,000 per year and were given the following options:

Option A: Annual salary increase of $1,200

Option B: Semiannual salary increase of $300

Option C: Quarterly salary increase of $75

Option D: Monthly salary increase of $10

Each person should write the arithmetic series for the total amount of money earned in 10 years under a different option. Your group should reach a consensus as to which is the best option. Give reasons and show your calculations in the paper that your group submits.

G39. It is not uncommon for the owner of a home to receive a letter similar to the one shown below. Write a paper based on this letter. Different members of your group can work on different parts of the question, but you should submit one paper from your group.

Dear Customer:

Previously we provided you an enrollment package for our BiWeekly Advantage Plan. We have had an excellent response from our mortgagors, yet we have not received your signed enrollment form and program fee to start your program.

How effective is the BiWeekly Advantage Plan? Reviewing your loan as of the week of this letter we estimate:

        MORTGAGE INTEREST SAVINGS OF $99,287.56
        LOAN TERM REDUCED BY 7 YEARS.

Many financial advisors agree it is a sound investment practice to pay off a mortgage early, particularly in light of growing economic uncertainty.

Act today! Don't let procrastination or indecision deny you and your family the opportunity to obtain mortgage-free homeownership sooner than you ever expected.

Please call us toll-free at 1-800-555-6060 if you would like more information about our BiWeekly Advantage Plan and a free personalized mortgage analysis. Our telephone representatives are available to serve you from 9 am to 5 pm (EST).

                                    Sincerely,

Interest Rate:	8.3750
Current Balance:	$ 416,640.54
Monthly Payment:	**$ 3,180.91**

Homeownership: Remaining Terms		
	Years	**Months**
Current Payment Plan	29	5
BiWeekly Plan	22	5
REDUCTION	**7**	**0**

Total Remaining **Principal & Interest Payments:**	
Current Payment Plan	$ 1,122,849.24
BiWeekly Plan	$ 923,561.68
INTEREST SAVINGS	**$ 199,287.56**

a. What is the letter about?

b. A computer printout (shown above) was included with the letter. Assuming that these calculations are correct, discuss the advantages or disadvantages of accepting this offer.

c. The plan as described in the letter costs $375 to sign up. I called the company and asked what their plan would do that I could not do myself by simply making 13 payments a year to my mortgage holder. The answer I received was that the plan would do nothing more, but the reason people do sign up is because they do not have the self-discipline to make the bimonthly payments by themselves. Why is a biweekly payment equivalent to 13 annual payments instead of equivalent to a monthly payment?

d. The representative of the company told me that more than 250,000 people have signed up. How much income has the company received from this offer?

e. You calculated the income the company has received from this offer in part **d**, but that is not all it receives. It acts as a bonded and secure "holding company" for your funds (because the mortgage company does not accept "two-week" payments). This means that the company receives the use (interest value) of your money for two weeks out of every month. This is equivalent to half the year. Let's assume that the average monthly payment is $1,000 and that the company has 250,000 payments that it holds for half the year. If the interest rate is 5% (a secure guaranteed rate), how much potential interest can be received by this company?

Individual RESEARCH PROJECTS

 www.mathnature.com

Learning to use sources outside your classroom and textbook is an important skill, and here are ideas for extending some of the ideas in this chapter. You can find references to these projects in a library or at **www.mathnature.com.**

PROJECT 11.1 Conduct a survey of banks, savings and loan companies, and credit unions in your area. Prepare a report on the different types of savings accounts available and the interest rates they pay. Include methods of payment as well as interest rates.

PROJECT 11.2 Do you expect to live long enough to be a millionaire? Suppose that your annual salary today is $52,000. If inflation continues at 6%, how long will it be before $52,000 increases to an annual salary of a million dollars?

PROJECT 11.3 Consult an almanac or some government source, and then write a report on the current inflation rate. Project some of these results to the year of your own expected retirement.

PROJECT 11.4 Historical Quest   Write a short paper about Fibonacci numbers. You might check *The Fibonacci Quarterly,* particularly "A Primer on the Fibonacci Sequence," Parts I and II, in the February and April 1963 issues. The articles, written by Verner Hogatt and S. L. Basin, are considered classic articles on the subject. One member of your group should investigate the relationship of the Fibonacci numbers to nature, another the algebraic properties of the sequence, and another the history of the sequence.

PROJECT 11.5 Karen says that she has heard something about APR rates but doesn't really know what the term means. Wayne says he thinks it has something to do with the prime rate, but he isn't sure what. Write a short paper explaining APR to Karen and Wayne.

PROJECT 11.6 Some savings and loan companies advertise that they pay interest *continuously.* Do some research to explain what this means.

PROJECT 11.7 Select a car of your choice, find the list price, and calculate 5% and 10% price offers. Check out available money sources in your community, and prepare a report showing the different costs for the same car. Back up your figures with data.

PROJECT 11.8 Outline a program for your own retirement. In the process of writing this paper, answer the following questions. You will need to state your assumptions about interest and inflation rates.

a. What monthly amount of money today would provide you a comfortable living?

b. Using the answer to part **a**, project that amount to your own retirement, calculating the effects of inflation. Use your own age and assume that you will retire at age 65.

c. How much money would you need to have accumulated to provide the amount you found in part **b**, if you decide to live on the interest only?

d. If you set up a sinking fund to provide the amount you found in part **c**, how much would you need to deposit each month?

e. Offer some alternatives to the sinking fund you considered in part **d**.

f. Draw some conclusions about your retirement.

17 THE NATURE OF VOTING AND APPORTIONMENT

What in the World?

"Heather, how was Girls' State?" asked Bill. "I'll bet you met a lot of neat people, but was it as great as advertised?"

"It was a mountain-top event for me!" exclaimed Heather. "We met senators, representatives, and even the governor! And I learned a lot about how our government works. What I didn't expect was the subtleties of voting, and the many different ways there are for voting. I'll bet you didn't know that there is no perfect voting method. . . ."

Courtesy Charlie Daniels, Arkansas Secretary of State

Overview

This chapter investigates the question of how groups can best arrive at decisions. We refer to the study of the decision making process as **social choice theory.** This study considers the possibilities by which individual preferences are translated into a single group choice. Social choice theory arose to help explain the processes of **voting,** or indicating an individual's preferences. You have no doubt participated as a voter in many contexts, but you may not realize that the voting method used can significantly affect the outcome of the election.

Historically, certain voting inconsistencies were discussed by Jean-Charles de Borda (1733–1799) and Marie Jean Antoine Nicolas Caritat, the Marquis of Condorcet (1743–1794). It was not until 1951 that the mathematician Kenneth Arrow (1921–) proved that all attempts to arrive at a suitable technique for voting are doomed to failure!

Since all voting methods have inherent fallacies, we will investigate in this chapter different voting methods, as well as some reasons why we need to carefully consider the election process. We also look at the process of selecting a representative government using the apportionment of votes.

17.1 Voting

I think that society must choose among a number of alternative policies. These policies may be thought of as quite comprehensive, covering a number of aspects: foreign policy, budgetary policy, or whatever. Now, each individual member of the society has a preference, or a set of preferences, over these alternatives. I guess that you can say one alternative is better than another.

KENNETH J. ARROW

CHAPTER **CHALLENGE**

See if you can fill in the question mark.

$$2 \rightarrow 4 \rightarrow 8 \rightarrow 11 \rightarrow 19 \rightarrow 19 \rightarrow \text{?}$$

The process of selection can be accomplished in many different ways. If one person alone makes the decision, we call it a **dictatorship.** If the decision is made by a group, it is called a **vote.** The different methods of selection using a vote, such as voting on a proposal, resolution, law, or a choice between candidates, is an area of study called *social choice theory*. In this section we will discuss several ways of counting the votes to declare a winner.

Majority Rule

2008 Democratic National Convention

One common method of voting is by *majority rule*. By **majority rule,** we mean voting to find an alternative that receives more than 50% of the vote. Be careful how you interpret this. If there are 11 voters with two alternatives A and B, then 6 votes for A is a majority. If there are 12 voters and A receives 6 votes, then A does not have a majority. Finally, if there are more than two alternatives, say, A, B, and C, with 12 voters and A receives 5 votes, B receives 3 votes, and C receives 4 votes, then no alternative has a majority. We summarize with the following box.

Majority Rule

If the number of votes is n and n is even, then a majority is

$$\frac{n}{2} + 1$$

If the number of votes is odd, then a majority is

$$\frac{n + 1}{2}$$

Example 1 Find a winner using the majority rule

Consider an election with three alternatives. These might be Republican, Democrat, and Green party candidates. To keep our notation simple, we will designate the candidates as A, B, and C. There are 6 possible rankings, regardless of the number of voters. We list these using the following notation:

Choices: (ABC) (ACB) (BAC) (BCA) (CAB) (CBA)

The symbol "(ACB)" means that the ranking of a voter is candidate A for first place, C for second place, and B for third place. The six sets of three letters here indicate all possible ways for a voter to rank three candidates. Now, suppose there are 12 voters and we list the rankings of these voters using the following notation:

Choices:	(ABC)	(ACB)	(BAC)	(BCA)	(CAB)	(CBA)
No. of Votes:	5	0	2	1	0	4

This means that 5 of the 12 voters ranked the candidates ABC, while none of the voters ranked the candidates in the order ACB. Notice that we have accounted for all 6 possibilities even though in some cases some possibilities have no voters. The sum of the number of votes for all possibilities equals the number of voters—12 for this example. Use the majority rule to find a winner.

Solution   For the election we look only at first choices (even though the voters ranked all the candidates). We see A received 5 votes ($5 + 0 = 5$), B received 3 votes ($2 + 1 = 3$), and C received 4 votes ($0 + 4 = 4$). If we use the majority rule, $\frac{12}{2} + 1 = 7$ votes, and we see that there is no winner.

Notice from Example 1 that with three candidates, we listed 6 possibilities. In social choice theory, the principle that asserts that any set of individual rankings is possible is called the *principle of unrestricted domain.* If there are n candidates, then there are n first choices, $n - 1$ second choices, and so on. So, by the fundamental counting principle, the total number of choices is

$$n(n - 1)(n - 2) \cdot \cdots \cdot 3 \cdot 2 \cdot 1$$

We denote this product by writing $n!$. That is, $5! = 5 \cdot 4 \cdot 3 \cdot 2 \cdot 1$.

The majority rule satisfies a principle called **symmetry.** This principle ensures that if one voter prefers choice A to choice B and another prefers choice B to A, then their votes should cancel each other out.

Plurality Method

In the case of no winner by majority rule, we often want to have an alternative way to select a winner. With the **plurality method,** the winner is the candidate with the highest number of votes.

Plurality Method

Each voter votes for one candidate.
The candidate receiving the most votes is declared the winner.

Example 2 Find a winner using the plurality rule

Reconsider the Republican, Democrat, and Green Party vote from Example 1.

Choices:	(ABC)	(ACB)	(BAC)	(BCA)	(CAB)	(CBA)
No. of Votes:	5	0	2	1	0	4

Who is the winner using the plurality method?

Solution   A: $5 + 0 = 5$ votes; B: $2 + 1 = 3$ votes; C: $0 + 4 = 4$ votes. The winner is the candidate with the most votes, namely, candidate A.

Example 3 | Find a winner using the plurality method

Consider the following voting situation:

Choices:	(ABC)	(ACB)	(BAC)	(BCA)	(CAB)	(CBA)
No. of Votes:	3	2	2	0	1	4

Who is the winner using the plurality method?

Solution   We see the outcome is A: 5 votes $(3 + 2 = 5)$, B: 2 votes $(2 + 0 = 2)$, and C: 5 votes $(1 + 4 = 5)$. There is no majority winner, and there is no winner using the plurality method.

Somehow we cannot be satisfied with the result of Example 3. The very nature of voting seems to imply that we want a winner, so we need some set of tie-breaking rules. In situations governed by *Robert's Rules of Order,* the chairperson is allowed to vote to make or break a tie. Social choice theory calls this the *principle of decisiveness.*

Borda Count

A common way of determining a winner when there is no majority is to assign a point value to each voter's ranking. The last-place candidate is given 1 point, each next-to-the-last candidate is given 2 points, and so on. This counting scheme, called a **Borda count,** is defined in the following box.

Borda Count

Each voter ranks the candidates. If there are n candidates, then n points are assigned to the first choice for each voter, with $n - 1$ points for the next choice, and so on. The points for each candidate are added and if one has more votes, that candidate is declared the winner.

We illustrate this process with the following example.

Example 4 | Find a winner using a Borda count

Consider the following election with four candidates, A, B, C, and D. There are $4! = 4 \times 3 \times 2 \times 1 = 24$ possible rankings for these four candidates, so instead of listing all those possibilities as we did with the previous examples of this section, we ask the voters to rank their choices.

Voter	Ranking
#1	B, D, C, A
#2	D, C, A, B
#3	B, A, C, D
#4	B, A, D, C
#5	D, A, B, C
#6	A, B, C, D

Note the results: A: 1 vote; B: 3 votes; C: 0 votes; D: 2 votes. There is a total of 6 voters, so a majority would require $6/2 + 1 = 4$ votes, so there is no majority. Declare a winner using a Borda count.

Solution   A Borda count with 4 candidates awards 4 points for each first-place ranking, 3 points for each second-place ranking, followed by 2 points and 1 point. We summarize the voters' ranking in table form:

			Voter				
Candidate	#1	#2	#3	#4	#5	#6	Total
A	1	2	3	3	3	4	16
B	4	1	4	4	2	3	18
C	2	3	2	1	1	2	11
D	3	4	1	2	4	1	15

The winner is B, since this candidate has the highest total.

An example of voting using the Borda method with which you may be familiar is the annual voting for the Heisman Trophy in collegiate football. In 2010, the winner Mark Ingram of the University of Alabama was selected after 870 ballots were mailed to media personnel across the country, 55 still-living Heisman winners, and 1 fan ballot for a total of 926 electors. Each elector votes for three choices and a point total is reached by a system of three points for a first place vote, two for a second, and one for a third. It was reported that Ingram received 1,304 points, with the runner-up Toby Gerhart of Stanford University garnering 1,276 points is the closest Heisman race ever.

The principle of decisiveness forces us to consider a structure for selecting a winner when the method we use does not produce a winner. One such method is to hold a *runoff election.* A **runoff election** is an attempt to obtain a majority vote by eliminating one or more alternatives and voting again on the remaining choices.

Hare Method

The first runoff method we will consider was proposed in 1861 by Thomas Hare (1806–1891). In this method, votes are transferred from eliminated candidates to remaining candidates. We summarize this method in the following box.

Hare Method

Each voter votes for one candidate. If a candidate receives a majority of the votes, that candidate is declared to be a *first-round winner.* If no candidate receives a majority of the votes, then with the **Hare method,** also known as the *plurality with an elimination runoff method,* the candidate(s) with the fewest number of first-place votes is (are) eliminated.

Each voter votes for one candidate in the second round. If a candidate receives a majority, that candidate is declared to be a *second-round winner.* If no candidate receives a majority of the second-round votes, then eliminate the candidate(s) with the fewest number of first-place votes. Repeat this process until a candidate receives a majority.

Example 5 **Find a winner using the Hare method**

Reconsider Example 3.

Choices:	(ABC)	(ACB)	(BAC)	(BCA)	(CAB)	(CBA)
No. of Votes:	3	2	2	0	1	4

There is neither a majority winner nor a plurality winner. Find a solution using the Hare method.

Solution   We see that A received 5 (3 + 2 = 5) first-round votes; B received 2 votes; and C received 5 votes. We hold a runoff election by eliminating the alternative with the fewest votes; this is choice B. For convenience, in this book we assume that a voter's order of preference will remain the same for subsequent rounds of voting. Thus, we now have the following possibilities, where we have crossed out candidate B:

Choices:	(AB̸C)	(ACB̸)	(B̸AC)	(B̸CA)	(CAB̸)	(CB̸A)
No. of Votes:	3	2	2	0	1	4
	↓	↓	↓	↓	↓	↓

Choices:	(AC)	(CA)
No. of Votes:	3 + 2 + 2 = 7	0 + 1 + 4 = 5

We now declare a second-round winner, A, using the *majority rule*.

The assumption that we made in Example 5 about consistent voting has a name in social choice theory. It is called the *principle of independence of irrelevant alternatives*. In other words, we assume consistent voting, which means that if a voter prefers A to B with C a possible choice, then the voter still prefers A to B when C is not a possible choice.

In countries with many political parties, such as France, the Hare method is used for electing their president.

Pairwise Comparison Method

Runoff elections are not always appropriate. It seems reasonable that if everyone in a group of voters prefers candidate X over candidate Y, then under its voting method, the group should prefer X to Y. Social choice theory calls this the *Pareto principle*. Thus, it is desirable that the pairwise methods we consider satisfy this principle. The characteristic property of these pairwise methods is that they pair up the competitors, two at a time. Such methods are called **binary voting.** We begin with the most important of these methods.

Historical NOTE

Karl Smith library

**Vilfredo Pareto
(1848–1923)**

Pareto was an economist and sociologist known for his application of mathematics to economic analysis and for his theory of the "circulation of elites." This theory says there will always be new Bill Gateses in the world to replace the old Bill Gateses of the world. The Pareto principle we use in this book is **not** the same as "Pareto's principle," known as the "80:20 rule." The latter has many forms and asserts, "A minority of input produces the majority of results." For example, "80% of the work is usually done by 20% of the people," or "80% of the problems are usually caused by 20% of the people."

Pairwise Comparison Method

In the **pairwise comparison method** of voting, the voters rank the candidates by making a series of comparisons in which each candidate is compared to each of the other candidates. If choice A is preferred to choice B, then A receives 1 point. If B is preferred to A, then B receives 1 point. If the candidates tie, each receives $\frac{1}{2}$ point. The candidate with the most points is declared the winner.

Example **6**   **Find the winner using the pairwise comparison method**

Consider the election described by Example 1:

Choices:	(ABC)	(ACB)	(BAC)	(BCA)	(CAB)	(CBA)
No. of Votes:	5	0	2	1	0	4

Find the winner using the pairwise comparison method.

Solution

A over B: $5 + 0 + 0 = 5$; B over A: $2 + 1 + 4 = 7$;   B obtains 1 point.

A over C: $5 + 0 + 2 = 7$; C over A: $1 + 0 + 4 = 5$;   A obtains 1 point.

B over C: $5 + 2 + 1 = 8$; C over B: $0 + 0 + 4 = 4$;   B obtains 1 point.

Totals: A: 1 point

B: $1 + 1 = 2$ points

C: 0 points

Candidate B wins the election by the pairwise comparison method.

Tournament Method

Another form of binary voting is a *king-of-the-hill* situation in which the competitors are paired, the winner of one pairing taking on the next competitor. This type of runoff election is sometimes called **sequential voting.**

One of the most common examples of sequential voting is called the **tournament method,** or **tournament elimination method.** With this method, candidates are teamed head-to-head, with the winner of one pairing facing a new opponent for the next election. Tennis matches and other sporting events are often decided in this fashion.

Example 7 Find a winner using the tournament method

Consider the following election:

Choices:	(ABC)	(ACB)	(BAC)	(BCA)	(CAB)	(CBA)
No. of Votes:	5	0	3	0	0	4

Find the winner using the tournament method.

Solution

Do you see how this vote of 5:7 is found? (5:7 means 5 for A and 7 for B.)
5 people voted (ABC), A over B.
3 people voted (BAC), B over A, and 4 people voted (CBA), B over A; this is a total of 3 + 4 = 7.

Since all three possible tournaments result in B as the winner, we see that the tournament method finds B to be the winner. We will see later that different pairings *may* result in different winners.

In Example 7 there were three candidates, and the number of comparison charts was three (A with B, A with C, and B with C). In general, the number of necessary comparisons for n candidates is

$$\frac{n(n-1)}{2}$$

In this book we will not have examples with more than 5 candidates, so Table 17.1 shows the number of choices for n between 3 and 6 (inclusive).

Even though we can use some tie-breaking voting procedures, ties may still exist. Decisiveness requires that we specify some method for breaking ties. Sometimes *breaking a tie* can be accomplished by using another voting method, by choosing the candidate with the most first-place votes, by voting by the presiding officer, or even by flipping a coin. If the voting process is to be fair, the tie-breaking procedure should be specified before the vote.

TABLE 17.1

	Number of Pairwise Comparisons	
n	Number
3	3
4	6
5	10
6	15

Example 8 Declare a winner with the possibility of a tie

Consider the following voting situation:

Choices:	(ABC)	(ACB)	(BAC)	(BCA)	(CAB)	(CBA)
No. of Votes:	2	0	0	2	1	0

a. Is there a majority winner?
b. Is there a plurality winner?

c. If there is a tie, break it by deleting the candidate with the fewest first-place votes.

d. If there is a tie, break it by deleting the candidate with the most last-place votes.

Solution

a. A majority of the 5 votes is 3 votes; there is no majority.

b. There is no plurality.

c. There is a tie; we drop the candidate with the *fewest first-place votes*. (Recall that this is called the Hare method.) Number of first-place votes:

A: $2 + 0 = 2$

B: $0 + 2 = 2$

C: $1 + 0 = 1$

Choice C has the fewest first-place votes; compress the ratings:

Choices:	(AB)	(BA)
No. of Votes:	$2 + 0 + 1 = 3$	$0 + 2 + 0 = 2$

The winner is A.

d. There is a tie; we drop the candidate with the *most last-place votes.*

A is in last place for $2 + 0 = 2$ of the votes;

B is in last place for $0 + 1 = 1$ of the votes;

C is in last place for $2 + 0 = 2$ of the votes.

There is a tie, so we use this rule again; drop the candidate with the *most last-place votes* or *next-to-last-place votes.*

A has $0 + 1 = 1$ next-to-last-place votes and 2 last-place votes, for a total of 3 votes.

B has $2 + 0 = 2$ next-to-last-place votes and 1 last-place vote, for a total of 3 votes.

C has $0 + 2 = 2$ next-to-last-place votes and 2 last-place votes, for a total of 4 votes.

Delete C and compress the ratings:

Choices:	(AB)	(BA)
No. of Votes:	$2 + 0 + 1 = 3$	$0 + 2 + 0 = 2$

The winner is A.

Approval Voting

Historically, the most recent voting method replaces the "one person, one vote" method with which we are familiar in the United States with a system that allows a voter to cast one vote for each of the candidates. There is no limit on the number of candidates for whom an individual can vote.

Approval Voting Method

The **approval voting method** allows each voter to cast one vote for each candidate that meets with his or her approval. The candidate with the most votes is declared the winner.

This is the method used to select the secretary general of the United Nations and is popular in those countries in which there are many candidates. It was designed, in part, to prevent the election of minority candidates in multicandidate contests.

Example 9 Find a winner using approval voting

The Milwaukee Booster Club (7 members) is meeting to decide ways to bring people to the downtown area, and its members are brainstorming ideas. Here is a list of their suggestions:

A: Hold an art show.
B: Hire a big-time consultant.
C: Hold a contest.
R: Advertise on the radio.
N: Advertise in the newspaper.

Here are the members' rankings and the number of choices within each ranking that they intend to vote for.

Choices:	(ABCRN)	(RNCAB)	(NRACB)	(CANRB)
No. of Votes:	1	2	1	3
Intent:	vote for 5	vote for 3	vote for 5	vote for 2

a. What is the maximum number of votes that can be cast?
b. What is the outcome if each voter votes for his or her top three?
c. What is the outcome if each voter votes the number shown by his or her intent?

Solution

a. Since there are 7 members and 5 choices, the maximum number of possible votes occurs if every member votes for every choice; namely, $7 \times 5 = 35$.

b.

					Total
A:	1		1	3	**5**
B:	1				**1**
C:	1	2		3	**6**
R:		2	1		**3**
N:		2	1	3	**6**

We see that advertising in the newspaper (N) and holding a contest (C) is a tie with 6 votes each.

c.

					Total
A:	1		1	3	**5**
B:	1		1		**2**
C:	1	2	1	3	**7**
R:	1	2	1		**4**
N:	1	2	1		**4**

We see that holding a contest (C) wins with 7 votes.

We conclude with an example comparing some of the voting methods introduced in this section. These methods are summarized in Table 17.2.

Example 10 Find a winner—compare methods

The town of Ferndale has four candidates running for mayor: the town barber, Darrell; the fire chief, Clough; the grocer, Abel; and a homemaker, Belle. A poll of 1,000 of the voters shows the following results:

Choices:	(DABC)	(CABD)	(CADB)	(BADC)
No. of Votes:	225	190	210	375

a. How many different votes are possible (4 are shown)? What is the vote for the possibilities not shown?

b. Is there a majority winner?

c. Is there a winner using the plurality method?

d. What is the Borda count, and is there a winner using this method?

Solution

a. There are $4! = 24$ possibilities; there are no votes for the 20 possibilities not shown.

b. A: 0 votes; B: 375 votes; C: $190 + 210 = 400$ votes; D: 225 votes. A majority is $\frac{1,000}{2} + 1 = 501$ or more votes; there is no majority winner.

c. The plurality winner is C (because it has the most votes).

d. We show the Borda count in the following table:

	A	B	C	D		A	B	C	D
							Total		
225:	3	2	1	4		675	450	225	900
190:	3	2	4	1		570	380	760	190
210:	3	1	4	2		630	210	840	420
375:	3	4	1	2		1,125	1,500	375	750
TOTAL:						3,000	2,540	2,200	2,260

The Borda count declares A the winner.

TABLE 17.2

Summary of Voting Methods

Method	Description
Majority Method	Each voter votes for one candidate. If the number of voters is n and n is even, then the candidate with $\frac{n}{2} + 1$ or more votes wins. If the number n is odd, then the candidate with $\frac{n+1}{2}$ or more votes wins.
Plurality Method	Each voter votes for one candidate. The candidate receiving the most votes wins.
Borda Count Method	Each voter ranks the candidates. Each last-place candidate is given 1 point, each next-to-last candidate is given 2 points, and so on. The candidate with the highest number of points wins.
Hare Method	Each voter votes for one candidate. If a candidate receives a majority of the votes, that candidate is the winner. If no candidate receives a majority, eliminate the candidate with the fewest first-place votes and repeat the process until there is a majority candidate, who wins.
Pairwise Comparison Method	Each voter ranks the candidates. Each candidate is compared to each of the other candidates. If choice A is preferred to choice B, then A receives 1 point. If B is preferred to A, then B receives one point. If the candidates tie, then each receives $\frac{1}{2}$ point. The candidate with the most points wins.
Tournament Method	This method compares the entire slate of candidates two at a time, in a predetermined order. The first and second candidates are compared, the candidate with the fewer votes is eliminated, and the winner is then compared with the third candidate. These pairwise comparisons continue until the final pairing, which selects the winner.
Approval Method	Each voter casts one vote for all the candidates that meet with his or her approval. The candidate with the most votes is declared the winner.

Problem Set 17.1

1. **IN YOUR OWN WORDS** Describe and discuss the plurality voting method.

2. **IN YOUR OWN WORDS** Describe and discuss the Borda count voting method.

3. **IN YOUR OWN WORDS** Describe and discuss the Hare voting method.

4. **IN YOUR OWN WORDS** Describe and discuss the pairwise comparison method.

5. **IN YOUR OWN WORDS** Describe and discuss the tournament method.

6. **IN YOUR OWN WORDS** Describe and discuss the approval voting method.

7. **IN YOUR OWN WORDS** Give one example in which you have participated in voting where the count was tabulated by the plurality voting method. Your example can be made up or factual, but you should be specific.

8. **IN YOUR OWN WORDS** Give one example in which you have participated in voting where the count was tabulated by the Borda count method. Your example can be made up or factual, but you should be specific.

9. **IN YOUR OWN WORDS** Give one example in which you have participated in voting where the count was tabulated by the Hare voting method. Your example can be made up or factual, but you should be specific.

10. **IN YOUR OWN WORDS** Give one example in which you have participated in voting where the count was tabulated by using the tournament method. Your example can be made up or factual, but you should be specific.

11. **IN YOUR OWN WORDS** Give one example in which you have participated in voting where the count was tabulated by the approval voting method. Your example can be made up or factual, but you should be specific.

In voting among three candidates, the outcomes are reported as:

(ABC)	(ACB)	(BAC)	(BCA)	(CAB)	(CBA)
8	4	3	0	2	5

Use this information to answer the questions in Problems 12–17.

12. What is the total number of votes?

13. How many votes would be necessary for a majority?

14. **a.** What does the notation (CAB) mean?
    b. What does the "5" under (CBA) mean?

15. **a.** What does the notation (ACB) mean?
    b. What does the "4" under (ACB) mean?

16. **a.** If a person ranks A as their first choice, B as their second choice, and C last, how would this be written?
    b. How many voters have this preference?

17. **a.** What does the notation (BCA) mean?
    b. What does the "0" under (BCA) mean?

In voting among four candidates, the outcomes are reported as:

(ADBC)	(DACB)	(BADC)	(BDCA)	(DCAB)
8	5	3	1	2

Use this information to answer the questions in Problems 18–23.

18. What is the total number of votes?

19. How many votes would be necessary for a majority?

20. **a.** What does the notation (DACB) mean?
    b. What does the "5" under (DACB) mean?

21. **a.** What does the notation (ADBC) mean?
    b. What does the "8" under (ADBC) mean?

22. **a.** If a person ranks B as his first choice, C as his second choice, D as his third choice, and A last, how would this be written?
    b. How many voters have this preference?

23. **a.** How many possibilities are there for voter preferences with four candidates?
    b. Name those possibilities that have 0 voter preferences.

24. Which of the following are examples of a dictatorship?

    a. Dad comes home with a surprise for the family—he just bought tickets for the family to vacation in Hawaii.

    b. The choice of selecting the champagne for the toast is left to the cellar master at the restaurant.

    c. The chairperson makes a decision to poll the members of the committee regarding their opinion about the impeachment vote.

    d. The department chair decides that the meeting will be held at 4:00 P.M. on Thursday.

25. **a.** How many different ways can a voter rank 3 candidates (no ties are allowed)?
    b. How many different ways can a voter rank 4 candidates (no ties are allowed)?
    c. How many different ways can a voter rank 5 candidates (no ties are allowed)?

26. **a.** If there are 10 voters and 5 candidates, how many total points would there be in a Borda count?
    b. If there are 20 voters and 4 candidates, how many total points would there be in a Borda count?
    c. If there are 200 voters and 3 candidates, how many total points would there be in a Borda count?

BALLOT BOX
For Official Use Only

27. How many different ways can a voter rank *n* candidates (no ties are allowed)?

28. It can be shown that

$$1 + 2 + 3 + \cdots + m = \frac{m(m + 1)}{2}$$

Use this formula to determine how many total points there would be in a Borda count with *n* voters and *m* candidates.

In voting among three candidates, the outcomes are reported as:

(ABC)	(ACB)	(BAC)	(BCA)	(CAB)	(CBA)
8	4	3	0	2	5

Determine the winner, if any, using the voting methods in Problems 29–34.

29. Majority rule

30. Plurality method

31. Borda count method

32. Hare method

33. Pairwise comparison method

34. Tournament method

35. Twelve board members are voting on after-meeting activities, and they are asked to check any that they might like. The outcome of their choices is shown here:

	1	2	3	4	5	6	7	8	9	10	11	12
Snacks	✓	✓	✓	✓	✓	✓		✓	✓	✓	✓	
Drinks	✓	✓		✓	✓	✓		✓		✓	✓	
Travel talk					✓				✓	✓		
Speaker	✓	✓		✓	✓		✓	✓	✓		✓	✓

What is the outcome using approval voting?

36. Twelve board members are voting on admitting two new board members. They interview 5 candidates and vote "x" for an acceptable candidate and no vote for an unacceptable candidate. The outcome of their choices is shown here:

	1	2	3	4	5	6	7	8	9	10	11	12
A	x	x	x	x	x	x		x	x	x	x	
B	x	x	x	x		x	x	x		x	x	x
C	x	x	x	x	x	x	x	x		x	x	x
D	x	x			x		x	x	x	x	x	x
E	x	x	x				x	x	x		x	x

What is the outcome using approval voting?

37. In the 2000 race for the governor of Vermont, the state vote was as follows:

Marilyn Christian	1,054
Howard Dean	148,059
Ruth Dwyer	111,359
Richard Gottlieb	337
Hardy Macia	785
Anthony Pollina	28,116
Phil Stannard	2,148
Joel Williams	1,359
Others	255
TOTAL	293,472

Was there a majority winner in this election, and if so, who was it?

38. In the 2000 race for the 36th Congressional District of California, the vote was as follows:

Jane Harman	106,975
John Konopka	3,297
Steven Kuykendall	103,142
Matt Ornati	2,078
Daniel Sherman	5,615
TOTAL	221,107

Was there a majority winner in this election, and, if so, who was it?

Twelve people serve on a board and are considering three alternatives: A, B, and C. Here are the choices followed by vote:

(ABC)	(ACB)	(BAC)	(BCA)	(CAB)	(CBA)
2	4	2	1	2	1

Determine the winner, if any, using the voting methods in Problems 39–44.

39. Majority rule

40. Plurality method

41. Borda count method

42. Hare method

43. Pairwise comparison method

44. Tournament method

Seventeen people serve on a board and are considering three alternatives: A, B, and C. Here are the choices followed by vote:

(ABC)	(ACB)	(BAC)	(BCA)	(CAB)	(CBA)
1	3	4	3	5	1

Determine the winner, if any, using the voting methods in Problems 45–50.

45. Majority rule

46. Plurality method

47. Borda count method

48. Hare method

49. Pairwise comparison method

50. Tournament method

Level 3

Suppose your college transcripts show the following distribution of grades:

A: 2
B: 6
C: 5
D: 1
F: 0

If all of these grades are in three-unit classes, use this information to answer the questions in Problems 51–52.

51. a. Which grade is the most common?
   b. Which voting method describes how you answered part **a**?

52. a. What is your GPA?
   b. Which voting method describes how you answered part **a**?

Suppose your college transcripts show the following distribution of grades:

A: 14
B: 21
C: 35
D: 5
F: 2

If all of these grades are in three-unit classes, use this information to answer the questions in Problems 53–54.

53. a. Which grade is the most common?
   b. Which voting method describes how you answered part **a**?

54. a. What is your GPA?
   b. Which voting method describes how you answered part **a**?

In Problems 55–59, consider the following situation. A political party holds a national convention with 1,100 delegates. At the convention, five persons (which we will call A, B, C, D, and E) have been nominated as the party's presidential candidate. After the speeches and hoopla, the delegates are asked to rank all five candidates according to choice. However, before the vote, caucuses have narrowed the choices down to six different possibilities. The results of the first ballot are shown (choices, followed by the number of votes):

(ADEBC)	(BEDCA)	(CBEDA)
360	240	200
(DCEBA)	(EBDCA)	(ECDBA)
180	80	40

Answer the following questions and give reasons for your responses.

55. How many possible rankings are there?

56. a. Is there a majority winner? If so, who?
   b. Is there a plurality winner? If so, who?

57. Who would win in a runoff election using the principle of eliminating the candidate with the fewest first-place votes?

58. Who would win in a runoff election using the principle of eliminating the candidate with the most last-place votes?

59. What is the Borda count for each person? Who wins the Borda count?

Problem Solving 3

60. IN YOUR OWN WORDS   By looking at your answers to Problems 55–59, who would you say should be declared the winner? Look at the title of the next section. Relate your answer to this question for the need to study the next section.

17.2 Voting Dilemmas

Principles in social choice theory do not behave in the same fashion as principles of mathematics. In mathematics, a correctly stated principle has no exceptions. On the other hand, we frequently find exceptions to voting principles. In the last section, we considered four reasonable and often-used voting methods. In this section, we will consider four voting principles that most would agree are desirable, and then we will show that all of the voting methods will fail one or more of the principles. We will call these **fair voting principles:** *majority criterion, Condorcet criterion, monotonicity criterion,* and *irrelevant alternatives criterion.* Let us consider these voting principles, one at a time.

Majority Criterion

The first and most obvious criterion is called the **majority criterion.**

Majority Criterion

If a candidate receives a majority of the first-place votes, then that candidate should be declared the winner.

Only a Borda count method can violate this criterion. Consider the following example.

Example 1   Find a winner using the majority criterion

The South Davis Faculty Association is using the Borda count method to vote for its collective bargaining representative. Members' choices are the All Faculty Association (A), American Federation of Teachers (B), and California Teachers Association (C). Here are the results of the voting:

Choices:	(ABC)	(ACB)	(BAC)	(BCA)	(CAB)	(CBA)
No. of Votes:	16	0	0	8	0	7

a. Which organization is selected for collective bargaining?
b. Does the choice in part a violate the majority criterion?

Solution
a. Here is a tally of the Borda count:

				Total		
	A	B	C	A	B	C
(ABC) 16:	3	2	1	48	32	16
(BCA) 8:	1	3	2	8	24	16
(CBA) 7:	1	2	3	7	14	21
TOTAL:				63	70	53

The highest Borda count number goes to choice B, the American Federation of Teachers.
b. Choice A received 16 votes, which is a majority of the 31 votes that were cast, so the Borda count violates the majority criterion.

Example 1 shows that the Borda count method can violate the majority criterion. However, all the other methods must satisfy this criterion. Suppose that a candidate X is the first choice for more than half the voters. It follows that X will have more first-place votes than any other single candidate and must win by the plurality method. If the Hare method is used, then X would always have at least the votes that it started with, and since that is more than half the votes, X could never be eliminated and would wind up the winner. And finally, since X has the majority of the votes in each of its pairwise matchups, X would win in each of those matchups. So no other candidate can win as many pairs as X does, so X wins the election.

Thus we conclude that the Borda count method presents a dilemma. Although it takes into account voters' preferences by having all candidates ranked, a candidate with a majority of first-place votes can lose an election!

Condorcet Criterion

About a decade after Borda proposed his counting procedure, the mathematician Marquis de Condorcet became interested in some of the apparent dilemmas raised by the Borda count methods. He proposed a head-to-head election to rank the candidates. The candidate who wins all the one-to-one matchups is the **Condorcet candidate.** The **Condorcet criterion** asserts that the Condorcet candidate should win the election. Some elections do not yield a Condorcet candidate because none of the candidates can win over *all* the others.

Condorcet Criterion

If a candidate is favored when compared one-on-one with every other candidate, then that candidate should be declared the winner.

Before most major elections in the United States, we hear the results of polls for each of the political parties pairing candidates and telling preferences in a one-on-one election. Is this a valid way of considering the candidates? Consider the following example.

**Marquis de Condorcet
(1743–1794)**

Condorcet, also known as Marie Nicolas de Caritat, was a mathematician who wrote an important book on probability. He was a friend of Anne Robert Turgot, a French economist and Controller General of Finance in France, and was considerably influenced by him. He is known for the Condorcet paradox, which points out that it is possible that a majority prefers A over B, and B over C, and yet the majority prefers C over A. In mathematical terms, "majority prefers" is not a transitive operation. Condorcet died in a prison cell on March 27, 1794. He was imprisoned for his political beliefs, and it is not known whether he died from natural causes, suicide, or was murdered.

Example 2 Compare the Condorcet criterion with other methods

The seniors at Weseltown High School are voting on where to go for their senior trip. They are deciding on Angel Falls (A), Bend Canyon (B), Cedar Lake (C), or Danger Gap (D). The results of the preferences are:

Choices:	(DABC)	(ACBD)	(BCAD)	(CBDA)	(CBAD)
No. of Votes:	120	100	90	80	45

a. Who is the Condorcet candidate?
b. Is there a majority winner? If not, is there a plurality winner? Does this violate the Condorcet criterion?
c. Who wins the Borda count? Does this violate the Condorcet criterion?
d. Who wins using the Hare method? Does this violate the Condorcet criterion?
e. Who wins using the pairwise comparison method? Does this violate the Condorcet criterion?

Solution

a. The best way to examine the one-on-one matchups is to construct a table with all possibilities listed as the row and column headings.*

	A	B	C	D
A	—	*		
B	*	—		
C			—	
D				—

$$\underbrace{\text{(DABC)(ACBD)}}_{\substack{\text{A wins.}}} \qquad \underbrace{\text{(BCAD)(CBDA)(CBAD)}}_{\text{B wins.}}$$

Look at the line right under the preferences.

$$120 + 100 = 220 \qquad 90 + 80 + 45 = 215$$

A wins, since $220 > 215$, so we fill in these entries in the table.

	A	B	C	D
A	—	A		
B	A	—		
C			—	
D				—

We similarly fill in the rest of the table by comparing the items, one-on-one:

A with C:　A: $120 + 100 = 220$; C: $90 + 80 + 45 = 215$; A wins.

A with D:　A: $100 + 90 + 45 = 235$; D: $120 + 80 = 200$; A wins.

B with C:　B: $120 + 90 = 210$; C: $100 + 80 + 45 = 225$; C wins.

B with D:　B: $100 + 90 + 80 + 45 = 315$; D: 120; B wins.

C with D:　C: $100 + 90 + 80 + 45 = 315$; D: 120; C wins.

We complete the table as shown:

	A	B	C	D
A	—	A	A	A
B	A	—	C	B
C	A	C	—	C
D	A	B	C	—

We see that the Condorcet choice is A (Angel Falls) since the column headed A (and the row headed A) each have all entries of A.

*This is for A with B; this means that A and B are matched.

b. The first-place votes are:

A: 100
B: 90
C: 80 + 45 = 125
D: 120

Since there were 435 votes cast, a majority would be

$$\frac{435 + 1}{2} = 218 \text{ votes}$$

There is no majority. The winner of the plurality vote is C, Cedar Lake. This example shows that the plurality method can violate the Condorcet criterion.

c. The Borda count is shown in the following table:

	A	B	C	D	A	B	C	D
					\multicolumn{4}{c}{Total}
120:	3	2	1	4	360	240	120	480
100:	4	2	3	1	400	200	300	100
90:	2	4	3	1	180	360	270	90
80:	1	3	4	2	80	240	320	160
45:	2	3	4	1	90	135	180	45
TOTAL:					1,110	1,175	1,190	875

Location C, Cedar Lake, wins the Borda count. This example shows that the Borda count can violate the Condorcet criterion.

d. Using the Hare method, there is no majority, so we eliminate the candidate with the fewest first-place votes; this is choice B. The remaining tally is

A: 100   C: 90 + 80 + 45 = 215   D: 120

Since a majority vote is 216, there is still no majority, so we now eliminate A. The result now is:

C: 100 + 90 + 80 + 45 = 315   D: 120

The declared winner is C, Cedar Lake. This example demonstrates that the Hare method can violate the Condorcet criterion.

e. For the pairwise comparison method, we can use the table of pairings we had in part **a** to award the points:

A is favored over B, C, and D, giving A 3 points.

B is favored over D, giving B 1 point.

C is favored over B and D, giving C 2 points.

D is not favored.

The choice is A, Angel Falls. Note that if a certain choice is favored over all other candidates, then this candidate will have the largest point value. Thus, the pairwise comparison method can never violate the Condorcet criterion.

Monotonicity Criterion

Another property of voting has to do with elections that are held more than once. Historically, there have been many pairings of the same two candidates, and at a personal level, we are often part of a process in which a nonbinding vote is taken before all the discussion takes place. Such a vote is known as a **straw vote**. It would seem obvious that if a winning candidate in the first election gained strength before the second election, then that candidate should win the second election. A statement of this property is called the **monotonicity criterion.**

Monotonicity Criterion

A candidate who wins a first election and then gains additional support, without losing any of the original support, should also win a second election.

As obvious as this criterion may seem, the following example introduces another voting dilemma by showing it is possible for the winner of the first election to gain additional support before a second election, and then lose that second election.

Example 3 | Use the monotonicity criterion

In 1995 the 105th International Olympic Committee (IOC) met in Budapest to select the 2002 Winter Olympic site. The cities in the running were Québec (Q), Salt Lake City (L), Ostersund (T) and Sion (S). Consider the following fictional account of how the voting might have been conducted. The voting takes place over a two-day period using the Hare method. The first day, the 87 members of the IOC take a nonbinding vote, and then on the second day they take a binding vote.

a. On the first day, the rankings of the IOC members were

(TLSQ)	(LQTS)	(QSTL)	(TQSL)	(TSLQ)
21	24	30	6	6

What are the results of the election using the Hare method for the first (nonbinding) day of voting?

b. On the evening of the first day of voting, representatives from Salt Lake City offered bribes to the 12 members with the bottom votes. They were able to convince these IOC members to move Québec to the top of their list, because, after all, Québec won the day's straw votes anyway. Now for the second day, the rankings of the IOC committee were:

(TLSQ)	(LQTS)	(QSTL)	(QTSL)	(QTSL)
21	24	30	6	6

What are the results of the election using the Hare method for the second (binding) day of voting?

Solution

a. A majority is $\frac{87 + 1}{2} = 44$ votes.

On the first day, Round 1:   T: $21 + 6 + 6 = 33$
                               L: 24
                               Q: 30
                               S: 0

No city has a majority (44) of votes, so Sion is eliminated from the voting.

Round 2:   T: $21 + 6 + 6 = 33$
            L: 24
            Q: 30

No city has a majority, so now Salt Lake City is eliminated from the voting.

Round 3:   T: $21 + 6 + 6 = 33$
            Q: $24 + 30 = 54$

Québec has a majority of the votes and is the winner from the first (nonbinding) day of voting using the Hare method.

b. On the second day, Round 1:   T: 21
                                      L: 24
                                      Q: $30 + 6 + 6 = 42$
                                      S: 0

No city has a majority (44) of votes, so Sion is eliminated from the voting.

Round 2:   T: 21
           L: 24
           Q: 30 + 6 + 6 = 42

No city has a majority, so now Ostersund (T) is eliminated from the voting.

Round 3:   L: 21 + 24 = 45 votes
           Q: 30 + 6 + 6 = 42

Salt Lake City has a majority of the votes and is the winner from the second (binding) day of voting using the Hare method.

As you can see from this remarkable example, it is possible for the winning candidate on a first vote (Québec) to receive more votes and end up losing the election! We see (from Example 3) that the Hare method can violate the monotonicity criterion. It is also possible to find examples showing that the pairwise comparison method can also violate the monotonicity criterion. The plurality and Borda count methods cannot violate the monotonicity criterion.

Irrelevant Alternatives Criterion

In the controversial 2000 presidential election, there was much talk about the final vote of the election. Although there is no such thing as an official final figure, the numbers in Table 17.3 are an aggregate of state numbers that appear to be final.

TABLE 17.3

		2000 U.S. Presidential Election Results		
Candidate	Party	Vote	Percentage	Electoral College Vote
Harry Browne	Libertarian	386,024	0.37	0
Pat Buchanan	Reform	448,750	0.42	0
George W. Bush	Republican	50,456,167	47.88	271
Al Gore	Democrat	50,996,277	48.39	267
Ralph Nader	Green	2,864,810	2.72	0
14 others		238,300	0.23	0
TOTAL		105,390,328		538

Suppose the president were selected by popular vote (rather than the Electoral College). As close as the election was, if we use the numbers in Table 17.3, we see that the winner would have been Al Gore. Now, suppose that another election were held, and this time Ralph Nader dropped out before the vote. Since Nader really had no chance of winning, we might conclude this action should not have any effect on the outcome. But as you can see from these numbers, such is not the case. The Nader voters could have swung the election either way. We might consider this a voting dilemma because it would violate the following criterion, called the **irrelevant alternatives criterion.**

Irrelevant Alternatives Criterion

If a candidate is declared the winner of an election, and in a second election one or more of the other candidates is removed, then the previous winner should still be declared the winner.

Example 4 | Illustrate the irrelevant alternatives criterion

The mathematics department (22 members) has interviewed five candidates for a new instructor position. They are Alicia (A), Benito (B), Carmelia (C), Doug (D), and Erin (E). There are 5! = 120 possible rankings, but the voting process has narrowed the voting to seven possible rankings:

(BDCEA) (BDEAC) (EDACB) (ACEBD) (DECBA) (CBDEA) (CEDBA)
 6   4   4   4   2   1   1

Just before the voting, Carmelia withdraws from the hiring process.
a. Is there a majority winner? If not, who is the plurality winner?
b. Who is the Borda count winner?
c. Who wins using the Hare method?
d. Use the pairwise comparison method to determine the winner.
e. Suppose one of the department members convinces the others that voting should take place without excluding Carmelia. Who wins the pairwise comparison method?

Solution If we delete Carmelia from the process, the vote becomes:

(BDEA) (BDEA) (EDAB) (AEBD) (DEBA) (BDEA) (EDBA)
 6   4   4   4   2   1   1

We now combine those shown in color (6 + 4 + 1 = 11) to record the vote as:

(BDEA) (EDAB) (AEBD) (DEBA) (EDBA)
 11   4   4   2   1

a. The first place votes are

 A: 4

 B: 11

 D: 2

 E: 4 + 1 = 5

A majority is $\frac{22}{2} + 1 = 12$, so there is no majority winner. We see that Benito is the plurality winner.

b. The Borda count numbers are

	A	B	D	E	Total A	B	D	E
11:	1	4	3	2	11	44	33	22
4:	2	1	3	4	8	4	12	16
4:	4	2	1	3	16	8	4	12
2:	1	2	4	3	2	4	8	6
1:	1	2	3	4	1	2	3	4
TOTAL:					38	62	60	60

Benito is the Borda count winner.

c. The fewest first-place votes are for Doug, so when he is eliminated for the second round, the results of this round are

 A: 4

 B: 11

 E: 4 + 2 + 1 = 7

There is still no majority, so on this round Alicia is eliminated. The third-round results are:

 B: 11

 E: 4 + 4 + 2 + 1 = 11

There is a tie. The chairperson could break the tie, or another method could be chosen to break the tie.

d. A over B: $4 + 4 = 8$; and B over A: $11 + 2 + 1 = 14$; B wins 1 point.

A over D: 4; and D over A: $11 + 4 + 2 + 1 = 18$; D wins 1 point.

A over E: 4; and E over A: $11 + 4 + 2 + 1 = 18$; E wins 1 point.

B over D: $11 + 4 = 15$; and D over B: $4 + 2 + 1 = 7$; B wins 1 point.

B over E: 11; and E over B: $4 + 4 + 2 + 1 = 11$; Tie; B wins 1/2 point and E wins 1/2 point.

D over E: $11 + 2 = 13$; and E over D: $4 + 4 + 1 = 9$; D wins 1 point.

The tally of points is

A: 0

B: $2\frac{1}{2}$ points

D: 2 points

E: $1\frac{1}{2}$ points

Benito is the winner using the pairwise comparison method.

e. From the solutions to parts **a–d,** it certainly appears that Benito should be the victor. But what effect did Carmelia's withdrawal from the process have on the outcome? The irrelevant alternatives criterion says it should have no effect. However, this example shows us otherwise. Consider the original rankings, and calculate the winner using the pairwise comparison method.

A over B: $4 + 4 = 8$; and B over A: $6 + 4 + 2 + 1 + 1 = 14$; B wins 1 point.

A over C: $4 + 4 + 4 = 12$; and C over A: $6 + 2 + 1 + 1 = 10$; A wins 1 point.

A over D: 4; and D over A: $6 + 4 + 4 + 2 + 1 + 1 = 18$; D wins 1 point.

A over E: 4; and E over A: $6 + 4 + 4 + 2 + 1 + 1 = 18$; E wins 1 point.

B over C: $6 + 4 = 10$; and C over B: $4 + 4 + 2 + 1 + 1 = 12$; C wins 1 point.

B over D: $6 + 4 + 4 + 1 = 15$; and D over B: $4 + 2 + 1 = 7$; B wins 1 point.

B over E: $6 + 4 + 1 = 11$; and E over B: $4 + 4 + 2 + 1 = 11$; Tie; B wins 1/2 point and E wins 1/2 point.

C over D: $4 + 1 + 1 = 6$; and D over C: $6 + 4 + 4 + 2 = 16$; D wins 1 point.

C over E: $6 + 4 + 1 + 1 = 12$; and E over C: $4 + 4 + 2 = 10$; C wins 1 point.

D over E: $6 + 4 + 2 + 1 = 13$; and E over D: $4 + 4 + 1 = 9$; D wins 1 point.

The tally of points is

A: 1

B: $2\frac{1}{2}$ points

C: 2 points

D: 3 points

E: $1\frac{1}{2}$ points

Doug is the winner using the pairwise comparison method, and this violates the irrelevant alternatives criterion.

An outstanding factual example illustrating this dilemma occurred in the 1991 Louisiana gubernatorial race. The candidates were the incumbent Governor "Buddy" Roemer and his challengers, former governor Edwin Edwards and David Duke. Now, David Duke was a former leader of the Ku Klux Klan, and the former governor was indicted for corruption, so it is reasonable to assume that Roemer would have beaten either of his opponents in a one-on-one race, but instead he came in last.

Arrow's Impossibility Theorem

We have now considered four criteria that would seem to be desirable properties of any voting system. We refer to these four criteria as the **fairness criteria.**

Spend a few minutes with these criteria. Read, then reread; create some small examples and test them.

Fairness Criteria

Majority criterion

If a candidate receives a majority of the first-place votes, then that candidate should be declared the winner.

Condorcet criterion

If a candidate is favored when compared one-on-one with every other candidate, then that candidate should be declared the winner.

Monotonicity criterion

A candidate who wins a first election and then gains additional support, without losing any of the original support, should also win a second election.

Irrelevant alternatives criterion

If a candidate is declared the winner of an election, and in a second election one or more of the other candidates is removed, then the previous winner should still be declared the winner.

We compare these criteria with the voting methods we have considered in Table 17.4.

TABLE 17.4	Comparison of Voting Methods and Fairness Criteria			
Voting Method:	**Plurality**	**Hare**	**Borda Count**	**Pairwise Comparison**
Majority criterion:	Satisfied	Satisfied	Not satisfied (See Example 1)	Satisfied
Condorcet criterion:	Not satisfied (Example 2b)	Not satisfied (Example 2d)	Not satisfied (Example 2c)	Satisfied
Monotonicity criterion:	Satisfied	Not satisfied (Example 3)	Satisfied	Not satisfied
Irrelevant alternatives criterion:	Not satisfied	Not satisfied	Not satisfied	Not satisfied (Example 4)

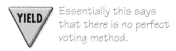

Essentially this says that there is no perfect voting method.

In 1951, the economist Kenneth Arrow (1921–) proved that there is exactly one method for voting that satisfies all four of these principles, and this method is a *dictatorship.* Stated in another way, it is known as *Arrow's paradox:* Perfect democratic voting is, not just in practice but in principle, impossible.

Example 5   Compare voting methods

In the voting for the 2004 Olympics site, five cities were in the running: Athens (A), Buenos Aires (B), Cape Town (C), Rome (R), and Stockholm (S). Four rounds of voting by the 107 IOC members are summarized here:

City	Round #1	Round #2	Round #3	Round #4
A:	32	38	52	66
B:	16			
C:	16	22	20	
R:	23	28	35	41
S:	20	19		

Who wins by the
a. majority/plurality methods?
b. Hare method?
c. pairwise comparisons method?
   (*Note*: The voters' rankings are not available, so we can't do the Borda count.)

Solution
a. A majority would require $\frac{107 + 1}{2} = 54$ votes. There is no majority. The plurality vote goes to Athens.
b. The Hare method eliminates the choice with the smallest number of first-place votes. There is a tie (16), so a runoff election is held between Buenos Aires and Cape Town. Suppose the result of this election is B: 45, C: 62, so Buenos Aires is eliminated from round 2. In the round 2 votes, there is no majority, so Stockholm is eliminated. The results from round 3 also show no majority, so Cape Town is eliminated. In round 4 voting, the majority choice is Athens.
c. For the pairwise matchings, A wins 4 points because it has more votes than any of the other choices. No other choice can beat 4 points, so Athens is the choice.

The previous example illustrates that it is not *necessary* to have a vote with contradictions. It is possible to satisfy all of the fairness criteria. However, the following example illustrates a situation in which any of the candidates A, B, or C could be declared the winner using the tournament method!

Example 6 Find a winner using the tournament method

Consider the following election:

Choices:	(ABC)	(ACB)	(BAC)	(BCA)	(CAB)	(CBA)
No. of Votes:	1	0	0	1	1	0

Determine the winner using the tournament method.

Solution   The pairing AB gives A one point; the pairing AC gives C one point; and the pairing BC gives B one point. All three are tied in points.

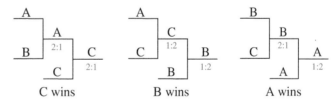

However, if we play this as a tournament, we see that any of A, B, or C could win, depending on the initial pairing. This shows that there is tremendous power in the hands of the tournament director or committee chair who has the opportunity to set the agenda, if the group choice is to be made using a tournament (pairwise) voting method.

CAUTION Different agendas may produce different winners. This is called the agenda effect.

A variation of the agenda effect is **insincere voting,** or the offering of amendments with the purpose of changing an election. Consider the following example.

Assume that Tom, Ann, and Linda each have the choice of voting on whether to lower the drinking age to 18. The current law sets the drinking age at 21. Voting against the new law (age 18) means that the old law (age 21) will prevail. Let's assume that Tom and Ann are in favor of the new law, but Linda is against it. Here is a table of their preferences:

	First Choice	*Second Choice*
Tom:	new law (age 18)	old law (age 21)
Ann:	new law (age 18)	old law (age 21)
Linda:	old law (age 21)	new law (age 18)

Let's also assume that this law will pass or fail, depending on the outcome of the votes of these three people. If the vote is taken now, all three persons know the vote will be 2 for the new law and 1 against the new law. However, Linda decides to defeat the new law by insincere voting, and she introduces an amendment that she knows Tom would like most of all, but Ann likes least of all. Suppose that Linda knows Tom would like to have no law regarding drinking, but that Ann would find that offensive. Linda offers an (insincere) amendment (no age limit). Now here are the choices:

	First Choice	*Second Choice*	*Third Choice*
Tom:	amendment (no age)	new law (age 18)	old law (age 21)
Ann:	new law (age 18)	old law (age 21)	amendment (no age)
Linda:	old law (age 21)	amendment (no age)	new law (age 18)

The vote is taken first for the amendment, and it passes with a vote of 2 to 1 because Tom votes for it and Linda votes insincerely by voting for the amendment. Now, the vote on the floor is for no age limitation or for the old law. Tom votes for no age limitation and Linda and Ann vote for the old law, which carries by a vote of 2 to 1.

What does this say? If you are sitting through a meeting conducted by *Robert's Rules of Order,* it may be better to enter the more preferred outcomes at a later stage of the discussion. The chances of success are better when there are fewer remaining votes.

There is a curious possibility that seems to violate the transitive law in mathematics. The **transitive law** states:

If A beats B, and B beats C, then A should beat C.

Example 6 violates this law and leads to a paradox. Notice that A beats B by a vote of 2 to 1; B beats C by a vote of 2 to 1. The transitive law says that A should beat C, but that is NOT the case! C beats A by a vote of 2 to 1. This paradox was first described by Marquis de Condorcet. He wrote a treatise, *Essay on the Application of Analysis to the Probability of Majority Decisions,* in 1785, and he described this paradox, which today is known as **Condorcet's paradox** or *the paradox of voting.*

We now state the result known as **Arrow's impossibility theorem,** which Kenneth Arrow proved in 1951.

Arrow's Impossibility Theorem

No social choice rule satisfies all of the following conditions.
1. **Unrestricted domain**   Any set of rankings is possible; if there are n candidates, then there are $n!$ possible rankings.
2. **Decisiveness**   Given any set of individual rankings, the method produces a winner.
3. **Symmetry and transitivity**   The voting system should be symmetric and transitive over the set of all outcomes.
4. **Independence of irrelevant alternatives**   If a voter prefers A to B with C as a possible choice, then the voter still prefers A to B when C is not a possible choice.
5. **Pareto principle**   If each voter prefers A over B, then the group chooses A over B.
6. There should be **no dictator.**

We conclude with an example that forces "everyone to get along" because everyone wins!

Example 7 Illustrate Arrows impossibility theorem

Example 5 used the historical vote of the International Olympic Committee to select the site for the 2004 Olympics. Remember, there were five cities in the running: Athens (A),

Buenos Aires (B), Cape Town (C), Rome (R), and Stockholm (S). In this example, we replace the actual vote with a fictitious preference schedule:

Choices:	(ARSCB)	(BSRCA)	(CBSRA)	(RCSBA)	(SBRCA)	(SCRBA)
No. of Votes:	36	24	20	18	8	4

a. How many preference schedules received 0 votes?
b. Who is the majority/plurality winner?
c. What is the Borda count, and who is the winner from this method?
d. Who is the winner using the Hare method?
e. Who wins from the pairwise comparison method?
f. Suppose there is a runoff in which the top two contenders of the plurality method face each other. (What, you say . . . we have not previously considered this method! You are right, but we didn't want one of the cities to feel left out.)

Solution

a. Since there are 5 cities, there are $5! = 5 \times 4 \times 3 \times 2 \times 1 = 120$ possible preference schedules. Since we have shown 6 of them, it follows that there are 114 that received 0 votes.

b. There are 110 votes, so a majority is $110/2 + 1 = 56$ votes; there is no majority. The plurality winner is Athens (A), with 36 votes.

c. We set up a table for the Borda count:

	A	B	C	R	S		Total A	B	C	R	S
36:	5	1	2	4	3		180	36	72	144	108
24:	1	5	2	3	4		24	120	48	72	96
20:	1	4	5	2	3		20	80	100	40	60
18:	1	2	4	5	3		18	36	72	90	54
8:	1	4	2	3	5		8	32	16	24	40
4:	1	2	4	3	5		4	8	16	12	20
TOTAL:							254	312	324	382	378

The Borda count winner is Rome (R).

d. There is no majority winner; the fewest first-place votes are for Stockholm, so the second-round vote is

Athens:	36
Buenos Aires:	$24 + 8 = 32$
Cape Town:	$20 + 4 = 24$
Rome:	18

The least number of votes is for Rome, so that city is eliminated. The third-round vote is

Athens:	36
Buenos Aires:	$24 + 8 = 32$
Cape Town:	$20 + 18 + 4 = 42$

The least number of votes for this round is for Buenos Aires, so the final-round votes are

Athens:	36
Cape Town:	$24 + 20 + 18 + 8 + 4 = 74$

The Hare method winner is Cape Town (C).

e. For the pairwise comparison method, there are $\frac{(5)(4)}{2} = 10$ matchups. The vote is (the details are left for you)

A: 0 points	R: 3 points
B: 1 point	S: 4 points
C: 2 points	

Stockholm (S) is the winner from the pairwise comparison method.

f. A faces off against B:

A: 36
B: 24 + 20 + 18 + 8 + 4 = 74

Buenos Aires (B) wins the election.

Admittedly, the numbers used in Example 7 were contrived to make a point, but nevertheless this example shows that we used five different common voting procedures to come up with five different winners. You can see that those with the power to select the voting method may have the power to determine the outcome of the election.

Problem Set 17.2

Level **1**

1. IN YOUR OWN WORDS What is the majority criterion?

2. IN YOUR OWN WORDS What is the Condorcet criterion?

3. IN YOUR OWN WORDS What is the monotonicity criterion?

4. IN YOUR OWN WORDS What is the irrelevant alternatives criterion?

5. IN YOUR OWN WORDS What are the fairness criteria?

6. IN YOUR OWN WORDS If you could have only one of the fairness criteria, which one would you choose and why?

7. IN YOUR OWN WORDS If you could have only two of the fairness criteria, which ones would you choose and why?

8. IN YOUR OWN WORDS What is insincere voting?

9. IN YOUR OWN WORDS Why is Arrow's impossibility theorem important?

10. IN YOUR OWN WORDS What is the Pareto principle?

11. The South Davis Faculty Association is using the Hare method to vote for its collective bargaining representative. Member's choices are the All Faculty Association (A), American Federation of Teachers (B), and California Teachers Association (C). Here are the results of the voting:

(ABC)	(ACB)	(BAC)	(BCA)	(CAB)	(CBA)
11	1	3	6	3	7

a. Which organization is selected for collective bargaining using the Hare method?

b. Does the choice in part **a** violate the majority criterion?

12. An election with three candidates has the following rankings:

(ABC)	(BCA)	(CBA)
5	4	3

© Michael Newman/PhotoEdit

a. Is there a majority? If not, who wins the plurality vote?

b. Who wins using the Borda count method?

c. Does the Borda method violate the majority criterion?

13. An election with three candidates has the following rankings:

(BAC)	(ACB)	(CAB)
5	6	3

a. Is there a majority? If not, who wins the plurality vote?

b. Who wins using the Borda count method?

c. Does the Borda method violate the majority criterion?

14. The South Davis Faculty Association is using the Borda count method to vote for its collective bargaining unit. Member's choices are the All Faculty Association (A),

American Federation of Teachers (B), and California Teachers Association (C). Here are the results of the voting:

(ABC)	(ACB)	(BAC)	(BCA)	(CAB)	(CBA)
16	0	0	5	0	9

a. Is there a majority? If not, who wins the plurality vote?
b. Who wins using the Borda count method?
c. Does the Borda method violate the majority criterion?

15. Consider the following voting situation:

(ABC)	(ACB)	(BAC)	(BCA)	(CAB)	(CBA)
2	0	0	2	1	0

Notice that there is no winner using the majority or plurality rules.
a. Who would win in a runoff election by dropping the choice with the fewest first-place votes?
b. Who would win if B withdraws before the election?
c. Does this violate any of the fairness criteria?

16. Consider the following voting situation:

(ABC)	(ACB)	(BAC)	(BCA)	(CAB)	(CBA)
9	0	9	0	0	7

Notice that there is no winner using the majority or plurality rules.
a. Who would win in a runoff election by dropping the choice of the fewest first-place votes?
b. Who would win if C withdraws before the election?
c. Does this violate any of the fairness criteria?

17. The philosophy department is selecting a chairperson, and the candidates are Andersen (A), Bailey (B), and Clark (C). Here are the preferences of the 27 department members:

(ABC)	(BCA)	(BAC)	(CAB)
8	5	8	6

a. Who is the Condorcet candidate, if there is one?
b. Is there a majority winner? If not, who wins the plurality vote? Does this violate the Condorcet criterion?

18. The philosophy department is selecting a chairperson, and the candidates are Andersen (A), Bailey (B), and Clark (C). Here are the preferences of the 27 department members:

(ABC)	(BCA)	(BAC)	(CAB)
8	5	8	6

a. Who is the Condorcet candidate, if there is one?
b. Who wins according to the Borda count method? Does this violate the Condorcet criterion?

19. The Adobe School District is hiring a vice principal and has interviewed four candidates: Andrew (A), Bono (B), Carol (C), and Davy (D). The hiring committee has indicated their preferences:

(ACDB)	(CBAD)	(BCDA)	(DBCA)
7	5	3	2

a. Who is the winner using the plurality method?
b. Suppose that Carol drops out of the running before the vote is taken. Who is the winner using the plurality method?
c. Do the results of parts **a** and **b** violate the irrelevant alternatives criterion?

The seniors at Weseltown High School are voting for where to go for their senior trip. They are deciding on Angel Falls (A), Bend Canyon (B), Cedar Lake (C), or Danger Gap (D). The results of the preferences are:

(DABC)	(ACBD)	(BCAD)	(CBDA)	(CBAD)
30	25	22	20	11

Use this information for Problems 20–24.

20. Who is the Condorcet candidate, if there is one?
21. Is there a majority winner? If not, is there a plurality winner? Does this violate the Condorcet criterion?
22. Who wins the Borda count? Does this violate the Condorcet criterion?
23. Who wins using the Hare method? Does this violate the Condorcet criterion?
24. Who wins using the pairwise comparison method? Does this violate the Condorcet criterion?

The seniors at Weseltown High School are voting for where to go for their senior trip. They are deciding on Angel Falls (A), Bend Canyon (B), Cedar Lake (C), or Danger Gap (D). The results of the preferences are:

(DABC)	(ACBD)	(BCAD)	(CBDA)	(CBAD)
80	45	30	10	50

Use this information for Problems 25–29.

25. Who is the Condorcet candidate?
26. Is there a majority winner? If not, is there a plurality winner? Does this violate the Condorcet criterion?
27. Who wins the Borda count? Does this violate the Condorcet criterion?
28. Who wins using the Hare method? Does this violate the Condorcet criterion?
29. Who wins using the pairwise comparison method? Does this violate the Condorcet criterion?

A focus group of 33 people for ABC TV were asked to rank the government spending priorities of education (E), military spending (M), health care (H), immigration (I), and lowering taxes (T). Here are the preferences:

(EIHTM)	(MIEHT)	(HMETI)	(TMEIH)
15	6	6	6

Use this information to answer Problems 30–35.

30. Who is the winner using the pairwise comparison method?
31. Who is the winner using a Borda count?
32. Suppose that the losing issues of health care and lowering taxes are removed from the table. Now, who is the winner using the pairwise comparison method? Does this violate the irrelevant alternatives criterion?

33. Suppose that the losing issues of health care and lowering taxes are removed from the table. Now, who is the winner using the Borda count method? Does this violate the irrelevant alternatives criterion?

34. Suppose that the losing issues of health care, lowering taxes, and immigration are removed from the table. Now, who is the winner using the pairwise comparison method? Does the pairwise comparison method violate the irrelevant alternatives criterion?

35. Suppose that the losing issues of health care, lowering taxes, and immigration are removed from the table. Now, who is the winner using the Borda count method? Does the Borda count method violate the irrelevant alternatives criterion?

   HISTORICAL QUEST   *In* 1988 *the 94th International Olympic Committee (IOC) met in Seoul to select the* 1994 *Winter Olympics site. The cities in the running were Anchorage* (A), *Lillehammer* (L), *Ostersund* (T), *and Sofia* (S). *Consider the following fictional account of how the voting might have been conducted. The voting takes place over a two-day period using the Hare method. The first day the 93 members of the IOC take a nonbinding vote, and then on the second day they take a binding vote. Use this information for Problems* 36 *and* 37.

36. On the first day, the rankings of the IOC members were:

(TLSA)	(LATS)	(ASLT)	(ASTL)	(STLA)
31	35	20	4	3

   What is the result of the election using the Hare method for the first (nonbinding) day of voting?

AP/Wide World Photos

37. On the evening of the first day of voting (see Problem 36), representatives from Ostersund wined, dined, and sweet-talked the 7 members with the bottom votes. They were able to convince seven of those IOC members to move Lillehammer to the top of their list. After all, they argued, Lillehammer won the straw vote anyway—everyone likes to vote for the winner. Also, one of the (TLSA) voters changed to (LTSA). The second day, the rankings of the IOC committee were:

(TLSA)	(LTSA)	(LATS)	(ASLT)	(LAST)	(LSTA)
30	1	35	20	4	3

   What is the result of the election using the Hare method for the second binding day of voting? Does this vote count violate the monotonicity criterion?

   HISTORICAL QUEST   *In* 1993 *the 101st International Olympic Committee met in Monaco to select the* 2000 *Winter Olympics site. The cities in the running were Beijing* (B),

Berlin (L), *Istanbul* (I), *Manchester* (M), *and Sydney* (S). *Suppose we look at their voting preferences:*

(BLIMS)	(LBSIM)	(IBLSM)	(MSBLI)
32	3	5	8

(LSBIM)	(SBLMI)	(IMSBL)	(MBSLI)
6	30	2	3

Use this information to answer the questions in Problems 38 and 39.

38. **a.** Is there a majority winner? If not, which city wins the plurality vote?
   b. Find the results of the election using the Hare method. Just after the third vote, one of the committee members voting for Manchester was accused of cheating and was disqualified. Because of that scandal, one member admitted she was voting insincerely, and changed her vote from Manchester to Sydney. What is the result of using the Hare method?
   c. Do the results of parts **a** and **b** violate any of the fairness criteria?

39. **a.** Find the result of the election using a Borda count.
   b. Using the result of part **a**, determine whether any of the fairness criteria have been violated.

40. The U.S. president is elected with a vote of the Electoral College. However, if the vote were conducted using the Hare method, what would be the outcome? Use the data in Table 17.3, and assume that the second choice of the Browne voters is Gore, and the second choice of the Buchanan voters is Bush. Assume that the second choice of 80% of the Nader voters is Gore and for 20% of them the second choice is Bush. Finally, assume that the other voters split the second choice 50%–50% between Gore and Bush. Who is the winner of this election?

41. **HISTORICAL QUEST**   Article 7 of the French constitution states, "The President of the Republic is elected by an absolute majority of votes cast. If this is not obtained on the first ballot, a second round of voting must be held, to take place two Sundays later. Only two candidates may stand for election on the second ballot, these being the two that obtained the greatest number of votes in the first round."

Musee de la Revolution Francaise, Vizille, France/The Bridgeman Art Library International

The 2002 French presidential election incumbent president Jacques Chirac (center-right political party) and Prime Minister

Lionel Jospin (Socialist party) were shoo-ins for the second round, but the strength of the extreme right candidate Jean-Marie Le Pen was unanticipated. Here are the results of the first-round voting (rounded to the nearest percent):

Jacques Chirac:	20%
Jean-Marie Le Pen:	17%
Lionel Jospin:	16%
Others:	47%

These percents are of the votes cast. It was estimated that 28% of the voters abstained.

a. Who are the two candidates in the runoff election?

b. Jean-Marie Le Pen is described as a racist. Here is a statement from *À la française forum*:

"Today, the strongest feeling I have is SHAME. For the first time in my life, I'm ashamed to be French. All of the values that I believe in (culture, tolerance, integration . . .) have been scorned and denounced by 17% of my country's voters."

Comment on this quotation in light of the fairness criteria.

c. The vote in the second round of the election was:

| Jacques Chirac: | 82% |
| Jean-Marie Le Pen: | 18% |

It was estimated that 19% of the voters abstained for this ballot. Give at least one possible change in the voting preferences to account for both the first and the second votes.

A group of fun-loving people have decided to play a practical joke on one of their friends, but they can't decide which friend, Alice (A), Betty (B), or Connie (C). Their preferences are

(ABC)	(CBA)	(BCA)
6	5	4

Use this information to answer the questions in Problems 42–45.

42. a. Is there a Condorcet candidate?
    b. Is there a majority? If not, who wins the plurality vote? Does this violate the Condorcet criterion?

43. Who wins using the Borda count method? Does this violate the Condorcet criterion?

44. Who wins the election using the Hare method? Does this violate the Condorcet criterion?

45. Who wins the election using the pairwise comparison method? Does this violate any of the conditions in Arrow's impossibility theorem?

The fraternity ΣΔΓ is electing a national president, and there are four candidates: Alberto (A), Bate (B), Carl (C), and Dave (D). The voter preferences are:

(BDCA)	(BDAC)	(CDAB)	(ADCB)
100	120	130	150

Use this information to answer the questions in Problems 46–49.

46. a. How many votes were cast?
    b. Is there a majority? If not, who wins the plurality vote?
    c. Is there a Condorcet candidate?

47. Who wins using the Borda count method? Does this violate any of the fairness criteria?

48. Who wins the election using the Hare method? Does this violate any of the fairness criteria?

49. Who is the winner by using the pairwise comparison method? Does this violate any of the fairness criteria?

50. Consider an election with three candidates with the following results:

(ABC)	(BCA)	(CBA)
5	3	3

a. Is there a majority winner? If not, who is the plurality winner?

b. Who wins using the pairwise comparison method?

c. Is the ordering for the choices for candidates in part **b** transitive?

51. Consider an election with four candidates with the following results:

(ABCD)	(ABDC)	(CDAB)	(CDBA)	(DACB)
10	9	8	7	6

a. Is there a winner using the pairwise comparison method?

b. Is there a winner using the tournament method?

c. Do either of these methods violate any conditions of Arrow's impossibility theorem?

52. Repeat Problem 50, with 10 votes for each listed possibility.

53. Consider an election with four candidates with the following results:

(ABCD)	(BCAD)	(CABD)
20	20	10

a. Who wins the election using a Borda count method?

b. Does the Borda count method violate the irrelevant alternative criterion?

54. Consider an election with three candidates with the following results:

(ACB)	(BAC)	(CAB)
4	2	5

a. Is there a majority winner? If not, who is the plurality winner?

b. If a majority is required for election, there must be a runoff between the second and third choices. Who will win that runoff?

c. How can the voters who support C vote insincerely to enable C to win the election?

55. Consider an election with three candidates with the following results:

(ACB)	(BAC)	(CBA)	(CAB)
2	5	4	2

a. Is there a majority winner? If not, who is the plurality winner?

b. Who wins the election using the Borda count method?

c. Who wins if he or she first eliminates the one with the most last-place votes and then has a runoff between the other two?

d. Could the two voters with preference (CAB) change the outcome of the election in part **c** if they voted insincerely and pretended to have the preference (CBA)?

56. Suppose that 100 Senators must vote on an appropriation: a new bridge in Alabama (A), a new freeway interchange in California (C), or a grain subsidy for Iowa (I). The Senate Whip estimates that the preferences of the senators is

(ACI)	(CIA)	(ICA)
10	38	52

a. Which project wins using the Borda count method?
b. Iowa argues that it should win because it has a majority vote. However, since the vote is to be by Borda count, those who favor California believe that Iowa could win and thus they vote insincerely for Alabama as their second choice. How would this affect the Borda count?
c. If those who favor Iowa believe that the insincere voting in part **b** might take place, should they still vote so as to cause the funds to go to Iowa?

57. IN YOUR OWN WORDS Suppose that Jane, Linda, Ann, and Melissa are members of a committee of the Tuesday Afternoon Club and Jane, Linda, and Ann all prefer a new rule that says the meeting time will change to the evenings. Jane proposed this new rule because she absolutely cannot come if it is not in the evening, and Linda prefers it because Jane picks her up for the meetings, but she could drive herself if Jane were not available. Ann, on the other hand, says she will go along with anything that does not interfere with her Wednesday morning golf lessons. Melissa argues that if they adopt the new rule, they will need to change the name of their club, which will require a by-law change, so she is opposed to the new rule. Can you suggest an amendment that Melissa could offer to force the vote in her favor? Note that for a new rule to pass, three votes are required, and on a tie vote of two to two, the old rule stands.

58. IN YOUR OWN WORDS Make up an example of a vote that is not transitive.

59. IN YOUR OWN WORDS Suppose there are ten serious, but almost indistinguishable, candidates for a U.S. presidential primary. Also suppose that at the last possible minute a very radical candidate enters the race. He is so radical, in fact, that 90% of the voters rank this candidate at the bottom. Show how it might be possible for voters to elect this candidate.

60. The Game of WIN. Construct a set of nonstandard dice as shown in Figure 17.1.

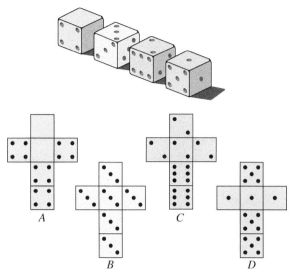

FIGURE 17.1 Faces on the dice for a game of WIN

Suppose that one player picks die *A* and that the other picks die *B*, the dice are rolled, and the higher number wins. We can enumerate the sample space as shown here.

B*A*	0	0	4	4	4	4
3	(3, 0)	(3, 0)	(3, 4)	(3, 4)	(3, 4)	(3, 4)
3	(3, 0)	(3, 0)	(3, 4)	(3, 4)	(3, 4)	(3, 4)
3	(3, 0)	(3, 0)	(3, 4)	(3, 4)	(3, 4)	(3, 4)
3	(3, 0)	(3, 0)	(3, 4)	(3, 4)	(3, 4)	(3, 4)
3	(3, 0)	(3, 0)	(3, 4)	(3, 4)	(3, 4)	(3, 4)
3	(3, 0)	(3, 0)	(3, 4)	(3, 4)	(3, 4)	(3, 4)

| *B wins* | *A wins* |

We see that *A*'s probability of winning is $\frac{24}{36}$, or $\frac{2}{3}$. There are, of course, many other possible choices for the dice played. If you were to play the game of WIN, would you choose your die first or second? What is your probability of winning at WIN? This problem reminds you of which concept introduced in this section?

17.3 | Apportionment

The framing of the United States Constitution during the Constitutional Convention in 1787 has been the subject of books, movies, and plays. Many issues of grave importance were introduced and debated, but one of the most heated and important debates concerned how the states would be represented in the new legislature. The large states wanted proportional representation based on population, and the smaller states wanted representation by state. From this debate came the Great Compromise, which led to the formation of two sides of the legislative branch of government. The compromise allowed the Senate to have two representatives per state (advantageous for the smaller states) and the House of Representatives to determine the number of representatives for a particular state by the size of the population (advantageous for the larger states). The accompanying gives the exact wording from the United States Constitution, and if you read it you will notice that it does not specify *how* to determine the number of representatives for each state. The process of making this decision is called **apportionment.** To *apportion* means to divide or share according to a plan. It usually refers to dividing representatives in Congress or taxes to the states, but it can refer to judicial decisions or to the assignment of goods or people to different jurisdictions. In this section, we will consider five apportionment plans: *Adams' plan, Jefferson's plan, Hamilton's plan, Webster's plan, and Huntington-Hill's plan (HH plan).* You recognize, no doubt, some of these names from American history.

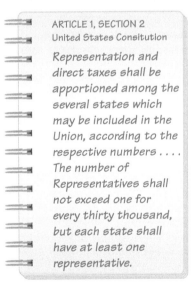

ARTICLE 1, SECTION 2
United States Consitution

Representation and direct taxes shall be apportioned among the several states which may be included in the Union, according to the respective numbers . . . . The number of Representatives shall not exceed one for every thirty thousand, but each state shall have at least one representative.

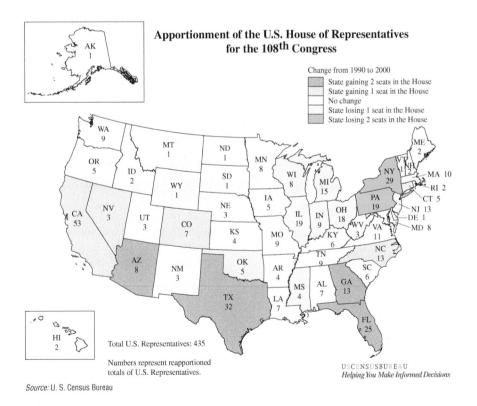

Apportionment of the U.S. House of Representatives for the 108th Congress

Change from 1990 to 2000

- State gaining 2 seats in the House
- State gaining 1 seat in the House
- No change
- State losing 1 seat in the House
- State losing 2 seats in the House

Total U.S. Representatives: 435

Numbers represent reapportioned totals of U.S. Representatives.

U.S. CENSUS BUREAU
Helping You Make Informed Decisions

Source: U. S. Census Bureau

The Approtionment Process

We begin with a simple example to introduce us to some of the terminology used with apportionment. Table 17.5 shows the population (in thousands) over the years for five New York Boroughs.

TABLE 17.5						
					Populations of New York Boroughs	
Year	Total	Manhattan	Bronx	Brooklyn	Queens	Staten Island
1790	49	32	2	5	6	4
1800	81	61	2	6	7	5
1840	697	516	8	139	19	15
1900	3,438	1,850	201	1,167	153	67
1940	7,454	1,890	1,395	2,698	1,297	174
1990	7,324	1,488	1,204	2,301	1,952	379
2000	8,007	1,537	1,333	2,465	2,229	443

One of the recurring problems with apportionment is working with approximate data and the problems caused by rounding. For example, if you look at the total population for the five New York Boroughs in the year 2000, you will find the total to be 8,008,000. If you add the numbers in Table 17.5, you will find the total to be 8,007,000. The discrepancy is caused by rounding, and we should not just sweep it under the rug and ignore such discrepancies. How we handle rounding is a large part of distinguishing apportionment problems. Consider the following example.

Example　1　Apportionment in 1790

In 1790 the population in New York City was 49,000. Suppose the city council at that time consisted of 8 members.
a. How many people did each city council member represent?
b. If the assignment of council seats is proportional to the borough's population, use Table 17.5 to allocate the council seats.

Solution

a. Since the population was 49,000, each council member should represent

$$\frac{49,000}{8} = 6,125$$

This number is called the *standard divisor.*

b. To find the appropriate representation, we need to divide the population of each borough by the standard divisor; the resulting number is known as the *standard quota.* Round your results to the nearest hundredth. We show rounding the standard quota to the nearest whole number, and we also show the result of rounding up and of rounding down. The result of rounding up is called the **upper quota** and the result of rounding down is called the **lower quota.**

	Standard Quota	Nearest	Upper Quota	Lower Quota
Manhattan:	$\frac{32,000}{6,125} \approx 5.22$	5	6	5
Bronx:	$\frac{2,000}{6,125} \approx 0.33$	0	1	0
Brooklyn:	$\frac{5,000}{6,125} \approx 0.82$	1	1	0
Queens:	$\frac{6,000}{6,125} \approx 0.98$	1	1	0
Staten Island:	$\frac{4,000}{6,125} \approx 0.65$	1	1	0
TOTAL:		8	10	5

Now, seats on a city council must be whole numbers, so we should use the numbers from one of the columns of rounded numbers. But which column? Since we need to fill 8 seats, we see for this example that if we round to the nearest unit, we will fill the 8 seats.

Example 1 raises some questions. First, how would you like it if you lived in the Bronx? You would have no representation. On the other hand, if you rounded each of the numbers up, the number of seats would increase to 10, and certainly rounding down for this example would not satisfy anyone (except perhaps those from Manhattan). There are other difficulties caused by the rounding in Example 1, but before we take a closer look, we need the following definitions.

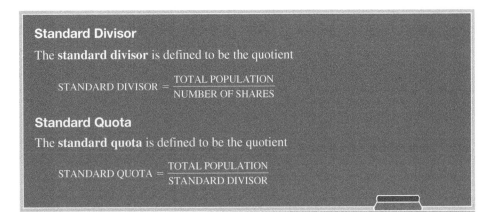

Standard Divisor

The **standard divisor** is defined to be the quotient

$$\text{STANDARD DIVISOR} = \frac{\text{TOTAL POPULATION}}{\text{NUMBER OF SHARES}}$$

Standard Quota

The **standard quota** is defined to be the quotient

$$\text{STANDARD QUOTA} = \frac{\text{TOTAL POPULATION}}{\text{STANDARD DIVISOR}}$$

Example 2   Find the standard divisor and standard quota

Use the data for New York City in 1790 to find the standard divisor and standard quota for each borough for the number of seats requested. Round these standard quotas to the nearest integer, up (upper quota), and down (lower quota).
a. 12 seats   **b.** 13 seats

Solution   The total population is 49,000. Let d be the standard divisor and q be the standard quota for each borough.

a. 12 seats; standard divisor: $d = \frac{49,000}{12} \approx 4,083.33$

	Standard Quota	Nearest	Upper Quota	Lower Quota
Manhattan:	$\frac{32,000}{d} \approx 7.84$	8	8	7
Bronx:	$\frac{2,000}{d} \approx 0.49$	0	1	0
Brooklyn:	$\frac{5,000}{d} \approx 1.22$	1	2	1
Queens:	$\frac{6,000}{d} \approx 1.47$	1	2	1
Staten Island:	$\frac{4,000}{d} \approx 0.98$	1	1	0
TOTAL:		11	14	9

b. 13 seats; $d = \frac{49,000}{13} \approx 3,769.23$

	Standard Quota	Nearest	Upper Quota	Lower Quota
Manhattan:	$\frac{32,000}{d} \approx 8.49$	8	9	8

	Standard Quota	Nearest	Upper Quota	Lower Quota
Bronx:	$\dfrac{2{,}000}{d} \approx 0.53$	1	1	0
Brooklyn:	$\dfrac{5{,}000}{d} \approx 1.33$	1	2	1
Queens:	$\dfrac{6{,}000}{d} \approx 1.59$	2	2	1
Staten Island:	$\dfrac{4{,}000}{d} \approx 1.06$	1	2	1
TOTAL:		13	16	11

Take a look at the results of Example 2, and you will see that if the required number of seats is 12, none of the rounding methods shown will work. Also note that if there are fewer than 13 seats, there is no representation for the Bronx. You may also have noticed that the apportionment we seek must be either the upper quota or the lower quota. This is known as the **quota rule.**

Quota Rule

The number assigned to each represented unit must be either the standard quota rounded down to the nearest integer or the standard quota rounded up to the nearest integer.

Before we decide on a rounding scheme, we will consider one more historical example from the United States Congress. The first congressional apportionment was to occur after the 1790 census. (It actually occurred in 1794.) The results of the census of 1790 are shown in Table 17.6.

TABLE 17.6
U.S. Population in the 1790 Census State Population

State	Population
Connecticut	237,655
Delaware	59,096
Georgia	82,548
Kentucky	73,677
Maryland	319,728
Massachusetts	475,199
New Hampshire	141,899
New Jersey	184,139
New York	340,241
North Carolina	395,005
Pennsylvania	433,611
Rhode Island	69,112
South Carolina	249,073
Vermont	85,341
Virginia	747,550
TOTAL	3,893,874

Note: We are using demographic information from the Consortium for Political and Social Research, Study 00003. The population numbers actually used for the 1794 apportionment were slightly different from these, so the historical record does not exactly match these academic examples. Among the reasons for this discrepancy is that prior to 1870, the population base included the total free population of the states and three-fifths of the number of slaves, and it excluded American Indians who, as a group, were not taxed.

> ## Example 3 Find the standard divisor and standard quota

Use the results of Table 17.6, and the fact that the number of seats in the House of Representatives was to be raised from 65 to 105. Find the standard divisor and the standard quota for each state. Round each of the standard quotas to the nearest number, as well as to give the lower and upper quotas.

Solution   Standard divisor: $d = \frac{3,893,874}{105} \approx 37,084.51$

	Standard Quota	Nearest	Upper Quota	Lower Quota
Connecticut:	$\frac{237,655}{d} \approx 6.41$	6	6	7
Delaware:	$\frac{59,096}{d} \approx 1.59$	2	1	2
Georgia:	$\frac{82,548}{d} \approx 2.23$	2	2	3
Kentucky:	$\frac{73,677}{d} \approx 1.99$	2	1	2
Maryland:	$\frac{319,728}{d} \approx 8.62$	9	8	9
Massachusetts:	$\frac{475,199}{d} \approx 12.81$	13	12	13
New Hampshire:	$\frac{141,899}{d} \approx 3.83$	4	3	4
New Jersey:	$\frac{184,139}{d} \approx 4.97$	5	4	5
New York:	$\frac{340,241}{d} \approx 9.17$	9	9	10
North Carolina:	$\frac{395,005}{d} \approx 10.65$	11	10	11
Pennsylvania:	$\frac{433,611}{d} \approx 11.69$	12	11	12
Rhode Island:	$\frac{69,112}{d} \approx 1.86$	2	1	2
South Carolina:	$\frac{249,073}{d} \approx 6.72$	7	6	7
Vermont:	$\frac{85,341}{d} \approx 2.30$	2	2	3
Virginia:	$\frac{747,550}{d} \approx 20.16$	20	20	21
TOTAL:		106	96	111

The quota rule tells us that the actual representation for each state must be the lower quota or the upper quota.

The First Congress of the United States needed to decide how to round the standard quotas, q, of Example 3. There were three plans proposed initially, and we will consider them one at a time. One of them rounded up, one rounded down, and a third rounded down with some additional conditions.

Adams' Plan

The first plan we will consider was proposed by the sixth president of the United States, John Quincy Adams, so it is known as **Adams' plan.**

Adams' Plan

Any standard quota with a decimal portion must be *rounded up* to the next whole number. To find the appropriate number of seats, use the following procedure.

Step 1 Compute the standard divisor, d.

Step 2 Compute the standard quota, q, for each state.

Step 3 Round the standard quotas up and add these quotas to find the total number of seats. It will be correct, or it will be too large. Raise the standard divisor in small increments until the rounded quotas provide the appropriate total; this divisor is called a **modified divisor**, D. The number Q for each state is called the **modified quota.**

Back in 1790 the process of finding the modified quota was quite a task, but with the help of spreadsheets today it is not very difficult. Look at Example 3 and note that the upper quotas total 111 and we are looking for a total of 105 seats. Look at the spreadsheet in Figure 17.2. Note that $d = 37{,}084.51$ (from Example 3) and if we raise this to $D = 38{,}000$, the total number of seats is 108, so we raised d too little. Next, we raise d to $D = 40{,}000$, and the total number of seats is now 103, so we raised d too much. (Remember, the goal is 105.) Finally, you will see that if we choose $D = 39{,}600$, we obtain the target number of seats, which is 105. The number of seats for each of the original states according to Adams' apportionment plan is shown in Figure 17.2.

Spreadsheet Application

	A	B	C	D	E	F	G	H	I	J	K
1		CN	DE	GA	KY	MD	MS	NH	NJ	NY	
2	Population	237,655	59,096	82,548	73,677	319,728	475,199	141,899	184,139	340,241	
3	q	6.41	1.59	2.23	1.99	8.62	12.81	3.83	4.97	9.17	
4	Nearest	6	2	2	2	9	13	4	5	9	
5	Round up	7	2	3	2	9	13	4	5	10	
6	Round dn	6	1	2	1	8	12	3	4	9	
7	Trial 1	7	2	3	2	9	13	4	5	9	
8	Q	6.25	1.56	2.17	1.94	8.41	12.51	3.73	4.85	8.95	
9	Trial 2	6	2	3	2	8	12	4	5	9	
10	Q	5.94	1.48	2.06	1.84	7.99	11.88	3.55	4.60	8.51	
11	Adams	6	2	3	2	9	13	4	5	9	
12	Q	6.00	1.49	2.06	1.86	8.07	12.00	3.58	4.65	8.59	
13											
14											
15		NC	PA	RI	SC	VT	VA	TOTAL	No. of Seats	d	
16	Population	395,005	433,611	69,112	249,073	85,341	747,550	3,893,874	105	37,084.51	
17	q	10.65	11.69	1.86	6.72	2.30	20.16	105			
18	Nearest	11	12	2	7	2	20	106			
19	Round up	11	12	2	7	3	21	111			
20	Round dn	10	11	1	6	2	20	96		D	
21	Trial 1	11	11	2	7	3	20	106	Raise d to:	38,000	too little
22	Q	10.39	11.41	1.82	6.55	2.25	19.67				
23	Trial 2	10	11	2	7	3	19	103	Raise d to:	40,000	too much
24	Q	9.88	10.84	1.73	6.23	2.13	18.69				
25	Adams	10	11	2	7	3	19	105	Raise d to:	39,600	just right
26	Q	9.97	10.95	1.75	6.29	2.16	18.88				

FIGURE 17.2 Apportionment calculations for Adams' apportionment plan

Example 4 Find the apportionment for students

Advanced mathematics is taught at five high schools in the Santa Rosa Unified School District. The district has just received a grant of 200 TI-Nspire™ calculators that are to be distributed to the five high schools. If these calculators are distributed according to Adams' plan, how should they be apportioned to the schools? Use the data in Table 17.7.

Table 17.7

Statistics for Santa Rosa Unified School District High Schools

School	No. of Students	No. Advanced Math Students
Elsie Allen	1,524	72
Maria Carrillo	1,687	131
Montgomery	1,755	243
Piner	1,519	95
Santa Rosa	1,797	71
TOTAL:	8,282	612

Solution   The standard divisor is $d = \frac{612}{200} = 3.06$. The standard and upper quotas are

	Population	Standard Quota, q	Upper Quota
Elsie Allen	72	$\frac{72}{d} \approx 23.53$	24
Maria Carrillo	131	$\frac{131}{d} \approx 42.81$	43
Montgomery	243	$\frac{243}{d} \approx 79.41$	80
Piner	95	$\frac{95}{d} \approx 31.05$	32
Santa Rosa	71	$\frac{71}{d} \approx 23.20$	24
TOTAL:			203

We now find the modified divisor, D, by raising d until the sum of the upper quotas
gives us 200. Suppose we raise $d = 3.06$ to $D = 3.1$. Now, the modified quotas are

	Modified Quota, Q	Adams' Plan
Elsie Allen	$\frac{72}{D} \approx 23.23$	24
Maria Carrillo	$\frac{131}{D} \approx 42.26$	43
Montgomery	$\frac{243}{D} \approx 78.39$	79
Piner	$\frac{95}{D} \approx 30.65$	31
Santa Rosa	$\frac{71}{D} \approx 22.90$	23
TOTAL:		200

Jefferson's Plan

Since the second plan was proposed by the third president of the United States, Thomas
Jefferson, it is known as **Jefferson's plan.** It is the same as Adams' plan, except you
round down instead of rounding up.

Round down!

CAUTION

Jefferson's Plan

Any standard quota with a decimal portion must be *rounded down* to the next whole
number. To find the appropriate number of seats, use the following procedure.

Step 1   Compute the standard divisor, d.

Step 2   Compute the standard quota, q, for each state.

Step 3   Round the standard quotas down and add these quotas to find the total
number of seats. It will be correct, or it will be too small. Lower the
standard divisor in small increments to find a modified divisor that will
give modified quotas that provide the appropriate total.

We again turn to Example 3 and note that the lower quotas total 96 and we are look-ing for a total of 105 seats. Look at the spreadsheet in Figure 17.3. This time we look at the lower quotas. Note that $d = 37,084.51$ (from Example 3) and if we lower this to $D = 36,000$, the total number of seats is 104, so we lowered d too little. (Remember, the goal is 105.) Next, we lower d to $D = 33,000$, and the total number of seats is now 111, so we lowered d too much. Finally, if we choose $D = 35,000$, we obtain the target num-ber of seats, which is 105. The number of seats for each of the original states according to Jefferson's apportionment plan is shown in Figure 17.3.

Spreadsheet Application   _ □ ✕

	A	B	C	D	E	F	G	H	I	J	
1		CN	DE	GA	KY	MD	MS	NH	NJ	NY	
2	Population	237,655	59,096	82,548	73,677	319,728	475,199	141,899	184,139	340,241	
3	q	6.41	1.59	2.23	1.99	8.62	12.81	3.83	4.97	9.17	
4	Nearest	6	2	2	2	9	13	4	5	9	
5	Round up	7	2	3	2	9	13	4	5	10	
6	Round dn	6	1	2	1	8	12	3	4	9	
7	Trial 1	6	1	2	2	8	13	3	5	9	
8	Q	6.80	1.64	2.29	2.05	8.88	13.20	3.94	5.11	9.45	
9	Trial 2	7	1	2	2	9	14	4	5	10	
10	Q	7.20	1.79	2.50	2.23	9.69	14.40	4.30	5.58	10.31	
11	Jefferson	6	1	2	2	9	13	4	5	9	
12	Q	6.79	1.69	2.36	2.11	9.14	13.58	4.05	5.26	9.72	
13											
14											
15		NC	PA	RI	SC	VT	VA	TOTAL	No. of Seats	d	
16	Population	395,005	433,611	69,112	249,073	85,341	747,550	3,893,874	105	37,084.51	
17	q	10.65	11.69	1.86	6.72	2.30	20.16	105			
18	Nearest	11	12	2	7	2	20	106			
19	Round up	11	12	2	7	3	21	111			
20	Round dn	10	11	1	6	2	20	96		D	
21	Trial 1	10	12	1	6	2	20	100	Lower d to:	36,000	too little
22	Q	10.97	12.04	1.92	6.92	2.37	20.77				
23	Trial 2	11	13	2	7	2	22	111	Lower d to:	33,000	too much
24	Q	11.97	13.14	2.09	7.55	2.59	22.65				
25	Jefferson	11	12	1	7	2	21	105	Lower d to:	35,000	just right
26	Q	11.29	12.39	1.97	7.12	2.44	21.36				

FIGURE 17.3 Apportionment calculations for Jefferson's apportionment plan

Example **5** **Distribute calculators to five high schools**

Use Table 17.7 and Jefferson's plan to distribute the 200 calculators to the five high schools based on the number of advanced math students.

Solution   The standard divisor is $d = \frac{612}{200} = 3.06$. The standard and upper quotas are:

	Population	Standard Quota, q	Lower Quota
Elsie Allen	72	$\frac{72}{d} \approx 23.53$	23
Maria Carrillo	131	$\frac{131}{d} \approx 42.81$	42
Montgomery	243	$\frac{243}{d} \approx 79.41$	79
Piner	95	$\frac{95}{d} \approx 31.05$	31
Santa Rosa	71	$\frac{71}{d} \approx 23.20$	23
TOTAL:			198

Suppose we lower $d = 3.06$ to $D = 3.01$ (this is the modified divisor). Now, the standard and lower quotas are calculated.

	Modified Quota, Q	Jefferson's Plan
Elsie Allen	$\frac{72}{D} \approx 23.92$	23
Maria Carrillo	$\frac{131}{D} \approx 43.52$	43
Montgomery	$\frac{243}{D} \approx 80.73$	80
Piner	$\frac{95}{D} \approx 31.56$	31
Santa Rosa	$\frac{71}{D} \approx 23.59$	23
TOTAL:		200

Hamilton's Plan

As you might have guessed by now, both Adams' and Jefferson's plans are a bit complicated. Historically, many complained that using this "modified divisor" to "tweak" the numbers is a bit "like magic." Alexander Hamilton, secretary of the treasury under George Washington, proposed the next plan we will consider, which is called, of course, **Hamilton's plan.** It is easier and more straightforward than the previous two plans we have considered.

Round down, but. . .

CAUTION

Hamilton's Plan

To find the appropriate number of seats, use the following procedure.

Step 1 Compute the standard divisor, d.

Step 2 Compute the standard quota, q, for each state.

Step 3 Round the standard quotas down to the nearest integer, but each *must be at least one.*

Step 4 Give any additional seats, one at a time (until no seats are left), to the states with the largest fractional parts of their standard quotas.

Note that Hamilton took into account the problem we discovered in Example 1. It just does not seem right that a district should have no representation, so if Hamilton's plan is used, all voters will have *some* representation.

Once again, look at Example 3 and note that the lower quotas total 96 and we are looking for a total of 105 seats. In the spreadsheet in Figure 17.4, we show you all three methods for easy comparison.

To carry out Hamilton's plan, start by looking at the value of q in the second row. Look across and locate the one with the greatest decimal portion; it is Kentucky (1.99, but look just at the decimal portion, 0.99); add one seat to Kentucky (see #1). Next, pick New Jersey (0.97); add one seat to New Jersey (see #2). Next, pick Rhode Island because it has the next largest decimal portion, (0.86); add one seat to Rhode Island (see #3). Continue to add seats in order (see #4 to #9). Note that now the total is 105 seats, so the process is complete.

Spreadsheet Application   _ □ ✕

	A	B	C	D	E	F	G	H	I	J
1		CN	DE	GA	KY	MD	MS	NH	NJ	NY
2	Population	237,655	59,096	82,548	73,677	319,728	475,199	141,899	184,139	340,241
3	q	6.41	1.59	2.23	1.99	8.62	12.81	3.83	4.97	9.17
4	Nearest	6	2	2	2	9	13	4	5	9
5	Round up	7	2	3	2	9	13	4	5	10
6	Round dn	6	1	2	1	8	12	3	4	9
7	Adams	6	2	3	2	9	13	4	5	9
8	Jefferson	6	1	2	2	9	13	4	5	9
9	Hamilton	6	1	2	2	9	13	4	5	9
10						#1	#9	#5	#4	#2	
11											
12		NC	PA	RI	SC	VT	VA	TOTAL	No. of Seats	d
13	Population	395,005	433,611	69,112	249,073	85,341	747,550	3,893,874	105	37,084.51
14	q	10.65	11.69	1.86	6.72	2.30	20.16	105		
15	Nearest	11	12	2	7	2	20	106		
16	Round up	11	12	2	7	3	21	111		
17	Round dn	10	11	1	6	2	20	96		
18	Adams	10	11	2	7	3	19	105		
19	Jefferson	11	12	1	7	2	21	105		
20	Hamilton	11	12	2	7	2	20	105		
21		#8	#7	#3	#6					

FIGURE 17.4 Apportionment calculations for Adams', Jefferson's, and Hamilton's apportionment plans

Example **6** **Use Hamilton's plan to distribute calculators**

Use Table 17.7 and Hamilton's plan to distribute the 200 calculators to the five high schools based on the number of advanced mathematics students.

Solution   The standard divisor is $d = \frac{612}{200} = 3.06$. The standard and lower quotas, along with Hamilton's plan, are shown:

	Population	Standard Quota, q	Lower Quota	Hamilton's Plan	
Elsie Allen	72	$\frac{72}{d} \approx 23.53$	23	24	#2 (0.53)
Maria Carrillo	131	$\frac{131}{d} \approx 42.81$	42	43	#1 (0.81)
Montgomery	243	$\frac{243}{d} \approx 79.41$	79	79	
Piner	95	$\frac{95}{d} \approx 31.05$	31	31	
Santa Rosa	71	$\frac{71}{d} \approx 23.20$	23	23	
TOTAL:			198	200	

The following example projects these mathematical methods of apportionment into the political process.

Example **7** **Compare small state and large state compromise**

Take a good look at Figure 17.4 to answer the following questions.
a. If you were from a small state, which plan would you probably favor?
b. If you were from a large state, which plan would you probably favor?
c. Which plan do you think was the first plan to be adopted by the First Congress?
    (*Hint*: remember, the First Congress was the congress of compromise.)

Solution

a. There are seven states (out of 15) for which the representation changes depending on the adopted plan. Adams' plan favors Delaware and Georgia, but hurts North Carolina and Pennsylvania. Jefferson's plan hurts Rhode Island. It seems as if *Adams' plan favors the smaller states.*

b. By the analysis in part a, it seems that the larger states would favor Jefferson's plan. It is not a coincidence that *Jefferson's plan favors the larger states* and that Jefferson was from Virginia.

c. It would seem that the plan to compromise the positions should be Hamilton's plan.

By considering Example 7, we can understand why the first apportionment plan to pass was Hamilton's plan. When the bill that would have adopted Hamilton's plan reached President Washington's desk, it became the first presidential veto in the history of our country. Washington objected to the fourth step in Hamilton's plan. Congress was not able to override the veto, so with a second bill Congress adopted Jefferson's plan, which was used until 1840 when it was replaced because flaws in Jefferson's plan showed up after the 1820 and 1830 censuses. We will discuss these flaws in the next section.

Webster's Plan

Daniel Webster, a senator from Massachusetts, ran for president on the Whig party, and was appointed secretary of state by President William H. Harrison. When the reapportionment based on the 1830 census was done, New York had a standard quota of 38.59 but was awarded 40 seats using Jefferson's plan. Webster argued that this was unconstitutional (violated the *quota rule*) and suggested a compromise, which became known as **Webster's plan.** His plan is similar to both Adams' and Jefferson's plans. Instead of rounding up or down from the modified quota, Webster proposed that any quota with a decimal portion must be rounded to the *nearest* whole number. This method is based on the *arithmetic mean*; round down if the standard quota is less than the *arithmetic mean* and round up otherwise.

> ⬦ CAUTION Use the arithmetic mean to round.

Webster's Plan

Any standard quota with a decimal portion must be *rounded to the nearest whole number.* To find the appropriate number of seats, use the following procedure.

Step 1 Compute the standard divisor, d.

Step 2 Compute the standard quota, q, for each state.

Step 3 Round the standard quotas down if the fractional part is less than 0.5 and up if the fractional part is greater than or equal to 0.5. The total will be correct, or it will not.

Step 4 If it is not, lower or raise the standard divisor in small increments to find a modified divisor that will give modified quotas that provide the appropriate total.

Example 8 Use Webster's plan to apportion cameras

The city St. Louis, Missouri, passed a ballot measure to provide and pay for 130 surveillance cameras for high crime areas. The city council mandated that these cameras be apportioned among the five highest crime areas, based on the 2001 crime statistics, summarized in Table 17.8. Use Webster's plan.

TABLE 17.8	
Serious Crimes in St. Louis, Missouri, in 2001	
Precinct	**Number of Violent Crimes (per 100 residents)**
Downtown	24.45
Fairground	10.04
Columbus Square	9.75
Downtown West	9.43
Peabody	9.01
TOTAL	62.68

Solution   In this case, the "population" is the total number of crimes per 100 residents. This is 62.68, and the number of items is 130. Thus, the standard divisor is $d = \frac{62.68}{130} \approx 0.48$. The standard quotas are shown in tabular form.

Precinct	Standard Quota, q	Rounded Value
Downtown	$\frac{24.45}{d} \approx 50.71$	51
Fairground	$\frac{10.04}{d} \approx 20.82$	21
Columbus Square	$\frac{9.75}{d} \approx 20.22$	20
Downtown West	$\frac{9.43}{d} \approx 19.56$	20
Peabody	$\frac{9.01}{d} \approx 18.69$	19
TOTAL:		131

The total of the standard quotas is too large, so we should raise the standard divisor to form a modified divisor. By trial and error we find that three-decimal-place rounding is necessary in order to give the correct number of cameras. The modified quotas are shown for a modified divisor $D = 0.484$.

Precinct	Modified Quota, Q	Rounded Value
Downtown	$\frac{24.45}{D} \approx 50.52$	51
Fairground	$\frac{10.04}{D} \approx 20.74$	21
Columbus Square	$\frac{9.75}{D} \approx 20.14$	20
Downtown West	$\frac{9.43}{D} \approx 19.48$	19
Peabody	$\frac{9.01}{D} \approx 18.62$	19
TOTAL:		130

At the time that Webster's plan was adopted, no one suspected that it had the same flaw as Jefferson's plan. It was used after the 1840 census and from 1900 to 1941, when it was replaced by Huntington-Hill's plan. Oddly enough, from 1850 to 1900 Hamilton's plan was used, so the only method never actually used in Congress was Adams' plan.

Huntington-Hill's Plan

Edward Huntington, a professor of mechanics and mathematics at Harvard University, and Joseph Hill, chief statistician for the Bureau of the Census, devised a rounding method currently used by the U.S. legislature. From 1850 to 1911, the size of the House of Representatives (number of seats) changed as states were added. In 1911, the House size was fixed at 433, with a provision for the addition of one seat each for Arizona and New Mexico. The House size has remained at 435 since, except for a temporary increase to 437 at the time of admission of Alaska and Hawaii. The seats went back to 435 after the subsequent census. In 1910, a plan called *Huntington-Hill's plan*, which we will abbreviate as the *HH's plan*, was adopted. It is the same as Webster's plan except it rounds using the *geometric mean,* rather than the *arithmetic mean* used by Webster's plan. First, we present an example reviewing the concept of geometric mean.

Example 9   Compare the arithmetic and geometric means

The following modified quotas are given. Find the upper and lower quotas, and the arithmetic and geometric means of the upper and lower quotas. Then round the modified quota by comparing it to the arithmetic mean and then to the geometric mean.
a. 9.49   **b.** 1.42   **c.** 4.53   **d.** 6.42

Solution   If a and b are two numbers, then

$$\text{arithmetic mean (A.M.)} = \frac{a+b}{2} \qquad\qquad \text{geometric mean (G.M.)} = \sqrt{ab}$$

Q	Down	Up	A.M.	A.M. Round	G.M.	G.M. Round
a. 9.49	9	10	$\frac{9+10}{2}=9.5$	9	$\sqrt{9\times10}\approx9.486$	10
b. 1.42	1	2	$\frac{1+2}{2}=1.5$	1	$\sqrt{1\times2}\approx1.414$	2
c. 4.53	4	5	$\frac{4+5}{2}=4.5$	5	$\sqrt{4\times5}\approx4.472$	5
d. 6.42	6	7	$\frac{6+7}{2}=6.5$	6	$\sqrt{6\times7}\approx6.48$	6

CAUTION   *Use the geometric mean to round.*

Huntington-Hill's Plan

To find the appropriate number of seats, use the following procedure.

Step 1   Compute the standard divisor, d.

Step 2   Compute the standard quota, q, for each state. Let a = lower quota and b = upper quota for each state.

Step 3   Round the standard quotas down if the fractional part is less than $\sqrt{ab}$ and up if the fractional part is greater than or equal to $\sqrt{ab}$. Add these rounded numbers; the total will be correct, or it will not.

Step 4   If it is not, lower or raise the standard divisor in small increments to find a modified divisor that will give modified quotas that provide the appropriate total.

Example 10   Apportion using Huntington-Hill's plan

Disney World has several resorts with lakes:

   Grand Floridian, 904 rooms

   Contemporary Resort, 1,041 rooms

   Polynesian Resort, 853 rooms

   Yacht Club Resort, 630 rooms

   Beach Club Resort, 584 rooms

If Disney World purchases 400 paddle boats, how many boats would each resort be assigned if they were assigned according to the number of rooms using HH's plan?

Solution There are 4,012 rooms. The standard divisor is $d = \frac{4012}{400} = 10.03$. The standard quotas are found and rounded according to the geometric mean.

Resort	Standard Quota, q	Geometric Mean	Rounded Value
Contemporary	$\frac{1,041}{d} \approx 103.79$	$\sqrt{103 \times 104} \approx 103.499$	104
Polynesian	$\frac{853}{d} \approx 85.04$	$\sqrt{85 \times 86} \approx 85.499$	85
Grand Floridian	$\frac{904}{d} \approx 90.13$	$\sqrt{90 \times 91} \approx 90.499$	90
Yacht Club	$\frac{630}{d} \approx 62.81$	$\sqrt{62 \times 63} \approx 62.498$	63
Beach Club	$\frac{584}{d} \approx 58.23$	$\sqrt{58 \times 59} \approx 58.498$	58
TOTAL:			400

We conclude this section with an example that allows us to compare and contrast the apportionment methods introduced in this section. We have summarized these in Table 17.9.

TABLE 17.9

Summary of Apportionment Methods

Method	Divisor	Apportionment
Adams' Plan	Round **up; raise** the standard divisor to find the modified divisor.	Round the standard quotas up. Apportion to each group its modified upper quota. It favors the smaller states.
Jefferson's Plan	Round **down; lower** the standard divisor to find the modified divisor.	Round the standard quotas down. Apportion to each group its modified lower quota. It favors the larger states.
Hamilton's Plan	Use the standard divisor. Round **down.**	Round the standard quotas down. Distribute additional seats one at a time until all items are distributed.
Webster's Plan	Use modified divisors. May round up or down.	Round by comparing with the **arithmetic mean** of the upper and lower quotas.
HH's Plan	Use modified divisors. May round up or down.	Round by comparing with the **geometric mean** of the upper and lower quotas.

Example **11** **Compare apportionment plans** Pólya's Method

Consider College Town with district populations as follows:

North: 8,600   South: 5,400   East: 7,200   West: 3,800

Suppose there are exactly 10 council seats. Apportion the current seats according to the indicated method.*

a. Adams' plan   **b.** Jefferson's plan
c. Hamilton's plan   **d.** Webster's plan
e. HH's plan

Solution We use Pólya's problem-solving guidelines for this example.

Understand the Problem. Suppose that 10 years ago the population of College Town was 24,000. At that time, the standard divisor was

$$d = \frac{24,000}{10} = 2,400$$

*This problem and solution are adapted from the article "Decimals, Rounding, and Apportionment," by Kay I. Meeks, *The Mathematics Teacher*, October 1992, pp. 523–525.

Over time, populations change, and the ten seats must be divided fairly for the four districts. Let's begin by doing some simple arithmetic. The present population is 25,000 and the number of seats is 10, so we begin by calculating the standard divisor:

$$\text{standard divisor} = \frac{25,000}{10} = 2,500$$

Next, calculate the standard quotas for the revised population:

North: $\frac{8,600}{2,500} = 3.144$ South: $\frac{5,400}{2,500} = 2.16$ East: $\frac{7,200}{2,500} = 2.88$ West: $\frac{3,800}{2,500} = 1.52$

Devise a Plan. Historically, there were five plans devised, and this example asks us to use each of these plans.

Carry Out the Plan. The results using the standard quota for each of these five plans are shown in the following table.

Results of City Council Apportionment

District	Population	Std Quota	Adams	Jefferson	Webster	Hamilton	HH
North	8,600	3.44	4	3	3	3	3
South	5,400	2.16	3	2	2	2	2
East	7,200	2.88	3	2	3	3	3
West	3,800	1.52	2	1	2	2	2
TOTAL	25,000		12	8	10	10	10

We see that the results from Adams' and Jefferson's plans require that we consider modified quotas.

a. Adams' plan: The modified divisor should be greater than the standard divisor. Try $D = 3,000$. The modified quotas are shown in the following table.

b. Jefferson's plan: The modified divisor should be less than the standard divisor. Try $D = 2,000$. The modified quotas are shown in the following table.

Additional Results of City Council Apportionment

District	Population	Std Quota $d = 2,400$	Adams $D = 3,000$	Jefferson $D = 2,000$	Adams	Jefferson
North	8,600	3.44	2.87	4.30	3	4
South	5,400	2.16	1.80	2.70	2	2
East	7,200	2.88	2.40	3.60	3	3
West	3,800	1.52	1.27	1.90	2	1
TOTAL	25,000				10	10

c. Hamilton's plan: Rank the original standard quotas:

North: $\frac{8,600}{25,000} \cdot 10 \approx 3.44$ Decimal rank is 3.

South: $\frac{5,400}{25,000} \cdot 10 \approx 2.16$ Decimal rank is 4.

East: $\frac{7,200}{25,000} \cdot 10 \approx 2.88$ Decimal rank is 1.

West: $\frac{3,800}{25,000} \cdot 10 \approx 1.52$ Decimal rank is 2.

Hamilton's plan adds one seat to the East (highest decimal, so it is rank 1) and one to the West (second highest decimal, so it is rank 2).

d. Webster's plan: The results of rounding to the nearest whole number (that is, rounding by comparing with the arithmetic mean) provided the correct apportionment.

Historical NOTE

Alexander Hamilton (1757–1804)

In 1780, Hamilton outlined a plan with a strong central government to replace the weak Articles of Confederation. He was the first secretary of the treasury and had a great deal of influence on the formation of our government in its first decade. He was a political adversary of Jefferson, and was part of the formation of two politically opposing parties: the Federalists, led by Hamilton and John Adams, and the Democratic Republicans, led by Jefferson and James Madison. Hamilton's proposal for apportionment was the first one passed, but it was the victim of the first presidential veto.

e. Huntington–Hill's plan: Consider the calculations shown in the table:

	Geometric Mean (G.M.)	Compare with G.M.	Round	Seats
North:	G.M. $= \sqrt{3 \cdot 4} \approx 3.46$	less	down	3
South:	G.M. $= \sqrt{2 \cdot 3} \approx 2.45$	less	down	2
East:	G.M. $= \sqrt{2 \cdot 3} \approx 2.45$	greater	up	3
West:	G.M. $= \sqrt{1 \cdot 2} \approx 1.41$	greater	up	2
TOTAL:				10

Notice that the total equals the required number of city council seats.

Look Back. Do all the methods provide the appropriate number of seats? Do any violate the quota rule?

In the next section we will see that since Adams', Jefferson's, Webster's, and HH's methods all use modified quotas, they can, under certain circumstances, violate the quota rule. We also see in the next section that every apportionment process will have some sort of anomaly under certain conditions.

Problem Set 17.3

Level 1

1. **IN YOUR OWN WORDS** Discuss the idea of apportionment. Describe some different apportionment schemes.

2. **IN YOUR OWN WORDS** Discuss the ideas of arithmetic mean and geometric mean.

3. **IN YOUR OWN WORDS** Which apportionment schemes for the U.S. Congress favor the smaller states? Which ones favor the larger states? Are any neutral as far as state size is concerned?

4. **IN YOUR OWN WORDS** What is the quota rule? Does this rule make sense to you? Discuss.

5. **IN YOUR OWN WORDS** If you round the standard quotas down, how do you need to change the standard divisor to find the modified quotas?

6. **IN YOUR OWN WORDS** If you round the standard quotas up, how do you need to change the standard divisor to find the modified quotas?

Modified quotas are given in Problems 7–14. Round your answers to two decimal places.
a. *Find the lower and upper quotas.*
b. *Find the arithmetic mean of the lower and upper quotas.*
c. *Find the geometric mean of the lower and upper quotas.*
d. *Round the given modified quota by comparing it with first the arithmetic mean, and then with the geometric mean.*

7. 3.81

8. 1.24

9. 1.46

10. 3.48

11. 2.49

12. 2.51

13. 1,695.4

14. 1,695.6

Find the standard divisor (to two decimal places) for the given populations and number of representative seats in Problems 15–22.

	Population	# seats		Population	# seats
15.	52,000	8	16.	135,000	8
17.	630	5	18.	540	7
19.	1,450,000	12	20.	8,920,000	12
21.	23,000,000	125	22.	62,300,000	225

For the given year, find the standard quotas for the New York City boroughs given in Table 17.5 in Problems 23–28. Assume there are eight council seats.

23. 1800

24. 1840

25. 1900

26. 1940

27. 1990

28. 2000

Consider the populations given in Problems 29–32.
a. *Find the standard divisor.*
b. *Find the standard quota for each precinct.*
c. *Total, rounding the standard quotas down.*
d. *Find a modified divisor that will give modified quotas to produce the desired number of seats.*

29. 10 seats

Population	
1st Precinct	35,000
2nd Precinct	21,000
3rd Precinct	12,000
4th Precinct	48,000
TOTAL	116,000

30. 12 seats

Population	
1st Precinct	35,000
2nd Precinct	21,000
3rd Precinct	12,000
4th Precinct	48,000
TOTAL	116,000

31. 10 seats

Population	
1st Precinct	135,000
2nd Precinct	231,000
3rd Precinct	118,000
4th Precinct	316,000
TOTAL	800,000

32. 12 seats

Population	
1st Precinct	135,000
2nd Precinct	231,000
3rd Precinct	118,000
4th Precinct	316,000
TOTAL	800,000

Consider the populations given in Problems 33–36.
a. *Find the standard divisor.*
b. *Find the standard quota for each precinct.*
c. *Total, rounding the standard quotas up.*
d. *Find a modified divisor that will give modified quotas to produce the desired number of seats.*

33. 10 seats

Population	
1st Precinct	35,000
2nd Precinct	21,000
3rd Precinct	12,000
4th Precinct	48,000
TOTAL	116,000

34. 12 seats

Population	
1st Precinct	35,000
2nd Precinct	21,000
3rd Precinct	12,000
4th Precinct	48,000
TOTAL	116,000

35. 10 seats

Population	
1st Precinct	135,000
2nd Precinct	231,000
3rd Precinct	118,000
4th Precinct	316,000
TOTAL	800,000

36. 12 seats

Population	
1st Precinct	135,000
2nd Precinct	231,000
3rd Precinct	118,000
4th Precinct	316,000
TOTAL	800,000

Level 2

HISTORICAL QUEST   *In the apportionment of the House of Representatives based on the 1790 Census (Example 3), there are 15 states. At that time Maine was still considered part of Massachusetts. If Maine had been a separate state, it would have shared in the distribution of the seats in the House. In the 1790 census, Maine's population was 96,643. Subtract this number from Massachusetts' population and then answer the questions in Problems 37–40 based on 16 states.*

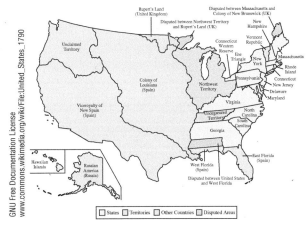

United States in 1790

37. What are the standard quotas for the 16 states?

38. What is the total of the quotas rounded to the nearest number?

39. What is the sum of the lower quotas?

40. What is the sum of the upper quotas?

Consider the following apportionment problem for College Town:

North:	8,700	East:	7,200
South:	5,600	West:	3,500

Suppose each council member is to represent approximately 2,500 citizens. Use the apportionment plan requested in Problems 41–45 assuming that there must be 10 representatives.

41. Adams' plan

42. Jefferson's plan

43. Hamilton's plan

44. Webster's plan

45. HH plan

Consider the following apportionment problem:

North:	18,200	East:	17,600
South:	12,900	West:	13,300

Use the apportionment plan requested in Problems 46–50 assuming that there must be 26 representatives.

46. Adams' plan

47. Jefferson's plan

48. Hamilton's plan

49. Webster's plan

50. HH's plan

Consider the following apportionment problem:

North:	18,200
South:	12,900
East:	17,600
West:	13,300

Use the apportionment plan requested in Problems 51–55 assuming that there must be 16 representatives.

51. Adams' plan

52. Jefferson's plan

53. Hamilton's plan

54. Webster's plan

55. HH's plan

Consider the following apportionment problem:

North:	1,820,000
Northeast:	2,950,000
East:	1,760,000
Southeast:	1,980,000
South:	1,200,000
Southwest:	2,480,000
West:	3,300,000
Northwest:	1,140,000

If there are to be 475 representatives, use the apportionment plan requested in Problems 56–60.

56. Adams' plan

57. Jefferson's plan

58. Hamilton's plan

59. Webster's plan

60. HH's plan

17.4 | Apportionment Paradoxes

As we saw in the last section, the U.S. Constitution mandated that representation in the House of Representatives be based on proportional representation by state. The first three apportionment plans, Adams', Jefferson's, and Hamilton's plans, were debated in Congress with regard to implementing this mandate using the population numbers from the 1790 census. The easiest to apply was Hamilton's plan, which, as we saw, was vetoed by Washington. This left two plans that relied on modified divisors. Remember, the quota rule states that the actual number of seats assigned to each state must be the lower or the upper quota. Consider the following historical example.

Example 1   Apportionment in 1830

In the 1830 election, New York's population was 1,918,578 and the U.S. population was 11,931,000. At that time, there were 240 seats in the House of Representatives. Determine the standard, upper, and lower quotas for New York in the 1830 election.

Solution $d = \dfrac{11,931,000}{240}$; the standard quota was $\dfrac{1,918,578}{d} \approx 38.59$. The lower quota is 38 and the upper quota is 39.

Remember, in 1830 Jefferson's plan was in place and the modified divisor used for that election produced a number with a standard quota that rounded down to 40 (see Example 1; this violated the quota rule). Daniel Webster was outraged, and he argued that the result was unconstitutional. Unfortunately, he proposed a method that had the same flaw (namely, it violated the quota rule). Any plan that uses a modified divisor can violate the quota rule.

Example **2**   **Discover an apportionment paradox**

Packard-Hue manufactures testing equipment at four locations and has just hired 200 new employees. Those employees are to be apportioned by production levels at the four locations using Jefferson's plan. The locations and production levels per week are

Atlanta:	12,520
Buffalo:	4,555
Carson City:	812
Denver:	947

a. What is the standard divisor?
b. What are the standard quotas?
c. What are the lower and upper quotas?
d. Find a modified divisor that will produce an appropriate modified quota totaling the 200 new employees.
e. Show that this apportionment violates the quota rule.

Solution

a. The total production is the sum of the production levels per week at each of the four plants: 18,834. The standard divisor is $d = \dfrac{18,834}{200} \approx 94.17$.

b. We calculate the production quotas:

Factory	Production/wk	q	Lower Quota	Upper Quota
A:	12,520	132.95	132	133
B:	4,555	48.37	48	49
C:	812	8.62	8	9
D:	947	10.06	10	11
TOTALS:			198	202

c. The lower and upper quotas are found by rounding, as shown in the table in part **b**.
d. We need to *lower d* so that the values of *q increase* to give us a total of 200 when we round them down. Let $D = 93$. We calculate the modified quotients.

Factory	Production/wk	Q	Round Down
A:	12,520	134.62	134
B:	4,555	48.98	48
C:	812	8.73	8
D:	947	10.18	10
TOTALS:			200

e. Notice that factory A's lower quota is 132 and its upper quota is 133, but the modified quota produces a rounded-down value that is *higher* than the upper quota. Thus, we say this example violates the quota rule.

The same kind of inconsistencies can happen with any of the methods that use modified divisors and modified quotas to form the sum. Only Hamilton's plan is immune to this behavior, and all the other plans may violate the quota rule. You might ask, Why, then, don't we use Hamilton's plan? We have another paradox to consider.

Alabama Paradox

Alabama

A serious inconsistency in Hamilton's plan was discovered in the 1880 census. Before the number of seats in the House of Representatives was fixed at 435, there was a debate on whether to have 299 or 300 seats in the House. Using Hamilton's method with 299 members, Alabama was to receive eight seats. But if the total number of representatives were *increased* to 300, Alabama would receive only seven seats!

Alabama Paradox

A reapportionment in which an increase in the total number of seats results in a loss in the seats for some state is known as the **Alabama paradox.**

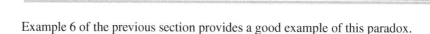

Example 6 of the previous section provides a good example of this paradox.

Example 3 Illustrate the Alabama paradox

Use Hamilton's plan to distribute 46 computers to five high schools based on the number of remedial mathematics students. The standard divisor $d = \frac{559}{46} \approx 12.152$, and the apportionment according to Hamilton's plan as shown here:

	Population	Standard Quota, q	Lower Quota	Hamilton's Plan
Elsie Allen	39	$\frac{39}{d} \approx 3.21$	3	3
Maria Carrillo	70	$\frac{70}{d} \approx 5.76$	5	6 #1 (0.76)
Montgomery	18	$\frac{18}{d} \approx 1.48$	1	2 #2 (0.48)
Piner	222	$\frac{222}{d} \approx 18.27$	18	18
Santa Rosa	210	$\frac{210}{d} \approx 17.28$	17	17
TOTAL:			44	46

Now, suppose that a parent at Montgomery High School heard of the computer distribution and contributed one additional computer to raise the number to 47 computers. What is the apportionment according to Hamilton's plan?

Solution The standard divisor is $d = \dfrac{559}{47} \approx 11.89$. We recalculate the apportionment according to Hamilton's plan, using this new value of d.

	Population	Standard Quota, q	Lower Quota	Hamilton's Plan
Elsie Allen	39	$\frac{39}{d} \approx 3.28$	3	3
Maria Carrillo	70	$\frac{70}{d} \approx 5.89$	5	6 #1 (0.89)
Montgomery	18	$\frac{18}{d} \approx 1.51$	1	1
Piner	222	$\frac{222}{d} \approx 18.67$	18	19 #2 (0.67)
Santa Rosa	210	$\frac{210}{d} \approx 17.66$	17	18 #3 (0.66)
TOTAL:			44	47

As you can see, the extra computer from the Montgomery parent caused that school to receive one less computer!

If you look at the preceding example, it is easy to see how this paradox can occur. Raising the number can cause a decimal part of one number to increase faster than the decimal part of another, changing their "rank" in their decimal parts.

Population Paradox

Shortly after the discovery of the Alabama paradox, another paradox was discovered around 1900 while Congress was still using Hamilton's plan. It is possible for the population of one state to be growing at a faster rate than another state, but still lose seats to the slower-growing state.

Population Paradox

When there is a fixed number of seats, a reapportionment that causes a state to lose a seat to another state even though the percent increase in the population of the state that loses the seat is larger than the percent increase of the state that wins the seat is called the **population paradox.**

For an example of the population paradox, consider the following example.

Example 4   Illustrate the population paradox

Suppose there are 100 new teachers to be apportioned to the three boroughs according to their 1990 population using Hamilton's plan. The population of each borough is

	1990	2000
Anderson Valley	3,755	3,800
Bennett Valley	10,250	10,350
Central Valley	36,100	36,150
TOTAL	50,105	50,300

Show that this example illustrates the population paradox.

Solution   In 1990, $d = \dfrac{50,105}{100} = 501.05$. The standard quotas are (in thousands)

Borough	Population	q	Lower Quota	Hamilton's Plan
A	3,755	7.49	7	8 (#1)
B	10,250	20.46	20	20
C	36,100	72.05	72	72
TOTAL	50,105		99	100

In 2000, $d = \dfrac{50,300}{100} = 503$.

Borough	Population	q	Lower Quota	Hamilton's Plan
A	3,800	7.55	7	7
B	10,350	20.58	20	21 (#2)
C	36,150	71.87	71	72 (#1)
TOTAL	50,300		98	100

Now, here are the percent increases:

Borough	1990	2000	Increase	Percent Increase
A	3,755	3,800	45	$\dfrac{45}{3,755} \approx 1.20\%$
B	10,250	10,350	100	$\dfrac{100}{10,250} \approx 0.98\%$
C	36,100	36,150	50	$\dfrac{50}{36,100} \approx 0.14\%$

Anderson Valley had the largest percent increase, but lost one teacher to Bennett Valley. This is an example of the population paradox.

New States Paradox

The last paradox we will discuss was discovered in 1907 when Oklahoma joined the Union. If a new state is added to the existing states and the number of seats being apportioned is increased to prevent decreasing the existing apportionment, addition may cause a shift in some of the original allocations.

> **New States Paradox**
>
> A reapportionment in which an increase in the total number of seats causes a shift in the apportionment of the existing states is known as the **new states paradox.**

The following example is a simplified version of Example 3.

 **Example 5   Illustrate the new states paradox**

Suppose a school received a grant of 20 calculators to distribute to two schools:

Elsie Allen	71 advanced math students
Maria Carrillo	119 advanced math students
TOTAL	190 advanced math students

The standard divisor is $d = \frac{190}{20} = 9.5$. That is, there is one calculator for each 9 or 10 students. The calculators are to be apportioned according to Hamilton's plan.

School	Number	q	Round Down	Hamilton's Plan
Elsie Allen	71	7.47	7	7
Maria Carrillo	119	12.53	12	13 (#1)
TOTAL	190		19	20

Now, suppose a parent decides to donate 5 more calculators for Ridgeway High, with a student population of 51 advanced math students. Shouldn't that be just right to accommodate the new school? Show that this example illustrates the new states paradox by calculating the new apportionment using this added contribution.

Solution

Elsie Allen	71 advanced math students
Maria Carrillo	119 advanced math students
Ridgeway	51 advanced math students
TOTAL	241 advanced math students

The standard divisor is $d = \dfrac{241}{25} = 9.64$. The calculators are to be apportioned according to Hamilton's plan.

School	Number	q	Round Down	Hamilton's Plan
Elsie Allen	71	7.37	7	8 (#1)
Maria Carrillo	119	12.34	12	12
Ridgeway	51	5.29	5	5
TOTAL	241		24	25

Notice that even though the five new calculators went to Ridgeway (as intended), the addition (new state) caused an adjustment on the prior apportionment. This is an example of the new states paradox.

Balinski and Young's Impossibility Theorem

In 1980 two mathematicians proved that if any apportionment plan satisfies the quota rule, then it must permit the possibility of some other paradox. Here is a statement of **Balinski and Young's impossibility theorem.**

Balinski and Young's Impossibility Theorem

Any apportionment plan that does not violate the quota rule must produce paradoxes. And any apportionment plan that does not produce paradoxes must violate the quota rule.

There is a footnote, however, to this theorem. The second part of this theorem is true only when the number of seats to be apportioned is fixed up front, as it is fixed with the U.S. House of Representatives to be 435.

We conclude with a summary of the paradoxes of this section, along with the quota rule, in Table 17.10.

TABLE 17.10

		Comparison of Apportionment Paradoxes				
Paradox	**Comment**	**Adams'**	**Jefferson's**	**Hamilton's**	**Webster's**	**HH**
Quota rule	Apportionment must be either the lower or upper quota.	Yes	Yes	No	Yes	Yes
Alabama paradox	An increase in the total may result in a loss for a state.	No	No	Yes	No	No
Population paradox	One state may lose seats to another even though its percent increase is larger.	No	No	Yes	No	No
New states paradox	The addition of a new state may change the apportionment of another group.	No	No	Yes	No	No

Note: "Yes" means that the apportionment method may violate the stated paradox. "No" means that the apportionment method may not violate the stated paradox.

Problem Set 17.4

Level 1

1. **IN YOUR OWN WORDS** What is the Alabama paradox?

2. **IN YOUR OWN WORDS** What is the population paradox?

3. **IN YOUR OWN WORDS** What is the new states paradox?

4. **IN YOUR OWN WORDS** What does Balinski and Young's impossibility theorem say?

Use Adams' plan in Problems 5–6. Show that it violates the quota rule.

5. | State: | A | B | C | D |
   |---|---|---|---|---|
   | Population: | 68,500 | 34,700 | 14,800 | 9,500 |

   Number of seats: 100

6. | State: | A | B | C | D |
   |---|---|---|---|---|
   | Population: | 685 | 347 | 160 | 95 |

   Number of seats: 100

Use Jefferson's plan in Problems 7–10. Show that it violates the quota rule.

7. State: A   B   C   D
Population: 68,500   34,700   16,000   9,500
Number of seats: 100

8. State: A   B   C   D
Population: 17,179   7,500   49,400   5,824
Number of seats: 132

9. State: A   B   C   D   E
Population: 1,100   1,100   1,515   4,590   2,010
Number of seats: 200

10. State: A   B   C   D   E
Population: 1,700   3,300   7,000   24,190 8,810
Number of seats: 150

In Problems 11–14, use Hamilton's plan to apportion the new seats to the existing states. Then increase the number of seats by one and decide whether the Alabama paradox occurs. Assume that the populations are in thousands.

11. State: A   B   C   D
Population: 181   246   812   1,485
Number of seats: 246

12. State: A   B   C   D
Population: 235   318   564   938
Number of seats: 45

13. State: A   B   C   D   E
Population: 300   301   340   630   505
Number of seats: 50

14. State: A   B   C   D   E
Population: 300   700   800   800   701
Number of seats: 82

In Problems 15–18, apportion the indicated number of representatives to three states, A, B, and C, using Hamilton's plan. Next, use the revised populations to reapportion the representatives. Decide whether the population paradox occurs.

15. State: A   B   C
Population: 55,200   124,900   190,000
Revised pop.: 61,100   148,100   215,000
Number of seats: 11

16. State: A   B   C
Population: 90,000   124,800   226,000
Revised pop.: 98,000   144,900   247,100
Number of seats: 13

17. State: A   B   C
Population: 89,950   124,800   226,000
Revised pop.: 97,950   144,900   247,100
Number of seats: 13

18. State: A   B   C
Population: 7,510   20,500   72,000
Revised pop.: 7,650   20,800   72,200
Number of seats: 100

In Problems 19–22, apportion the indicated number of representatives to two states, A and B, using Hamilton's plan. Next, recalculate the apportionment using Hamilton's plan for the three states, C and the original states. Decide whether the new states paradox occurs.

19. State: A   B   C
Population: 144,899   59,096   38,240
Number of original seats: 12
Number of additional seats: 2

20. State: A   B   C
Population: 394,990   753,950   138,550
Number of original seats: 16
Number of additional seats: 1

21. State: A   B   C
Population: 7,000,500   9,290,500   1,450,000
Number of original seats: 50
Number of additional seats: 4

22. State: A   B   C
Population: 265,000   104,000   69,000
Number of original seats: 16
Number of additional seats: 2

Level 2

23. Packard-Hue manufactures testing equipment at four locations, and has just hired 300 new employees. Those employees are to be apportioned using production levels at the four locations according to Jefferson's plan. The locations and production are as follows:

> Atlanta: 12,520
> Buffalo: 4,555
> Carson City: 812
> Denver: 947

   a. What is the standard divisor?
   b. What are the standard quotas?
   c. What are the lower and upper quotas?
   d. Find a modified divisor that will produce appropriate modified quotas totaling the 300 new employees.
   e. Does this violate the quota rule?

24. The English enrollments at five high schools in the Santa Rosa Unified School District are as follows:

> Elsie Allen: 154
> Maria Carillo: 142
> Montgomery: 165
> Piner: 307
> Santa Rosa: 231
> TOTAL: 999

Suppose that 45 copies of an important instructional video are to be allocated to the schools by using Hamilton's plan and the school population.
   a. What is the standard divisor?
   b. What are the standard quotas?
   c. What are the lower and upper quotas?
   d. What are the allocations for the 45 videos?
   e. What are the allocations for 46 videos?
   f. Does this illustrate the Alabama paradox?

25. The township of Bella Rosa is divided into two districts, uptown (pop. 16,980) and downtown (pop. 3,350), and is governed by 100 council members.
  a. What is the standard divisor?
  b. What are the standard quotas?
  c. How should the seats be apportioned using Hamilton's plan?
  d. Suppose the township annexes a third district (pop. 2,500). Using the standard divisor from part **a**, it was agreed that the new district should add 12 new seats. Carry out this new apportionment for the township using Hamilton's plan.
  e. Does this example illustrate the new states paradox?

26. Suppose the annual salaries of three people are

Employee #1	$43,100
Employee #2	$42,150
Employee #3 (half-time)	$20,000

  a. What are their salaries if they are given a 5% raise, and then the result is rounded to the nearest $1,000 using Hamilton's plan with a cap on the total salaries of $111,000?

  b. Suppose the salary increase is to be 6% with a cap of $111,000. What are the salaries if they are rounded to the nearest $1,000 using Hamilton's plan?
  c. If you compare parts **a** and **b**, are any of the paradoxes illustrated?

Problem Solving ③

27. A fair apportionment of dividing a leftover piece of cake between two children is to let child #1 cut the cake into two pieces and then to let child #2 pick which piece he or she wants. Consider the following apportionment of dividing the leftover piece of cake among three children. Let the first child cut the cake into two pieces. Then the second child is permitted to cut one of those pieces into two parts. Child #3 can select any of the pieces, followed by child #2 selecting one of the remaining pieces, followed by child #1 who gets the remaining piece. Is this allocation process fair if each child's goal is to maximize the size of his/her own piece of cake?

28. An elderly rancher died and left her estate to her three children. She bequeathed her 17 prize horses in the following manner: 1/2 to the eldest, 1/3 to the second child, and 1/9 to the youngest. How would you divide this estate?

29. The children (see Problem 28) decided to call in a very wise judge to help in the distribution of the rancher's estate. The judge arrived with a horse of his own. He put his horse in with the 17 belonging to the estate, and then told each child to pick from among the 18 in the proportions stipulated by the will (but be careful, he warned, not to pick *his* horse). The first child took nine horses, the second child took six, and the third child, two. The 17 horses were thus divided among the children. The wise judge took his horse from the corral, took a fair sum for his services, and rode off into the sunset.

   The youngest son complained that the oldest son received 9 horses (but was entitled to only $17/2 = 8.5$ horses). The judge was asked about this, and he faxed the children the following message: "You all received more than you deserved. The eldest received 1/2 of an 'extra' horse, the middle child received 1/3 more, and the youngest, 1/9 of a horse 'extra.'" Apportion the horses according to Adams', Jefferson's, and Webster's plans. Which plan gives the appropriate distribution of horses?

30. The children (see Problem 28) decided to call in a very wise judge to help in the distribution of the rancher's estate. They informed the judge that the 17 horses were not of equal value. The children agreed on a ranking of the 17 horses (#1 being the best and #17 being a real dog of a horse). They asked the judge to divide the estate fairly so that each child would receive not only the correct number of horses but horses whose average rank would also be the same. For example, if a child received horses 1 and 17, the number of horses is two and the average value is $\frac{1 + 17}{2} = 9$. How did the judge apportion the horses?

17.5   CHAPTER SUMMARY

Representatives and direct Taxes shall be apportioned among the several States which may be included in this Union, according to their respective numbers . . .

ARTICLE I, SECTION 2 OF THE
CONSTITUTION OF THE UNITED STATES

Important Ideas

Voting procedures [17.1]
Summary of voting methods, Table 17.2 [17.1]
Fair voting principles: majority criterion, Condorcet criterion, monotonicity criterion, irrelevant alternatives criterion [17.2]
Arrow's impossibility theorem [17.2]
Legislative seats or other resources [17.3]
Flaws or inconsistencies in the apportionment process [17.4]

Take some time getting ready to work the review problems in this section. First review these important ideas. Look back at the definition and property boxes. If you look online, you will find a list of important terms introduced in this chapter, as well as the types of problems that were introduced. You will maximize your understanding of this chapter by working the problems in this section only after you have studied the material.

You will find some review help online at **www.mathnature.com**. There are links giving general test help in studying for a mathematics examination, as well as specific help for reviewing this chapter.

Chapter **17** Review Questions

A taste test is conducted on the Atlantic City Boardwalk. People are given samples of Coke, Pepsi, and Safeway brands of cola in unmarked cups, and are then asked to rank them in order of preference. The first cup is labeled A, the second, B, and the third, C. Here are the results of the voting:

(CBA)	(ABC)	(BAC)
18	15	12

Use this information in Problems 1–5.

1. Does any item have a majority? If not, how about a plurality?
2. How many rankings of the three colas received no votes?
3. Who wins using the Hare method?
4. Who wins a pairwise comparison?
5. Are any of the fairness criteria violated?

In an election with three candidates, A, B, and C, we find the following results of the voting:

(ABC)	(ACB)	(BAC)	(BCA)	(CBA)	(CAB)
22%	23%	15%	29%	7%	4%

Use this information in Problems 6–7.

6. Does anyone receive a plurality?
7. Is there a Condorcet winner?
8. In 2001 the voting for the Heisman Trophy involved 925 ballots voting for three college football players. The results (in alphabetical order) were as follows:

> David Carr (Fresno State): 34, 60, 58
>
> Eric Crouch (Nebraska): 162, 98, 88
>
> Ken Dorsey (Miami): 109, 122, 67
>
> Dwight Freeney (Syracuse): 2, 6, 24
>
> Rex Grossman (Florida): 137, 105, 87
>
> Joey Harrington (Oregon): 54, 68, 66
>
> Bryant McKinnie (Miami): 26, 12, 14
>
> Julius Peppers (North Carolina): 2, 10, 15
>
> Antwaan Randle El (Indiana): 46, 39, 51
>
> Roy Williams (Oklahoma): 13, 36, 35

What was the Borda count for each player? Who was the winner according to the Borda count?

Consider a vote for four candidates with the following results:

(ADBC)	(CABD)	(BCDA)	(DBAC)
7	5	4	1

Use this information for Problems 9–11. If there is a tie, break the tie by having a runoff of the tied candidates.

9. Who wins by the Hare method?
10. Who wins by the pairwise comparison method?
11. If B pulls out before the election, who wins? Does this violate the irrelevant alternatives criterion?

Chemistry is taught at five high schools in the Santa Rosa Unified School District. The district has just received a grant of 100 microscopes, which are to be apportioned to the five high schools based on each school's chemistry population. Use the data in Table 17.11 for Problems 12–19.

TABLE 17.11

Statistics for Santa Rosa Unified School District High Schools

School	# Students	# Chemistry Students
Elsie Allen	1,524	90
Maria Carrillo	1,687	215
Montgomery	1,755	268
Piner	1,519	133
Santa Rosa	1,797	84
TOTAL	8,282	790

12. Find the standard divisor.
13. What are the standard, lower, and upper quotas?
14. Apportion the microscopes using Adams' plan.
15. Apportion the microscopes using Jefferson's plan.
16. Apportion the microscopes using Hamilton's plan.
17. Apportion the microscopes using Webster's plan.
18. Apportion the microscopes using HH's plan.
19. Can you point out any apportionment paradoxes?

20. The city of St. Louis, Missouri, passed a ballot measure to provide and pay for 180 surveillance cameras for high-crime areas. The city council mandated that these cameras be apportioned among the five highest crime areas, based on the 2001 crime statistics, summarized in Table 17.12. Use Webster's plan.

TABLE 17.12

Serious Crimes in St. Louis, Missouri in 2001	
Precinct	Number of Violent Crimes/ 100 Residents
Downtown	24.45
Fairground	10.04
Columbus Square	9.75
Downtown West	9.43
Peabody	9.01

BOOK REPORTS

Write a 500-word report on one of these books:

Voting Procedures, Michael Dummett (Oxford, UK: Oxford University Press, 1984).

Considerations on Representative Government, John Stuart Mill (New York: Harper and Brothers, 1862).

Group | RESEARCH PROJECTS

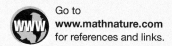

Go to
www.mathnature.com
for references and links.

Working in small groups is typical of most work environments, and learning to work with others to communicate specific ideas is an important skill. Work with three or four other students to submit a single report based on each of the following questions.

G55. Historical Quest   Write a history of apportionment in the United States House of Representatives. Pay particular attention to the paradoxes of apportionment.

G56. Of all possible collections of states that yield 270 or more electoral votes—enough to win a presidential election—which collection has the smallest geographical area?

REFERENCES   Frederick S.Hillier, and Gerald J. Lieberman. *Introduction to Operations Research.* 4th ed. Oakland: Holden Day, 1986.

Charles Redmond, Michael Federici, and Donald Platte, "Proof by Contradiction and the Electoral College," *The Mathematics Teacher,* Vol. 91, No. 8, November 1998, pp. 655–658.

G57. Historical Quest   Prepare a list of women mathematicians from the history of mathematics. Answer the question, "Why were so few mathematicians female?"

REFERENCES   Teri Perl, *Math Equals: Biographies of Women Mathematicians plus Related Activities.* (Reading, MA: Addison-Wesley Publishing Co., 1978).

Loretta Kelley, "Why Were So Few Mathematicians Female?" *The Mathematics Teacher,* October 1996.

Barbara Sicherman and Carol H. Green, eds. *Notable American Women: The Modern Period.* A Biographical Dictionary. (Cambridge, MA: Belknap Press, Harvard University Press, 1980).

Outstanding Women in Mathematics and Science (National Women's History Project, Windsor, CA 95492, 1991).

G58. Historical Quest   Prepare a list of black mathematicians from the history of mathematics.

REFERENCE   Virginia Newell et al., eds. *Black Mathematicians and Their Works* (Ardmore, PA: Dorrance & Company, 1980).

G59 Historical Quest   Prepare a list of mathematicians with the first name of Karl.

G60. Investigate some item of interest to your group. It might be to predict the outcome of an upcoming election, or your favorite song or movie. Your group should make up a list of 5 or 6 choices; for example, you might be researching which is the best of the *Star Wars* movies. Make up a written ballot and ask at least 50 people to rank the items on your list. Summarize the outcome of your poll. Was there a majority winner? A plurality winner? Who wins according to the Borda count and the Hare methods? What about the pairwise comparison method? Present a summary of your results.

Individual RESEARCH PROJECTS

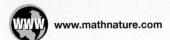 www.mathnature.com

Learning to use sources outside your classroom and textbook is an important skill, and here are some ideas for extending some of the ideas discussed in this chapter. You can find references to these projects in a library or at **www.mathnature.com.**

PROJECT 17.1 Research how voting is conducted for the following events. Use the terminology of this chapter, not the terminology used in the original sources.

    a. Heisman Trophy Award
    b. Selecting an Olympic host city
    c. The Academy Awards
    d. The Nobel Prizes
    e. The Pulitzer Prize

PROJECT 17.2 Compare and contrast the voting paradoxes. Which one do you find the most disturbing, and why? Which do you find the least disturbing, and why?

PROJECT 17.3 Compare and contrast the different apportionment plans. Which method do you think is best? Support your position with examples and facts.

PROJECT 17.4 Compare and contrast the apportionment paradoxes. Which one of these do you find the most disturbing, and why? Which one of these do you find the least disturbing, and why?

MATHEMATICS IN THE NATURAL SCIENCES, SOCIAL SCIENCES, AND HUMANITIES

We began this book with a prologue that asked the question, "Why study math?" so it seems appropriate that we end the book with an epilogue asking, "Why not study math?" Mathematics is the foundation and lifeblood of nearly all human endeavors. The German philosopher John Frederick Herbart (1776–1841) summarizes this idea:

All quantitative determinations are in the hands of mathematics, and it at once follows from this that all speculation which is heedless of mathematics, which does not enter into partnership with it, which does not seek its aid in distinguishing between the manifold modifications that must of necessity arise by a change of quantitative determinations, is either an empty play of thoughts, or at most a fruitless effort.

Historically, mathematics has always been at the core of a liberal arts education. This is a book of mathematics for the liberal arts. Karl Gauss, one of the greatest mathematicians of all time, called mathematics the "Queen of the Sciences," but mathematics goes beyond the sciences. Bertrand Russell claimed, "Mathematics, rightly viewed, possesses not only truth, but supreme beauty. . . . " And finally, Maxine Bôcher concludes, "I like to look at mathematics almost more as an art than as a science. . . . " If fact, the mathematics degree at UCLA is classified as an art, not a science. Mathematics seems to be part of the structure of our minds, more akin to memory than to a learnable discipline. Enjoyment and use of mathematics are not dependent on "book learning," and even a casual perusal of the topics in this book will clearly illustrate that mathematics is many things to many people.

Like music, mathematics resists definition. Bertrand Russell had this to say about mathematics: "Mathematics may be defined as the subject in which we never know what we are talking about, nor whether what we are saying is true." Einstein, with his customary mildness, tells us, "So far as the theorems of mathematics are about reality, they are not certain; so far as they are certain, they are not about reality." Aristotle, who was as sure of everything as anyone can be of anything, thought mathematics to be the study of quantity, whereas Russell, in a less playful mood, thinks of it as the "class of all propositions of the type '*p* implies *q*,' which seems to have little to do with quantity." Willard Gibbs thought of mathematics as a language; Hilbert thought of it as a game. Hardy stressed its uselessness, Hogben its practicality. Mill thought it an empirical science, whereas to Sullivan it was an art, and to the wonderful J. J. Sylvester, it was "the music of reason."

math·e·mat·ics\'math-ǝ-'mat-iks\ *n pl but usu sing in constr* **1:** the science of numbers and their operations, interrelations, combinations, generalizations, and abstractions and of space configurations and their structure, measurement, transformations, and generalizations **2:** a branch of, operation in, or use of mathematics

This is what it is.

This ambiguity should be consoling. It suggests that mathematics has so many mansions that there is room for everyone. In this epilogue we will discuss mathematics in the natural sciences, in the social sciences, and in the humanities.

Mathematics in the Natural Sciences

When most of us think about applications of mathematics, we think of those in the natural sciences, or those sciences that deal with matter, energy, and the interrelations and transformations. Some of the major categories include (alphabetically) astronomy, biology, chemistry (and biochemistry), computer science, ecology, geology, medicine, meteorology, physics (and biophysics), statistics, and zoology.

We began this text by looking at reasoning, both inductive and deductive reasoning. Inductive reasoning in the natural sciences is called the *scientific method*. With this type of reasoning, we are trying to recognize and formulate hypotheses, and then collect data through observation and experimentation in an effort to test our hypotheses and to make further conclusions or conjectures based on the obtained data.

Using mathematics to make real-life predictions involves a process known as **mathematical modeling,** which we discussed in Chapter 18. Since most models are dynamic, a feedback and reevaluation process is part of the formulation of a good model. It involves *abstraction, deriving results, interpretation*, and then *verification*. An illustration of what we mean is shown in Figure 1.

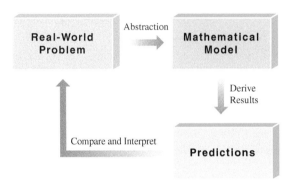

FIGURE 1 Mathematical modeling

A good example of mathematics modeling in the natural sciences, but with implications to history and the social sciences (not to mention golf!), is modeling the path of a cannonball. The *real-world* problem is to hit a target.

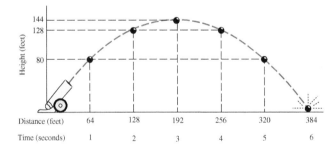

Fire a cannonball at 63 m/s at a 57° angle. We might begin by using trial and error. One possible trial is shown in Figure 2.

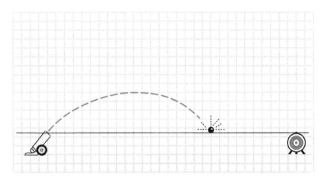

FIGURE 2 Trying to hit a target by trial and error

 You can try this experiment (it's fun!) at **www .mathnature. com.** *Choose "Epilogue links.*

The first use of a cannon was primarily to demoralize the enemy by its overwhelming power with little hope of actually hitting a specific target. In World War I, the trajectory of a cannon was trial and error, and we all remember old World War II movies where a "spotter" would phone directions to a gunner to adjust the angle of the cannon. We now need to make some assumptions; this is called *abstraction.* We assume that we are on earth (the earth's gravitational acceleration is 32 ft/s^2 or 9.8 m/s^2; we also assume that the density of the cannonball is constant, and that wind and friction are negligible). When we look at the path of a cannonball, we recognize it as having a parabolic shape, so our first attempt at modeling the path is to guess that it has an equation like $y = ax^2$ for an appropriate a. We also know that it opens downward, so a is negative. We now need to *derive some results* for the modeling process. We begin with the equation of a parabola that opens down (from Section 15.4): $x^2 = -4cy$. This equation assumes that the vertex of the parabola is at (0, 0). It can be shown that if the vertex is at a point *(h, k),* then the equation has the form

$$(x - h)^2 = -4c(y - h)$$

The vertex of the parabola formed by the path of the cannonball has a vertex at (192, 144), so the equation we seek has the form

$$(x - 192)^2 = -4c(y - 144)$$

We also see that the curve passes through (0, 0), so

$$(0 - 192)^2 = -4c(0 - 144)$$
$$36,864 = 576c$$
$$c = 64$$

We guess that the equation for the path of the cannonball can be described by the equation

$$(x - 192)^2 = -256(y - 144)$$

The graph is shown in Figure 3.

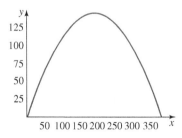

FIGURE 3 Path of a cannonball

Modeling is an iterative process, so we now must *interpret and compare.* Even though the path of the cannonball seems correct (it passes through all of the appropriate points), it does not correctly model the given information. The path should somehow be dependent on the angle of elevation as well as the speed of the cannonball.

In order to model the path as a function of the angle of trajectory and initial velocity, we need some concepts from calculus, specifically Newton's laws of motion. Even though the derivation of these equations is beyond the scope of this course, we can understand these equations once they are stated as follows:

$$x = (v_0 \cos \theta)t \qquad y = h_0 + (v_0 \sin \theta)t - 16t^2$$

where h_0 is the initial height off the ground, and v_0 is the initial velocity of the projectile in the direction of θ with the horizontal $(0° \le \theta \le 180°)$. You might wish to review the meaning of $\cos \theta$ and $\sin \theta$ discussed in Section 7.5. The variables x and y represent the horizontal and vertical distances, respectively, measured in feet, and the variable t represents the time, in seconds, after firing the projectile.

Example 1 Graph of a projectile

Graph the equations

$$x = (v_0 \cos \theta)t \qquad y = h_0 + (v_0 \sin \theta)t - 4.9t^2$$

where $\theta = 57°$, $v_0 = 63$ ft/s, and $h_0 = 0$.

Solution   The desired equations are

$$x = (63 \cos 57°)t \qquad y = (63 \sin 57°)t - 4.9t^2$$

We can set up a table of values (as shown in the margin) or use a graphing calculator to sketch the curve as shown in Figure 4.

t	x	y
0	0	0
1	34	48
2	69	86
3	103	114
4	137	133
5	172	142
6	206	141
7	240	130
8	274	109
9	309	79
10	343	38

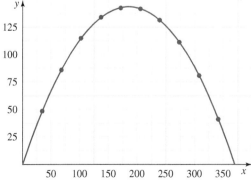

FIGURE 4 Graph of the path of a cannonball

We compare Figure 4 with the real-world problem and it seems to model the situation correctly. In modeling, it may be necessary to go back and modify the assumptions several times before obtaining a result that appropriately models what we seek to find.

Astronomy is the study of objects and matter outside the earth's atmosphere, their motions and paths, as well as their physical and chemical properties. Science often deals with the very small (such as cells, atoms, and electrons) or the very large (as with planets and galaxies). In the text, we defined scientific notation and developed the laws of exponents to help us deal with large and small numbers.

Example 2 Number of miles in a light year

One light-year is approximately

$$5,870,000,000,000 = 5.87 \times 10^{12} \text{ miles.}$$

The closest star is Alpha Centauri, a distance of 4.35 light-years from the sun. How far is this in miles?

Solution   We use the properties of exponents:

$$\begin{aligned} 4.35 \text{ light-years} &= 4.35 \times (1 \text{ light-year}) \\ &= 4.35 \times (5.87 \times 10^{12} \text{ miles}) \\ &= 25.5345 \times 10^{12} \text{ miles} \\ &= 2.55 \times 10^{13} \text{ miles} \end{aligned}$$

Note: Because we are working with approximate numbers, all of these equal signs would generally be "$\approx$," meaning "approximately equal to," but common usage is to write equal signs.

The subsection on scientific notation and estimation (Section 1.3) is particularly important in astronomy. These large numbers are necessary in Example 8, p. 739, Section 15.4, which finds the equation for the earth's orbit around the sun. This example is revisited in the following example.

Example 3 Investigate the orbit of a planet

Describe the meaning of the equation

$$\frac{x^2}{8.649 \times 10^{15}} + \frac{y^2}{8.647 \times 10^{15}} = 1$$

which models the path of the earth's orbit around the sun. The given distances are in miles. Find the eccentricity. The closer the eccentricity is to zero, the more circular the orbit.

Solution   We compare this with the equation of a *standard-form ellipse* centered at the origin.

$$\frac{x^2}{a^2} + \frac{y^2}{b^2} = 1$$

We note that $a = \sqrt{8.649 \times 10^{15}} \approx 93{,}000{,}000$ and $b = \sqrt{8.647 \times 10^{15}} \approx 92{,}990{,}000$. Since $a \approx b$ we note that the elliptic orbit is almost circular. The measure of the circularity of the orbit is the *eccentricity,* which is defined as

$$\epsilon = \frac{c}{a} = \sqrt{1 - \frac{b^2}{a^2}}$$

$$= \sqrt{1 - \frac{8.647 \times 10^{15}}{8.649 \times 10^{15}}} \approx 0.015$$

Note: In reality, ϵ for the earth is about 0.016678, which we could obtain with better accuracy on the measurement of the lengths of the sides. The *aphelion* (the greatest distance from the sun) is $a \approx 93{,}000{,}000$ miles and the *perihelion* (the closest distance from the sun) is $b \approx 92{,}990{,}000$.

Biology is defined as that branch of knowledge that deals with living organisms and vital processes and includes the study of the plant and animal life of a region or environment. In Section 6.3, we considered a significant example from biology, specifically an application from genetics.

Example 4 Find the proportion of genotypes and phenotypes

Suppose a certain population has two eye color genes: *B* (brown eyes, dominant) and *b* (blue eyes, recessive). Suppose we have an isolated population in which 60% of the genes in the gene pool are dominant *B*, and the other 40% are recessive *b*. What fraction of the population has each genotype? What percent of the population has each phenotype?

Solution   Let $p = 0.6$ and $q = 0.4$. Since p and q give us 100% of all the genes in the gene pool, we see that $p + q = 1$. Since

$$(p + q)^2 = p^2 + 2pq + q^2$$

we can find the percents:

Genotype *BB:* $p^2 = (0.6)^2 = 0.36,$
                  so 36% have *BB* genotype.
Genotype *bB* or *Bb:* $2pq = 2(0.6)(0.4) = 0.48,$ so
                  48% have this genotype.
Genotype *bb:* $q^2 = (0.4)^2 = 0.16,$
                  so 16% have *bb* genotype.
Check genotypes: $0.36 + 0.48 + 0.16 = 1.00$

As for the phenotypes, we look only at outward appearances, and since brown is dominant, *BB*, *bB*, and *Bb* all have brown eyes; this accounts for 84%, leaving 16% with blue eyes.

Another area of biology that relates closely with mathematics is the issue of *scale*. For example, we say that to predict a child's height as an adult, use a *scaling factor* of 2, which means if a two-year-old is 31 in. tall, then we predict that this child will be 62 in. tall as an adult. If we scale up a linear measure by a factor of two, then a two-dimensional measure will increase by a factor of $2^2 = 4$, and a three-dimensional measure will increase by a factor of $2^3 = 8$. We considered this idea relative to scaling on graphs in Section 14.1.

Example 5 Discuss the effect of area due to scaling factor changes

Consider a tissue sample as shown in Figure 5.

FIGURE 5 Small tissue sample

If this sample is scaled up by a factor of 2, how does the area of the new sample compare with the area of the original? Repeat for scaling up by a factor of 3.

Solution   Since the area function is a square $(A = s^2)$, we know that the area of the sample is scaled up by a factor of $2^2 = 4$ when doubled or $3^2 = 9$ when tripled.

Doubling the width and length results
in increasing the area by 4.

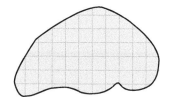

Tripling the width and length results
in increasing the area by 9.

Chemistry is the science that deals with the composition, structure, and properties of substances and with the transformations that they undergo. A popular and exciting natural science called **biochemistry** deals with the chemical compounds and processes occurring in organisms.

Computer science is the study of computers, their design, and programming and includes artificial intelligence, networking, computer graphics, and computer languages. Computers, calculators, and spreadsheets are discussed throughout the text.

Geology is the science that deals with the history of the earth and its life, especially as recorded in rocks. **Ecology** is the science that is concerned with the interrelationship of organisms and their environments. **Medicine** is the science and art dealing with the maintenance of health and the prevention, alleviation, or cure of disease. **Meteorology** is the science that deals with the atmosphere and its phenomena, and especially with weather and weather forecasting.

Physics is the science that deals with matter and energy and their interactions. **Biophysics** deals with the application of physical principles and methods to biological systems and problems.

Statistics is a branch of mathematics dealing with the collection, analysis, interpretation, and presentation of masses of numerical data. Chapter 14 of this text introduces some topics in statistics—namely, frequency distributions and graphs; measures of central tendency, position, and dispersion; normal curves; and correlation and regression analysis.

And last, but not least, on our list of major categories of the natural sciences is **zoology**, which is concerned with classification and properties of animals, including their structure, function, growth, origin, evolution, and distribution. Zoology is often considered to be a branch of biology.

An excellent discussion of mathematics in modeling a projectile's path can be found in the following article in the classic book, *World of Mathematics* (New York, Simon and Schuster, 1956): "Mathematics of Motion," by Galileo Galilei. You will find other references to mathematics in the natural sciences on the World Wide Web at

 **www.mathnature.com**

Mathematics in the Social Sciences

The social sciences are the study of human society and of individual relationships in and to society. Some of the major categories include (arranged alphabetically) anthropology, archaeology, civics, history, languages, political science, psychology, and sociology.

Anthropology refers to the study of human beings in relation to distribution, origin, classification, and relationship of races, physical character, environmental and social relations, and culture. In its broadest sense, it also includes theology.

Example 6 **Discussion**

Discuss the invention of the zero symbol.

Solution The term zero, written 0, is defined to be the *additive identity*, which is that number with the property that $x + 0 = 0 + x$ for any number x. The Babylonians used written symbols for thousands of years before they invented a symbol for 0, which was initially introduced as a position

marker to differentiate between numbers such as 123 and 1230. The first documented use of the *number* 0 is found around the first century A.D. in the Mayan numeration system. The Hindus customarily wrote numbers in columns and used a zero symbol to represent a blank column, which is necessary for our present place-value numeration system.

Another application of mathematics to anthropology is carbon dating of artifacts using the decay formula. Problem 57 of Problem Set 10.3, p. 499 asked you to use the gathered data to set a probable date for the Shroud of Turin. If you worked this problem, you found that it is not dated from the time of Christ.

Example 7 **Age of Shroud of Turin**

In 1988, a small sample of the Shroud of Turin was taken and scientists from Oxford University, the University of Arizona, and the Swiss Federal Institute of Technology were permitted to test it. Suppose the cloth contained 90.7% of the original amount of carbon. According to this information, how old is the Shroud?

Solution We use the decay formula $A = A_0 e^{rt}$, where $A/A_0 = 0.907$ and $r = -1.209680943E - 4$ (from Example 5, p. 492, Section 10.3):

$$A = A_0 e^{rt} \qquad \text{Decay formula}$$

$$\frac{A}{A_0} = e^{rt} \qquad \text{Divide both sides by } A_0.$$

$$0.907 = e^{rt} \qquad \text{Remember, } t \text{ is the unknown; } r \text{ is known.}$$

$$rt = \ln 0.907 \qquad \text{Definition of logarithm}$$

$$t = \frac{\ln 0.907}{r} \qquad r = -1.209680943E - 4$$

$$\approx 806.9 \qquad \text{This is the most probable age (in years).}$$

The probable date for the Shroud is about A.D. 1200. Since the first recorded evidence of the Shroud is about 1389, we see that A.D. 1200 is not only possible, but plausible.

"Human sacrifices and human compassion. Greek artists and American cannibals. The birth of language and the death of civilizations. Mongol hordes and ancient toys. Missing aviators and sunken ships. Egyptian politicians and modern saints. The first human and the latest war. The past hides the key to the future. Find it in. . . ." This advertisement for the periodical *Discovering Archaeology* does a good job of describing **archaeology.**

Civics is the subject that deals with the rights and duties of citizens. **History** refers to a chronological record of significant events, often including an explanation of their causes. (The prologue of this book focused on mathematical history.) **Linguistics** is the study of human speech, including the units, nature, structure, and modification of language, whereas **language** refers to the actual knowledge of the words and vocabulary used to communicate ideas and feelings.

Political science is a branch of social science that is the study of the description and analysis of political and especially governmental institutions and processes. Related to this idea is the problem of representation in government, namely, the issue of voting and apportionment. In the text we examined different forms of representative government, including dictatorship, majority, and plurality rules. What effect does a runoff election or a third party have on the results of an election?

Apportionment was an important issue for the framers of the U.S. Constitution, and historically there were four plans that are important to government planning today. These plans were advanced by Thomas Jefferson, John Quincy Adams, Daniel Webster, and Alexander Hamilton. We discussed apportionment at length in the text.

Psychology, broadly defined, refers to the science of mind and behavior. Mathematical tools used in psychology include sets, statistics, and the analysis of data, which we discuss at length in Chapter 14. The organization of data and surveys using Venn diagrams is introduced in Chapter 2.

Sociology is the study of society, social institutions, and social relationships, specifically the systematic study of the development, structure, interaction, and collective behavior of organized groups of human beings. Throughout the book, we encountered a secret sect of intellectuals called the Pythagoreans. Every evening each member of the Pythagorean Society had to reflect on three questions:

PYTHAGOREAN CREED

1. What good have I done today?
2. What have I failed at today?
3. What have I not done today that I should have done?

Example   8   Show that 28 is perfect

The Pythagoreans studied *perfect numbers.* A perfect number is a counting number that is equal to the sum of all its divisors that are less than the number itself. Show that 28 is a perfect number.

Solution   We first find all divisors of 28 that are less than 28: 1, 2, 4, 7, and 14. Their sum is

$$1 + 2 + 4 + 7 + 14 = 28$$

So we see that 28 is perfect!

Understanding population growth is an essential part of understanding the underlying principles used in the social sciences. Population growth, along with a working knowledge of the number e, is used to predict population

sizes for different growth rates. Recall the growth formula:

$$A = A_0 e^{rt}$$

which gives the future population A after t years for an initial population A_0 and a growth rate of r; this relationship was considered extensively in Chapter 10.

The principal use of mathematics in the social sciences is in its heavy use of statistics. In the text, we studied surveys and sampling, which are important to social scientists. To choose an unbiased sample from a target population, we must ask two questions: *Is the procedure random?* and *Does the procedure take into account the target population?* Finally, matrices, an important topic in mathematics, are used to organize and manipulate data in the social sciences. This topic is introduced and discussed extensively in the text.

Social Choice

The study of the decision-making process by which individual preferences are translated into a single group choice is known as *social choice theory.* It is an important topic in mathematics (see Chapter 17) and culminates with the surprising mathematical result that it is impossible to find a suitable technique for voting.

Related to voting is the process by which a representative government is chosen, called *apportionment*, which is also discussed in Chapter 17.

Stable Marriages

Suppose there are n graduates of a well-known medical school, and those graduates will be matched to n medical centers to serve their internship programs. Each graduate must select his or her preferences for medical school, and in turn, each medical school must make a list of preferences for graduates. We will call this pairing a **marriage.** A pairing is called **unstable** if there are a graduate and a school who have not picked each other and who would prefer to be married to each other rather than to their current selection. Otherwise, the pairing is said to be **stable.**

Example   9   Showing that a marriage possibility is stable

Suppose there are three graduates, *a, b, c,* and three schools, *A, B, C,* with choices as follows:

$a(ABC)$ means that *a* ranks the schools as *A*, first choice; *B*, second choice; and *C*, third choice.

$b(ACB)$ means that *b* ranks the schools *A*, *C*, and *B*, respectively.

$c(ABC)$ means that *c* ranks the schools *A*, *B*, and then *C*.

On the other hand, the schools' rankings of candidates are:

$A(cab)$, $B(cba)$,   and $C(bca)$

How many possible marriages are there, and how many of these are stable?

Solution   We begin by representing the choices for this example in matrix form (we considered matrices in Section 16.3):

$$
\begin{array}{c}
\\
a \\ b \\ c
\end{array}
\begin{array}{ccc}
A & B & C \\
\left[\begin{array}{ccc}
(1,2) & (2,3) & (3,3) \\
(1,3) & (3,2) & (2,1) \\
(1,1) & (2,1) & (3,2)
\end{array}\right]
\end{array}
$$

The entry (1, 2) means that a picks A as its 1st choice, and A picks a as its 2nd choice.

To answer the first question, we use the fundamental counting principle. Person a can be paired with any of three schools, and then (since the matching is one school to one student) there are two schools left for person b, and finally one for person c:

Number of possibilities: $3 \cdot 2 \cdot 1 = 6$

We show these choices using a tree diagram in Figure 6.

FIGURE 6 Possible pairings

We need to consider each of these six possibilities, one at a time. The first one listed is aA, bB, and cC. We repeat the above matrix, this time with these highlighted pairings:

$$
\begin{array}{c}
\\
a \\ b \\ c
\end{array}
\begin{array}{ccc}
A & B & C \\
\left[\begin{array}{ccc}
(1,2) & (2,3) & (3,3) \\
(1,3) & (3,2) & (2,1) \\
(1,1) & (2,1) & (3,2)
\end{array}\right]
\end{array}
$$

We look for a pairing in which both partners would rather be paired with someone else. This will not occur for a row in which the pairing shows a first choice, so we do not look at row a to find dissatisfaction; instead we look at row b. The pairing (3, 2) tells us that b is associated with his or her third choice. We are looking for another pair *in the same row* where the second component is smaller than its corresponding choice in *its column*. Note that in row b the entry (2, 1) has a second component of 1, which means that C would rather be paired with b than with its current pairing of c. We also see that person b would also prefer to be married to c (second choice) than with its current pairing, so this is *unstable*.

Let's move to the second pairing shown in Figure 6. It is aA, bC, and cB. We show this pairing:

$$
\begin{array}{c}
\\
a \\ b \\ c
\end{array}
\begin{array}{ccc}
A & B & C \\
\left[\begin{array}{ccc}
(1,2) & (2,3) & (3,3) \\
(1,3) & (3,2) & (2,1) \\
(1,1) & (2,1) & (3,2)
\end{array}\right]
\end{array}
$$

Row a is OK because a is paired with his or her first choice.

Row b is OK because b is paired with his or her second choice, but C is paired with a first choice.

Row c shows that c is paired with his or her second choice, but would rather be with A. A would also rather be with c, so this marriage is unstable.

The other possibilities are listed here:

$$
\begin{array}{c}
\\
a \\ b \\ c
\end{array}
\begin{array}{ccc}
A & B & C \\
\left[\begin{array}{ccc}
(1,2) & (2,3) & (3,3) \\
(1,3) & (3,2) & (2,1) \\
(1,1) & (2,1) & (3,2)
\end{array}\right]
\end{array}
$$

Not stable; a prefers A, and A prefers a to b.

$$
\begin{array}{c}
\\
a \\ b \\ c
\end{array}
\begin{array}{ccc}
A & B & C \\
\left[\begin{array}{ccc}
(1,2) & (2,3) & (3,3) \\
(1,3) & (3,2) & (2,1) \\
(1,1) & (2,1) & (3,2)
\end{array}\right]
\end{array}
$$

a prefers A, but A is paired with first choice.
b prefers A, but A is paired with first choice.
Stable

$$
\begin{array}{c}
\\
a \\ b \\ c
\end{array}
\begin{array}{ccc}
A & B & C \\
\left[\begin{array}{ccc}
(1,2) & (2,3) & (3,3) \\
(1,3) & (3,2) & (2,1) \\
(1,1) & (2,1) & (3,2)
\end{array}\right]
\end{array}
$$

c prefers A, and A prefers c, so this is unstable.

$$
\begin{array}{c}
\\
a \\ b \\ c
\end{array}
\begin{array}{ccc}
A & B & C \\
\left[\begin{array}{ccc}
(1,2) & (2,3) & (3,3) \\
(1,3) & (3,2) & (2,1) \\
(1,1) & (2,1) & (3,2)
\end{array}\right]
\end{array}
$$

b prefers C, and C prefers b, so this is unstable.

Example 9 has five unstable pairings and one stable one. It can be proved that every marriage has at least one stable pairing. In the problem set you are asked to consider the situation where the number of candidates is greater than the number of schools.

An excellent discussion of mathematics and the social sciences can be found in the following list of articles in the classic book, *World of Mathematics* (New York, Simon and Schuster, 1956):

"Gustav Theodor Fechner," a commentary on the founder of psychophysics, by Edwin G. Boring. Fechner's contribution was to introduce measurement as a tool.

"Mathematics of Population and Food," by Thomas Robert Malthus, explores the thesis that all animated life tends to increase beyond the nourishment prepared for it.

"A Mathematical Approach to Ethics," by George Birkhoff

 You will find other references to mathematics in the social sciences on the World wide at **www.mathnature.com**

Mathematics in the Humanities

By humanities we mean art, music, and literature. One of the major themes of this book has been the analysis of shapes and patterns, and shapes and patterns are the basis for a great deal of art and music.

There is an interdependence of mathematics and art (see Chapter 7). The shape that seems to be the most appealing to human intellect is the so-called golden rectangle, which was used in the design of the Parthenon in Athens and in *La Parade* by the French impressionist Georges Seurat.

Example 10   **Verify a golden ratio**

An unfinished canvas by Leonardo da Vinci entitled *St. Jerome* was painted about 1481. Find a golden rectangle that fits neatly around a prominent part of this painting. Measure the length and width of the rectangle and then find the ratio of the width to length.

Solution   A portion of the work of art is shown below (with a rectangle superimposed). The width and length of the rectangle will vary with the size of the reproduction, but the ratio of width to length is about 0.61.

© Scala/Art Resource, NY

St. Jerome by Leonardo da Vinci, 1481

© Scala/Art Resource, NY

A golden rectangle

In order to draw realistic-looking drawings, mathematical ideas from projective geometry are necessary. Early attempts at three-dimensional art failed miserably because they did not use projective geometry. We cite as examples Duccio's *Last Supper* (Figure 7.63, p. 376) or the Egyptian art shown in Figure 7.

© Historical Picture/Archive/CORBIS

FIGURE 7 *Judgment of the Dead-Pai on papyrusca.* 14th century B.C.

Projective geometry was an early mathematical attempt to represent three-dimensional objects on a canvas (see Dürer's *Recumbent Woman* on page 377). Finally, a plan for perspective was developed, as shown in Figure 8.

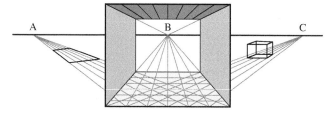

FIGURE 8 Perspective in Art

The rule of optical perspective begins with the horizon (line $\overleftrightarrow{AC}$). One point B on line $\overleftrightarrow{AC}$ is selected to be the vanishing point, and all other lines recede directly from the viewer and converge at the vanishing point. All other lines (except verticals and parallels to the horizon) have their own vanishing points, governed by their particular angle to the plane of the picture. The vanishing point for the rectangle in Figure 8 is point A, and for the cube at the right, it is point C.

Music is very mathematical, and the Greeks included music when studying arithmetic, geometry, and astronomy. Today, with a great deal of music created on a synthesizer, it is not uncommon for a computer programmer to be a musician and for a musician to be a computer programmer. The modern musical scale is divided into 13 tones, as shown in Figure 9.

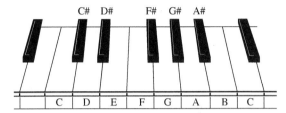

FIGURE 9 Piano keyboard showing one octave

The Greeks plucked strings and found what types of string vibrations made pleasing sounds. They found that the sound was pleasing if it was plucked at a location that was in the ratio of 1 to 2 (which we call an *octave*), 2 to 3 (*a fifth*), 3 to 4 (*a fourth*), and so on. You might notice that the piano keyboard is divided into 8 white keys (diatonic scale) and 5 black keys (pentatonic scale). These numbers 5 and 8 are two consecutive Fibonacci numbers. The middle C is tuned so the string vibrates 264 times per second, whereas the note A above middle C vibrates 440 times per second. Note that the ratio of 440 to 264 reduces to 5 to 3, two other Fibonacci numbers.

A mathematical concept known as the sine function (see Section 7.5) can be used to record the motion of the vibrations over time. These vibrations (known as sound) are shown in the following example.

Example 11 Graph tuning fork sound wave

A tuning fork vibrates at 264 Hz [frequency $f = 264$ and Hz is an abbreviation for Hertz meaning "cycles per unit of time," after the physicist Heinrich Hertz (1857–1894)]. This sound produces middle C on the musical scale and can be described by an equation of the form

$$y = 0.0050 \sin(528 \cdot 360x)$$

Use a graphing calculator to look at this curve.

Solution The graph is shown in Figure 10, along with the necessary input values. Technology does not do a good job of graphing an equation such as this, and you may

obtain many different looking graphs, depending on the window values.

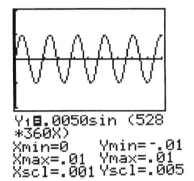

FIGURE 10 Graph of a musical note described by $y = 0.0050 \sin(528 \cdot 360x)$

A composition by Mozart is interesting not only for its music, but also because it illustrates the mathematical idea of an inversion transformation, introduced in Section 7.1. This unique piece for violin, reproduced in Figure 11, can be played simultaneously by two musicians facing each other and reading the music, laid flat between them, in opposite directions. The two parts, though different, will be in perfect harmony, without violating a single rule of classical composition. Another piece, Bach's *Art of the Fugue,* made use of mirror reflections in passages between the upper treble and lower bass figures.

FIGURE 11 Mozart composition

An excellent discussion of mathematics and the humanities can be found in the following list of articles from the classic book, *World of Mathematics* (New York, Simon and Schuster, 1956):

"Mathematics of Aesthetics," by George David Birkhoff

"Mathematics as an Art," by John William Navin Sullivan

"Mathematics and Music," by James Jeans

"Geometry in the South Pacific," by Sylvia Townsend Warner. The story is an example of mathematics in literature.

 You will find other references to mathematics in the humanities on the World Wide Web at **www.mathnature.com**

Mathematics in Business and Economics

The focus of Chapter 11 in the text forms the foundations for business and economics. A fundamental, and essential, idea in business and economics is the concept of **interest.** Interest is an amount paid for the use of someone else's money. It can be compounded once, or it can be compounded at regular intervals. Related to interest are annuities (future value of interest and deposits), sinking funds (monthly payment when the future value is known), present value of an annuity (the amount you can borrow, given the monthly payment), and amortization (the monthly payment when the present value is known). All of these concepts are essential ideas for understanding the processes of business, borrowing, and economics, and they are all important topics in mathematics.

An excellent discussion of mathematics in business and economics can be found in the following list of articles from the classic book, *World of Mathematics* (New York, Simon and Schuster, 1956):

"Mathematics of Value and Demand," by Augustin Cournot

"Theory of Political Economy," by William Stanley Jevons. This essay begins with the declaration, "It is clear that economics, if it is to be a science at all, must be a mathematical science. . . . Wherever the things treated are capable of being *greater or less*, there the laws and relations must be mathematical in nature."

"The Theory of Economic Behavior," by Leonid Hurwicz, introduces the important application of *theory of games and economic behavior.* Game theory is primarily concerned with the logic of strategy and was first envisioned by the great mathematician Gottfried Leibniz (1646–1716). However, the theory of games as we know it today was developed in the 1920s by John von Neumann and Emile Borel. It gained wide acceptance in 1944 in a book entitled *Theory of Games and Economic Behavior* by von Neumann and Oskar Morgenstern.

"Theory of Games," by S. Vajda provides further study in game theory.

Epilogue Problem Set

1. **IN YOUR OWN WORDS**   Describe some similarities between the scientific method and mathematical modeling.

2. **IN YOUR OWN WORDS**   Pick one of the areas that is of most interest to you: natural sciences, social sciences, humanities, or business and economics. Write a paper discussing at least one application of mathematics to this area that was not discussed in this epilogue.

3. Classify each of the disciplines as humanities, a natural science, or a social science.
   - **a.** psychology
   - **b.** physics
   - **c.** meteorology
   - **d.** music
   - **e.** history

4. Classify each of the disciplines as humanities, a natural science, or a social science.
   - **a.** chemistry
   - **b.** art
   - **c.** French
   - **d.** geology
   - **e.** computer programming

5. Classify each of the disciplines as humanities, a natural science, or a social science.
   - **a.** civics
   - **b.** medicine
   - **c.** anthropology
   - **d.** political science
   - **e.** biology
   - **f.** ecology

6. Classify each of the disciplines as humanities, a natural science, or a social science.
   - **a.** dance
   - **b.** theology
   - **c.** women's studies
   - **d.** social work
   - **e.** linguistics
   - **f.** conflict studies

7. Classify each of the disciplines as humanities, a natural science, or a social science.
   - **a.** plant pathology
   - **b.** geography
   - **c.** horticulture
   - **d.** food science
   - **e.** entomology
   - **f.** forestry

8. Classify each of the disciplines as humanities, a natural science, or a social science.
   - **a.** literature
   - **b.** Jewish studies
   - **c.** human nutrition
   - **d.** agriculture
   - **e.** gender studies
   - **f.** kinesiology

9. If a star is located at a distance of 858,000,000,000,000,000,000 miles, what is this distance in light-years?

10. If a star is located at a distance of 5.61 light-years, what is this distance in miles?

11. The eccentricities of the planets are given in the following table:

   Mercury, 0.21
   Venus, 0.01
   Earth, 0.02
   Mars, 0.09
   Jupiter, 0.04
   Saturn, 0.06
   Uranus, 0.05
   Neptune, 0.01
   Pluto, 0.24

   Which planet has the most circular orbit?

12. Each person has 23 pairs of chromosomes. If we inherit one of each pair from each parent, what is the number of possibilities?

13. An average chicken egg is 2 in. from top to bottom, and an ostrich egg is 6 in. from top to bottom. What is the scaling factor? If a chicken egg weighs 2 oz, what is the expected weight of an ostrich egg?

14. Eggs are graded for both quantity and size. Jumbo eggs must have a minimum weight of 56 lb per 30-doz case, and small eggs must have a minimum weight of 34 lb per 30-doz case. What is the scaling factor for the weight of one small egg compared to one jumbo egg?

15. Suppose a pea has two skin characteristics: S (smooth, dominant) and w (wrinkled, recessive). Suppose we have an isolated population in which 55% of the genes in the gene pool are dominant S and the other 45% are recessive w. What fraction of the population has each genotype?

16. Suppose a pea has two skin characteristics: S (smooth, dominant) and w (wrinkled, recessive). Suppose we have an isolated population in which 48% of the genes in the gene pool are dominant S and the other 52% are recessive w. What fraction of the population has each genotype?

17. The area of a cell magnified 2,000 times is about 20 cm². What is the area of the unmagnified cell?

18. **a.** If you change the angle in Example 1 to 45°, would you expect the cannonball to go farther or shorter than shown in the example?
    b. Use a calculator to sketch the path of a cannonball with initial velocity 63 ft/s at a 45° angle. Was your conjecture in part **a** correct?

19. What is the path of a cannonball fired at 64 ft/s at an angle of 60°?

20. Describe the meaning of the equation

$$\frac{x^2}{4.5837 \times 10^{15}} + \frac{y^2}{4.5835 \times 10^{15}} = 1$$

which models the path of Venus' orbit around the sun. The given distances are in miles.
    a. What is the eccentricity?
    b. Graph this equation.

21. Describe the meaning of the equation

$$\frac{x^2}{2.015 \times 10^{16}} + \frac{y^2}{1.995 \times 10^{16}} = 1$$

which models the path of Mars' orbit around the sun. The given distances are in miles.
    a. What is the eccentricity?
    b. Graph this equation.

22. Four professors, A, B, C, and D, are each going to hire a student. Six students have applied. How many possible marriages are there?

23. Each of four women is going to marry one of four men. How many possible marriages are there?

24. Four professors, A, B, C, and D, are each going to hire a student. Six students have applied. Here are the preferences:

$$\begin{array}{ll} A(a, f, b, c, d, e) & a(C, B, D, A) \\ B(a, b, f, e, d, c) & b(C, D, B, A) \\ C(b, a, e, c, d, f) & c(B, A, C, D) \\ D(a, b, e, f, c, d) & d(A, B, D, C) \\ & e(A, B, C, D) \\ & f(B, D, A, C) \end{array}$$

    a. Show the matrix of their choices.
    b. List one pairing and state whether it is stable or unstable.

25. Four women are going to marry four men. Here are their preferences:

$$\begin{array}{ll} a(A, D, B, C) & A(d, a, b, c) \\ b(D, A, C, B) & B(a, d, c, b) \\ c(D, A, B, C) & C(a, b, d, c) \\ d(D, B, A, C) & D(b, a, c, d) \end{array}$$

    a. Show the matrix of their choices.
    b. List one pairing and state whether it is stable or unstable.

26. An equation for middle C with frequency $f = 261.626$ and amplitude 8 is

$$y = 8 \sin(360fx)$$

Use a calculator to graph this note.

27. Graph the sound wave with equation

$$y = 8 \sin(360fx) + 4 \sin(720fx)$$

for $f = 261.626$.

28. Suppose there are three graduates, a, b, c, and three schools, A, B, C, with choices as follows:

$$\begin{array}{lll} a(CAB) & b(CAB) & c(CBA) \\ A(abc) & B(bac) & C(acb) \end{array}$$

    a. How many possible marriages are there?
    b. How many of these are stable?

29. Suppose there are three graduates, a, b, c, and three schools A, B, C, with choices as follows:

$$\begin{array}{lll} a(BCA) & b(CAB) & c(ABC) \\ A(abc) & B(bca) & C(cab) \end{array}$$

    a. How many possible marriages are there?
    b. How many of these are stable?

30. The moon's orbit is elliptical with the earth at one focus. The point at which the moon is farthest from the earth is called the *apogee,* and the point at which it is closest is called the *perigee.* If the moon is 199,000 miles from the earth at apogee and the length of the major axis of its orbit is 378,000 miles, what is the eccentricity of the moon's orbit?

Abelian group   A group that is also commutative.

Abscissa   The horizontal coordinate in a two-dimensional system of rectangular coordinates, usually denoted by x.

Absolute value   The absolute value of a number is the distance of that number from the origin. Symbolically,

$$|n| = \begin{cases} n & \text{if } n \geq 0 \\ -n & \text{if } n < 0 \end{cases}$$

Accuracy   One speaks of an *accurate statement* in the sense that it is true and correct, or of an *accurate computation* in the sense that it contains no numerical error. *Accurate to a certain decimal place* means that all digits preceding and including the given one are correct.

Acre   A unit commonly used in the United States system for measuring land. It contains $43{,}560 \text{ ft}^2$.

Acute angle   An angle whose measure is smaller than a right angle.

Acute triangle   A triangle with three acute angles.

Adams' apportionment plan   An apportionment plan in which the representation of a geographical area is determined by finding the quotient of the number of people in that area divided by the total number of people and then rounding the result as follows: Any quotient with a decimal portion must be rounded up to the next whole number.

Addition   One of the fundamental undefined operations applied to the set of counting numbers.

Addition law of exponents   To multiply two numbers with like bases, add the exponents; that is,

$$b^m \cdot b^n = b^{m+n}$$

Addition law of logarithms   The log of the product of two numbers is the sum of the logs of those numbers. In symbols,

$$\log_b (AB) = \log_b A + \log_b B$$

Addition method   The method of solution of a system of equations in which the coefficients of one of the variables are opposites so that when the equations are added, one of the variables is eliminated.

Addition of integers   If the integers to be added have the same sign, the answer will also have that same sign and will have a magnitude equal to the sum of the absolute values of the given integers. If the integers to be added have opposite signs, the answer will have the sign of the integer with the larger absolute value, and will have a magnitude equal to the difference of the absolute values. Finally, if one or both of the given integers is 0, use the property that $n + 0 = n$ for any integer n.

Addition of matrices $[M] + [N] = [S]$ if and only if $[M]$ and $[N]$ are the same order and the entries of $[S]$ are found by adding the corresponding entries of $[M]$ and $[N]$.

Addition of rational numbers

$$\frac{a}{b} + \frac{c}{d} = \frac{ad}{bd} + \frac{bc}{bd} = \frac{ad + bc}{bd}$$

Addition principle   A method of representing numbers by repeating a symbol in a numeration system and repeatedly adding the symbol's value. For example, ∩∩∩|||| means $10 + 10 + 10 + 1 + 1 + 1 + 1$.

Addition property (of equations)   The solution of an equation is unchanged by adding the same number to both sides of the equation.

Addition property of inequality   The solution of an inequality is unchanged if you add the same number to both sides of the inequality.

Addition property of probabilities   For any events E and F, the probability of their union can be found by

$$\begin{aligned} P(E \cup F) &= P(E \text{ or } F) \\ &= P(E) + P(F) - P(E \cap F) \end{aligned}$$

Additive identity   The number 0, which has the property that $a + 0 = a$ for any number a.

Additive inverse   See *Opposites*. The additive inverse of a matrix $[M]$ is denoted by $[-M]$ and is defined by $(-1)[M]$.

Add-on interest   A method of calculating interest and installments on a loan. The amount of interest is calculated according to the formula $I = Prt$ and is then added to the amount of the loan. This sum, divided by the number of payments, is the amount of monthly payment.

Address   Designation of the location of data within internal memory or on a magnetic disk or tape.

Adjacent angles   Two angles are adjacent if they share a common side.

Adjacent side   In a right triangle, an acute angle is made up of two sides; one of those sides is the hypotenuse, and the other side is called the adjacent side.

Adjusted balance method   A method of calculating credit card interest using the formula $I = Prt$ in which P is the balance owed after the current payment is subtracted.

Alabama paradox   An increase in the total numbers of items to be apportioned resulting in a loss for a group is called the Alabama paradox.

Algebra   A generalization of arithmetic. Letters called variables are used to denote numbers, which are related by laws that hold (or are assumed) for any of the numbers in the set. The four main processes of algebra are (1) simplify, (2) evaluate, (3) factor, and (4) solve.

Algebraic expression   Any meaningful combination of numbers, variables, and signs of operation.

Alternate exterior angles   Two *alternate angles* are angles on opposite sides of a transversal cutting two parallel lines, each having one of the lines for one of its sides. They are *alternate exterior angles* if neither lies between the two lines cut by the transversal.

Alternate interior angles   Two *alternate angles* are angles on opposite sides of a transversal cutting two parallel lines, each having one of the lines for one of its sides. They are *alternate interior angles* if both lie between the two lines cut by the transversal.

Alternating series   A series that alternates in sign.

Amortization   The process of paying off a debt by systematically making partial payments until the debt (principal) and interest are repaid.

Amortization schedule   A table showing the schedule of payments of a loan detailing the amount of each payment that goes to repay the principal and how much goes to pay interest.

Amortized loan   A loan that is fully paid off with the last periodic payment.

Analytic geometry   The geometry in which position is represented analytically (or by coordinates) and algebraic methods of reasoning are used for the most part.

And   See *Conjunction*. In everyday usage, it is used to join together elements that are connected in two sets simultaneously.

AND-gate   An electrical circuit that simulates conjunction; that is, the circuit is on when two switches are on.

Angle   Two rays or segments with a common endpoint.

Angle of depression   The angle between the line of sight to an object below measured from a horizontal.

Angle of elevation   The angle between the line of sight to an object above measured from a horizontal.

Annual compounding   In the compound interest formula, it is when $n = 1$.

Annual percentage rate   The percentage rate charged on a loan based on the actual amount owed and the actual time it is owed. The approximation formula for annual percentage rate (APR) is

$$APR = \frac{2Nr}{N + 1}$$

Annuity   A sequence of payments into or out of an interest-bearing account. If the payments are made into an interest-bearing account at the end of each time period, and if the frequency of payments is the same as the frequency of compounding, the annuity is called an *ordinary annuity*.

Antecedent   See *Conditional*.

Antiderivative   If the derivative of a function defined by $y = F(x)$ is $f(x)$, then the *antiderivative* of $f(x)$ is

$$\int f(x)\,dx = F(x)$$

This means that $F'(x) = f(x)$.

Apportionment   process of dividing the representation in a legislative body according to some plan.

Approval voting   The approval voting method allows each voter to cast one vote for each candidate who meets with his or her approval. The candidate with the most votes is declared winner.

APR   Abbreviation for annual percentage rate. See *Annual percentage rate*.

Arc   (1) Part of the circumference of a circle. (2) In networks, it is a connection between two vertices.

Area   A number describing the two-dimensional content of a set. Specifically, it is the number of square units enclosed in a plane figure.

Area formulas   Square, s^2; rectangle, ℓw; parallelogram, bh; triangle, $\frac{1}{2}bh$; circle, πr^2; trapezoid, $\frac{1}{2}h(b_1 + b_2)$.

Area function   The function that is the area bounded below by the x-axis, above by a function $y = f(x)$, on the left by the y-axis, and on the right by the vertical line $x = t$.

Area under a curve   The area of the region bounded by the graph of a function f, the x-axis, and the vertical lines $x = a$ and $x = b$ is given by

$$A = \int_a^b f(x)\,dx$$

Argument   (1) The statements and conclusion as a form of logical reasoning. (2) In a logarithmic expression $\log_b N$, it is the number N.

Arithmetic mean   The arithmetic mean of the numbers a and b is $\dfrac{a + b}{2}$.

Arithmetic sequence   A sequence, each term of which is equal to the sum of the preceding term and a constant, written $a_1, a_2 = a_1 + d, a_3 = a_1 + 2d, \ldots$; the nth term of an arithmetic sequence is

$$a_1 + (n - 1)d$$

where a_1 is the first term and d is the *common difference*. Also called an *arithmetic progression*. See also *Sequence*.

Arithmetic series   The indicated sum of the terms of an arithmetic sequence. The sum of n terms is denoted by A_n and

$$A_n = \tfrac{n}{2}(a_1 + a_n) \text{ or } A_n = \tfrac{n}{2}[2a_1 + (n - 1)d]$$

Arrangement   Same as *Permutation*.

Array   An arrangement of items into rows and columns. See *Matrix*.

Arrow's impossibility theorem   No social choice rule satisfies all six of the following conditions.

1. **Unrestricted domain**   Any set of rankings is possible; if there are n candidates, then there are $n!$ possible rankings.
2. **Decisiveness**   Given any set of individual rankings, the method produces a winner.
3. **Symmetry and transitivity**   The voting system should be symmetric and transitive over the set of all outcomes.
4. **Independence of irrelevant alternatives**   If a voter prefers A to B with C as a possible choice, then the voter still prefers A to B when C is not a possible choice.
5. **Pareto principle**   If each voter prefers A over B, then the group chooses A over B.
6. There should be **no dictator**.

Artificial intelligence   A field of study devoted to computer simulation of human intelligence.

ASCII code   A standard computer code used to facilitate the interchange of information among various types of computer equipment.

Assignment   A computer term for setting the value of one variable to match the value of another.

Associative property   A property of grouping that applies to certain operations (addition and multiplication, for example, but not to subtraction or division): If a, b, and c are real numbers, then

$$(a + b) + c = a + (b + c)$$

and

$$(ab)c = a(bc)$$

Assuming the antecedent   Same as *direct reasoning*.

Assuming the consequent   A logical fallacy; same as the *fallacy of the converse*.

Augmented matrix   A matrix that results after affixing an additional column to an existing matrix.

Average   A single number that is used to typify or represent a set of numbers. In this book, it refers to the *mean, median*, or *mode*.

Average daily balance method   A method of calculating credit card interest using the formula $I = Prt$ in which P is the average daily balance owed for a current month, and t is the number of days in the month divided by 365.

Average rate of change   The average rate of change of a function f from x to $x + h$ is

$$\frac{f(x + h) - f(x)}{h}$$

Axes   The intersecting lines of a Cartesian coordinate system. The horizontal axis is called the x-axis, and the vertical axis is called the y-axis. The axes divide the plane into four parts called *quadrants*.

Axiom   A statement that is accepted without proof.

Axis of a parabola   The line through the focus of a parabola drawn perpendicular to the directrix.

Axis of symmetry   A curve is symmetric with respect to a line, called the axis of symmetry, if for any point P on the curve, there is a point Q also on the curve such that the axis of symmetry is the perpendicular bisector of the line segment $\overline{PQ}$.

Balinski and Young's impossibility theorem   Any apportionment plan that does not violate the quota rule must produce paradoxes. And any apportionment method that does not produce paradoxes must violate the quota rule.

Balloon payment   A single larger payment made at the end of the time period of an installment loan that is not amortized.

Bar graph   See *Graph*.

Base   (1) *See Exponent*. (2) In a percent problem, it is the whole quantity.

Base angles   In an isosceles triangle, the angles formed by the base with each of the equal sides.

Base b numeration system   A numeration system with b elements.

Base of an exponential   In $y = b^x$, the *base* is $b (b \neq 1)$.

Base of a triangle   In an isosceles triangle, the side that is not the same length as the sides whose lengths are the same.

Because   A logical operator for p because q, which is defined to mean

$$(p \wedge q) \wedge (q \to p).$$

Bell-shaped curve   See *Normal curve*.

Belong to a set   To be an element of a set.

Bernoulli trial   A Bernoulli trial is an experiment with two possible, mutually exclusive outcomes (usually called success and failure).

Biconditional   A logical operator for simple statements p and q which is true when p and q have the same truth values, and is false when p and q have different truth values.

Billion   A name for $10^9 = 1,000,000,000$.

Bimodal   A distribution with two modes.

Binary numeration system   A numeration system with two numerals, 0 and 1.

Binary voting   Selecting a winner by pairing two competitors and then pairing up the winners to select the final victor.

Binomial   A polynomial with exactly two terms.

Binomial distribution theorem   Let X be a random variable for the number of successes in n independent and identical repetitions of an experiment with two possible outcomes, success and failure. If p is the probability of success, then

$$P(X = k) = \binom{n}{k} p^k (1 - p)^{n-k}$$

where $k = 0, 1, \ldots, n$.

Binomial experiment   A *binomial experiment* is an experiment that meets four conditions:
1. There must be a fixed number of trials. Denote this number by n.
2. There must be two possible mutually exclusive outcomes for each trial. Call them *success* and *failure*.
3. Each trial must be independent. That is, the outcome of a particular trial is not affected by the outcome of any other trial.
4. The probability of success and failure must remain constant for each trial.

Binomial random variable   A random variable that counts the number of successes in a binomial experiment.

Binomial theorem   For any positive integer n,

$$(a + b)^n = \sum_{k=0}^{n} \binom{n}{k} a^{n-k} b^k$$

Birthday problem   The probability that two unrelated people will have their birthdays on the same day (not counting the year of birth).

Bisect   To divide into two equal or congruent parts.

Bit   Binary digit, the smallest unit of data storage with a value of either 0 or 1, thereby representing whether a circuit is open or closed.

Bond   An interest-bearing certificate issued by a government or business, promising to pay the holder a specified amount (usually $1,000) on a certain date.

Boot   To start a computer. To do this the computer must have access to an operating system on a CD or hard disk.

Borda count   A common way of determining a winner when there is no majority is to assign a point value to each voter's ranking. If there are n candidates, then n points are assigned to the first choice for each voter, with $n - 1$ points for the next choice, and so on. The points for each candidate are added and if one has more votes, that candidate is declared the winner.

Boundary   See *Half-plane*.

Box plot   A rectangular box positioned above a numerical scale associated with a given set of data. It shows the maximum value, the minimum value, and the quartiles for the data.

Braces   See *Grouping symbols.*

Brackets   See *Grouping symbols.*

Bug   An error in the design or makeup of a computer program (software bug) or a hardware component of the system (hardware bug).

Bulletin boards   An online means of communicating with others on a particular topic.

Byte   The fundamental block of data that can be processed by a computer. In most microcomputers, a byte is a group of eight adjacent bits and the rough equivalent of one alphanumeric symbol.

Calculus   The field of mathematics that deals with differentiation and integration of functions, and related concepts and applications.

Canceling   The process of reducing a fraction by dividing the same number into both the numerator and the denominator.

Canonical form   When a given number is written as a product of prime factors in ascending order, it is said to be in canonical form.

Capacity   A measurement for the amount of liquid a container holds.

Cardinal number   A number that designates the manyness of a set; the number of units, but not the order in which they are arranged.

Cardinality   The number of elements in a set.

Cards   A deck of 52 matching objects that are identical on one side and on the other side are divided into four suits (hearts, diamonds, spades, and clubs). The objects, called cards, are labeled A, 2, . . . , 9, 10, J, Q, and K in each suit.

Cartesian coordinate system   Two intersecting lines, called *axes*, used to locate points in a plane called a *Cartesian plane.* If the intersecting lines are perpendicular, the system is called a *rectangular coordinate system.*

Cartesian plane   See *Cartesian coordinate system.*

CD-ROM   A form of mass storage. It is a cheap read-only device, which means that you can only use the data stored on it when it was created, but it can store a massive amount of material, such as an entire encyclopedia.

Cell   A specific location on a spreadsheet. It is designated using a letter (column heading) followed by a numeral (row heading). A cell can contain a letter, word, sentence, number, or formula.

Celsius   A metric measurement for temperature for which the freezing point of water is 0° and the boiling point of water is 100°.

Center of a circle   See *Circle.*

Center of an ellipse   The midpoint of the line segment connecting the foci of the ellipse.

Center of a hyperbola   The midpoint of the line segment connecting the foci of the hyperbola.

Centi-   A prefix that means 1/100.

Centigram   One hundredth of a gram.

Centiliter   One hundredth of a liter.

Centimeter   One hundredth of a meter.

Change of base theorem

$$\log_a x = \frac{\log_b x}{\log_b a}$$

Ciphertext   A secret or coded message.

Circle   The set of points in a plane that are a given distance from a given point. The given point is called the *center,* and the given distance is called the *radius.* The diameter is twice the radius. The *unit circle* is the circle with center at (0, 0) and $r = 1$.

Circle graph   See *Graph.*

Circuit   A complete path of electrical current including a power source and a switch. It may include an indicator light to show when the circuit is complete.

Circular definition   A definition that relies on the use of the word being defined, or other words that rely on the word being defined.

Circumference   The distance around a circle. The formula for finding the circumference is $C = \pi D$ or $C = 2\pi r$.

Classes   One of the groupings when organizing data. The difference between the lower limit of one class and the lower limit of the next class is called the *interval* of the class. The number of values within a class is called the *frequency.*

Closed   See *Closure property.*

Closed curve   A curve that has no endpoints.

Closed-ended loan   An installment loan.

Closed half-plane   See *Half-plane.*

Closed network   A network that connects each point.

Closed set   A set that satisfies the closure property for some operation.

Closing   The process of settlement on a real estate loan.

Closing costs   Costs paid at the closing of a real estate loan.

Closure property   A set S is *closed* for an operation $\circ$ if $a \circ b$ is an element of S for all elements a and b in S. This property is called the *closure property.*

Coefficient   Any factor of a term is said to be the coefficient of the remaining factors. The *numerical coefficient* is the numerical part of the term, usually written before the variable part. In $3x$, it is the number 3, in $9x^2y^3$ it is the number 9. Generally, the word *coefficient* is taken to be the numerical coefficient of the variable factors.

Column   A vertical arrangement of numbers or entries of a matrix. It is denoted by letters $A, B, C, \ldots$ on a spreadsheet.

Combination   A selection of objects from a given set without regard to the order in which they are selected. Sometimes it refers to the number of ways this selection can be done and is denoted by $_nC_r$ or $\binom{n}{r}$ and is pronounced "n choose r." The formula for finding it is

$$\binom{n}{r} = \frac{n!}{r!(n-r)!}$$

Common denominator   For two or more fractions, a common multiple of the denominators.

Common difference   The difference between successive terms of an arithmetic sequence.

Common factor   A factor that two or more terms of a polynomial have in common.

Common fraction   Fractions written in the form of one integer divided by a whole number are common fractions. For example, 1/10 is common fraction representation and 0.1 is the decimal representation of the same number.

Common logarithm   A logarithm to the base 10; written log N.

Common ratio   The ratio between successive terms of a geometric sequence.

Communication matrix   A square matrix in which the entries symbolize the occurrence of some facet or event with a 1 and the nonoccurrence with a 0.

Communications package   A program that allows one computer to communicate with another computer.

Commutative group   A group that also satisfies the property that

$$a \circ b = b \circ a$$

for some operation $\circ$ and elements a and b in the set.

Commutative property   A property of order that applies to certain operations (addition and multiplication, for example, but not to subtraction and division). If a and b are real numbers, then

$$a + b = b + a$$

and

$$ab = ba$$

Comparison property   For any two numbers x and y, exactly one of the following is true: (1) $x = y$; x is equal to y (the same as) (2) $x > y$; x is greater than y (bigger than) (3) $x < y$; x is less than y (smaller than). This is sometimes known as the *trichotomy property*.

Comparison rate for home loans   A formula for comparing terms of a home loan. The formula is

$$\text{APR} + 0.125\left(\text{POINTS} + \tfrac{\text{ORIGINATION FEE}}{\text{AMOUNT OF LOAN}}\right)$$

Compass   An instrument for scribing circles or for measuring distances between two points.

Compiler   An operating system program that converts an entire program written in a higher-level language into machine language before the program is executed.

Complement   (1) Two numbers less than 1 are called complements if their sum is 1. (2) The complement of a set is everything not in the set relative to a given universe.

Complementary angles   Two angles are complementary if the sum of their measures is 90°.

Complementary probabilities

$$P(E) = 1 - P(\overline{E})$$

that is, two probabilities are *complementary* if

$$P(E) + P(\overline{E}) = 1$$

Completely factored   An expression is completely factored if it is a product and there are no common factors and no difference of squares—that is, if no further factoring is possible.

Complex decimal   A form that mixes decimal and fractional form, such as $0.12\tfrac{1}{2}$.

Complex fraction   A rational expression a/b where a or b (or both) have fractional form.

Components   See *Ordered pair*.

Composite number   Sometimes simply referred to as a *composite*; it is a positive integer that has more than two divisors.

Compound interest   A method of calculating interest by adding the interest to the principal at the end of the compounding period so that this sum is used in the interest calculation for the next period.

Compound interest formula

$$A = P(1 + i)^N$$

where A = future value; P = present value (or principal); r = annual interest rate (APR); t = number of years; n = number of times compounded per year; $i = \tfrac{r}{n}$; and $N = nt$.

Compound statement   A statement formed by combining simple statements with one or more operators.

Compounding   The process of adding interest to the principal so that in the next time period the interest is calculated on this sum.

Computer   A device which, under the direction of a program, can process data, alter its own program instructions, and perform computations and logical operations without human intervention.

Computer abuse   A misuse of a computer.

Computer program   A set of step-by-step directions that instruct a computer how to carry out a certain task.

Conclusion   The statement that follows (or is to be proved to follow) as a consequence of the hypothesis of the theorem. Also called a *logical conclusion*.

Conditional   The statement "if p, then q," symbolized by $p \rightarrow q$. The statement p is called the *antecedent* and q is called the *consequent*.

Conditional equation   See *Equation*.

Conditional inequality   See *Inequality*.

Conditional probability   A probability that is found on the condition that a certain event has occurred. The notation $P(E \mid F)$ is the probability of event E *on the condition* that event F has occurred.

Condorcet candidate   A candidate who wins all the one-to-one matchups.

Condorcet criterion   If a candidate is favored when compared one on one with every other candidate, then that candidate should be declared the winner.

Condorcet's paradox   There are three citizens, A, B, and C, and each citizen ranks three different policies as shown:

$$
\begin{aligned}
A&: x > y > z \\
B&: y > z > x \\
C&: z > x > y
\end{aligned}
$$

Then two citizens prefer x to y, two prefer y to z, and two prefer z to x, which is not transitive. Each voter is consistent, but the social choice is inconsistent. This is known as Condorcet's paradox.

Cone   A solid with a circle for its base and a curved surface tapering evenly to an apex so that any point on this surface is in a straight line between the circumference of the base and the apex.

Congruent   Of the same size and shape; if one is placed on top of the other, the two figures will coincide exactly in all their parts.

Congruent angles   Two angles that have the same measure.

Congruent modulo m   Two real numbers a and b are congruent modulo m, written $a \equiv b \pmod{m}$, if a and b differ by a multiple of m.

Congruent triangles   Two triangles that have the same size and shape.

Conic sections   The set of points that results from the intersection of a cone and a plane is a two-dimensional curve known as a conic section. The conic sections include the parabola, ellipse (special case, circle), and hyperbola.

Conjecture   A guess or prediction based on incomplete or uncertain evidence.

Conjugate axis   The line passing through the center perpendicular to the transverse axis of a hyperbola.

Conjunction   The conjunction of two simple statements p and q is true whenever both p and q are true, and is false otherwise. The common translation of conjunction is "and."

Connected network   A network that connects each point.

Connective   A rule that operates on one or two simple statements. Some examples of connectives are *and, or, not,* and *unless.*

Consecutive integers   Integers that differ by 1.

Consequent   See *Conditional.*

Consistent system   If a system of equations has at least one solution, it is consistent; otherwise it is said to be *inconsistent.*

Constant   Symbol with exactly one possible value.

Constant function   A function of the form $f(x) = c$.

Constant multiple   The following property of integrals:

$$\int af(x)dx = a\int f(x)dx$$

Constraint   A limitation placed on an objective function. See *Linear programming.*

Construct   The process of drawing a figure that will satisfy certain given conditions.

Contained in a set   An element is contained in a set if it is a member of the set.

Continuous compounding   If we let the number of compounding periods in a year increase without limit, the result is called continuous compounding. The formula is

$$A = Pe^{rt}$$

for a present value of P, future value A at a rate of r for t years.

Continuous distribution   A probability distribution that includes all x-values (as opposed to a discrete distribution, which allows a finite number of x-values).

Contradiction   An open equation for which the solution set is empty.

Contrapositive   For the implication $p \rightarrow q$, the contrapositive is $\sim q \rightarrow \sim p$.

Converge   To draw near to. A series is said to converge when the sum of the first n terms approaches a limit as n increases without bound. We say that the sequence converges to a limit L if the values of the successive terms of the sequence get closer and closer to the number L as $n \rightarrow \infty$.

Converse   For the implication $p \rightarrow q$, the converse is $q \rightarrow p$.

Convex set   A set that contains the line segment joining any two of its points.

Coordinate plane   See *Cartesian coordinate system.*

Coordinates   A numerical description for a point. Also see *Ordered pair.*

Correlation   The interdependence between two sets of numbers. It is a relationship between two quantities, such that when one changes the other does (simultaneous increasing or decreasing is called *positive correlation;* and one increasing, the other decreasing, *negative correlation*).

Corresponding angles   Angles in different triangles that are similarly related to the rest of the triangle.

Corresponding parts   Points, angles, lines, etc., in different figures, similarly related to the rest of the figures.

Corresponding sides   Sides of different triangles that are similarly related to the rest of the triangle.

Cosine   In a right triangle ABC with right angle C,

$$\cos A = \frac{\text{LENGTH OF ADJACENT SIDE OF } A}{\text{LENGTH OF HYPOTENUSE}}$$

Countable set   A set with cardinality $\aleph_0$. That is, a set that can be placed into a one-to-one correspondence with the set of counting numbers.

Count-down property $n! = n(n - 1)!$

Counterclockwise   In the direction of rotation opposite to that in which the hands move around the dial of a clock.

Counterexample   An example that is used to disprove a proposition.

Counting numbers   See *Natural numbers.*

CPU   Central Processing Unit, the primary section of the computer that contains the memory, logic, and arithmetic procedures necessary to process data and perform computations. The CPU also controls the functions performed by the input, output, and memory devices.

Credit card   A card signifying that the person or business issued the card has been approved for open-ended credit. It can be used at certain restaurants, airlines, and stores accepting that card.

Cryptography   The writing or deciphering of messages in code.

Cube   (1) A solid with six equal square sides. (2) In an expression such as x^3, which is pronounced "x cubed," it means xxx.

Cube root   See *Root of a number.*

Cubed   See *Cube.*

Cubic unit   A three-dimensional unit. It is the result of cubing a unit of measurement.

Cumulative frequency   A frequency that is the total number of cases having any given score or a score that is lower.

Cup   A unit of measurement in the United States measurement system that is equivalent to 8 fluid ounces.

Cursor   Indicator (often flashing) on a computer or calculator display to designate where the next character input will be placed.

Cylinder   Suppose we are given two parallel planes and two simple closed curves C_1 and C_2 in these planes for which lines joining corresponding points of C_1 and C_2 are parallel to a given line L. A cylinder is a closed surface consisting of two bases that are plane regions bounded by such curves C_1 and C_2 and a lateral surface that is the union of all line segments joining corresponding points of C_1 and C_2.

Daily compounding   In the compound interest formula, it is when $n = 365$ (exact interest) or when $n = 360$ (ordinary interest). In this book, use ordinary interest unless otherwise indicated.

Data processing   The recording and handling of information by means of mechanical or electronic equipment.

Database   A collection of information. A data-base manager is a program that is in charge of the information stored in a database.

Database manager   A computer program that allows a user to interface with a database.

Dealer's cost   The actual amount that a dealer pays for the goods sold.

Debug   The organized process of testing for, locating, and correcting errors within a program.

Decagon   A polygon having ten sides.

Decay formula Refers to exponential decay. It is described by the equation

$$A = A_0 e^{rt}$$

where r is the annual decay rate (and consequently is negative), t is the time (in years), A_0 is the amount present initially (present value), and A is the future value. If r is positive, this formula models growth, and if r is negative, the formula models decay.

Deci- A prefix that means 1/10.

Decibel A unit of measurement for measuring sounds. It is defined as a ratio of the intensity of one sound, I, and another sound $I_0 \approx 10^{-16}$ watt/cm^2, the intensity of a barely audible sound for a person with normal hearing.

Deciles Nine values that divide a data set into ten equal parts.

Decimal Any number written in decimal notation. The digits represent powers of ten with whole numbers and fractions being separated by a period, called a *decimal point*. Sometimes called a Hindu-Arabic numeral.

Decimal fraction A number in decimal notation that has fractional parts, such as 23.25. If a common fraction p/q is written as a decimal fraction, the result will be either a *terminating decimal* as with $\frac{1}{4} = 0.25$ or a *repeating decimal* as with $\frac{2}{3} = 0.6666\ldots$.

Decimal notation The representation of a number using the decimal number system. See *Decimal*.

Decimal numeration system A numeration system with base 10.

Decimal point See *Decimal*.

Decisiveness Given any set of individual rankings, the method produces a winner when voting.

Decoding key A key that allows one to unscramble a coded message.

Deductive reasoning A formal structure based on a set of axioms and a set of undefined terms. New terms are defined in terms of the given undefined terms and new statements, or *theorems*, are derived from the axioms by proof.

Definite integral Let f be a function defined over the interval $[a, b]$. Then the definite integral of f over the interval is denoted by

$$\int_a^b f(x)dx$$

and is the net change of an antiderivative of f over that interval. Thus, if $F(x)$ is an antiderivative of $f(x)$, then

$$\int_a^b f(x)dx = F(x)\big|_a^b = F(b) - F(a)$$

Degree (1) The degree of a term in one variable is the exponent of the variable, or it is the sum of the exponents of the variables if there are more than one. The degree of a polynomial is the degree of its highest-degree term. (2) A unit of measurement of an angle that is equal to 1/360 of a revolution.

Deka- A prefix that means 10.

Deleted point A single point that is excluded from the domain.

De Morgan's laws For sets X and Y,

$$\overline{X \cup Y} = \overline{X} \cap \overline{Y}$$

and

$$\overline{X \cap Y} = \overline{X} \cup \overline{Y}$$

Demand The number of items that can be sold at a given price.

Denominator See *Rational number*.

Dense set A set of numbers with the property that between any two points of the set, there exists another point in the set that is between the two given points.

Denying the antecedent A logical fallacy; same as the *fallacy of the inverse*.

Denying the consequent Same as *indirect reasoning*.

Dependent events Two events are dependent if the occurrence of one influences the probability of the occurrence of the other.

Dependent system If *every* ordered pair satisfying one equation in a system of equations also satisfies every other equation of the given system, then we describe the system as dependent.

Dependent variable The variable associated with the second component of an ordered pair.

Derivative One of the fundamental operations of calculus; it is the instantaneous rate of change of a function with respect to the variable. Formally, for a given function f, we define the derivative of f at x, denoted by $f'(x)$, to be

$$f'(x) = \lim_{h \to 0} \frac{f(x + h) - f(x)}{h}$$

provided this limit exists. If the limit exists, we say f is a differentiable function of x.

Description method A method of defining a set by describing the set (as opposed to listing its elements).

Descriptive statistics Statistics that is concerned with the accumulation of data, measures of central tendency, and dispersion.

Diagonal form A matrix with the terms arranged on a diagonal, from upper left to lower right, and zeros elsewhere.

Diameter See *Circle*.

Dice Plural for the word *die*, which is a small, marked cube used in games of chance.

Dictatorship A selection process where one person alone makes a decision.

Die See *Dice*.

Difference The result of a subtraction.

Difference quotient If f is a function, then the *difference quotient* is defined to be the function

$$\frac{f(x + h) - f(x)}{h}$$

Difference of squares A mathematical expression in the form $a^2 - b^2$.

Differentiable function See *Derivative*.

Differential calculus That branch of calculus that deals with the derivative and applications of the derivative.

Dimension (1) A configuration having length only is said to be of one dimension; area and not volume, two dimensions; volume, three dimensions. (2) In reference to matrices, dimension is the numbers of rows and columns.

Direct reasoning One of the principal forms of logical reasoning. It is an argument of the form

$$[(p \to q) \wedge p] \to q$$

Directrix See *Parabola*.

Discount A reduction from a usual or list price.

Discrete mathematics That part of mathematics that deals with sets of objects that can be counted or processes that consist of a sequence of individual steps.

Disjoint sets   Sets that have no elements in common.

Disjunction   The disjunction of two simple statements p and q is false whenever both p and q are false, and is true otherwise. The common translation of disjunction is "or."

Disk drive   A mechanical device that uses the rotating surface of a magnetic disk for the high-speed transfer and storage of data.

Distinguishable permutation   The number of distinguishable permutations of n objects in which n_1 are of one kind, n_2 are of another kind, $\ldots$, and n_k are of a further kind, so that $n = n_1 + n_2 + \cdots + n_k$ is denoted by $\begin{pmatrix} n \\ n_1, n_2, \ldots, n_k \end{pmatrix}$ and is defined by

$$\begin{pmatrix} n \\ n_1, n_2, \ldots, n_k \end{pmatrix} = \frac{n!}{n_1!\, n_2! \cdots\, n_k!}$$

Distributive law of exponents

$$(1)\ (ab)^m = a^m b^m; \qquad (2)\ \left(\frac{a}{b}\right)^m = \frac{a^m}{b^m}$$

Distributive property (for multiplication over addition)   If a, b, and c are real numbers, then $a(b + c) = ab + ac$ and $(a + b)c = ac + bc$ for the basic operations. That is, the number outside the parentheses indicating a sum or difference is distributed to each of the numbers inside the parentheses.

Diverge   A sequence that does not converge is said to diverge.

Dividend   The number or quantity to be divided. In a/b, the dividend is a.

Divides   See *Divisibility*.

Divine proportion   If two lengths h and w satisfy the proportion

$$\frac{h}{w} = \frac{w}{h + w}$$

then the lengths are said to be in a *divine proportion*.

Divisibility   If m and d are counting numbers, and if there is a counting number k so that $m = d \cdot k$, we say that d is a divisor of m, d is a factor of m, d divides m, and m is a multiple of d.

Division $\frac{a}{b} = x$ *is* $a \div b = x$ and means $a = bx$.

Division by zero   In the definition of division, $b \neq 0$, because if $b = 0$, then $bx = 0$, regardless of the value of x. If $a \neq 0$, then there is no such number. On the other hand, if $a = 0$, then $0/0 = 1$ checks from the definition, and so also does $0/0 = 2$, which means that $1 = 2$, another contradiction. Thus, division by 0 is excluded.

Division of integers   The quotient of two integers is the quotient of the absolute values, and is positive if the given integers have the same sign, and negative if the given numbers have opposite signs. Furthermore, division by zero is not possible and division into 0 gives the answer 0.

Division of rational numbers

$$\frac{a}{b} \div \frac{c}{d} = \frac{ad}{bc} \quad (c \neq 0)$$

Division property (of equations)   The solution of an equation is unchanged by dividing both sides of the equation by the same nonzero number.

Division property of inequality   See *Multiplication property of inequality*.

Divisor   The quantity by which the dividend is to be divided. In a/b, b is the divisor.

Dodecagon   A polygon with 12 sides.

Domain   The *domain* of a variable is the set of replacements for the variable. The *domain* of a graph of an equation with two variables x and y is the set of permissible real-number replacements *for x*.

Double negative $-(-a) = a$

Double subscripts   Two subscripts on a variable as in a_{12}. (Do not read this as "twelve.")

Down payment   An amount paid at the time a product is financed. The purchase price minus the down payment is equal to the amount financed.

Download   The process of copying a program form the network to your computer.

Dummy variable   A variable in a mathematical expression whose only function is as a placeholder.

e   Euler's number, defined by

$$e = \lim_{n \to \infty} \left(1 + \frac{1}{n}\right)^n$$

Eccentricity   For a conic section, it is defined as the ratio

$$\epsilon = \frac{c}{a}$$

For the ellipse, $0 \leq \epsilon < 1$, where ϵ measures the amount of roundness. If $\epsilon = 0$, then the conic is a circle. For the parabola, $\epsilon = 1$; and for the hyperbola, $\epsilon > 1$.

Edge   A line or a line segment that is the intersection of two plane faces of a geometric figure, or that is in the boundary of a plane figure.

Either . . . or   A logical operator for "either p or q," which is defined to mean

$$(p \vee q) \wedge \sim(q \wedge p)$$

Element   One of the individual objects that belong to a set.

Elementary operations   Refers to the operations of addition, subtraction, multiplication, and division.

Elementary row operations   There are four elementary row operations for producing equivalent matrices: (1) *RowSwap:* Interchange any two rows. (2) *Row+:* Row addition—add a row to any other row. (3) **Row:* Scalar multiplication—multiply (or divide) all the elements of a row by the same nonzero real number. (4) **Row+:* Multiply all the entries of a row (*pivot row*) by a nonzero real number and add each resulting product to the corresponding entry of another specified row (*target row*).

Ellipse   The set of all points in a plane such that, for each point on the ellipse, the sum of its distances from two fixed points (called the **foci**) is a constant.

Elliptic geometry   A non-Euclidean geometry in which a Saccheri quadrilateral is constructed with summit angles obtuse.

e-mail   Electronic mail sent from one computer to another.

Empirical probability   A probability obtained empirically by experimentation.

Empty set   See *Set*.

Encoding key   A key that allows one to scramble, or encode a message.

Encrypt   To scramble a message so that it cannot be read by an unwanted person.

Equal angles   Two angles that have the same measure.

Equal matrices   Two matrices are equal if they are the same order (dimension) and also the corresponding elements are the same (equal).

Equal sets   Sets that contain the same elements.

Equal to   Two numbers are equal if they represent the same quantity or are identical. In mathematics, a relationship that satisfies the axioms of equality.

Equality, axioms of   For $a, b, c \in \mathbb{R}$,

Reflexive:	$a = a$
Symmetric:	If $a = b$, then $b = a$.
Transitive:	If $a = b$ and $b = c$, then $a = c$.
Substitution:	If $a = b$, then a may be replaced throughout by b (or b by a) in any statement without changing the truth or falsity of the statement.

Equally likely outcomes   Outcomes whose probabilities of occurring are the same.

Equation   A statement of equality. If always true, an equation is called an *identity*; if always false, it is called a *contradiction*. If it is sometimes true and sometimes false, it is called a *conditional equation*. Values that make an equation true are said to *satisfy* the equation and are called *solutions* or *roots* of the equation. Equations with the same solutions are called *equivalent equations*.

Equation of a graph   Every point on the graph has coordinates that satisfy the equation, and every ordered pair that satisfies the equation has coordinates that lie on the graph.

Equation properties   There are four equation properties:

(1) *Addition property:* Adding the same number to both sides of an equation results in an equivalent equation.

(2) *Subtraction property:* Subtracting the same number from both sides of an equation results in an equivalent equation.

(3) *Multiplication property:* Multiplying both sides of a given equation by the same nonzero number results in an equivalent equation.

(4) *Division property:* Dividing both sides of a given equation by the same nonzero number results in an equivalent equation.

Equilateral triangle   A triangle whose three sides all have the same length.

Equilibrium point   A point for which the supply and demand are equal.

Equivalent equations   See *Equation*.

Equivalent matrices   Matrices that represent equivalent systems.

Equivalent sets   Sets that have the same cardinality.

Equivalent systems   Systems that have the same solution set.

Estimate   An approximation (usually mental) of size or value used to form an opinion.

Euclidean geometry   The study of geometry based on the assumptions of Euclid. These basic assumptions are called Euclid's postulates.

Euclid's postulates   1. A straight line can be drawn from any point to any other point. 2. A straight line extends infinitely in either direction. 3. A circle can be described with any point as center and with a radius equal to any finite straight line drawn from the center. 4. All right angles are equal to each other. 5. Given a straight line and any point not on this line, there is one and only one line through that point that is parallel to the given line.

Euler circles   The representation of sets using interlocking circles.

Euler circuit   Begin at some vertex of a graph, travel on each edge exactly once, and return to the starting vertex. The path that is a trace of the tip is called an *Euler circuit*.

Euler's circuit theorem   Every vertex on a graph which is an Euler circuit has an even degree, and conversely, if in a connected graph every vertex has an even degree, then the graph is an Euler circuit.

Euler's number   It is the number e.

Evaluate   To *evaluate* an expression means to replace the variables by given numerical values and then simplify the resulting numerical expression. To *evaluate* a trigonometric ratio means to find its approximate numerical value. To *evaluate* a summation means to find its value.

Even vertex   In a network, a vertex with even degree—that is, with an even number of arcs or line segments connected at that vertex.

Event   A subset of a sample space.

Exact interest   The calculation of interest assuming that there are 365 days in a year.

Exact solution   The simplified value of an expression before approximation by calculator.

Exclusive or   A translation of *p or q* which includes *p* or *q*, but not both. In this book we translate the *exclusive or* as "either *p* or *q*."

Expand   To simplify by carrying out the given operations.

Expand a summation   To write out a summation notation showing the individual terms without a sigma.

Expanded notation   A way of writing a number that lists the meaning of each grouping symbol and the number of items in that group. For example, 382.5 written in expanded notation is

$$3 \times 10^2 + 8 \times 10^1 + 2 \times 10^0 + 5 \times 10^{-1}$$

Expectation   See *Mathematical expectation*.

Expected value   See *Mathematical expectation*.

Experiment   An observation of any physical occurrence.

Exponent   Where b is any nonzero real number and n is any natural number, *exponent* is defined as follows:

$$b^n = \underbrace{b \cdot b \cdot \cdots \cdot b}_{n \text{ factors}} \qquad b^0 = 1 \qquad b^{-n} = \frac{1}{b^n}$$

b is called the *base*, n is called the *exponent*, and b^n is called a *power* or *exponential*.

Exponential   See *Exponent*.

Exponential curve   The graph of an exponential equation. It indicates an increasingly steep rise, and passes through the point (0, 1).

Exponential equation   An equation of the form $y = b^x$, where b is positive and not equal to 1.

Exponential function   A function that can be written as $f(x) = b^x$, where $b > 0$, $b \neq 1$.

Exponential notation   A notation involving exponents.

Exponentiation   The process of raising a number to some power. See *Exponent*.

Expression   Numbers, variables, functions, and their arguments that can be evaluated to obtain a single result.

Extended order of operations   1. Perform any operations enclosed in parentheses. 2. Perform any operations that involve raising to a power. 3. Perform multiplications and divisions as they occur by working from left to right.

4. Finally, perform additions and subtractions as they occur by working from left to right.

Exterior angle   An exterior angle of a triangle is the angle on the other side of an extension on one side of the triangle.

Extraneous root   A number obtained in the process of solving an equation that is not a root of the equation to be solved.

Extremes   See *Proportion.*

Factor   (*noun*) Each of the numbers multiplied to form a product is called a factor of the product. (*verb*) To write a given number as a product.

Factor tree   The representation of a composite number showing the steps of successive factoring by writing each new pair of factors under the composite.

Factorial   For a natural number n, the product of all the positive integers less than or equal to n. It is denoted by $n!$ and is defined by

$$n! = n(n - 1)(n - 2) \cdot \cdots \cdot 4 \cdot 3 \cdot 2 \cdot 1$$

Also, $0! = 1$.

Factoring   The process of determining the factors of a product.

Factorization   The result of factoring a number or an expression.

Fahrenheit   A unit of measurement in the United States system for measuring temperature based on a system where the freezing point of water is 32° and the boiling point of water is 212°.

Fair coin   A coin for which heads and tails are equally likely.

Fair game   A game for which the mathematical expectation is zero.

Fair voting principles   See *Fairness criteria.*

Fairness criteria   Properties that would seem to be desirable in any voting system.

Majority criterion: If a candidate receives a majority of the first-place votes, then that candidate should be declared the winner.

Condorcet criterion: If a candidate is favored when compared one-on-one with every other candidate, then that candidate should be declared the winner.

Monotonicity criterion: A candidate who wins a first election and then gains additional support, without losing any of the original support, should also win a second election.

Irrelevant alternatives criterion: If a candidate is declared the winner of an election, and in a second election one or more of the other candidates is removed, then the previous winner should still be declared the winner.

Fallacy   An invalid form of reasoning.

Fallacy of exceptions   Reasoning or forming a conclusion by looking at one particular case, which may be an exception.

Fallacy of the converse   An invalid form of reasoning that has the form $[(p \rightarrow q) \wedge q]$ and reaches the incorrect conclusion p.

Fallacy of the inverse   An invalid form of reasoning that has the form

$$[(p \rightarrow q) \wedge (\sim p)]$$

and reaches the incorrect conclusion $\sim q$.

False chain pattern   An invalid form of reasoning that has the form

$$[(p \rightarrow q) \wedge (p \rightarrow r)]$$

and reaches the incorrect conclusion $q \rightarrow r$.

Feasible solution   A set of values that satisfies the set of constraints in a linear programming problem.

Fibonacci sequence   The sequence 1, 1, 2, 3, 5, 8, 13, 21, ... The general term is $s_n = s_{n-1} + s_{n-2}$, for any given s_1 and s_2.

Fibonacci-type sequence   A sequence with general term $s_n = s_{n-1} + s_{n-2}$, for any given s_1 and s_2. *The* Fibonacci sequence has first terms 1, 1, . . . , but *a* Fibonacci-type sequence can have any two first terms.

Field   A set with two operations satisfying the closure, commutative, associative, identity, and inverse properties for both operations. A field also satisfies a distributive property combining both operations.

Finance charge   A charge made for the use of someone else's money.

Finite series   A series with n terms, where n is a counting number.

Finite set   See *Set.*

First component   See *Ordered pair.*

First-degree equation   With one variable, an equation of the form $ax + b = 0$; with two variables, an equation of the form $y = mx + b$.

Five-percent offer   An offer made that is 105% of the price paid by the dealer. That is, it is an offer that is 5% over the cost.

Fixed-point form   The usual decimal representation of a number. It is usually used in the context of writing numbers in scientific notation or in floating-point form. See *Floating-point form.*

Floating-point form   A calculator or computer variation of scientific notation in which a number is written as a number between one and ten times a power of ten where the power of ten is understood. For example, 2.678×10^{11} is scientific notation and 2.678E 11 or 2.678 + 11 are floating-point representations. The fixed-point representation is the usual decimal representation of 267,800,000,000.

Floor-plan problem   Given a floor plan of some building you wish to find a path from room to room that will proceed through all of the rooms exactly once.

Floppy disk   Storage medium that is a flexible platter ($3\frac{1}{2}$ or $5\frac{1}{4}$ inches in diameter) of mylar plastic coated with a magnetic material. Data are represented on the disk by electrical impulses.

Foci   Plural *for focus.*

Focus   See *Parabola, Ellipse,* and *Hyperbola.*

FOIL   (1) A method for multiplying binomials that requires First terms, Outer terms + Inner terms, Last terms:

$$(a + b)(c + d) = ac + (ad + bc) + bd$$

(2) A method for factoring a trinomial into the product of two binomials.

Foot   A unit of linear measure in the United States system that is equal to 12 inches.

Foreclose   If the scheduled payments are not made, the lender takes the right to redeem the mortgage and keeps the collateral property.

Formula   A general answer, rule, or principle stated in mathematical notation.

Fractal   A family of shapes involving chance whose irregularities are statistical in nature. They are shapes used, for example, to model coastlines, growth, and boundaries of clouds. Fractals model curves as well as surfaces. The term *fractal set* is also used in place of the word *fractal.*

Fractal geometry   The branch of geometry that studies the properties of fractals.

Fraction   See *Rational number*.

Frequency   See *Classes*.

Frequency distribution   For a collection of data, the tabulation of the number of elements in each class.

Function   A rule that assigns to each element in the domain a single (unique) element.

Function machine   A device used to help us understand the nature of functions. It is the representation of a function as a machine into which some number is input and "processed" through the machine; the machine then outputs a single value.

Functional notation   The representation of a function f using the notation $f(x)$.

Fundamental counting principle   If one task can be performed in m ways and a second task can be performed in n ways, then the number of ways that the tasks can be performed one after the other is mn.

Fundamental operators   In symbolic logic, the fundamental operators are the connectives *and, or,* and *not*.

Fundamental property of equations   If P and Q are algebraic expressions, and k is a real number, then each of the following is equivalent to $P = Q$:

Addition	$P + k = Q + k$
Subtraction	$P - k = Q - k$
Nonzero multiplication	$kP = kQ, k \neq 0$
Nonzero division	$\dfrac{P}{k} = \dfrac{Q}{k}, k \neq 0$

Fundamental property of fractions   If both the numerator and denominator are multiplied by the same nonzero number, the resulting fraction will be the same. That is,

$$\frac{PK}{QK} = \frac{P}{Q} \quad (Q, K \neq 0)$$

Fundamental property of inequalities   If P and Q are algebraic expressions, and k is a real number, then each of the following is equivalent to $P < Q$:

Addition	$P + k < Q + k$
Subtraction	$P - k < Q - k$
Positive multiplication	$kP < kQ, k > 0$
Positive division	$\frac{P}{k} < \frac{Q}{k}, k > 0$
Negative multiplication	$kP > kQ, k < 0$
Negative division	$\frac{P}{k} > \frac{Q}{k}, k < 0$

This property also applies for $\leq$, $>$, and $\geq$.

Fundamental theorem of arithmetic   Every counting number greater than 1 is either a prime or a product of primes, and the prime factorization is unique (except for the order in which the factors appear).

Future value   See *Compound interest formula*.

Future value formula   For simple interest: $A = P(1 + rt)$; for compound interest:

$$A = P(1 + i)^N$$

Fuzzy logic   A relatively new branch of logic used in computer programming that does not use the law of the excluded middle.

Gallon   A measure of capacity in the United States system that is equal to 4 quarts.

Gates   In circuit logic, it is a symbolic representation of a particular circuit.

Gauss-Jordan elimination   A method for solving a system of equations that uses the following steps. *Step 1*: Select as the first pivot the element in the first row, first column, and pivot. *Step 2*: The next pivot is the element in the second row, second column; pivot. *Step 3*: Repeat the process until you arrive at the last row, or until the pivot element is a zero. If it is a zero and you can interchange that row with a row below it, so that the pivot element is no longer a zero, do so and continue. If it is zero and you cannot interchange rows so that it is not a zero, continue with the next row. The final matrix is called the **row-reduced form**.

g.c.f.   An abbreviation for *greatest common factor*.

General form   In relation to second-degree equations (or conic sections), it refers to the form

$$Ax^2 + Bxy + Cy^2 + Dx + Ey + F = 0$$

where A, B, C, D, E, and F are real numbers and (x, y) is any point on the curve.

General term   The nth term of a sequence or series.

Genus   The number of cuts that can be made without cutting a figure into two pieces. The genus is equivalent to the number of holes in the object.

Geometric mean   The geometric mean of the numbers a and b is $\sqrt{ab}$.

Geometric sequence   A sequence for which the ratio of each term to the preceding term is a constant, written $g_1, g_2, g_3, \ldots$. The nth term of a geometric sequence is $g_n = g_1 r^{n-1}$, where g_1 is the first term and r is the *common ratio*. It is also called a *geometric progression*.

Geometric series   The indicated sum of the terms of a geometric sequence. The sum of n terms is denoted by G_n and

$$G_n = \frac{g_1(1 - r^n)}{1 - r}, r \neq 1$$

If $|r| < 1$, then $G = \frac{g_1}{1 - r}$, where G is the sum of the infinite geometric series. If $|r| \geq 1$, the infinite geometric series has no sum.

Geometry   The branch of mathematics that treats the shape and size of things. Technically, it is the study of invariant properties of given elements under specified groups of transformations.

GIGO   Garbage In, Garbage Out, an old axiom regarding the use of computers.

Golden ratio   The division of a line segment $\overline{AB}$ by an interior point P so that

$$\frac{|\overline{AB}|}{|\overline{AP}|} = \frac{|\overline{AP}|}{|\overline{PB}|}$$

It follows that this ratio is a root of the equation $x^2 - x - 1 = 0$, or $x = \frac{1}{2}(1 + \sqrt{5})$. This ratio is called the golden ratio and is considered pleasing to the eye.

Golden rectangle   A rectangle R with the property that it can be divided into a square and a rectangle similar to R; a rectangle whose sides form a golden ratio.

Googol   The number with 1 followed by 100 zeros—that is, 10,000,000,000,000,000,000,000,000,000,000,000,000,000,000,000,000,000,000,000,000,000,000,000,000,000,000,000,000,000,000,000,000,000,000.

Grace period   A period of time between when an item is purchased and when it is paid during which no interest is charged.

Gram   A unit of weight in the metric system. It is equal to the weight of one cubic centimeter of water at 4°C.

Grant's tomb properties   Two fundamental properties of logarithms:

1. $\log_b b^x = x$
2. $b^{\log_b x} = x, x > 0$

Graph   (1) In statistics, it is a drawing that shows the relation between certain sets of numbers. Common forms are bar graphs, line graphs, pictographs, and pie charts (circle graphs). (2) A drawing that shows the relation between certain sets of numbers. It may be one-dimensional ($\mathbb{R}$), two-dimensional ($\mathbb{R}^2$), or three-dimensional ($\mathbb{R}^3$). (3) A set of vertices connected by arcs or line segments.

Graph of an equation   See *Equation of a graph.*

Graphing method   A method of solving a system of equations that finds the solution by looking at the intersection of the individual graphs. It is an approximate method of solving a system of equations, and depends on the accuracy of the graph that is drawn.

Great circle   A circle on a sphere that has its diameter equal to that of the sphere.

Greater than   If a lies to the right of b on a number line, then a is greater than b, $a > b$. Formally, $a > b$ if and only if $a - b$ is positive.

Greater than or equal to   Written $a \geq b$ means $a > b$ or $a = b$.

Greatest common factor   The largest divisor common to a given set of numbers.

Group   A set with one defined operation that satisfies the closure, associative, identity, and inverse properties.

Grouped frequency distribution   If the data are grouped before they are tallied, then the resulting distribution is called a *grouped frequency distribution.*

Grouping symbols   Parentheses ( ), brackets [ ], and braces { } indicate the order of operations and are also sometimes used to indicate multiplication, as in $(2)(3) = 6$. Also called *symbols of inclusion.*

Growth formula   Refers to exponential growth. It is described by the equation

$$A = A_0 e^{rt}$$

where r is the annual growth rate (and consequently is positive), t is the time (in years), A_0 is the amount present initially (present value), and A is the future value. If r is positive, this formula models growth, and if r is negative, the formula models decay.

Half-life   The time that it takes for a particular radioactive substance to decay to half of its original amount.

Half-line   A ray, with or without its endpoint. The half-line is said to be closed if it includes the endpoint, and open if it does not include the endpoint.

Half-plane   The part of a plane that lies on one side of a line in the plane. It is a *closed* half-plane if the line is included. It is an *open* half-plane if the line is not included. The line is the *boundary* of the half-plane in either case.

Hamiltonian cycle   A path that begins at some vertex and then visits each vertex exactly once, ending up at the original vertex.

Hamilton's apportionment plan   An apportionment plan in which the representation of a geographical area is determined by finding the quotient of the number of people in that area divided by the total number of people and then the result is rounded as follows: Allocate the remainder, one at a time, to districts on the basis of the decreasing order of the decimal portion of the quotients. This method is sometimes called the *method of the largest fractions.*

Hare method   Each voter votes for one candidate. If a candidate receives a majority of the votes, that candidate is declared to be a *first-round winner.* If no candidate receives a majority of the votes, then with the *Hare method,* also known as the *plurality with an elimination runoff method,* the candidate(s) with the fewest number of first-place votes is (are) eliminated. Each voter votes for one candidate in the second-round. If a candidate receives a majority, that candidate is declared to be a *second-round winner.* If no candidate receives a majority of the second-round votes, then eliminate the candidate(s) with the fewest number of votes is (are) eliminated. Repeat this process until a candidate receives a majority.

Hecto-   A prefix meaning 100.

Heptagon   A polygon having seven sides.

Hexagon   A polygon having six sides.

HH method   See *Huntington-Hill's plan.*

Higher-level language   A computer programming language (e.g., BASIC, PASCAL, LOGO) that approaches the syntax of English and is easier both to use and to learn than machine language. It is also not system-dependent.

Hindu-Arabic numerals   Same as the usual decimal numeration system that is in everyday use.

Horizontal ellipse   An ellipse whose major axis is horizontal.

Horizontal hyperbola   A hyperbola whose transverse axis is horizontal.

Horizontal line   A line with zero slope. Its equation has the form $y = $ constant.

Hundred   Ten 10s.

Huntington-Hill's plan   An apportionment plan currently in use by the U.S. legislature. It is based on the geometric mean of two numbers, a and b, where a is the value of the exact ratio rounded down and b is the value of the exact ratio rounded up. It rounds down if the exact quota is less than the geometric mean and rounds up if it is greater than the geometric mean.

Hyperbola   The set of all points in a plane such that, for each point on the hyperbola, the difference of its distances from two fixed points (called the *foci*) is a constant.

Hyperbolic geometry   A non-Euclidean geometry in which a Saccheri quadrilateral is constructed with summit angles acute.

Hypotenuse   The longest side in a right triangle.

Hypothesis   An assumed proposition used as a premise in proving something else.

Identity   (1) A statement of equality that is true for all values of the variable. It also refers to a number I so that for some operation $\circ$, $\text{I} \circ a = a \circ \text{I} = a$ for every number a in a given set. (2) An open equation that is true for all replacements of the variable.

Identity matrix   A matrix satisfying the identity property. It is a square matrix consisting of ones along the main diagonal and zeros elsewhere.

If-then   In symbolic logic, it is a connective also called *implication.*

Implication   A statement that follows from other statements. It is also a proposition formed from two given propositions by connecting them with an "if . . . , then . . . " form. It is symbolized by $p \rightarrow q$.

Impossible event   An event for which the probability is zero—that is, an event that cannot happen.

Improper fraction   A fraction for which the numerator is greater than the denominator.

Improper subset   See *Subset*.

Inch   A linear measurement in the United States system equal in length to the following segment: _____

Inclusive or   The same as *Disjunction*. The compound statement "*p* or *q*" is called the *inclusive or*.

Inconsistent system   A system for which no replacements of the variable make the equations true simultaneously.

Indefinite integral   An antiderivative.

Independence of irrelevant alternatives   If a voter prefers A to B with C as a possible choice, we assume that the voter still prefers A to B when C is not a possible choice.

Independent events   Events *E* and *F* are *independent* if the occurrence of one in no way affects the occurrence of the other.

Independent system   A system of equations such that no one of them is necessarily satisfied by a set of values of the variables that satisfy all the others.

Independent variable   The variable associated with the first component of an ordered pair.

Indirect reasoning   One of the principal forms of logical reasoning. It is an argument of the form

$$[(p \rightarrow q) \wedge \sim q] \rightarrow \sim p$$

Inductive reasoning   A type of reasoning accomplished by first observing patterns and then predicting answers for more complicated similar problems.

Inequality   A statement of order. If always true, an inequality is called an *absolute inequality*; if always false, an inequality is called a *contradiction*. If sometimes true and sometimes false, it is called a *conditional inequality*. Values that make the statement true are said to satisfy the inequality. A *string of inequalities* may be used to show the order of three or more quantities.

Inequality symbols   The symbols $>$, $\geq$, $<$, and $\leq$. Also called *order symbols*.

Inferential statistics   Statistics that is concerned with making generalizations or predictions about a population based on a sample from that population.

Infinite series   The indicated sum of an infinite sequence.

Infinite set   See *Set*.

Infinity symbol ∞

Inflation   An increase in the amount of money in circulation, resulting in a fall in its value and a rise in prices. In this book, we assume annual compounding with the future value formula; that is, use $A = P(1 + r)^n$, where r is the projected annual inflation rate, n is the number of years, and P is the present value.

Information retrieval   The locating and displaying of specific material from a description of its content.

Input   A method of putting information into a computer. *Input* includes downloading a program, typing on a keyboard, pressing on a pressure-sensitive screen.

Input device   Component of a system that allows the entry of data or a program into a computer's memory.

Installment loan   A financial problem in which an item is paid for over a period of time. It is calculated using add-on interest or compound interest.

Installments   Part of a debt paid at regular intervals over a period of time.

Instant Insanity   A puzzle game consisting of four blocks with different colors on the faces. The object of the game is to arrange the four blocks in a row so that no color is repeated on one side as the four blocks are rotated through 360°.

Instantaneous rate of change   The instantaneous rate of change of a function *f* from *x* to *x* + *h* is

$$\lim_{h \rightarrow 0} \frac{f(x + h) - f(x)}{h}$$

Integers $\mathbb{Z} = \{\ldots, -3, -2, -1, 0, 1, 2, 3, \ldots\}$, composed of the natural numbers, their opposites, and 0.

Integral   A fundamental concept of calculus, which involves finding the area bounded by a curve, the *x*-axis, and two vertical lines. Let *f* be a function defined over the interval $[a, b]$. Then the definite integral of *f* over the interval is denoted by

$$\int_a^b f(x)\, dx$$

and is the net change of an antiderivative of *f* over that interval. The numbers *a* and *b* are called the *limits of integration*.

Integral calculus   That branch of calculus that involves applications of the integral.

Integral of a sum   The following property of integrals:

$$\int [f(x) + g(x)]\, dx = \int f(x)\, dx + \int g(x)\, dx$$

Integrand   In an integral, it is the function to be integrated.

Integrated circuit   The plastic or ceramic body that contains a chip and the leads connecting it to other components.

Interactive   Software that allows continuous two-way communication between the user and the program.

Intercept form of the equation of a line   The form

$$\frac{x}{a} + \frac{y}{b} = 1$$

of a linear equation where the *x*-intercept is *a* and the *y*-intercept is *b*.

Intercepts   The point or points where a line or a curve crosses a coordinate axis. The *x*-intercepts are sometimes called the *zeros* of the equation.

Interest   An amount of money paid for the use of another's money. See *Compound interest*.

Interest-only loan   A loan in which periodic payments are for interest only so that the principal amount of the loan remains the same.

Interest rate   The percentage rate paid on financial problems. In this book it is denoted by *r* and is assumed to be an annual rate unless otherwise stated.

Interface   The electronics necessary for a computer to communicate with a peripheral.

Internet   A network of computers from all over the world that are connected together.

Intersection   The *intersection* of sets A and B, denoted by $A \cap B$ is the set consisting of elements in *both* A and B.

Interval   See *Classes*.

Invalid argument   An argument that is not valid.

Inverse   (1) In symbolic logic, for an implication $p \rightarrow q$, the inverse is the statement $\sim p \rightarrow \sim q$. (2) For addition, see *Opposites*.

For multiplication, see *Reciprocal*. (3) For matrices, if [A] is a square matrix, and if there exists a matrix $[A]^{-1}$ such that

$$[A]^{-1}[A] = [A][A]^{-1} = [I]$$

where [I] is the identity matrix for multiplication, then $[A]^{-1}$ is called the inverse of [A] for multiplication.

Inverse cosine   See *Inverse trigonometric ratios*.

Inverse property   For each $a \in \mathbb{R}$, there is a unique number $(-a) \in \mathbb{R}$, called the *opposite* (or *additive inverse*) of a, so that

$$a + (-a) = -a + a = 0$$

Inverse sine   See *Inverse trigonometric ratios*.

Inverse tangent   See *Inverse trigonometric ratios*.

Inverse trigonometric ratios   The inverse sine, inverse cosine, and inverse tangent are the *inverse trigonometric ratios*. For θ an acute angle in a right triangle,

$$\sin^{-1}\left(\frac{\text{OPP}}{\text{HYP}}\right) = \theta; \quad \cos^{-1}\left(\frac{\text{ADJ}}{\text{HYP}}\right) = \theta,$$

$$\tan^{-1}\left(\frac{\text{OPP}}{\text{ADJ}}\right) = \theta$$

Invert   In relation to the fraction a/b, it means to interchange the numerator and the denominator to obtain the fraction b/a.

Irrational number   A number that can be expressed as a nonrepeating, nonterminating decimal; the set of irrational numbers is denoted by $\mathbb{Q}'$.

Irrelevant alternatives criterion   If a candidate is declared the winner of an election, and in a second election one or more of the other candidates is removed, then the previous winner should still be declared the winner.

Isosceles triangle   A triangle with two sides the same length.

Isosceles triangle property   If two sides of a triangle have the same length, then angles opposite them are equal.

Jefferson's apportionment plan   An apportionment plan in which the representation of a geographical area is determined by finding the quotient of the number of people in that area divided by the total number of people and then rounding the result as follows: Any quotient with a decimal portion must be rounded down to the previous whole number.

Jordan curve   Also called a *simple closed curve*. For example, a curve such as a circle or an ellipse or a rectangle that is closed and does not intersect itself.

Juxtaposition   When two variables, a number and a variable, or a symbol and a parenthesis, are written next to each other with no operation symbol, as in *xy*, *2x*, or *3(x + y)*. Juxtaposition is used to indicate multiplication.

K   The symbol represents 1,024 (or 2^{10}). For example, 48K bytes of memory is the same as $48 \times 1,024$ or 49,152 bytes. It is sometimes used as an approximation for 1,000.

Keno   A lottery game that consists of a player trying to guess in advance which numbers will be selected from a pot containing n numbers. A certain number, say m, where $m < n$, of selections is randomly made from the pot of n numbers. The player then gets paid according to how many of the m numbers were selected.

Keyboard   Typewriter-like device that allows the user to input data and commands into a computer.

Kilo-   A prefix that means 1,000.

Kilogram   1,000 grams.

Kiloliter   1,000 liters.

Kilometer   1,000 meters.

Kruskal's algorithm   To construct a minimum spanning tree from a weighted graph: 1. Select any edge with minimum weight. 2. Select the next edge with minimum weight among those not yet selected. 3. Continue to choose edges of minimum weight from those not yet selected, but make sure not to select any edge that forms a circuit. 4. Repeat this process until the tree connect all of the vertices of the original graph.

Laptop   A small portable computer.

Law of contraposition   A conditional may always be replaced by its contrapositive without having its truth value affected.

Law of detachment   Same as *direct reasoning*.

Law of double negation $\sim(\sim p) \Leftrightarrow p$

Law of the excluded middle   Every simple statement is either true or false.

Laws of exponents   There are five laws of exponents.

Addition law	$b^m \cdot b^n = b^{m+n}$
Multiplication law	$(b^n)^m = b^{mn}$
Subtraction law	$\dfrac{b^m}{b^n} = b^{m-n}$
Distributive laws	$(ab)^m = a^m b^m$
	$\left(\dfrac{a}{b}\right)^m = \dfrac{a^m}{b^m}$

Laws of logarithms   If A, B, and b are positive numbers, p any real number, and $b \neq 1$, then

Addition law	$\log_b (AB) = \log_b A + \log_b B$
Subtraction law	$\log_b \frac{A}{B} = \log_b A - \log_b B$
Multiplication law	$\log_b A^p = p \log_b A$

Laws of square roots   There are 4 laws of square roots.

(1) $\sqrt{0} = 0$ (2) $\sqrt{a^2} = a$

(3) $\sqrt{ab} = \sqrt{a}\sqrt{b}$ (4) $\sqrt{\frac{a}{b}} = \frac{\sqrt{a}}{\sqrt{b}}$

l.c.d.   An abbreviation for least common denominator.

l.c.m.   An abbreviation for least common multiple.

Least common denominator (l.c.d.)   The smallest number that is exactly divisible by each of the given numbers.

Least common multiple (l.c.m.)   The smallest number that each of a given set of numbers divides into.

Least squares line   A line $y = mx + b$ so that the sum of the squares of the vertical distances of the data points from this line will be as small as possible.

Least squares method   A method based on the principle that the best prediction of a quantity that can be deduced from a set of measurements or observations is that for which the sum of the squares of the deviations of the observed values (from predictions) is a minimum.

Leg of a triangle   One of the two sides of a right triangle that are not the hypotenuse.

Length   A measurement of an object from end to end.

Less than   If a is to the left of b on a number line, then a is less than b, $a < b$. Formally, $a < b$ if and only if $b > a$.

Less than or equal to   Written $a \leq b$, means $a < b$ or $a = b$.

Like terms   Terms that differ only in their numerical coefficients. Also called *similar terms*.

Limit   The formal definition of a limit is beyond the scope of this course. Intuitively, it is the tendency of a function to approach some value as its variable approaches a given value.

Limit of a sequence   The formal definition of a limit of a sequence is beyond the scope of this course. Intuitively, it is an accumulation point such that there are an infinite number of terms of the sequence arbitrarily close to the accumulation point.

Limits of integration   See *Integral*.

Line   In mathematics, it is an undefined term. It is a curve that is straight, so it is sometimes referred to as a *straight line*. It extends in both directions and is considered one-dimensional, so it has no thickness.

Line graph   See *Graph*.

Line of credit   A preapproved credit limit on a credit account. The maximum amount of credit to be extended to a borrower. That is, it is a promise by a lender to extend credit up to some predetermined amount.

Line of symmetry   A line with the property that for a given curve, any point P on the curve has a corresponding point Q (called the reflection point of P) so that the perpendicular bisector of $\overline{PQ}$ is on the line of symmetry.

Line segment   A part of a line between two points on the line.

Linear   (1) A first-degree polynomial. (2) Pertaining to a line. In two variables, a set of points satisfying the equation $Ax + By + C = 0$.

Linear combination method   See *Addition method*.

Linear correlation coefficient   A measure to determine whether there is a statistically significant linear relationship between two variables.

Linear equation   An equation of the form

$ax + b = 0$ (one variable) or
$Ax + By + C = 0$ (two variables)

A first-degree equation with one or two variables. For example, $x + 5 = 0$ and $x + y + 5 = 0$ are linear. An equation is linear in a certain variable if it is first-degree in that variable. For example, $x + y^2 = 0$ is linear in x, but not y.

Linear function   A function whose equation can be written in the form $f(x) = mx + b$.

Linear inequality   A first-degree inequality with one or two variables.

Linear polynomial   A first-degree polynomial.

Linear programming   A type of problem that seeks to maximize or minimize a function called the *objective function* subject to a set of *restrictions* (linear inequalities) called *constraints*.

Linear programming theorem   A linear expression in two variables, $c_1x + c_2y$, defined over a convex set S whose sides are line segments, takes on its maximum value at a corner point of S and its minimum value at a corner point of S. If S is unbounded, there may or may not be an optimum value, but if there is, then it must occur at a corner point.

Linear system   A system of equations, each of which is first degree.

Liter   The basic unit of capacity in the metric system. It is the capacity of 1 cubic decimeter.

Literal equation   An equation with more than one variable.

Logarithm   For $A > 0, b > 0, b \neq 1$ $x = \log_b A$ means $b^x = A$ x is the called the logarithm and A is called the argument.

Logarithmic equation   An equation for which there is a logarithm on one or both sides.

Logarithmic function

$$f(x) = \log_b x, \quad b > 0, \quad x > 0$$

Logarithmic scale   A scale in which logarithms are used to make data more manageable by expanding small variations and compressing large ones.

Logic   The science of correct reasoning.

Logical conclusion   The statement that follows logically as a consequence of the hypotheses of a theorem.

Logical equivalence   Two statements are *logically equivalent* if they have the same truth values.

Logical fallacy   An invalid form of reasoning.

Log of both sides theorem   If A, B, and b are positive real numbers with $b \neq 1$, then $\log_b A = \log_b B$ is equivalent to $A = B$

Lower quota   In apportionment, the result of a quota found by rounding down.

Lowest common denominator   For two or more fractions, the smallest common multiple of the denominators. It is the same as the *lowest common multiple*.

Lump-sum problem   A financial problem that deals with a single sum of money, called a *lump sum*. Contrast with a *periodic payment* problem.

Main diagonal   The entries $a_{11}, a_{22}, a_{33}, \ldots$ in a matrix.

Major axis   In an ellipse, the line passing though the foci.

Majority   Voting to find an alternative that receives more than 50% of the vote.

Majority criterion   If a candidate receives a majority of the first-place votes, then that candidate should be declared the winner.

Marriage   A pairing of one couple where each partner is taken from a separate group. A marriage is *stable* if each partner is satisfied with the pairing and *unstable* if one or the other (or both) would prefer to be paired with another.

Mass   In this course, it is the amount of matter an object comprises. Formally, it is a measure of the tendency of a body to oppose changes in its velocity.

Mathematical expectation   A calculation defined as the product of an amount to be won and the probability that it is won. If there is more than one amount to be won, it is the sum of the expectations of all the prizes. It is also called the *expected value* or *expectation*.

Mathematical modeling   An iterative procedure that makes assumptions about real-world problems to formulate the problem in mathematical terms. After the mathematical problem is solved, it is tested for accuracy in the real world, and revised for the next step in the iterative process.

Mathematical system   A set with at least one defined operation and some developed properties.

Matrix   A rectangular array of terms called *elements*.

Matrix equation   An equation whose elements are matrices.

Maximum loan   In this book, it refers to the maximum amount of loan that can be obtained for a home with a given amount of income and a given amount of debt. To find this amount, use the present value of an annuity formula.

Mean   The number found by adding the data and dividing by the number of values in the data set. The sample mean is usually denoted by $\bar{x}$.

Means   See *Proportion*.

Measure   Comparison to some unit recognized as standard.

Measures of central tendency   Refers to the averages of mean, median, and mode.

Measures of dispersion   Refers to the measures of range, standard deviation, and variance.

Measures of position   Measures that divide a data set by position, which include median, quartiles, deciles, and percentiles.

Median   The middle number when the numbers in the data are arranged in order of size. If there are two middle numbers (in the case of an even number of data values), the median is the mean of these two middle numbers.

Member   See *Set*.

Meter   The basic unit for measuring length in the metric system.

Metric system   A decimal system of weights and measures in which the gram, the meter, and the liter are the basic units of mass, length, and capacity, respectively. One gram is the mass of one cm^3 of water and one liter is the same as 1,000 cm^3. In this book, the metric system refers to SI metric system as revised in 1960.

Micrometer   One millionth of a meter, denoted by μm.

Mile   A unit of linear measurement in the United States system that is equal to 5,280 ft.

Milli-   A prefix that means 1/1,000.

Milligram   1/1,000 of a gram.

Milliliter   1/1,000 of a liter.

Millimeter   1/1,000 of a meter.

Million   A name for $10^6 = 1,000,000$.

Minicomputer   An everyday name for a personal computer.

Minimum spanning tree   A spanning tree for which the sum of the numbers with the edges is a minimum.

Minor axis   In an ellipse, the axis perpendicular to the major axis passing though the center of the ellipse.

Minus   Refers to the operation of subtraction. The symbol "$-$" means minus only when it appears between two numbers, two variables, or between numbers and variables.

Mixed number   A number that has both a counting number part and a proper fraction part; for example, $3\frac{1}{2}$.

Mode   The value in a data set that occurs most frequently. If no number occurs more than once, there is no mode. It is possible to have more than one mode.

Modem   A device connected to a computer that allows the computer to communicate with other computers using electric cables, phone lines, or wireless.

Modified quotient   Adjust the standard divisor so that the desired number of seats are used. This adjusted number is known as the modified quotient.

Modular codes   A code based on modular arithmetic.

Modulo 5   A mathematical system consisting of five elements having the property that every number is equivalent to one of these five elements if they have the same remainder when divided by 5.

Modulo *n*   A mathematical system consisting of *n* elements having the property that every number is equivalent to one of these *n* elements if they have the same remainder when divided by *n*.

Modus ponens   Same as *direct reasoning*.

Modus tollens   Same as *indirect reasoning*.

Monitor   An output device for communicating with a computer. It is similar to a television screen.

Monomial   A polynomial with one and only one term.

Monotonicity criterion   A candidate who wins a first election and then gains additional support, without losing any of the original support, should also win a second election.

Monthly compounding   In the compound interest formula, it is when $n = 12$.

Monthly payment   In an installment application, it is a periodic payment that is made once every month.

Mortgage   An agreement, or loan contract, in which a borrower pledges a home or other real estate as security.

Mouse   A small plastic "box" usually with two buttons on top and a ball on the bottom so that it can be rolled around on a pad. It is attached to the computer by a long cord and is used to take over some of the keyboard functions.

Multiple   See *Divisibility*.

Multiplication   For $b \neq 0$, $a \times b$ means

$$\underbrace{b + b + b + \cdots + b}_{a \text{ addends}}$$

If $a = 0$, then $0 \times b = 0$.

Multiplication law of equality   If $a = b$, then $ac = bc$. Also called the *multiplication property of equality* or a *fundamental property of equations*.

Multiplication law of exponents   To raise a power to a power, multiply the exponents. That is, $(b^n)^m = b^{mn}$.

Multiplication law of inequality

1. If $a > b$ and $c > 0$, then $ac > bc$.
2. If $a > b$ and $c < 0$, then $ac < bc$.

Multiplication law of logarithms   The log of the *p*th power of a number is *p* times the log of that number. In symbols,

$$\log_b A^p = p \log_b A$$

Multiplication of integers   If the integers to be multiplied both have the same sign, the result is positive and the magnitude of the answer is the product of the absolute values of the integers. If the integers to be multiplied have opposite signs, the product is negative and has magnitude equal to the product of the absolute values of the given integers. Finally, if one or both of the given integers is 0, the product is 0.

Multiplication of matrices   Let [M] be an $m \times r$ matrix and [N] an $r \times n$ matrix. The product matrix [M][N] = [P] is an $m \times n$ matrix. The entry in the *i*th row and *j*th column of [M][N] is the sum of the products formed by multiplying each entry of the *i*th row of [M] by the corresponding element in the *j*th column of [N].

Multiplication of rational numbers

$$\frac{a}{b} \times \frac{c}{d} = \frac{ac}{bd}$$

Multiplication principle   In a numeration system, multiplication of the value of a symbol by some number. Also, see *Fundamental counting principle*.

Multiplication property (of equations)   Both sides of an equation may be multiplied or divided by any nonzero number to obtain an equivalent equation.

Multiplication property of factorials

$$n! = n(n - 1)!$$

Multiplication property of inequality   Both sides of an inequality may be multiplied or divided by a positive number, and the order of the inequality will remain unchanged. The order is reversed if both sides are multiplied or divided by a negative number. That is, if $a < b$ then $ac < bc$ if $c > 0$ and $ac > bc$ if $c < 0$. This also applies to $\leq$, $>$, and $\geq$.

Multiplication property of probability   If events E and F are independent events, then we can find the probability of an intersection as follows:

$$P(E \cap F) = P(E \text{ and } F) = P(E) \cdot P(F)$$

Multiplicative identity   The number 1, with the property that $1 \cdot a = a$ for any real number a

Multiplicative inverse   (1) See *Reciprocal.* (2) If [A] is a square matrix and if there exists a matrix $[A]^{-1}$ such that

$$[A]^{-1}[A] = [A][A]^{-1} = [I]$$

where [I] is the identity matrix for multiplication, then $[A]^{-1}$ is called the inverse of [A] for multiplication.

Multiplicity   If a root for an equation appears more than once, it is called a *root of multiplicity.* For example,

$$(x - 1)(x - 1)(x - 1)(x - 2)(x - 2)(x - 3) = 0$$

has roots 1, 2, and 3. The root 1 has multiplicity three and root 2 has multiplicity two.

Mutually exclusive   Events are *mutually exclusive* if their intersection is empty.

Natural base   The natural base is e; it refers to an exponential with a base e.

Natural logarithm   A logarithm to the base e, written $\ln N$.

Natural numbers $\mathbb{N} = \{1, 2, 3, 4, 5, \ldots\}$, the positive integers, also called the *counting numbers.*

Negation   A logical connective that changes the truth value of a given statement. The negation of p is symbolized by $\sim p$.

Negative of a conditional   The negative of a conditional, $p \rightarrow q$ is found by

$$\sim(p \rightarrow q) \Leftrightarrow p \wedge \sim q$$

Negative number   A number less than zero.

Negative sign   The symbol "—" when used in front of a number, as in -5. Do not confuse with the same symbol used for subtraction.

Neither . . . nor   A logical operator for "neither p nor q," which is defined to mean $\sim(p \vee q)$

Network   (1) A linking together of computers. (2) A set of points connected by arcs or by line segments.

New states paradox   When a reapportionment of an increased number of seats causes a shift in the apportionment of the existing states, it is known as the *new states paradox.*

n-gon   A polygon with n sides.

No p is q   A logical operator for "no p is q," which is defined to mean $p \rightarrow \sim q$.

Nonagon   A polygon with 9 sides.

Nonconformable matrices   Matrices that cannot be added or multiplied because their dimensions are not compatible.

Non-Euclidean geometries   A geometry that results when Euclid's fifth postulate is not accepted.

Nonrepeating decimal   A decimal representation of a number that does not repeat.

Nonsingular matrix   A matrix that has an inverse.

Nonterminating decimal   A decimal representation of a number that does not terminate.

Normal curve   A graphical representation of a normal distribution. Its high point occurs at the mean, it is symmetric with respect to this mean, and each side of the mean has an area that includes 34.1% of the population within on standard deviation, 13.6% from one to two standard deviations, and

about 2.3% of the population more than two standard deviations from the mean.

Not   A common translation for the connective of negation.

NOT-gate   A logical gate that changes the truth value of a given statement.

Null set   See *Set.*

Number   A *number* represents a given quantity, as opposed to a *numeral,* which is the symbol for the number. In mathematics, it generally refers to a specific set of numbers—for example, counting numbers, whole numbers, integers, rationals, or real numbers. If the set is not specified, the assumed usage is to the set of real numbers.

Number line   A line used to display a set of numbers graphically (the axis for a one-dimensional graph).

Numeral   Symbol used to denote a number.

Numeration system   A system of symbols with rules of combination for representing all numbers.

Numerator   See *Rational number.*

Numerical coefficient   See *Coefficient.*

Objective function   The function to be maximized or minimized in a linear programming problem.

Obtuse angle   An angle that is greater than a right angle and smaller than a straight angle.

Obtuse triangle   A triangle with one obtuse angle.

Octagon   A polygon with eight sides.

Octal numeration system   A numeration system with eight symbols.

Odd vertex   In a network, a vertex of odd degree—that is, with an odd number of arcs or line segments connected at that vertex.

Odds   If $s + f = n$, where s is the number of outcomes considered favorable to an event E and n is the total number of possibilities, then the *odds in favor* of E is s/f and the *odds against* E is f/s.

One   The first counting number; it is also called the *identity element for multiplication;* that is, it satisfies the property that

$$x \cdot 1 = 1 \cdot x = x$$

for all numbers x.

One-dimensional coordinate system   A real number line.

One-to-one correspondence   Between two sets A and B, this means each element of A can be matched with exactly one element of B and also each element of B can be matched with exactly one element of A.

Online   To be connected to a computer network or to the Internet.

Open-ended loan   A preapproved line of credit that the borrower can access as long as timely payments are made and the credit line is not exceeded. It is usually known as a credit card loan.

Open equation   An equation that has at least one variable.

Open half-plane   See *Half-plane.*

Operator   A rule, such as negation, that modifies the value of a simple statement, or a rule that combines two simple statements, such as conjunction or disjunction.

Opposite side   In a right triangle, an acute angle is made up of two sides. The opposite side of the angle refers to the third side that is not used to make up the sides of the angle.

Opposites   Opposites x and $-x$ are the same distance from 0 on the number line but in opposite directions; $-x$ is also called the *additive inverse* of x. Do not confuse the negative symbol "$-$"

meaning opposite with the same symbol as used to mean subtraction or negative.

Optimum solution   The maximum or minimum value in a linear programming problem.

Or   A common translation for the connective of disjunction.

OR-gate   An electrical circuit that simulates disjunction. That is, the circuit is on when either of two switches is on.

Order   Refers to the direction that an inequality symbol points. In reference to matrices, it refers to the number of rows and columns in a matrix. When used in relation to a matrix, it is the same as the *dimension* of the matrix.

Order of an inequality   Refers to $>$, $\geq$, $<$, or $\leq$ relationship.

Order of operations   If no grouping symbols are used in a numerical expression, first perform all multiplications and divisions from left to right, and then perform all additions and subtractions from left to right.

Order symbols   Refers to $>$, $\geq$, $<$, $\leq$ in an inequality. Also called inequality symbols.

Ordered pair   A pair of numbers, written (x, y), in which the order of naming is important. The numbers x and y are sometimes called the *first* and *second components* of the pair and are called the *coordinates* of the point designated by (x, y).

Ordered triple   Three numbers, written (x, y, z), in which the order of the components is important.

Ordinary annuity   See *Annuity*.

Ordinary interest   The calculation of interest assuming a year has 360 days. In this book, we assume ordinary interest unless otherwise stated.

Ordinate   The vertical coordinate in a two-dimensional system of rectangular coordinates, usually denoted by y.

Origin   The point designating 0 on a number line. In two dimensions, the point of intersection of the coordinate axes; the coordinates are $(0, 0)$.

Origination fee   A fee paid to obtain a real estate loan.

Ounce   (1) A unit of capacity in the United States system that is equal to 1/128 of a gallon. (2) A unit of mass in the United States system that is equal to 1/16 of a pound.

Output   A method of getting information out of a computer.

Output device   Component of a system that allows the output of data. The most common output device is a printer.

Overlapping sets   Sets whose intersection is not empty.

Pairwise comparison method   In the *pairwise comparison method* of voting, the voters rank the candidates. The method consists of a series of comparisons in which each candidate is compared to each of the other candidates. If choice A is preferred to choice B, then A receives 1 point. If B is preferred to A, then B receives 1 point. If the candidates tie, each receives $\frac{1}{2}$ point. The candidate with the most points is the winner.

Parabola   A set of points in the plane equidistant from a given point (called the *focus*) and a given line (called the *directrix*). It is the path of a projectile. The *axis of symmetry* is the axis of the parabola. The point where the axis cuts the parabola is the *vertex*.

Parallel circuit   Two switches connected together so that if either of the two switches is turned on, the circuit is on.

Parallel lines   Two nonintersecting straight lines in the same plane.

Parallelepiped   A polyhedron, all of whose faces are parallelograms.

Parallelogram   A quadrilateral with its opposite sides parallel.

Parentheses   See *Grouping symbols*.

Pareto principle   If each voter prefers A over B, then the group chooses A over B.

Partial sum   If $s_1, s_2, s_3, \ldots$ is a sequence, then the partial sums are

$$S_1 = s_1, S_2 = s_1 + s_2, S_3 = s_1 + s_2 + s_3, \ldots.$$

Pascal's triangle   A triangular array of numbers that is bordered by ones and the sum of two adjacent numbers in one row is equal to the number in the next row between the two numbers.

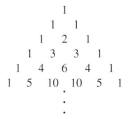

Password   A word or set of symbols that allows access to a computer account.

Pattern recognition   A computer function that entails the automatic identification and classification of shapes, forms, or relationships.

Pearson correlation coefficient   A number between -1 and $+1$ that indicates the degree of linear relationship between two sets of numbers. In the text, we call this the *linear correlation coefficient*.

Pentagon   A polygon with five sides.

Percent   The ratio of a given number to 100; hundredths; denoted by %; that is, 5% means 5/100.

Percent markdown   The percent of an original price used to find the amount of discount.

Percent problem A is $P\%$ of W is formulated as a proportion

$$\frac{P}{100} = \frac{A}{W}$$

Percentage   The given amount in a percent problem.

Percentile   Ninety-nine values that divide a data set into one hundred equal parts.

Perfect number   An integer that is equal to the sum of all of its factors except the number itself. For example, 28 is a perfect number since

$$28 = 1 + 2 + 4 + 7 + 14$$

Perfect square $1^2 = 1, 2^2 = 4, 3^2 = 9, \ldots$, so the perfect squares are 1, 4, 9, 16, 25, 36, 49, $\ldots$.

Perimeter   The distance around a polygon.

Periodic payment problem   A financial problem that involves monthly or other periodic payments.

Peripheral   A device, such as a printer, that is connected to and operated by a computer.

Permutation   A selection of objects from a given set with regard to the order in which they are selected. Sometimes it refers to the number of ways this selection can be done and is denoted by $_nP_r$. The formula for finding it is

$$_nP_r = \frac{n!}{(n - r)!}$$

Perpendicular lines   Two lines are perpendicular if they meet at right angles.

Personal computer   A computer kept for and used by an individual.

Pi (π)   A number that is defined as the ratio of the circumference to the diameter of a circle. It cannot be represented exactly as a decimal, but it is a number between 3.1415 and 3.1416.

Pictograph   See *Graph*.

Pie chart   See *Graph*.

Pirating   Stealing software by copying it illegally for the use of someone other than the person who paid for it.

Pivot   A process that uses elementary row operations to carry out the following steps: 1. Divide all entries in the row in which the pivot appears (called the *pivot row*) by the nonzero pivot element so that the pivot entry becomes a 1. This uses elementary row operation 3. 2. Obtain zeros above and below the pivot element by using elementary row operation 4.

Pivot row   In an elementary row operation, it is the row that is multiplied by a constant. See *Elementary row operations*.

Pivoting   See *Pivot*.

Pixel   Any of the thousands (or millions) of tiny dots that make up a computer or calculator image.

Place-value names   Trillions, hundred billions, ten billions, billions, hundred millions, ten millions, millions, hundred thousands, ten thousands, thousands, hundreds, tens, units, tenths, hundredths, thousandths, ten-thousandths, hundred-thousandths, and millionths (from large to small).

Planar curve   A curve completely contained in a plane.

Plane   In mathematics, it is an undefined term. It is flat and level and extends infinitely in horizontal and vertical directions. It is considered two-dimensional.

Plot a point   To mark the position of a point.

Plurality rule   The winner of an election is the candidate with the highest number of votes.

Point   (1) In the decimal representation of a number, it is a mark that divides the whole number part of a number from its fractional part. (2) In relation to a home loan, it represents 1% of the value of a loan, so that 3 points would be a fee paid to a lender equal to 3% of the amount of the loan. (3) In geometry, it is an undefinedword that signifies a position, but that has no dimension or size.

Point-slope form   An algebraic form of an equation of a line that is given in terms of a point (x_1, y_1) and slope m of a given line:

$$y - y_1 = m(x - x_1)$$

Police patrol problem   Suppose a police car needs to patrol a gated subdivision and would like to enter the gate, cruise all the streets exactly once, and then leave by the same gate.

Polygon   A geometric figure that has three or more straight sides that all lie in a plane so that the starting point and the ending point are the same.

Polynomial   An algebraic expression that may be written as a sum (or difference) of terms. Each *term* of a polynomial contains multiplication only.

Population   The total set of items (actual or potential) defined by some characteristic of the items.

Population growth   The population, P, at some future time can be predicted if you know the population P_0 at some time, and the annual growth rate, r. The predicted population t years after the given time is $P = P_0 e^{rt}$.

Population paradox   When there is a fixed number of seats, a reapportionment may cause a state to lose a seat to another state, even though the percent increase in the population of the state that loses the seat is larger than the percent increase of the state that wins the seat. When this occurs, it is known as the *population paradox*.

Positional system   A numeration system in which the position of a symbol in the representation of a number determines the meaning of that symbol.

Positive number   A number greater than 0.

Positive sign   The symbol "+" when used in front of a number or an expression.

Positive square root   The symbol $\sqrt{x}$ is the positive number that, when multiplied by itself, gives the number x. The symbol "$\sqrt{}$" is always positive.

Postulate   A statement that is accepted without proof.

Pound   A unit of measurement for mass in the United States system. It is equal to 16 oz.

Power   See *Exponent*.

Precision   The accuracy of the measurement; for example, a measurement is taken to the nearest inch, nearest foot, or nearest mile. It is not to be confused with accuracy that applies to the calculation.

Predecessor   In a sequence, the predecessor of an element a_n is the preceding element, a_{n-1}.

Premise   A previous statement or assertion that serves as the basis for an argument.

Present value   See *Compound interest formula*.

Present value formula   The present value, P, of a known future value A invested at an annual interest rate of r for t years compounded n times per year is found by the formula

$$P = A\left(1 + \frac{r}{n}\right)^{-nt}$$

Present value of an annuity   A financial formula that seeks the present value from periodic payments over a period of time. the formula is

$$P = m\left[\frac{1 - \left(1 + \frac{r}{n}\right)^{-nt}}{\frac{r}{n}}\right]$$

Previous balance method   A method of calculating credit card interest using the formula $I = Prt$ in which P is the balance owed before the current payment is subtracted.

Prime factorization   The factorization of a number so that all of the factors are primes and so that their product is equal to the given number.

Prime number $P = \{2, 3, 5, 7, 11, 13, 17, 19, 23, \ldots\}$: a number with exactly two factors: 1 and the number itself.

Principal   See *Compound interest formula*.

Printer   An output device for a computer.

Prism   In this book, it refers to a right prism, which is also called a parallelepiped or more commonly a box.

Probabilistic model   A model that deals with situations that are random in character and attempts to predict the outcomes of events with a certain stated or known degree of accuracy.

Probability   If an experiment can result in any of $n(n \geq 1)$ mutually exclusive and equally likely outcomes, and if s of these are considered favorable to event E, then $P(E) = s/n$.

Probability function   A function P that satisfies the following properties: $0 \leq P(E) \leq 1$, $P(S) = 1$, and if E and F are mutually exclusive events, then $P(E \cup F) = P(E) + P(F)$.

Problem-solving procedure   1. *Read the problem*. Note what it is all about. Focus on processes rather than numbers. You can't work a problem you don't understand. 2. *Restate the problem.* Write a verbal description of the problem using operation signs and an equal sign. Look for equality. If you can't find equal quantities, you will never formulate an equation. 3. *Choose a variable.* If there is a single unknown, choose a variable. 4. *Substitute.* Replace the verbal phrases by known numbers and by the variable. 5. *Solve the equation.* This is the easy step. Be sure your answer makes sense by checking it with the original question in the problem. Use estimation to eliminate unreasonable answers. 6. *State the answer.* There were no variables defined when you started, so $x = 3$ is not an answer. Pay attention to units of measure and other details of the problem. Remember to answer the question that was asked.

Product   The result of a multiplication.

Profit formula $P = S - C$, where P represents the profit, S represents the selling price (or revenue), and C the cost (or overhead).

Program   A set of step-by-step instructions that instruct a computer what to do in a specified situation.

Progression   See *Sequence*

Projective geometry   The study of those properties of geometric configurations that are invariant under projection. It was developed to satisfy the need for depth in works of art.

Prompt   In a computer program, a prompt is a direction that causes the program to print some message to help the user understand what is happening at a particular time.

Proper divisor   A divisor of a number that is less than the number itself.

Proper fraction   A fraction for which the numerator is less than the denominator.

Proper subset   See *Subset*.

Proof   A logical argument that establishes the truth of a statement.

Property of complements   See *Complementary probabilities*.

Property of proportions   If the product of the means equals the product of the extremes, then the ratios form a proportion. Also, if the ratios form a proportion, then the product of the means equals the product of the extremes.

Property of rational expressions   Let P, Q, R, S, and K be any polynomials such that all values of the variable that cause division by zero are excluded from the domain.

Equality $\dfrac{P}{Q} = \dfrac{R}{S}$ if and only if $PS = QR$.

Fundamental property $\dfrac{PK}{QK} = \dfrac{P}{Q}$

Addition $\dfrac{P}{Q} + \dfrac{R}{S} = \dfrac{PS + QR}{QS}$

Subtraction $\dfrac{P}{Q} - \dfrac{R}{S} = \dfrac{PS - QR}{QS}$

Multiplication $\dfrac{P}{Q} \cdot \dfrac{R}{S} = \dfrac{PR}{QS}$

Division $\dfrac{P}{Q} \div \dfrac{R}{S} = \dfrac{PS}{QR}$

Property of zero $AB = 0$ if and only if $A = 0$ or $B = 0$ (or both). Also called the *zero-product rule*.

Proportion   A statement of equality between two ratios. For example,

$$\frac{a}{b} = \frac{c}{d}$$

For this proportion, a and d are called the *extremes*; b and c are called the *means*.

Protractor   A device used to measure angles.

Pseudosphere   The surface of revolution of a tractrix about its asymptote. It is sometimes called a "four-dimensional sphere."

Pyramid   A solid figure having a polygon as a base, the sides of which form the bases of triangular surfaces meeting at a common vertex.

Pythagorean theorem   If a triangle with legs a and b and hypotenuse c is a right triangle, then $a^2 + b^2 = c^2$.

Quadrant   See *Axes*.

Quadratic   A second-degree polynomial

Quadratic equation   An equation of the form $ax^2 + bx + c = 0, a \neq 0$.

Quadratic formula   If $ax^2 + bx + c = 0$ and $a \neq 0$, then

$$x = \frac{-b \pm \sqrt{b^2 - 4ac}}{2a}$$

The radicand $b^2 - 4ac$ is called the *discriminant* of the quadratic.

Quadratic function

$$f(x) = ax^2 + bx + c, a \neq 0$$

Quadrilateral   A polygon having four sides.

Quart   A measure of capacity in the United States system equal to 1/4 of a gallon.

Quarterly compounding   In the compound interest formula, it is when $n = 4$.

Quartile   Three values that divide a data set into four equal parts.

Quota rule   The number assigned to each represented unit must be either the standard quota rounded down to the nearest integer, or the standard quota rounded up to the nearest integer.

Quotient   The result of a division.

Radical form   The $\sqrt{\ }$ symbol in an expression such as $\sqrt{2}$. The number 2 is called the *radicand* and an expression involving a radical is called a *radical expression*.

Radicand   See *Radical form*.

Radius   The distance of a point on a circle from the center of the same circle.

RAM   Random-Access Memory, or memory where each location is uniformly accessible, often used for the storage of a program and the data being processed.

Random variable   A *random variable X* associated with the sample space S of an experiment is a function that assigns a real number to each simple event in S.

Range   (1) In statistics, it is the difference between the largest and the smallest numbers in the data set. (2) The *range* of a graph of an equation with two variables x and y is the set of permissible real-number replacements for y.

Rate   (1) In percent problems, it is the percent. (2) In tax problems, it is the level of taxation, written as a percent. (3) In financial problems, it refers to the APR.

Ratio   The quotient of two numbers or expressions.

Rational equation   An equation that has at least one variable in the denominator.

Rational number   A number belonging to the set $\mathbb{Q}$ defined by

$$\mathbb{Q} = \left\{ \frac{a}{b} \,\middle|\, a \text{ is an integer, } b \text{ is a nonzero integer} \right\}$$

a is called the *numerator* and b is called the *denominator*. A rational number is also called *a fraction*.

Ray If P is a point on a line, then a ray from the point P is all points on the line on one side of P.

Real number line A line on which points are associated with real numbers in a one-to-one fashion.

Real numbers The set of all rational and irrational numbers, denoted by $\mathbb{R}$.

Reciprocal The reciprocal of n is $\frac{1}{n}$, also called the *multiplicative inverse of n*.

Rectangle A quadrilateral whose angles are all right angles.

Rectangular coordinate system See *Cartesian coordinate system*.

Rectangular coordinates See *Ordered pair*.

Rectangular parallelepiped In this book, it refers to a box all of whose angles are right angles.

Reduced fraction A fraction so that the numerator and denominator have no common divisors (other than 1).

Reducing fractions The process by which we make sure that there are no common factors (other than 1) for the numerator and denominator of a fraction.

Reflection Given a line L and a point P, we call the point P' the *reflection* about the line L if $\overline{PP'}$ is perpendicular to L and is also bisected by L.

Region In a network, a separate part of the plane.

Regression analysis The analysis used to determine the relationship between two variables.

Regular polygon A polygon with all sides the same length.

Relation A set of ordered pairs.

Relative frequency If an experiment is repeated n times and an event occurs m times, then the relative frequency is the ratio m/n.

Relatively prime Two integers are relatively prime if they have no common factors other than ± 1; two polynomials are relatively prime if they have no common factors except constants.

Remainder When an integer m is divided by a positive integer n, and a quotient q is obtained for which $m = nq + r$ with $0 \leq r < n$, then r is the remainder.

Repeating decimal See *Decimal fraction*.

Repetitive system numeration system for which a single symbol is repeated to represent a given number. For example, ∩∩∩ in the Babylonian system means $10 + 10 + 10 = 30$

Replication On a spreadsheet, the operation of copying a formula from one place to another.

Resolution The number of dots (or pixels) determines the clarity, or resolution, of the image on the monitor.

Revolving credit It is the same as open-ended or credit card credit.

Rhombus A parallelogram with adjacent sides equal.

Richter number A number used to denote the magnitude or size of an earthquake.

Richter scale Same as *Richter number*.

Right angle An angle of 90°.

Right circular cone A cone with a circular base for which the base is perpendicular to its axis.

Right circular cylinder A cylinder with a circular base for which the base is perpendicular to its axis.

Right prism A prism whose base is perpendicular to the lateral edges.

Right triangle A triangle with one right angle.

Rise See *Slope*.

ROM <u>R</u>ead-<u>O</u>nly <u>M</u>emory, or memory that cannot be altered either by the user or a loss of power. In microcomputers, the ROM usually contains the operating system and system programs.

Root of a number An nth root (n is a natural number) of a number b is a only if $a^n = b$. If $n = 2$, then the root is called a *square root*; if $n = 3$, it is called a *cube root*.

Root of an equation See *Solution*.

Roster method A method of defining a set by listing its members.

Rounding a number Dropping decimals after a certain significant place. The procedure for rounding is: 1. Locate the rounding place digit. 2. Determine the rounding place digit: It stays the same if the first digit to its right is a 0, 1, 2, 3, or 4; it increases by 1 if the digit to the right is a 5, 6, 7, 8, or 9. 3. Change digits: all digits to the left of the rounding digit remain the same (unless there is a carry) and all digits to the right of the rounding digit are changed to zeros. 4. Drop zeros: If the rounding place digit is to the left of the decimal point, drop all trailing zeros; if the rounding place digit is to the right of the decimal point, drop all trailing zeros to the right of the rounding place digit.

Row A horizontal arrangement of numbers or entries of a matrix. It is denoted by numerals 1, 2, 3, . . . on a spreadsheet.

Row+ An elementary row transformation that causes one row of a matrix (called the *pivot row*) to be added to another row (called the *target row*). The answer to this addition replaces the entries in the target row, entry by entry.

Row-reduced form The final matrix after the process of Gauss-Jordan elimination.

RowSwap An elementary row operation that causes two rows of a matrix to be switched, entry-by-entry.

Rubik's cube A three-dimensional cube that can rotate about all three axes. It is a puzzle that has the object of returning the faces to a single-color position.

Rules of divisibility A number N is divisible by:

1	
2	if the last digit is divisible by 2.
3	if the sum of the digits is divisible by 3.
4	if the number formed by the last two digits is divisible by 4.
5	if the last digit is 0 or 5.
6	if the number is divisible by 2 and by 3.
8	if the number formed by the last three digits is divisible by 8.
9	if the sum of the digits is divisible by 9.
10	if the last digit is 0.
12	if the number is divisible by 3 and by 4.

Run See *Slope*.

Runoff election An attempt to obtain a majority vote by eliminating one or more alternatives and voting again on the remaining choices.

Saccheri quadrilateral A rectangle with base angles A and B right angles, and with sides $\overline{AC}$ and $\overline{BD}$ the same length.

Sales price A reduced price usually offered to stimulate sales. It can be found by subtracting the discount from the original price, or by multiplying the original price by the complement of the markdown.

Sales tax A tax levied by government bodies that is based on the sale price of an item.

Sample A finite portion of a population.

Sample space   The set of possible outcomes for an experiment.

Satisfy   See *Equation* or *Inequality*.

Scalar   A real number.

Scalar multiplication   The multiplication of a real number and a matrix.

Scalene triangle   A triangle with no two sides having the same length.

Scatter diagram   A diagram showing the frequencies with which joint values of variables are observed. One variable is indicated along the *x*-axis and the other along the *y*-axis.

Scientific notation   Writing a number as the product of a number between 1 and 10 and a power of 10: For any real number n, $n = m \cdot 10^c$, $1 \leq m < 10$, and c is an integer. Calculators often switch to scientific notation to represent large or small numbers. The usual notation is 8.234 05, where the space separates the number from the power; thus 8.234 05 means 8.234×10^5.

Secant line   A line passing through two points of a given curve.

Second component   See *Ordered pair*.

Second-degree equation   With one variable, an equation of the form $ax^2 + bx + c = 0$; with two variables, an equation of the form

$$Ax^2 + Bxy + Cy^2 + Dx + Ey + F = 0$$

Semiannual compounding   In the compound interest formula, it is when $n = 2$.

Semicircle   Half a circle.

Sequence   An *infinite sequence* is a function whose domain is the set of counting numbers. It is sometimes called *a progression*. A *finite sequence* with *n* terms is a function whose domain is the set of numbers $\{1, 2, 3, \ldots, n\}$.

Sequential voting   A runoff election procedure that has one vote followed by another.

Series   The indicated sum of a finite or an infinite sequence of terms.

Series circuit   Two switches connected together so that the circuit is on only if both switches are on.

Set   A collection of particular things, called the *members* or *elements* of the set. A set with no elements is called the *null set* or *empty set* and is denoted by the symbol $\varnothing$. All elements of *a finite set* may be listed, whereas the elements of an *infinite set* continue without end.

Set-builder notation   A technical notation for defining a set. For example,

$$\{a \mid a \in \mathbb{Z}, 5 < a < 100\}$$

means "the set of all elements *a* such that *a* is an integer between 5 and 100."

Set theory   The branch of mathematics that studies sets.

SI system   See *Metric system*.

Sieve of Eratosthenes   A method for determining a set of primes less than some counting number *n*. Write out the consecutive numbers from 1 to *n*. Cross out 1, since it is not classified as a prime number. Draw a circle around 2, the smallest prime number. Then cross out every following multiple of 2, since each is divisible by 2 and thus is not prime. Draw a circle around 3, the next prime number. Then cross out each succeeding multiple of 3. Some of these numbers, such as 6 and 12, will already have been crossed out because they are also multiples of 2. Circle the next open prime, 5, and cross out all subsequent multiples of 5. The next prime number is 7; circle 7 and cross out multiples of 7. Continue this process until you have crossed out the primes up to $\sqrt{n}$. All of the remaining numbers on the list are prime.

Sigma notation   Sigma, the Greek letter corresponding to *S*, is written Σ. It is used to indicate the process of summing the first to the *n*th terms of a set of numbers $s_1, s_2, s_3, \ldots, s_n$, which is written as

$$\sum_{k=1}^{n} s_k$$

This notation is also called *summation notation*.

Signed number   An integer.

Significance level   Deviations between hypothesis and observations that are so improbable under the hypothesis as not to be due merely to sampling error or random fluctuations are said to be *statistically significant*. The significance level is set at an acceptable level for a deviation to be statistically significant.

Similar figures   Two geometric figures are similar if they have the same shape, but not necessarily the same size.

Similar terms   Terms that differ only in their numerical coefficients.

Similar triangle theorem   Two triangles are similar if two angles of one triangle are equal to two angles of the other triangle. If the triangles are similar, then their corresponding sides are proportional.

Similar triangles   Triangles that have the same shape.

Similarity   Two geometric figures are *similar* if they have the same shape.

Simple curve   A curve that does not intersect itself.

Simple event   An event that contains only one element of the sample space.

Simple grouping system   A numeration system is a grouping system if the position of the symbols is not important, and each symbol larger than 1 represents a group of other symbols.

Simple interest formula $I = Prt$

Simple statement   A statement that does not contain a connective.

Simplify   (1) A *polynomial*: combine similar terms and write terms in order of descending degree. (2) A fraction (a rational expression): Simplify numerator and denominator, factor if possible, and eliminate all common factors. (3) A square root: The *radicand* (the number under the radical sign) has no factor with an exponent larger than 1 when it is written in factored form; the radicand is not written as a fraction or by using negative exponents; there are no square root symbols used in the denominators of fractions.

Simulation   Use of a computer program to simulate some real-world situation.

Simultaneous solution   The solution of a simultaneous system of equations.

Sine   In a right triangle *ABC* with right angle *C*,

$$\sin A = \frac{\text{LENGTH OF OPPOSITE SIDE OF } A}{\text{LENGTH OF HYPOTENUSE}}$$

Singular matrix   A matrix that does not have an inverse.

Sinking fund   A financial problem in which the monthly payment must be found to obtain a known future value. The formula is

$$m = \frac{A\left(\frac{r}{n}\right)}{\left(1 + \frac{r}{n}\right)^{nt} - 1}$$

Skewed distribution   A statistical distribution that is not symmetric, but favors the occurrence on one side of the mean or the other.

Slant asymptotes   In graphing a hyperbola, the diagonal lines passing through the corners of the central rectangle.

Slope   The slope of a line passing through (x_1, y_1) and (x_2, y_2) is denoted by m, and is found by

$$m = \frac{y_2 - y_1}{x_2 - x_1} = \frac{\text{VERTICAL CHANGE}}{\text{HORIZONTAL CHANGE}} = \frac{\text{RISE}}{\text{RUN}}$$

Slope-intercept form $y = mx + b$

Slope point   A point that is found after counting out the rise and the run from the y-intercept.

Software   The routines, programs, and associated documentation in a computer system.

Software package   A commercially available computer program that is written to carry out a specific purpose, for example, a database program or a word-processing program.

Solution   The values or ordered pairs of values for which an equation, a system of equations, inequality, or system of inequalities is true. Also called *roots*.

Solution set   The set of all solutions to an equation.

Solve a proportion   To find the missing term of a proportion. Procedure: First, find the product of the means or the product of the extremes, whichever does not contain the unknown term; next, divide this product by the number that is opposite the unknown term.

Solve an equation   To find the values of the variable that make the equation true.

Solve an inequality   To find the values of the variable that make the inequality true.

Some   A word used to mean "at least one."

Spanning tree   A tree that is created from another graph by removing edges while keeping a path to each vertex.

Sphere   The set of all points in space that are a given distance from a given point.

Spreadsheet   A rectangular grid used to collect and perform calculations on data. *Rows* are horizontal and are labeled with numbers and *columns* are vertical and are labeled with letters to designate *cells* such as A4, P604. Each cell can contain text, numbers, or formulas.

Square   (1) A quadrilateral with all sides the same length and all angles right angles. (2) In an expression such as x^2, which is pronounced "x-squared," it means xx.

Square matrix   A matrix with the same number of rows and columns.

Square number   Numbers that are squares of the counting numbers: 1, 4, 9, 16, 25, 36, 49, 64, 81, 100, 121, 144, 169, ...

Square root   See *Root of a number.*

Square unit   A two-dimensional unit. It is the result of squaring a unit of measurement.

Stable marriage   A pairing in which both partners are satisfied.

Standard deviation   It is a measure of the variation of a data set. In particular, it is the square root of the mean of the squares of the deviations from the mean.

Standard divisor

$$\text{STANDARD DIVISOR} = \frac{\text{TOTAL POPULATION}}{\text{NUMBER OF SHARES}}$$

Standard form   The standard form of the equation of a line is

$$Ax + By + C = 0.$$

Standard quota

$$\text{STANDARD QUOTA} = \frac{\text{TOTAL POPULATION}}{\text{STANDARD DIVISOR}}$$

Statement   A declarative sentence that is either true or false, but not both true and false.

Statistics   Methods of obtaining and analyzing quantitative data.

Stem-and-leaf plot   A procedure for organizing data that can be divided into two categories. The first category is listed at the left, and the second category at the right.

Sticker price   In this book, it refers to the manufacturer's total price of a new automobile as listed on the window of the car.

Straight angle   An angle whose rays point in opposite directions; an angle whose measure is $180°$.

Straightedge   A device used as an aid in drawing a straight line segment.

Straw vote   A nonbinding vote taken before all the discussion has taken place. It precedes the actual vote.

Street problem   A problem that asks the number of possible routes from one location to another along some city's streets. The assumptions are that we always move in the correct direction and that we do not cut through the middle of a block, but rather stay on the streets or alleys.

Subjective probability   A probability obtained by experience and used to indicate a measure of "certainty" on the part of the speaker. These probabilities are not necessarily arrived at through experimentation or theory.

Subscript   A small number or letter written below and to the right or left of a letter as a mark of distinction.

Subset   A set contained within a set. There are 2^n subsets of a set with n distinct elements. A subset is *improper* if it is equivalent to the given set; otherwise it is *proper*.

Substitution method   The method of solution of a system of equations in which one of the equations is solved for one of the variables and substituted into another equation.

Substitution property   The process of replacing one quantity or unknown by another quantity. That is, if $a = b$, then a may be substituted for b in any mathematical statement without affecting the truth or falsity of the given mathematical statement.

Subtraction   The operation of subtraction is defined by:

$$a - b = x \text{ means } a = b + x$$

Subtraction law of exponents   To divide two numbers with the same base, subtract the exponents. That is,

$$\frac{b^m}{b^n} = b^{m-n}$$

Subtraction law of logarithms   The log of the quotient of two numbers is the log of the numerator minus the log of the denominator. In symbols,

$$\log_b\left(\frac{A}{B}\right) = \log_b A - \log_b B$$

Subtraction of integers

$$a - b = a + (-b)$$

Subtraction of matrices $[M] - [N] = [S]$ if and only if [M] and [N] are the same order and the entries of [S] are found by subtracting the corresponding entries of [M] and [N].

Subtraction of rational numbers

$$\frac{a}{b} - \frac{c}{d} = \frac{ad}{bd} - \frac{bc}{bd} = \frac{ad - bc}{bd}$$

Subtraction principle   In reference to numeration systems, it is subtracting the value of some symbol from the value of the other symbols. For example, in the Roman numeration system IX uses the subtraction principle because the position of the I in front of the X indicates that the value of I (which is 1) is to be subtracted from the value of X (which is 10). IX = 9.

Subtraction property of equations   The solution of an equation is unchanged by subtracting the same number from both sides of the equation.

Subtraction property of inequality   *See Addition property of inequality.*

Successor   In a sequence, the successor of an element a_n is the following element, a_{n+1}.

Sum   The result of an addition.

Summation notation   See *Sigma notation.*

Supercomputer   A large, very fast mainframe computer used especially for scientific computations.

Superfluous constraint   In a linear programming problem, a constraint that does not change the outcome if it is deleted.

Supermarket problem   Set up the shelves in a market or convenience store so that it is possible to enter the store at one door and travel each aisle once (and only once) and leave by the same door.

Supplementary angles   Two angles whose sum is 180°.

Supply   The number of items that can be supplied at a given price.

Surface   In mathematics, it is an undefined term. It is the outer face or exterior of an object; it has an extent or magnitude having length and breadth, but no thickness.

Surface area   The area of the outside faces of a solid.

Syllogism   A logical argument that involves three propositions, usually two premises and a conclusion, the conclusion necessarily being true if the premises are true.

Symbols of inclusion   See *Grouping symbols.*

Symmetric property of equality   If $a = b$, then $b = a$.

Symmetry   (1) In geometry, a graph or picture is *symmetric with respect to a line* if the graph is a mirror reflection along the line. (2) In voting, it means that if one voter prefers A to B and another B to A, then the votes should cancel each other out.

Syntax error   The breaking of a rule governing the structure of the programming language being used.

System of equations   A set of equations that are to be solved *simultaneously.* A brace symbol is used to show the equations belonging to the system.

System of inequalities   A set of inequalities that are to be solved simultaneously. The solution is the set of all ordered pairs (x, y) that satisfy all the given inequalities. It is found by finding the intersection of the half-planes defined by each inequality.

Tangent   In a right triangle ABC with right angle C,

$$\tan A = \frac{\text{LENGTH OF OPPOSITE SIDE OF } A}{\text{LENGTH OF ADJACENT SIDE OF } A}$$

Tangent line   A tangent line to a circle is a line that contains exactly one point of the circle. The tangent line to a curve at a point P is the limiting position, if this exists, of the secant line through a fixed point P on the curve and a variable point P' on the curve so that P' approaches P along the curve.

Target population   The population to be considered for a statistical application.

Target row   In an elementary row operation, it is the row that is changed. See *Elementary row operations.*

Tautology   A compound statement is a tautology if all values on its truth table are true.

Temperature   The degree of hotness or coldness.

Ten   A representation for "ΔΔΔΔΔΔΔΔΔΔ" objects

Term   (1) A number, a variable, or a product of numbers and variables. See *Polynomial.* (2) A *term of a sequence* is one of the elements of that sequence.

Terminating decimal   See *Decimal fraction.*

Tessellation   A mosaic, repetitive pattern.

Test point   A point that is chosen to find the appropriate half-plane when graphing a linear inequality in two variables.

Theorem   A statement that has been proved. See *Deductive reasoning.*

Theoretical probability   A probability obtained by logical reasoning according to stated definitions.

Time   In a financial problem, the length of time (in years) from the present value to the future value.

*Row   An elementary row operation that multiplies each entry of a row of a matrix (called the *target row)* by some number, called a *scalar.* The elements of the row are replaced term-by-term by the products. It is denoted by *Row.

*Row+   An elementary row operation that multiplies each entry of a row of a matrix (called the *pivot row)* by some number (called a *scalar*), and then adds that product, term by term, to the numbers in another row (called the *target row).* The results replace the entries in the target row, term by term. It is denoted by *Row+.

Ton   A measurement of mass in the United States system; it is equal to 2,000 lb.

Topologically equivalent   Two geometric figures are said to be *topologically equivalent* if one figure can be elastically twisted, stretched, bent, shrunk, or straightened into the same shape as the other. One can cut the figure, provided at some point the cut edges are "glued" back together again to be exactly the same as before.

Topology   That branch of geometry that deals with the *topological properties* of figures. If one figure can be transformed into another by stretching or contracting, then the figures are said to be *topologically equivalent.*

Tournament method   A method of selecting a winner by pairing candidates head-to-head with the winner of one facing a new opponent for the next election.

Trailing zeros   Sometimes zeros are placed after the decimal point or after the last digit to the right of the decimal point, and if these zeros do not change the value of the number, they are called *trailing zeros.*

Transformation   A passage from one figure or expression to another, such as a reflection, translation, rotation, contraction, or dilation.

Transformational geometry   The geometry that studies transformations.

Transitive law   If A beats B, and B beats C, then A should beat C. In symbols, equality: If $a = b$ and $b = c$, then $a = c$; *inequality:* If $a > b$ and $b > c$, then $a > c$. Also holds for $\geq, <$, and $\leq$.

Transitive reasoning   If $a = b$ and $b = c$, then $a = c$.

Translating symbols   The process of writing an English sentence in mathematical symbols.

Transversal   A line that intersects two parallel lines.

Transverse axis   The line passing through the foci is called the *transverse axis*.

Trapezoid   A quadrilateral that has two parallel sides.

Traveling salesperson problem (TSP)   A salesperson starts at home and wants to visit several cities without going through any city more than once and then returning to the starting city.

Traversable network   A network is said to be *traversable* if it can be traced in one sweep without lifting the pencil from the paper and without tracing the same edge more than once. Vertices may be passed through more than once.

Tree   A graph that is connected and has no circuits.

Tree diagram   A device used to list all the possibilities for an experiment.

Triangle   A polygon with three sides.

Trichotomy   Exactly one of the following is true, for any real numbers a and b: $a < b$, $a > b$, or $a = b$.

Trigonometric functions   The same as the *trigonometric ratios*.

Trigonometric ratios   The sine, cosine, and tangent ratios are known as the *trigonometric ratios*.

Trillion   A name for $10^{12} = 1,000,000,000,000$.

Trinomial   A polynomial with exactly three terms.

Truth set   The set of values that makes a given statement true.

Truth table   A table that shows the truth values of all possibilities for compound statements.

Truth value   The truth value of a simple statement is true or false. The truth value of a compound statement is true or false and depends only on the truth values of its simple component parts. It is determined by using the rules for connecting those parts with well-defined operators.

Two-point form   The equation of a line passing through (x_1, y_1) and (x_2, y_2) is

$$y - y_1 = \left(\frac{y_2 - y_1}{x_2 - x_1}\right)(x - x_1)$$

Type I error   Rejection of a hypothesis based on sampling when, in fact, the hypothesis is true.

Type II error   Acceptance of a hypothesis based on sampling when, in fact, it is false.

Undefined terms   To avoid circular definitions, it is necessary to include certain terms without specific mathematical definition.

Union   The union of sets A and B, denoted by $A \cup B$, is the set consisting of elements in A or in B or in both A and B.

Unit circle   A circle with radius 1 centered at the origin.

Unit distance   The distance between 0 and 1 on a number line.

Unit scale   The distance between the points marked 0 and 1 on a number line.

United States system   The measurement system used in the United States.

Universal set   The set that contains all of the elements under consideration for a problem or a set of problems.

Unless   A logical operator for "p unless q" that is defined to mean $\sim q \rightarrow p$.

Unrestricted domain   Any set of rankings is possible; if there are n candidates, then there are $n!$ possible rankings.

Unstable marriage   A pairing in which one (or both) of the partners would prefer to be paired with another partner.

Upload   The process of copying a program from your computer to the network.

Upper quota   In apportionment, the result of a quota found by rounding up.

User-friendly   A term used to describe software that is easy to use. It includes built-in safeguards to keep the user from changing important parts of a program.

Valid argument   In logic, refers to a correctly inferred logical argument.

Variable   A symbol that represents unspecified elements of a given set. On a calculator, it refers to the name given to a location in the memory that can be assigned a value.

Variable expression   An expression that contains at least one variable.

Variance   The square of the standard deviation. When the variance is based on a set of sample scores, it is called the *variance of a random sample* and is denoted by s^2, and when it is based on the entire population, it is called the *variance of the population* and is denoted by σ^2. The formulas for variance are

$$s^2 = \frac{\Sigma(x - \bar{x})^2}{n - 1} \qquad \sigma^2 = \frac{\Sigma(x - \mu)^2}{n}$$

Velocity   An instantaneous rate of change; a directed speed.

Venn diagram   A diagram used to illustrate relationships among sets.

Vertex   (1) A *vertex* of a polygon is a corner point, or a point of intersection of two sides. (2) A *vertex* of a parabola is the lowest point for a parabola that opens upward; the highest point for one that opens downward; the leftmost point for one that opens to the right; and the rightmost point for one that opens to the left.

Vertex angle   The angle included between the legs of an isosceles triangle.

Vertical angles   Two angles such that each side of one is a prolongation through the vertex of a side of the other.

Vertical ellipse   An ellipse whose major axis is vertical.

Vertical hyperbola   A hyperbola whose transverse axis is vertical.

Vertical line   A line with undefined slope. Its equation has the form $x = $ constant.

Vertical line test   Every vertical line passes through the graph of a function in at most one point. This means that if you sweep a vertical line across a graph and it simultaneous intersects the curve at more than one point, then the curve is not the graph of a function.

Volume   A number describing three-dimensional content of a set. Specifically, it is the number of cubic units enclosed in a solid figure.

Vote   A decision by a group on a proposal, resolution, law, or a choice between candidates for office.

Water-pipe problem   Consider a network of water pipes to be inspected. Is it possible to pass a hand over each pipe exactly once without lifting it from a pipe, and without going over the samepipe more than once?

Webster's apportionment plan   An apportionment plan in which the representation of a geographical area is determined by finding the quotient of the number of people in that area divided by the total number of people and then rounding the result as follows: Any quotient with a decimal portion must be rounded to the nearest whole number.

Weight   (1) In everyday usage, the heaviness of an object. In scientific usage, the gravitational pull on a body. (2) In a network or graph, a cost associated with an edge.

Weighted graph   A graph for which all its edges have weight.

Weighted mean   If the scores $x_1, x_2, x_3, \ldots, x_n$ occur $w_1, w_2, \ldots, w_n$ times, respectively, then the *weighted mean* is

$$\bar{x} = \frac{\Sigma(w \cdot x)}{\Sigma w}$$

Well-defined set   A set for which there is no doubt about whether a particular element is included in the given set.

Whole numbers   The positive integers and zero; $\mathbb{W} = \{0, 1, 2, 3, \ldots\}$.

Windows   A graphical environment for IBM format computers.

With replacement   If there is more than one step for an experiment, to perform the experiment with replacement means that the object chosen on the first step is replaced before the next steps are completed.

Without replacement   If there is more than one step for an experiment, to perform the experiment without replacement means that the object chosen on the first step is not replaced before the next steps are completed.

Word processing   The process of creating, modifying, deleting, and formatting textual materials.

World Wide Web   A network that connects together computers from all over the world. It is abbreviated by www.

WYSIWYG: An acronym for <u>W</u>hat <u>Y</u>ou <u>S</u>ee <u>I</u>s <u>W</u>hat <u>Y</u>ou <u>G</u>et.

***x*-axis**   The horizontal axis in a Cartesian coordinate system.

***x*-intercept**   The place where a graph passes through the x-axis.

***y*-axis**   The vertical axis in a Cartesian coordinate system.

***y*-intercept**   The place where a graph passes through the y-axis. For a line

$$y = mx + b$$

it is the point $(0, b)$.

Yard   A linear measure in the United States system; it has the same length as 3 ft.

Zero   The number that separates the positive and negative numbers; it is also called the *identity element* for addition; that is, it satisfies the property that

$$x + 0 = 0 + x = x$$

for all numbers x.

Zero matrix   A matrix with all entries equal to 0.

Zero multiplication   If a is any real number, then $a \cdot 0 = 0 \cdot a = 0$.

Zero-one matrix   A square matrix in which the entries symbolize the occurrence of some facet or event with a 1 and the nonoccurrence with a 0.

Zero-product rule   If $a \cdot b = 0$, then either $a = 0$ or $b = 0$.

***z*-score**   A measure to determine the distance (in terms of standard deviations) that a given score is from the mean of a distribution.

Appendix

B | Selected Answers

PROLOGUE

Prologue Problem Set, page P11

9. 181 **11.** 1,099 **13.** February and March **15.** 30 **17.** March 2011 **19.** 119 **21.** 945 **23.** $\frac{3}{8}$ **25.** 2 **27. a.** tetrahedron **b.** cube (hexahedron) **c.** octahedron **d.** dodecahedron **e.** icosahedron **29.** 1,499 **31.** More than a million trees must be cut down to print a trillion one-dollar bills. **33.** The area is approximately 13.7 in.^{2}. **35.** $\frac{1}{3}$ **37.** She had $22 at the start of the first day. **39.** The cost is $390 if 100 make the trip. **41.** Let x be the number of weeks enrolled, and y be the total cost. Then $y = 45(10 - x)$. The graph is shown.

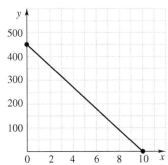

43. The rate at which percentage of alcohol is changing with respect to time is $\frac{dC}{dt} = -0.15e^{-t/2}$. **45.** There are 33 shortest paths. **47.** It will take until March 2125. **49.** $b = 2^{2/3}$ **51.** Answers vary; at least three cubes can be seen. **53.** $\frac{1}{120}$ **55.** This pattern of numbers has the property that the sum of the numbers in any row, column, or diagonal is the same (namely, 15). **57.** The population in 2000 was 153,000. The graph is shown.

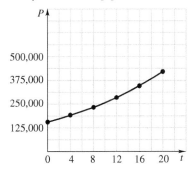

59. $2^{30} - 1$ dollars (more than a billion dollars)

CHAPTER 1

1.1 Problem Solving, page 14

5. first diagonal **7.** Yes; yes; answer is the same because the triangle is symmetric. **9. a.** 35 **b.** 56 **11.** 2 up, 3 over; 10 paths **13.** 4 up, 6 over; 210 paths **15.** 4 down, 3 over; 35 paths **17.** 2 up, 4 over; 15 paths **19.** Answers vary. **21.** There is a total of 27 boxes. **23.** The blind person says, "I need a pair of scissors." **25. a.** 2 **b.** 4 **c.** 8 **d.** 16 **27.** 49 paths **29.** 284 paths **31.** 12 **33.** 7 **35.** 11 **37.** 12:30

39. 54 **41.** 4 mm **43.** Answers vary. Put one lump in the first cup, four lumps in the second cup, and 5 lumps in the third cup. Now, put the first cup (containing the lump) inside the second cup. **45.** Answers vary. **47.** Answers vary. **49.** The fly flies 20 miles **51.** 8 miles or 12 miles **53.** puff **55.** 1.62 **57.** The number of routes from the start to the finish minus the number of routes passing through the barricade. **a.** 26 **b.** 23 **c.** 27 **59.** Answers vary.

1.2 Inductive and Deductive Reasoning, page 24

7. a. 17 **b.** 13 **9. a.** 45 **b.** 45 **11. a.** 14 **b.** 6 **13. a.** 50 **b.** 2 **15. a.** 38 **b.** 54 **17. a.** 13 **b.** 12 **19.** inductive reasoning; answers vary **21.** 3, 6, 9, . . . **23.** 5, 1, 6, 2, 7, 3, 8, 4, 9, . . . **25. a.** 625 **b.** 62,500

27.

2	7	6
9	5	1
4	3	8

29. valid **31.** valid **33.** valid **35.** not valid **37.** not valid **39.** not valid **41.** east; deductive reasoning **43.** probably Las Vegas; inductive reasoning **45.** eight persons; deductive reasoning **47.** probably Alabama; inductive reasoning **49.** There is no door seen, so this means that the bus is heading west (or to the left); this is an example of deductive reasoning. **51. a.** $9 \times 54,321 - 1$; 488,888 **b.** 8,888,888,888 **c.** 98,888,888,888 **53.** $34^2 = 1156$; $334^2 = 111556$; $3334^2 = 11115556$; $\cdots$; 111111111555555556, so the sum is $9(1) + 8(5) + 6 = 55$; inductive reasoning **55.** 91 squares **57.** Balance 3 with 3 to determine which group is heaver. Repeat with the heavier group. **59. a.** One diagonal is 38,307; other sums are 21,609. **b.** One diagonal is 13,546,875; other sums are 20,966,014.

1.3 Scientific Notation and Estimation, page 40

7. a. 3.2×10^3; 3.2 03 **b.** 4×10^{-4}; 4 −04 **c.** 6.4×10^{10}; 6.4 10 **9. a.** 5.629×10^3; 5.629 03 **b.** 6.3×10^5; 6.3 05 **c.** 3.4×10^{-8}; 3.4 −08 **11. a.** 49 **b.** 72,000,000,000 **c.** 4,560 **13. a.** 216 **b.** 0.00000 041 **c.** 0.00000 048 **15.** 9.3×10^7; 3.65×10^2 **17.** 2.2×10^8; 2.5×10^{-6} **19.** 3,600,000 **21.** 0.00000 003 *Estimates in Problems 23–30 may vary.* **23.** 35 mi **25.** Estimate $2,000 \times 500 = 1,000,000$; $1,850 \times 487 = 900,950$ **27.** Estimate $20 \times 15 = 300$; $23 \times 15 = 345$ **29.** Estimate $600,000 \div 60 = 10,000$ hours; $10,000 \div 25 = 400$ days; estimate one year. $525,600 \div 60 \div 24 = 365$ **31. a.** 1.2×10^9 **b.** 3×10^2 **33. a.** 1.2×10^{-3} **b.** 2×10^7 **35. a.** 4×10^{-8} **b.** 1.2 **37.** Estimate 10/cm^2, so about 120 oranges. **39.** Estimate 270 chairs **41.** Assume one balloon is about 1 ft^3 and also assume a typical classroom is 30 ft $\times$ 50 ft $\times$ 10 ft = 15,000 ft^3, so $10^6 \div (1.5 \times 10^4) \approx 67$; we estimate that it would take 60–70 classrooms. **43.** Assume there are 233 $1 bills per inch. A million dollars would form a stack about 119 yd high. **45.** Assume there are 2,260,000 grains in a pound of sugar. 1.356×10^{17} grains **47.** Assume that a box of chalk contains 12 four inch pieces, so one box is about 4 ft of chalk. Also assume that a box of chalk costs about $1. 400,000 ft $\approx$ 75 miles. **49. a.** Answers vary. **b.** 9^{9^9} **c.** $10^{369,692,902}$ to $10^{387,000,000}$ **51.** $3.36271772 \times 10^{23}$ **53.** Assume a brick is 8 in. by $3\frac{1}{2}$ in. by 2 in. Answers vary; the wall will contain between 27,000 and 31,000 bricks. **55.** 48 minutes, 13 seconds **57.** 192 zeros **59. a.** D **b.** 701.8 ft^2/person

Chapter 1 Review Questions, page 44

1. Understand the problem, devise a plan, carry out the plan, and then look back.   **2.** 126   **3.** 330 paths   **4.** 12,345,678,987,654,321   **5.** Order of operations: (1) First, perform any operations enclosed in parentheses. (2) Next, perform multiplications and divisions as they occur by working from left to right. (3) Finally, perform additions and subtractions as they occur by working from left to right.   **6.** The scientific notation for a number is that number written as a power of 10 times another number x, such that $1 \le x < 10$.   **7.** Inductive reasoning; the answer was found by looking at the pattern of questions.   **8.** Answers vary.   **a.** $\boxed{2}\,\boxed{y^x}\,\boxed{63}\,\boxed{=}$ or $\boxed{2}\,\boxed{\wedge}$ $\boxed{63}\,\boxed{\text{ENTER}}$ 9.223372037E18   **b.** $\boxed{9.22}\,\boxed{\text{EE}}\,\boxed{18}\,\boxed{\div}\,\boxed{6.34}\,\boxed{\text{EE}}\,\boxed{6}\,\boxed{=}$ 1.454258675E12   **9.** C   **10.** $\frac{3}{4}$ hr $\times$ 365 = 273.75 hr. This is approximately $2\frac{3}{4}$ hr/book. Could not possibly be a complete transcription of each book.   **11.** Answers vary. It is larger than the capacity of all of lakes behind all the world's dams, even the world's largest one to be completed in 2009 on the Yangzi River in China.   **12.** Each person's share is about $44,516.   **13.** Arrange the cards as $\begin{bmatrix} 2 & 7 & 6 \\ 9 & 5 & 1 \\ 4 & 3 & 8 \end{bmatrix}$.   **14.** Fill the classroom with $100 bills; it will take 857 classrooms.   **15.** not valid   **16.** not valid   **17.** valid   **18.** valid   **19.** Answers vary.   **20.** 7^{1000} ends in 1.

CHAPTER 2

2.1 Sets, Subsets, and Venn Diagrams, page 57

9. a. well defined   **b.** not well defined   **11. a.** not well defined   **b.** not well defined   **13. a.** $\{m, a, t, h, e, i, c, s\}$ **b.** {Barack Obama}   **15. a.** $\{7, 8, 9, 10, \ldots\}$ **b.** $\{1, 2, 3, 4, 5\}$ **17. a.** $\{p, i, e\}$ **b.** $\{151, 152, 153, \ldots\}$ *Answers to Problems 19–24 may vary.*   **19.** counting numbers less than 10   **21.** multiples of 10 between 0 and 101   **23.** odd numbers between 100 and 170   **25.** the set of all numbers, x, such that x is an odd counting number; $\{1, 3, 5, 7, \ldots\}$ **27.** the set of all natural numbers, x, except 8; $\{1, 2, 3, 4, 5, 6, 7, 9, 10, \ldots\}$ **29.** The set of all whole numbers, x, such that x is less than 8; $\{0, 1, 2, 3, 4, 5, 6, 7\}$ **31. a.** $\varnothing$ **b.** $\varnothing, \{1\}$ **c.** $\varnothing, \{1\}, \{2\}, \{1, 2\}$ **d.** $\varnothing, \{1\}, \{2\}, \{3\}, \{1, 2\}, \{1, 3\}, \{2, 3\}, \{1, 2, 3\}$ **e.** $\varnothing, \{1\}, \{2\}, \{3\}, \{4\}\{1, 2\}, \{1, 3\}, \{1, 4\}, \{2, 3\}, \{2, 4\}, \{3, 4\}, \{1, 2, 3\}, \{1, 2, 4\}, \{1, 3, 4\}, \{2, 3, 4\}, \{1, 2, 3, 4\}$

33. 32 subsets; yes

35. 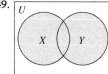   **37.**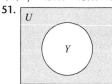

39. a. $|A| = 3, |B| = 1, |C| = 3, |D| = 1, |E| = 1, |F| = 1$ **b.** $A \leftrightarrow C; B \leftrightarrow D \leftrightarrow E \leftrightarrow F$ **c.** $A = C; D = E = F$ **41. a.** true   **b.** false   **43. a.** true   **b.** false   **45.** true   **47.** true   **49.** false   **51.** false   **53.** true   **55.** Answers vary; the set of real numbers, or the set of people alive in China today.   **57.** There will be five different ways, since each group of four will have one missing person.   **59.** The set of Chevrolets is a subset of the set of automobiles.

2.2 Operations with Sets, page 62

3. a. or   **b.** and   **c.** not   **5.** $\{2, 6, 8, 10\}$ **7.** $\{2, 3, 5, 6, 8, 9\}$ **9.** $\{3, 4, 5\}$ **11.** $\{1, 3, 4, 5, 6, 7, 10\}$ **13.** $\{2, 4, 6, 8, 10\}$ **15.** $\{2, 3, 4, 6, 8, 9, 10\}$ **17.** $\{1, 3, 5, 7, 9\}$ **19.** $\{x \,|\, x$ is a nonzero integer$\}$ **21.** $\mathbb{W}$ **23.** $\varnothing$ **25.** $\varnothing$ **27.** U **29.** $\{1, 2, 3, 4, 5, 6\}$ **31.** $\{1, 2, 3, 4, 5, 7\}$ **33.** $\{5\}$ **35.** $\{5, 6, 7\}$ **37.** $\{1, 2, 4, 6\}$ **39.** $\{1, 2, 3, 4\}$ **41.** $\{1, 2, 3, 4, 6, 7\}$ **43.** A **45.** $A \cap B$ **47.** $\overline{A \cap B}$

49. 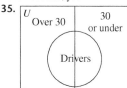   **51.**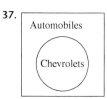

53. yes   **55.** 3   **57.** 51,000   **59.** 2^n regions

2.3 Applications of Sets, page 70

1. $\overline{X \cup Y} = \overline{X} \cap \overline{Y}$ and $\overline{X \cap Y} = \overline{X} \cup \overline{Y}$ **3.** $\{3, 5\}$ **5.** $\{7\}$ **7.** $\{5, 6, 7\}$ **9.** $\{1, 2, 4, 6, 7\}$ **11.** $\overline{X} \cup \overline{Y}$ **13.** $\overline{X \cap Y}$ **15.** $X \cup Y$ **17.** $\overline{X} \cap \overline{Y}$

19. 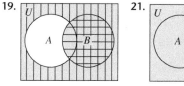   **21.**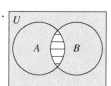

23. 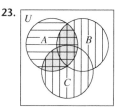   **25.**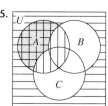

27. 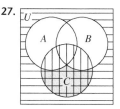   **29.**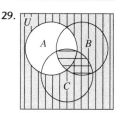

31. 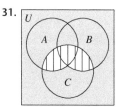   **33.**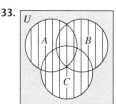

35. 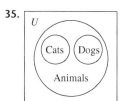   **37.**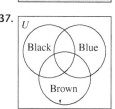

39.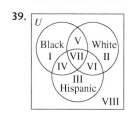

I: 24,985,000
II: 203,825,000
III: 15,780,000
IV: 5,260,000
V: 1,315,000
VI: 2,630,000
VII: 0
VIII: 9,205,000

41. Steffi Graf, II; Michael Stich, V; Martina Navratilova, III; Stefan Edberg, V; Chris Evert Lloyd, VI; Boris Becker, V; Evonne Goolagong, II; Pat Cash, V; Virginia Wade, II; John McEnroe, IV   **43.** $\overline{A} \cap B$ **45.** $[(\overline{A \cup B}) \cap C] \cup [(A \cap B) \cap C]$

47.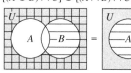

It is true.

49.

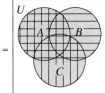

It is true.

51.

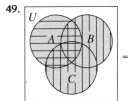

It is true.

53. No, there were 102 persons polled, not 100.

55. a.

$E = \{\text{favor Prop. 8}\}$
$T = \{\text{favor Prop. 13}\}$
$F = \{\text{favor Prop. 5}\}$
b. 12   **c.** 7

57.

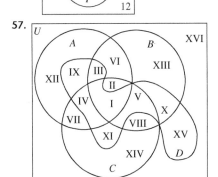

59. a. region 32   **b.** region 2

2.4 Finite and Infinite Sets, page 77

5. $A \times B = \{(c, w), (c, x), (d, w), (d, x), (f, w), (f, x)\}$ **7.** $\{(1, a), (1, b),$
$(1, c), (2, a), (2, b), (2, c), (3, a), (3, b), (3, c), (4, a), (4, b), (4, c), (5, a),$
$(5, b), (5, c)\}$ **9.** $\{(2, a), (2, e), (2, i), (2, o), (2, u), (3, a), (3, e), (3, i),$
$(3, o), (3, u), (4, a), (4, e), (4, i), (4, o), (4, u)\}$ **11.** 143   **13.** 85
15. 21   **17.** 0   **19.** $\aleph_0$ **21.** 460   **23.** $\aleph_0$ **25.** 260   **27.** 5,000
29. $\{m, a, t\}$; $\{m, a, t\}$; there are others.

$\{1, 2, 3\}; \{3, 2, 1\}$

31. $\{1, \quad 2, \ldots, \quad n, \quad n + 1, \ldots, \quad 353, 354, 355, 356 \ldots, 586,$
$587\}$

$\{550, 551, \ldots, n + 549, n + 550, \ldots, 902, 903\}$
Thus, the sets do not have the same cardinality.
33. a. finite   **b.** infinite
35. $\{1, \quad 2, \quad 3, \ldots, \quad n, \ldots\}$

$\{-1, -2, -3, \ldots, -n, \ldots\}$
Since these sets can be put into a one-to-one correspondence, they
have the same cardinality—namely, $\aleph_0$.
37. $\{1, 2, 3, \ldots, n, \ldots\}$

$\{\frac{1}{1}, \frac{1}{2}, \frac{1}{3}, \ldots, \frac{1}{n}, \ldots\}$
Since these sets can be put into a one-to-one correspondence, they
have the same cardinality—namely, $\aleph_0$.

39. $\mathbb{W} = \{0, 1, 2, 3, \ldots, \quad n, \ldots\}$

$\{1, 2, 3, 4, \ldots, n + 1, \ldots\}$
Since these sets can be put into a one-to-one correspondence, they
have the same cardinality—namely, $\aleph_0$.
41. $\{1, 3, 5, \ldots, 2n + 1, \ldots\}$

$\{1, 2, 3, \ldots, \quad n, \ldots\}$
Since these sets can be put into a one-to-one correspondence, they
have the same cardinality—namely, $\aleph_0$.
43. $\{1, 2, 3, \ldots, \quad n, \ldots\}$

$\{1, 3, 9, \ldots, \quad 3^{n-1}, \ldots\}$
Since these sets can be put into a one-to-one correspondence, they
have the same cardinality—namely, $\aleph_0$.
45. $\mathbb{W} = \{0, 1, 2, 3, \ldots, \quad n, \ldots\}$

$\{1, 2, 3, 4, \ldots, n + 1, \ldots\}$
Since $\mathbb{W}$ can be put into a one-to-one correspondence with a proper
subset of itself, it is infinite.
47. $\{12, 14, 16, \ldots, \quad n, \ldots\}$

$\{14, 16, 18, \ldots, n + 2, \ldots\}$
Thus, this set is infinite.
49. $\mathbb{W} = \{0, 1, 2, 3, \ldots, \quad n, \ldots\}$

$\{1, 2, 3, 4, \ldots, n + 1, \ldots\}$
Thus, $\mathbb{W}$ is countably infinite.
51. $\mathbb{Q}$ is countably infinite because it can be put into a one-to-one correspondence with the counting numbers (see Example 3).
53. $\{2, 4, 8, \ldots, 2^n, \ldots\}$

$\{1, 2, 3, \ldots, n, \ldots\}$
Thus, the set $\{2, 4, 8, 16, 32, \ldots\}$ is countably infinite.
55. If a set is uncountable, then it is infinite, by definition; the statement is
true.   **57.** Some infinite sets have cardinality $\aleph_0$. Whereas other infinite
sets may have larger cardinality; the statement is false.   **59.** Answers
vary; odd numbers + even numbers = counting numbers.

Chapter 2 Review Questions, page 80

1. a. $\{1, 2, 3, 4, 5, 6, 7, 9, 10\}$ **b.** $\{9\}$ **2. a.** $\{1, 3, 5, 7, 8\}$ **b.** 0
3. a. 10   **b.** 5   **4. a.** 25   **b.** 50   **5. a.** $\{1, 2, 3, 4, 5, 6, 7, 8, 10\}$
b. $\{1, 2, 3, 4, 5, 6, 7, 8, 10\}$ **c.** yes, from De Morgan's law
6. $\{2, 4, 6, 8, 10\}$ **7.** $\{2, 4, 6, 10\}$ **8. a.** $\subset$ or $\subseteq$ **b.** $\in$
c. $=$ or $\subseteq$ **d.** $=$ or $\subseteq$ **e.** $\subset$ or $\subseteq$ **9. a.** 25   **b.** 41
c. 20   **d.** 46
10. a.

b.

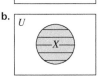

11. a.

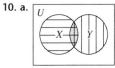

b.

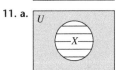

12. a.

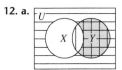

b.

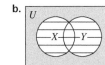

13. a. 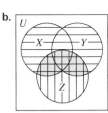   **b.**

14. 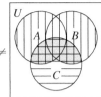 $\neq$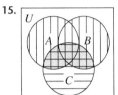

The statement has been disproved.

15. 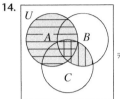 $=$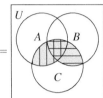

The statement has been proved.

16. a. The set of rational numbers is the set of all numbers of the form $\frac{a}{b}$ such that a is an integer and b is a counting number.
b. $\frac{2}{3}$; answers vary.

17. $\{5,\ 10, 15, \ldots, 5n, \ldots\}$
$\qquad \updownarrow \ \ \updownarrow \ \updownarrow \qquad \updownarrow$
$\{10,\ 20, 30, \ldots, 10n, \ldots\}$
Since the second set is a proper subset of the first set, we see that the set F is infinite.

18. a. $\{n \mid (-n) \in \mathbb{N}\}$; answers vary.
b. $\{\ 1,\quad 2,\quad 3, \ldots, \quad n, \ldots\}$
$\qquad \updownarrow \ \ \updownarrow \ \updownarrow \qquad \updownarrow$
$\{-1, -2, -3, \ldots, -n, \ldots\}$
Since the first set is the set of counting numbers, it has cardinality $\aleph_0$; so the given set also has cardinality $\aleph_0$ since it can be put into a one-to-one correspondence with the set of counting numbers.

19. 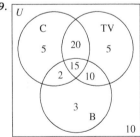   Ten students had none of the items.

20. a. $A^-, AB^-, B^-, A^+, AB^+, B^+, O^+, O^-$
b. $A^-, AB^-, B^-, A^+, AB^+, B^+, O^-$ **c.** A, B, O^+

CHAPTER 3

3.1 Deductive Reasoning, page 89

5. a, b, and d are statements.   **7.** a, b, and d are statements.   **9.** Claire
11. Charles, Joe   **13.** T   **15.** F   **17.** T   **19.** F   **21.** Some dogs do not have fleas.   **23.** Some triangles are squares.   **25.** Some counting numbers are not divisible by 1.   **27.** All integers are odd.   **29. a.** T   **b.** F   **c.** T
d. F   **31. a.** Prices or taxes will rise.   **b.** Prices will not rise and taxes will rise.   **c.** Prices will rise or taxes will not rise.   **d.** Prices will not rise or taxes will not rise.   **33. a.** T   **b.** F   **c.** T   **d.** F   **35. a.** T   **b.** F
37. a. F   **b.** T   **39. a.** T   **b.** T   **41.** $e \wedge d \wedge t$ **43.** $\sim t \wedge \sim m$
45. $(j \vee i) \wedge \sim p$ **47.** $d \vee e$ **49. a.** $(s \wedge t) \vee c$ **b.** $s \wedge (t \vee c)$ **51.** T
53. T   **55.** T   **57.** T   **59.** Melissa did change her mind.

3.2 Truth Tables and the Conditional, page 98

5.

p	q	$\sim p$	$\sim p \vee q$
T	T	F	T
T	F	F	F
F	T	T	T
F	F	T	T

7.

p	q	$p \wedge q$	$\sim(p \wedge q)$
T	T	T	F
T	F	F	T
F	T	F	T
F	F	F	T

9.

r	$\sim r$	$\sim(\sim r)$
T	F	T
F	T	F

11.

p	q	$\sim q$	$p \wedge \sim q$
T	T	F	F
T	F	T	T
F	T	F	F
F	F	T	F

13.

p	q	$\sim p$	$\sim p \wedge q$	$\sim q$	$(\sim p \wedge q) \vee \sim q$
T	T	F	F	F	F
T	F	F	F	T	T
F	T	T	T	F	T
F	F	T	F	T	T

15.

p	q	$p \to q$	$p \vee (p \to q)$
T	T	T	T
T	F	F	T
F	T	T	T
F	F	T	T

17.

p	q	$p \vee q$	$p \wedge (p \vee q)$	$[p \wedge (p \vee q)] \to p$
T	T	T	T	T
T	F	T	T	T
F	T	T	F	T
F	F	F	F	T

19.

p	q	r	$p \vee q$	$(p \vee q) \vee r$
T	T	T	T	T
T	T	F	T	T
T	F	T	T	T
T	F	F	T	T
F	T	T	T	T
F	T	F	T	T
F	F	T	F	T
F	F	F	F	F

21.

p	q	r	$p \vee q$	$\sim r$	$(p \vee q) \wedge \sim r$	$[(p \vee q) \wedge \sim r] \wedge r$
T	T	T	T	F	F	F
T	T	F	T	T	T	F
T	F	T	T	F	F	F
T	F	F	T	T	T	F
F	T	T	T	F	F	F
F	T	F	T	T	T	F
F	F	T	F	F	F	F
F	F	F	F	T	F	F

23. If the slash through "P" means no parking, then a slash through "No Parking" must mean park here (law of double negation).
25. Statement: $\sim p \to \sim q$; Converse: $\sim q \to \sim p$
Inverse: $p \to q$; Contrapositive: $q \to p$
27. Statement: $\sim t \to \sim s$; Converse: $\sim s \to \sim t$
Inverse: $t \to s$; Contrapositive: $s \to t$
29. Statement: If I get paid, then I will go Saturday.
Converse: If I go Saturday, then I got paid.
Inverse: If I do not get paid, then I will not go Saturday.
Contrapositive: If I do not go Saturday, then I do not get paid.
31. If it is a triangle, then it is a polygon.   **33.** If you are a good person, then you will go to heaven.   **35.** If we make a proper use of these means

which the God of Nature has placed in our power, then we are not weak. **37.** If it is work, then it is noble. **39.** T **41.** T **43. a.** T **b.** F **c.** F **45. a.** F **b.** T **c.** T **47.** $(q \wedge \sim d) \rightarrow n$, where q: The qualifying person is a child; d: This child is your dependent; n: You enter your child's name. **49.** $(b \vee c) \rightarrow n$, where b: The amount on line 32 is $86,025; c: The amount on line 32 is less than $86,025; n: You multiply the number of exemptions by $2,500. **51.** $(m \vee d) \rightarrow s$, where m: You are a student; d: You are a person with disabilities; s: you see line 6 of instructions. **53. a.** $a \rightarrow (e \vee f)$ **b.** $(a \wedge e) \rightarrow q$ **c.** $(a \wedge f) \rightarrow q$ **55.** $[(m \vee t \vee w \vee h) \wedge s] \rightarrow q$ **57.** $t \rightarrow (m \wedge s \wedge p)$ **59.** This is not a statement, since it gives rise to a paradox and is neither true nor false.

3.3 Operators and Laws of Logic, page 105

7. a. 9 hours **b.** if you look at the middle sign, 10 hours; if you look at the lower sign, 15 minutes **9.** no **11.** no **13.** yes **15.** no

17.

p	q	$p \vee q$	$\sim(p \vee q)$
T	T	T	F
T	F	T	F
F	T	T	F
F	F	F	T

19.

p	q	$\sim q$	$p \rightarrow \sim q$
T	T	F	F
T	F	T	T
F	T	F	T
F	F	T	T

21. Let h: I will buy a new house; p: All provisions of the sale are clearly understood. Not h unless p: $\sim p \rightarrow \sim h$. **23.** Let r: I am obligated to pay the rent; s: I signed the contract. r because s: $(r \wedge s) \wedge (s \rightarrow r)$ **25.** Let m: It is a man; i: It is an island. No m is i: $m \rightarrow \sim i$ **27.** Let n: You are nice to people on your way up; m: You will meet people on your way down. n because m: $(n \wedge m) \wedge (m \rightarrow n)$. **29.** Let f: The majority, by mere force of numbers, deprives a minority of a clearly written constitutional right; r: Revolution is justified. If f then r: $f \rightarrow r$. *Answers to Problems 30–35 may vary.* **31.** The cherries have not turned red or they are ready to be picked. **33.** If Hannah watches Jon Stewart, then she watches the NBC late-night orchestra. **35.** If the money is not available, then I will not take my vacation.

37.

p	$\sim p$	$\sim(\sim p)$	$p \leftrightarrow \sim(\sim p)$
T	F	T	T
F	T	F	T

Thus, $p \Leftrightarrow \sim(\sim p)$.

39.

p	q	$p \vee q$	$\sim(p \vee q)$	$\sim p$	$\sim q$	$\sim p \wedge \sim q$	$(p \vee q) \leftrightarrow (\sim p \wedge \sim q)$
T	T	T	F	F	F	F	T
T	F	T	F	F	T	F	T
F	T	T	F	T	F	F	T
F	F	F	T	T	T	T	T

Thus, $\sim(p \vee q) \Leftrightarrow \sim p \wedge \sim q$.

41.

p	q	$p \rightarrow q$	$\sim p$	$\sim p \vee q$	$(p \rightarrow q) \leftrightarrow (\sim p \vee q)$
T	T	T	F	T	T
T	F	F	F	F	T
F	T	T	T	T	T
F	F	T	T	T	T

Thus, $(p \rightarrow q) \Leftrightarrow (\sim p \vee q)$.

43. $\sim(p \rightarrow \sim q) \Leftrightarrow \sim(\sim p \vee \sim q) \Leftrightarrow \sim(\sim p) \wedge \sim(\sim q) \Leftrightarrow p \wedge q$
45. $\sim(\sim p \rightarrow \sim q) \Leftrightarrow \sim[\sim(\sim p) \vee \sim q] \Leftrightarrow \sim p \wedge \sim(\sim q) \Leftrightarrow \sim p \wedge q$
47. Jane did not go to the basketball game and she did not go to the soccer game. **49.** Missy is on time or she did not miss the boat. **51.** You are out of Schlitz and you have beer. **53.** $x - 5 = 4$ and $x \neq 1$. **55.** $x = 1$ and $y = 2$, and $2x + 3y \neq 8$. **57.** Let d: You purchase your ticket between January 5 and February 15; f: You fly round trip between February 20 and May 3; m: You depart on Monday; t: You depart on Tuesday; w: You depart on Wednesday; h: You return on Tuesday; i: You return on Wednesday; j: You return on Thursday; s: You stay over a Saturday night; e: You obtain 40% off regular fare. Symbolic statement: $[d \wedge f \wedge (m \vee t \vee w) \wedge (h \vee i \vee j) \wedge s] \rightarrow e$ **59.** Let ℓ: The tenant lets the premises; m: The tenant lets a portion of the premises; s: The tenant sublets the premises; t: The tenant

sublets a portion of the premises; p: Permission is obtained. Symbolic statement: $\sim p \rightarrow [\sim(\ell \vee m) \wedge \sim(s \vee t)]$

3.4 The Nature of Proof, page 113

1. reasoning that can be written in the form $[(p \rightarrow q) \wedge p] \rightarrow q$
3. reasoning that can be written in the form $[(p \rightarrow q) \wedge (q \rightarrow r)] \rightarrow (p \rightarrow r)]$ **7. a.** valid; indirect **b.** invalid; fallacy of the converse **9. a.** invalid; fallacy of the inverse **b.** valid; direct **11.** valid; direct **13.** valid; transitive **15.** valid; direct **17.** valid; direct **19.** invalid; false chain **21.** valid; indirect **23.** valid; indirect **25.** invalid; fallacy of the converse **27.** valid; transitive **29.** valid; transitive **31.** valid; indirect **33.** valid; contrapositive and transitive **35.** false chain pattern **37.** If you learn mathematics, then you understand human nature. (*transitive*) **39.** We do not go to the concert. (*indirect*) **41.** $b = 0$ (*excluded middle*) **43.** We do not interfere with the publication of false information. (*indirect*) **45.** I will not eat that piece of pie. (*indirect*) **47.** We will go to Europe. (*transitive; direct*) **49.** Babies cannot manage crocodiles. (*transitive*) **51.** None of my poultry are officers. (*transitive, contrapositive* twice, *indirect*) **53.** Airsecond Aircraft Company suffers financial setbacks. (*direct; indirect*) **55.** The janitor could not have taken the elevator because the building fuses were blown. **57.** Guinea pigs do not appreciate Beethoven. **59.** This is not an easy problem.

3.5 Problem Solving Using Logic, page 121

1. a. The playing board is an undefined term. The directions simply present the board, but do not define it. **b.** This is a stated rule of the game, so we would call this an axiom. **c.** Passing "GO" is an undefined term, because the rules of the game simply refer to GO. **d.** The "chance" cards are part of the definitions, so this is a defined term. **e.** This playing piece is simply given as part of the game, so it qualifies as an undefined term. **3. a.** The playing pieces in *Sorry* are not specifically defined, so this would be an undefined term. **b.** This is a stated rule of the game, so we would call this an axiom. **c.** "Home" is a defined term in *Sorry*. **d.** This is a stated rule of the game, so we would call this an axiom. **e.** This term is not defined, so it is an undefined term. **5. a.** This is a stated rule of the game, so we would call this an axiom. **b.** This is a stated rule of the game, so we would call this an axiom. **c.** It is assumed that you know what is meant by a "die," so we take this as an undefined term. **d.** A door's location is precisely located on the playing board, but the notion of a door itself is not defined, so this is an undefined term. **e.** This is a stated rule of the game, so we would call this an axiom. **7. a.** While the number, size, and specifications of permitted players are all part of the rules, the word "player" is not defined, so this is an undefined term. **b.** This is a stated rule of the game, so we would call this an axiom. **c.** This is a defined term. **d.** This is a defined term. **e.** This is a consequence of the rules of the game, so this would be considered a theorem.

9.

Statements	Reasons
MIII	Given
MIIIIII	Doubling (Rule 2)
MUU	Substitution (Rule 3)
M	Deletion (Rule 4)

11.

Statements	Reasons
MI	Given
MII	Doubling (Rule 2)
MIIII	Doubling (Rule 2)
MIIIIIIII	Doubling (Rule 2)
MIUIU	Substitution (Rule 3)

13.

Statements	Reasons
MIIIUUIIIII	Given
MIIIIIIII	Deletion (Rule 4)
MIIUU	Substitution (Rule 3)
MII	Deletion (Rule 4)
MIIU	Addition (Rule 1)

15.

Statements	Reasons
EA	Given
AE	Rule 3
AEE	Rule 1
A	Rule 5

17.

Statements	Reasons
AI	Given
AIII	Rule 1
AE	Rule 4
AEE	Rule 1
A	Rule 5

19.

Statements	Reasons
AE	Given
AEE	Rule 1
A	Rule 5

21. The first is a knight and the second is also a knight.   **23.** Bob is a knave and Cary is a knight.   **25.** white   **27.** need to choose three socks **29.** There must be 49 red and 1 yellow.   **31.** Alice has an ace on her head. **33.** Ben and Cole have kings and Alice has a lower card.   **35.** Ben says, "I lose" and Cole says, "I win." Cole has a queen and the others have lower cards. *You should take Problems 37–54 together.*   **37.** 6 **39.** 3 **41.** 6 **43.** 7 **45.** 3 **47.** 3 **49.** 4 **51.** 2 **53.** 2 **55.** Moe knows that his hat must be black.   **57.** Gary was 17 and had 15 marbles; Harry was 10 and had 12 marbles; Iggy was 3 and had 12 marbles; Jack was 18 and had 9 marbles. They shot in the order of Gary, Jack, Harry, and then Iggy. **59.** three weighings

3.6 Logic Circuits, page 128

5. light   **7.** AND-gate   **9.** NOT-gate   *Answers to Problems 10–15 may vary.*   **11.** $\sim p$ **13.** p or q; $p \vee q$ **15.** $p \wedge \sim q$

17.

p	q	$\sim p$	$\sim p \wedge q$
T	T	F	F
T	F	F	F
F	T	T	T
F	F	T	F

19.

p	q	$\sim q$	$p \vee \sim q$	$\sim(p \vee \sim q)$
T	T	F	T	F
T	F	T	T	F
F	T	F	F	T
F	F	T	T	F

21. $p \vee q$

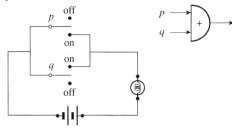

23. $p \wedge \sim q$

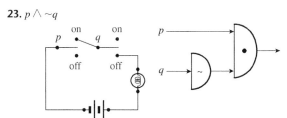

25. $\sim(p \wedge q)$

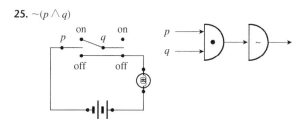

27. $q \to p$

p	q	$q \to p$
T	T	T
T	F	T
F	T	F
F	F	T

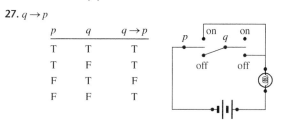

29. $q \to \sim p$ (note that this is the contrapositive of Problem 28, so the truth table and circuits are the same.)

p	q	$\sim p$	$q \to \sim p$
T	T	F	F
T	F	F	T
F	T	T	T
F	F	T	T

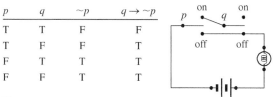

31. $\sim(q \to p)$

p	q	$q \to p$	$\sim(q \to p)$
T	T	T	F
T	F	T	F
F	T	F	T
F	F	T	F

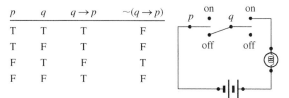

33. $(p \wedge q) \vee r$

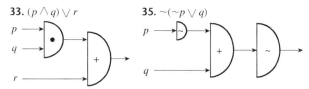

35. $\sim(\sim p \vee q)$

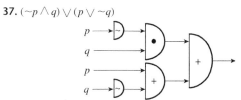

37. $(\sim p \wedge q) \vee (p \vee \sim q)$

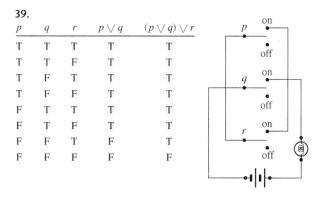

39.

p	q	r	$p \vee q$	$(p \vee q) \vee r$
T	T	T	T	T
T	T	F	T	T
T	F	T	T	T
T	F	F	T	T
F	T	T	T	T
F	T	F	T	T
F	F	T	F	T
F	F	F	F	F

41.

p	q	r	$q \vee r$	$p \vee (q \vee r)$
T	T	T	T	T
T	T	F	F	T
T	F	T	F	T
T	F	F	F	T
F	T	T	T	T
F	T	F	F	F
F	F	T	F	F
F	F	F	F	F

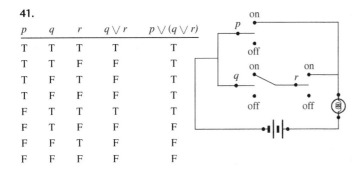

51.

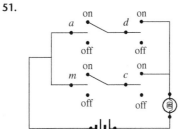

43.

p	q	r	$p \wedge q$	$(p \wedge q) \vee r$
T	T	T	T	T
T	T	F	T	T
T	F	T	F	T
T	F	F	F	F
F	T	T	F	T
F	T	F	F	F
F	F	T	F	T
F	F	F	F	F

53.

p	q	$p \rightarrow q$	$\sim p$	$\sim p \vee q$	$(p \rightarrow q) \leftrightarrow (\sim p \vee q)$
T	T	T	F	T	T
T	F	F	F	F	T
F	T	T	T	T	T
F	F	T	T	T	T

$(p \rightarrow q) \Leftrightarrow (\sim p \vee q)$

55. Notice that $p \rightarrow \sim q \Leftrightarrow \sim p \vee \sim q$.

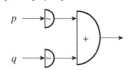

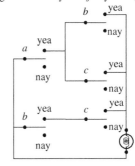

45.

p	q	r	$q \wedge r$	$p \wedge (q \vee r)$
T	T	T	T	T
T	T	F	F	F
T	F	T	F	F
T	F	F	F	F
F	T	T	F	F
F	T	F	F	F
F	F	T	F	F
F	F	F	F	F

57. a.

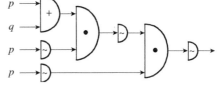

b. $140,000

59. Let the committee members be a, b, and c, respectively. Light *on* represents a majority. Light is on for a yea majority and light is off otherwise.

Note the circuit for this problem is the same as the one for Problem 38. This fact is sometimes called the *associative property for conjunction*. That is,

$$(p \wedge q) \wedge r = p \wedge (q \wedge r)$$

47. Let b_1: the first rest room is occupied; b_2: the second rest room is occupied; b_3: the third rest room is occupied.
a. $(b_1 \vee b_2) \vee b_3$; note that this is equivalent to $b_1 \vee (b_2 \vee b_3)$.
b.

b_1	b_2	b_3	$b_1 \vee b_2$	$(b_1 \vee b_2) \vee b_3$
T	T	T	T	T
T	T	F	T	T
T	F	T	T	T
T	F	F	T	T
F	T	T	T	T
F	T	F	T	T
F	F	T	F	T
F	F	F	F	F

c.

49. Let a: the thermostat is set on automatic mode; d: all the doors are closed; m: the thermostat is set on manual mode; c: the proper authorization code has been entered. A logical statement might be: $(a \wedge d) \vee (m \wedge c)$.

Chapter 3 Review Questions, page 130

1. a. A *logical statement* is a declarative sentence that is either true or false. **b.** A *tautology* is a logical statement in which the conclusion is equivalent to its premise. **c.** $(p \rightarrow q) \leftrightarrow (\sim q \rightarrow \sim p)$ or, in words: A conditional may always be replaced by its contrapositive without having its truth value affected.

2.

p	q	$\sim p$	$p \wedge q$	$p \vee q$	$p \rightarrow q$	$p \leftrightarrow q$
T	T	F	T	T	T	T
T	F	F	F	T	F	F
F	T	T	F	T	T	F
F	F	T	F	F	T	T

3.

p	q	$p \wedge q$	$\sim(p \wedge q)$
T	T	T	F
T	F	F	T
F	T	F	T
F	F	F	T

4.

p	q	$\sim q$	$p \vee \sim q$	$\sim p$	$(p \vee \sim q) \wedge \sim p$	$[(p \vee \sim q) \wedge \sim p] \to \sim q$
T	T	F	T	F	F	T
T	F	T	T	F	F	T
F	T	F	F	T	F	T
F	F	T	T	T	T	T

5.

p	q	r	$p \wedge q$	$(p \wedge q) \wedge r$	$[(p \wedge q) \wedge r] \to p$
T	T	T	T	T	T
T	T	F	T	F	T
T	F	T	F	F	T
T	F	F	F	F	T
F	T	T	F	F	T
F	T	F	F	F	T
F	F	T	F	F	T
F	F	F	F	F	T

6.

p	q	$\sim p$	$\sim q$	$p \wedge q$	$\sim(p \wedge q)$	$\sim p \vee \sim q$	$\sim(p \wedge q) \leftrightarrow (\sim p \vee \sim q)$
T	T	F	F	T	F	F	T
T	F	F	T	F	T	T	T
F	T	T	F	F	T	T	T
F	F	T	T	F	T	T	T

7. $p \to q$

p

$\therefore q$

p	q	$p \to q$	$(p \to q) \wedge p$	$[(p \to q) \wedge p] \to q$
T	T	T	T	T
T	F	F	F	T
F	T	T	F	T
F	F	T	F	T

8. Answers vary.

> If you study hard, then you will get an *A*.
> You do not get an *A*.
> Therefore, you did not study hard.

9. Answers vary; fallacy of the converse, fallacy of the inverse, or false chain pattern; for example:

> If you study hard, then you will get an *A*.
> You do not study hard, so you do not get an *A*. *(fallacy of the inverse.)*

10. Yes; it is indirect reasoning. **11. a.** Some birds do not have feathers. **b.** No apples are rotten. **c.** Some cars have two wheels. **d.** All smart people attend college. **e.** You go on Tuesday and you can win the lottery.
12. a. T **b.** T **c.** T **d.** T **e.** T **13. a.** If P is a prime number, then $P + 2$ is a prime number. **b.** Either P or $P + 2$ is a prime number.
14. a. Let p: This machine is a computer; q: This machine is capable of self-direction. $p \to \sim q$ **b.** Contrapositive: $\sim(\sim q) \to \sim p$; $q \to \sim p$. If this machine is capable of self-direction, then it is not a computer. **15.** Let p: There are a finite number of primes; q: There is some natural number, greater than 1, that is not divisible by any prime. Then the argument in symbolic form is:

$$p \to q$$
$$\sim q$$
$$\therefore \sim p$$

Conclusion: There are infinitely many primes (assuming that "not a finite number" is the same as "infinitely many"). This is indirect reasoning.
16. a.

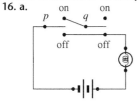

b.

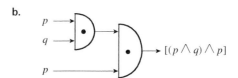

$[(p \wedge q) \wedge p]$

17. I do not attend to my duties. **18.** No prune is an artificial sweetener. **19.** All squares are polygons. **20.** North: Maureen (baker); East: Terry (hiker); South: Josie (gardener); West: Warren (surfer)

CHAPTER 4

4.1 Early Numeration Systems, page 143

7. a. Roman, Egyptian **b.** Roman, Babylonian **c.** Egyptian, Roman, Babylonian **d.** Egyptian, Roman, Babylonian **e.** Roman, Babylonian **f.** Roman **9. a.** $\frac{2}{3}$ **b.** 100,010 **11. a.** $24\frac{1}{2}$ **b.** $\frac{1}{100}$ **13. a.** 1,100 **b.** 1,997 **15. a.** 1,999 **b.** 2,001 **17. a.** 7,600 **b.** 9,712 **19. a.** 71 **b.** 671 **21. a.** 47 **b.** 25 **23.** 133 **25.** 1
27. ∩∩∩∩∩∩∩ |||||

29. 99999∩∩| **31.** [Egyptian numerals] |||||| **33.** LXXV
35. DXXI **37.** MMVII **39.** ▼ ⊲ ▼▼▼▼▼
41. ▼▼▼▼▼▼▼▼ ⊲⊲⊲⊲▼
43. ⊲⊲⊲▼▼▼⊲⊲▼▼▼▼▼▼▼
45. [Egyptian] 999999999∩∩∩∩∩∩∩||||| ||
47. ⊲⊲⊲⊲⊲ **49.** ⊲⊲▼▼▼▼▼ **51.** VIII
53. LXXXIX **55.** MMMCMXCIX **57. a.** MDCLXVI

b. MCDXLIV **59.** ▼▼▼▼▼ by ⊲▼▼

4.2 Hindu–Arabic Numeration System, page 147

9. 5 units **11.** 5 hundred-thousandths **13.** 5 thousandths
15. a. 100,000 **b.** 1,000 **17. a.** 0.0001 **b.** 0.001 **19. a.** 5,000 **b.** 500 **21. a.** 0.06 **b.** 0.00009 **23.** 10,234 **25.** 521,658
27. 7,000,000.03 **29.** 500,457.34 **31.** 20,600.40769
33. a. $9 \times 10^{-2} + 6 \times 10^{-3} + 4 \times 10^{-4} + 2 \times 10^{-5} + 1 \times 10^{-6}$
b. $2 \times 10^1 + 7 \times 10^0 + 5 \times 10^{-1} + 7 \times 10^{-2} + 2 \times 10^{-3}$
35. a. $6 \times 10^3 + 2 \times 10^2 + 4 \times 10^1 + 5 \times 10^0$
b. $2 \times 10^6 + 3 \times 10^5 + 5 \times 10^3 + 6 \times 10^2 + 8 \times 10^1 + 1 \times 10^0$
37. $5 \times 10^{-6} + 2 \times 10^{-7} + 7 \times 10^{-8}$
39. $8 \times 10^2 + 9 \times 10^1 + 3 \times 10^0 + 1 \times 10^{-4}$
41. $6 \times 10^5 + 7 \times 10^4 + 8 \times 10^3 + 1 \times 10^{-2}$
43. $5 \times 10^4 + 7 \times 10^3 + 2 \times 10^2 + 8 \times 10^1 + 5 \times 10^0 + 9 \times 10^{-1} + 3 \times 10^{-2} + 6 \times 10^{-3} + 1 \times 10^{-4}$ **45.** 3,201 **47.** 5,001,005
49. 8,009,026
51.

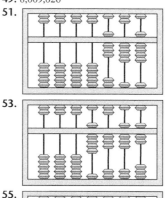

53.

55.

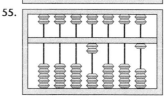

57.

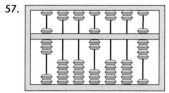

59. 22, 23, 24, 30, 31, 32, 33, 34, 40, . . .

4.3 Different Numeration Systems, page 152

5. a. 9 **b.** 14_{five} **c.** 100_{three} **d.** 11_{eight} **e.** 1001_{two} **f.** 10_{nine}
7. $6 \times 8^2 + 4 \times 8^1 + 3 \times 8^0$ **9.** $1 \times 2^5 + 1 \times 2^4 + 1 \times 2^2 + 1 \times 2^1$
$+ 1 \times 2^0 + 1 \times 2^{-1} + 1 \times 2^{-4}$ **11.** $6 \times 8^7 + 4 \times 8^6 + 2 \times 8^5$
$+ 5 \times 8^1 + 1 \times 8^0$ **13.** $3 \times 4^5 + 2 \times 4^4 + 3 \times 4^3 + 2 \times 4^{-1}$
15. $3 \times 5^0 + 4 \times 5^{-1} + 2 \times 5^{-3} + 3 \times 5^{-4} + 1 \times 5^{-5}$ **17.** 343
19. 4,307 **21.** 116 **23.** 11.625 **25.** 807 **27.** 66 **29.** 351.125
31. a. 10344_{five} **b.** 21310_{four} **33. a.** 3122_{five} **b.** 1147_{eight}
35. a. 1000000000_{two} **b.** 1002110_{three} **37. a.** 1132_{eight} **b.** 1030_{four}
39. 7 weeks, 3 days **41.** 4 ft, 7 in. **43.** 3 gross, 5 doz, 8 units
45. $84 = 314_{five}$, so eight coins are needed **47.** $954_{twelve} = 1,360$ pencils
49. $44 = 62_{seven}$; 6 weeks, 2 days **51.** $29 = 15_{twenty-four}$; 1 day, 5 hours
53. 6 years, 3 months **55.** 16 ft, 1 in. **57.** 4 gross, 6 dozen, 3 units
59. 4 years, 11 months, 6 days

4.4 Binary Numeration System, page 157

3. 39 **5.** 167 **7.** 13 **9.** 11 **11.** 29 **13.** 27 **15.** 99 **17.** 184
19. 1101_{two} **21.** 100011_{two} **23.** 110011_{two} **25.** 1000000_{two}
27. 10000000_{two} **29.** 1100011011_{two} **31.** 68 79 **33.** 69 78 68
35. HAVE **37.** STUDY **39.** 101_{two} **41.** 1101_{two} **43.** 10_{two}
45. 100011_{two} **47.** The computer is correct because there must be either
war or peace. **49. a.** 101_{two} **b.** 110_{two} **51. a.** $001\ 110\ 111_{two}$
b. $110\ 010\ 100_{two}$ **53. a.** 5_{eight} **b.** 7_{eight} **55.** 007750_{eight}
57. 773521_{eight}

4.5 History of Calculating Devices, page 168

11. a. 27 **b.** 63 **c.** 54 **13. a.** 243 **b.** 432 **c.** 504
15. ENIAC, UNIVAC, Cray, Altair, Apple
Answers to Problems 16–33 may vary.
17. Aristophanes developed a finger-counting system about 500 B.C.
19. Babbage built a calculating machine in the 19th century. **21.** Berry
helped Atanasoff build the first computer. **23.** Cray developed the first
supercomputer. **25.** Engelbart invented the computer mouse.
27. Jobs was the cofounder of Apple Computer and codesigned the
Apple II computer. **29.** Leibniz built a calculating device in 1695.
31. Napier invented a calculating device to do multiplication (in 1617).
33. Wozniak codesigned the Apple II computer. **35.** yes; speed,
complicated computations **37.** yes; speed, repetition **39.** yes;
repetition **41.** yes; ability to make corrections easily **43.** yes (but not
completely); it can help with some of the technical aspects **45.** yes;
speed, complicated computations, repetition **47.** E **49.** D

Chapter 4 Review Questions, page 171

1. Answers vary. The position in which the individual digits are listed is
relevant; examples will vary. **2.** Answers vary. Addition is easier in a
simple grouping system; examples will vary. **3.** Answers vary. It uses ten
symbols; it is positional; it has a placeholder symbol (0); and it uses 10 as
its basic unit for grouping. **4.** Answers vary. Should include finger
calculating, Napier's rods, Pascal's calculator, Leibniz' reckoning machine,
Babbage's difference and analytic engines, ENIAC, UNIVAC, Atanasoff's
and Eckert and Mauchly's computers, and the dispute they had in proving
their position in the history of computers. Should also include the role and
impact of the Apple and Macintosh computers, as well as the supercomput-
ers (such as the Cray). **5.** Answers vary. Should include illegal (breaking
into another's computer, adding, modifying, or destroying information;
copying programs without authorization or permission) and ignorance
(assuming that output information is correct, or not using software for
purposes for which it was intended). **6.** Answers vary. **a.** the physical
components (mechanical, magnetic, electronic) of a computer system
b. the routine programs, and associated documentation in a computer system **c.** the process of creating, modifying, deleting, and formatting text
and materials **d.** a system for communication between computers using
electronic cables, phone lines, or wireless devices **e.** electronic mail—
that is, messages sent along computer modems **f.** R̲andom-A̲ccess
M̲emory or memory where each location is uniformly accessible, often
used for the storage of a program and data being processed **g.** an
electronic place to exchange information with others, usually on a particular topic **h.** a computer component that reads and stores data **7.** 10^9
8. $4 \times 10^2 + 3 \times 10^1 + 6 \times 10^0 + 2 \times 10^{-1} + 1 \times 10^{-5}$
9. $5 \times 8^2 + 2 \times 8^1 + 3 \times 8^0$ **10.** $1 \times 2^6 + 1 \times 2^3 + 1 \times 2^2 + 1 \times 2^1$
11. 4,020,005.62 **12.** 29 **13.** 123 **14.** 17 **15.** 1,177 **16.** 1100_{two}
17. 110100_{two} **18.** 11111010111_{two} **19.** $11110100001001000000_{two}$
20. a. $92E_{twelve}$ **b.** 400_{five}

5.1 Natural Numbers, page 180

11. a. $4 + 4 + 4$ **b.** $3 + 3 + 3 + 3$ **13. a.** $184 + 184$
b. $2 + 2 + \cdots + 2$ (a total of 184 terms) **15. a.** $y + y + y + \cdots + y$
(a total of x terms) **b.** $x + x + x + \cdots + x$ (a total of y terms)
17. commutative **19.** associative **21.** commutative **23.** commutative
25. commutative **27.** commutative **29.** none are associative
31. Answers vary; dictionary definitions are often circular.
33. a. $-i$ **b.** -1 **c.** 1 **d.** $-i$ **e.** i **f.** -1 **35.** Answers vary; yes
37. Answers vary; **a.** yes **b.** yes **39.** yes; answers vary
41. a. $\square$ **b.** $\circ$ **c.** yes; no $[\circ \cdot \triangle \neq \triangle \cdot \circ]$ **d.** yes
43. Check: $a \downarrow (b \to c) = (a \downarrow b) \to (a \downarrow c)$. Try several examples; it holds.
45. a. $5 \times (100 - 1) = 500 - 5 = 495$ **b.** $4 \times (90 - 2) = 360 - 8 = 352$
c. $8 \times (50 + 2) = 400 + 16 = 416$ **47.** yes **49.** yes; even + even = even
51. yes; odd $\times$ odd = odd **53.** yes; let a and b be any elements in S. Then,
$a \odot b = 0 \cdot a + 1 \cdot b = b$ and we know that b is an element of S. **55.** It is
commutative but not associative: $2 \oslash 3 = 10$ and $3 \oslash 2 = 10$; try other
examples. $(2 \oslash 3) \oslash 4 \neq 2 \oslash (3 \oslash 4)$ **57.** yes **59.** Answers vary;
$0 + 1 + 2 - 3 - 4 + 5 - 6 + 7 + 8 - 9 = 1$

5.2 Prime Numbers, page 194

7. a. prime; use sieve **b.** not prime; $3 \cdot 19$ **c.** not prime; only 1
divisor **d.** prime; check primes under 45 **9. a.** prime; use sieve
b. prime; use sieve **c.** not prime; $3^2 \cdot 19$ **d.** not prime; $3^2 \cdot 223$
11. a. T **b.** F **c.** T **d.** F **13. a.** F **b.** T **c.** T **d.** T **15.** Use the
sieve of Eratosthenes; you need only to cross out the multiples of primes
up to 17. The list of primes is: 2, 3, 5, 7, 11, 13, 17, 19, 23, 29, 31, 37, 41,
43, 47, 53, 59, 61, 67, 71, 73, 79, 83, 89, 97, 101, 103, 107, 109, 113, 127,
131, 137, 139, 149, 151, 157, 163, 167, 173, 179, 181, 191, 193, 197, 199,
211, 223, 227, 229, 233, 239, 241, 251, 257, 263, 269, 271, 277, 281, 283,
and 293. **17. a.** $2^3 \cdot 3$ **b.** $2 \cdot 3 \cdot 5$ **c.** $2^2 \cdot 3 \cdot 5^2$ **d.** $2^4 \cdot 3^2$
19. a. $2^3 \cdot 3 \cdot 5$ **b.** $2 \cdot 3^2 \cdot 5$ **c.** $3 \cdot 5^2$ **d.** $3 \cdot 5^2 \cdot 13$ **21.** prime
23. prime **25.** $13 \cdot 29$ **27.** $3 \cdot 5 \cdot 7$ **29.** prime **31.** $3^2 \cdot 5 \cdot 7$
33. $3^4 \cdot 7$ **35.** $19 \cdot 151$ **37.** 12; 360 **39.** 3; 2,052 **41.** 1; 252
43. 15; 1,800 **45.** The least common multiple of 6 and 8 is 24, so the
next night off together is in 3 weeks, 3 days. **47.** Answers vary.
49. 1, 3, 7, 9, 13, 15, 21, 25, 31, 33, 37, 43, 45, 49, 51, 63, 67, 69, 73, 75,
79, 87, 93, and 99 **51.** Answers vary. **53. a.** yes **b.** yes **c.** yes
55. $2 \cdot 3 \cdot 5 \cdot 7 \cdot 11 \cdot 13 + 1 = 30,031$, which is not prime,
since $30,031 = 59 \cdot 509$ **57.** Answers vary; some other possibilities are:
2, 17, 37, 101, 197, 257, 401, 577, 677, 1297, 1601, 2917, 3137, 4357,
5477, 7057, 8101, 8837. A computer could also be used to answer this
question. **59.** If $N = 5$, $2^{5-1}(2^5 - 1) = 496$.

5.3 Integers, page 203

7. a. 30 **b.** 30 **c.** -30 **d.** 0 **9. a.** 8 **b.** -2 **11. a.** 10 **b.** -4
13. a. -7 **b.** 12 **15. a.** 3 **b.** -3 **17. a.** -18 **b.** -20
19. a. -70 **b.** 70 **21. a.** -3 **b.** 7 **23. a.** 132 **b.** -1 **25. a.** -56

b. −75   **27. a.** −4   **b.** 4   **29. a.** −12   **b.** 15   **31. a.** 150   **b.** −19
33. a. 5   **b.** 10   **35. a.** 0   **b.** −8   **37. a.** 0   **b.** −23   **39. a.** −7
b. 0   **41. a.** 8   **b.** −2   **43. a.** 6   **b.** 7   **45. a.** 1   **b.** 22   **47. a.** 4
b. 16   **49. a.** 44   **b.** 16   **51. a.** 1   **b.** 1   **c.** 1   **d.** 1   **e.** 1   **f.** 1
53. a. 1   **b.** −1   **c.** −1   **d.** 1   **e.** −1   **f.** −1   **55. a.** An operation ○ is
commutative for a set S if $a \circ b = b \circ a$ for all elements a and b in S.   **b.**
yes   **c.** no   **d.** yes   **e.** no   **59.** 12345668765433

5.4 Rational Numbers, page 210

7. a. $\frac{1}{5}$ **b.** $\frac{1}{4}$ **9. a.** 2   **b.** 2   **11. a.** 3   **b.** $\frac{2}{3}$ **13. a.** $\frac{1}{8}$ **b.** $\frac{1}{3}$
15. a. $\frac{6}{35}$ **b.** $\frac{3}{20}$ **17. a.** $\frac{17}{21}$ **b.** $\frac{7}{8}$ **19. a.** $\frac{-92}{105}$ **b.** $\frac{5}{6}$ **21. a.** $\frac{1}{9}$
b. $\frac{71}{63}$ **23. a.** $\frac{20}{7}$ **b.** $\frac{-7}{27}$ **25. a.** $\frac{8}{15}$ **b.** $\frac{7}{10}$ **27. a.** $\frac{10}{21}$ **b.** $\frac{1}{20}$ **29. a.** 1
b. −1   **31. a.** 36   **b.** −25   **33. a.** $\frac{18}{35}$ **b.** $\frac{4}{45}$ **35. a.** $\frac{80}{27}$ **b.** $\frac{-15}{56}$
37. a. 20   **b.** 6   **39. a.** $\frac{11}{15}$ **b.** $\frac{39}{5}$ **41. a.** $\frac{-3}{4}$ **b.** $\frac{-3}{4}$ **43.** $\frac{2{,}137}{10{,}800}$
45. $\frac{971}{3{,}060}$ **47.** $\frac{10{,}573}{13{,}020}$ **55.** $\frac{3}{4} = \frac{1}{2} + \frac{1}{4}$ **57.** $\frac{67}{120} = \frac{1}{3} + \frac{1}{8} + \frac{1}{10}$ or $\frac{1}{2} + \frac{1}{20} + \frac{1}{120}$
59. It checks.

5.5 Irrational Numbers, page 218

7. true   **9. a.** 30   **b.** 36   **c.** 807   **d.** 169   **11. a.** a **b.** xy **c.** $4b$
d. $40w$ **13. a.** irrational; 3.162   **b.** irrational; 5.477   **c.** irrational; 9.870
d. irrational; 7.389   **15. a.** rational; 13   **b.** rational; 20
c. irrational; 23.141   **d.** irrational; 22.459   **17. a.** rational; 32
b. rational; 44   **c.** irrational; 1.772   **d.** irrational; 1.253   **19. a.** $10\sqrt{10}$
b. $20\sqrt{7}$ **c.** $8\sqrt{35}$ **d.** $21\sqrt{10}$ **21. a.** $\frac{1}{2}\sqrt{2}$ **b.** $\frac{1}{3}\sqrt{3}$
c. $\frac{1}{5}\sqrt{15}$ **d.** $\frac{1}{7}\sqrt{21}$ **23. a.** $\frac{1}{2}\sqrt{2}$ **b.** $-\frac{1}{3}\sqrt{3}$ **c.** $\frac{2}{5}\sqrt{5}$ **d.** $\frac{1}{2}\sqrt{10}$
25. a. simplified   **b.** $x + 2$ **27. a.** $10\sqrt{2}$ **b.** 0   **29. a.** $3 + \sqrt{5}$
b. $2 - \sqrt{3}$ **31. a.** $1 - 3\sqrt{x}$ **b.** $-3 - \sqrt{x}$ **33. a.** $\frac{2x}{5y}\sqrt{y}$
b. $\frac{1}{4x}\sqrt{5xy}$ **35.** $\frac{1 - \sqrt{19}}{6}$ **37.** $6 + \sqrt{37}$ **39.** 24 ft   **41.** 10 ft
43. $\sqrt{8}$ in. or $2\sqrt{2}$ in.   **45.** 200 ft   **47.** 15 ft   **49.** Answers vary;
1.2323323332 . . .   **51.** Answers vary; 0.0919919991 . . .   **53.** Solution
comes from Pythagorean theorem.   **a.** 2-in. square   **b.** same   **c.** 7-in.
square   **d.** 9-in. square   **e.** 15-in. square
55.

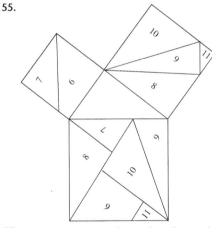

57. Answers vary; any number can be written as the sum of three triangular
numbers. He must have meant 3 or fewer triangular numbers because to
represent 2, for example, we write $1 + 1$.   **59.** Consider the second
diagonal: $1, 3, 6, 10, 15, 21, \ldots$. If we take the sum of any 2 adjacent terms,
we obtain square numbers: $4, 9, 16, 25, \ldots$. (*Note:* Don't forget that we start
counting with the 0th diagonal.)

5.6 Groups, Fields, and Real Numbers, page 228

5. Let $\mathbb{S}$ be any set, let ○ be any operation, and let a, b, and c be any
elements of $\mathbb{S}$. We say that $\mathbb{S}$ is a **group** for the operation of ○ if the

following properties are satisfied: 1. The set $\mathbb{S}$ is *closed* for ○: $(a \circ b) \in \mathbb{S}$.
2. The set $\mathbb{S}$ is *associative* for ○: $(a \circ b) \circ c = a \circ (b \circ c)$. 3. The set $\mathbb{S}$ satisfies the *identity* for ○: There exists a number $I \in \mathbb{S}$ so that
$x \circ I = I \circ x = x$ for *every* $x \in \mathbb{S}$. 4. The set $\mathbb{S}$ satisfies the *inverse* for ○:
For *each* $x \in \mathbb{S}$, there exists a corresponding $x^{-1} \in \mathbb{S}$ so that
$x \circ x^{-1} = x^{-1} \circ x = I$, where I is the identity element in $\mathbb{S}$.
7. a. $\mathbb{N}, \mathbb{Z}, \mathbb{Q}, \mathbb{R}$ **b.** $\mathbb{Q}, \mathbb{R}$ **c.** $\mathbb{Q}', \mathbb{R}$ **d.** $\mathbb{Q}', \mathbb{R}$ **e.** $\mathbb{Q}, \mathbb{R}$ **f.** $\mathbb{Q}, \mathbb{R}$
g. $\mathbb{Q}, \mathbb{R}$ **h.** $\mathbb{N}, \mathbb{Z}, \mathbb{Q}, \mathbb{R}$ **i.** $\mathbb{Z}, \mathbb{Q}, \mathbb{R}$ **9. a.** 1.5   **b.** 0.7   **c.** 0.6   **d.** 1.8
11. a. $0.\overline{6}$ **b.** $2.\overline{153846}$ **c.** 5   **d.** 1.09   **13. a.** $\frac{1}{2}$ **b.** $\frac{4}{5}$ **15. a.** $\frac{9}{20}$
b. $\frac{117}{500}$ **17. a.** $\frac{987}{10}$ **b.** $\frac{63}{100}$ **19. a.** $\frac{153}{10}$ **b.** $\frac{139}{20}$ **21. a.** 3.179   **b.** −5.504
c. 1.901   **d.** −6.31   **23. a.** −0.13112   **b.** −65.415   **c.** 12.4   **d.** 0.85
25. a. 7.46   **b.** −5.15   **c.** 72.6   **d.** 45.96   **27. a.** commutative
b. distributive   **29. a.** commutative   **b.** associative   **31.** identity
33. x **35.** no   **37.** $\mathbb{N}$ is not a group for − since it is not closed.
39. $\mathbb{W}$ is not a group for × since the inverse property is not satisfied.
41. $\mathbb{Z}$ is not a group for × since the inverse property is not satisfied.
43. $\mathbb{Q}$ is not a group for × since there is no multiplicative inverse for the
rational number 0.
45. a.

×	1	2	3	4
1	1	2	3	4
2	2	4	6	8
3	3	6	9	12
4	4	8	12	16

b.

*	1	2	3	4
1	2	2	2	2
2	4	4	4	4
3	6	6	6	6
4	8	8	8	8

c. Operation ×: not closed, associative, identity is 1, no inverse property,
commutative; Operation *: not closed, not associative, no identity, no inverse property, not commutative

Answers to Problems 46–50 may vary.
47. 2.5; $\frac{2\pi}{3}$ **49.** $4.\overline{5}$; 4.545545554 . . .
51. $\left\{ \frac{1}{2}, \frac{1}{3}, \frac{2}{3}, \frac{1}{4}, \frac{3}{4}, \frac{1}{5}, \frac{2}{5}, \frac{3}{5}, \frac{4}{5}, \frac{1}{6}, \frac{5}{6}, \frac{1}{7}, \frac{2}{7}, \ldots \right\}$
53. $a \circ b = ab$ **55.** $a \circ b = a + b + 1$ **57.** $a \circ b = 2(a + b)$
59. $a \circ b = a^2 + 1$

5.7 Discrete Mathematics, page 238

5. a. 3   **b.** 10   **c.** 3   **d.** 2   **7. a.** 12   **b.** 8   **c.** 8   **d.** 3
9. a. 8   **b.** 1   **11. a.** T   **b.** F   **13. a.** T   **b.** T   **15. a.** T   **b.** T
17. a. 0, (mod 5)   **b.** 8, (mod 12)   **c.** 2, (mod 5)   **d.** 3, (mod 5)
19. a. 2, (mod 5)   **b.** 2, (mod 8)   **21. a.** 3, (mod 5)   **b.** 10, (mod 11)
23. a. 4, (mod 7)   **b.** 4, (mod 5)   **25. a.** 5, (mod 6)   **b.** 3, (mod 7)
27. a. 1, 3, (mod 4)   **b.** 2, (mod 9)   **29. a.** 0, (mod 4)   **b.** 2, (mod 4)
31. all x's (mod 2)   **33. a.** Sunday   **b.** Thursday   **c.** Wednesday
d. Monday   **35.** The possible distances are 4, 14, 24, 34, . . . or
9, 19, 29, 39, ...   **37.** She lives 14 miles from your house.
39. It is a group for addition modulo 7.
41.

+	0	1	2	3	4	5	6	7	8	9	10
0	0	1	2	3	4	5	6	7	8	9	10
1	1	2	3	4	5	6	7	8	9	10	0
2	2	3	4	5	6	7	8	9	10	0	1
3	3	4	5	6	7	8	9	10	0	1	2
4	4	5	6	7	8	9	10	0	1	2	3
5	5	6	7	8	9	10	0	1	2	3	4
6	6	7	8	9	10	0	1	2	3	4	5
7	7	8	9	10	0	1	2	3	4	5	6
8	8	9	10	0	1	2	3	4	5	6	7
9	9	10	0	1	2	3	4	5	6	7	8
10	10	0	1	2	3	4	5	6	7	8	9

×	0	1	2	3	4	5	6	7	8	9	10
0	0	0	0	0	0	0	0	0	0	0	0
1	0	1	2	3	4	5	6	7	8	9	10
2	0	2	4	6	8	10	1	3	5	7	9
3	0	3	6	9	1	4	7	10	2	5	8
4	0	4	8	1	5	9	2	6	10	3	7
5	0	5	10	4	9	3	8	2	7	1	6
6	0	6	1	7	2	8	3	9	4	10	5
7	0	7	3	10	6	2	9	5	1	8	4
8	0	8	5	2	10	7	4	1	9	6	3
9	0	9	7	5	3	1	10	8	6	4	2
10	0	10	9	8	7	6	5	4	3	2	1

43. no **45.** no
47.

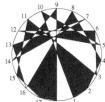

49.

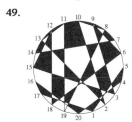

51.

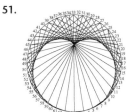

53. a. 8 **b.** 5 **55.** The check digit is 10. **57.** Assign eleven teams the numbers 1 to 11. On the first day, all teams whose sum is 1, (mod 11) play; day 2, matches those whose sum is 2, (mod 11); . . . . The last team plays the left over numbered team so each team plays every day. The schedule follows:

Day 1:	1-11;	2-10;	3-9;	4-8;	5-7;	6-12
Day 2:	2-11;	3-10;	4-9;	5-8;	6-7;	1-12
Day 3:	3-11;	4-10;	5-9;	6-8;	1-2;	7-12
Day 4:	4-11;	5-10;	6-9;	7-8;	1-3;	2-12
Day 5:	5-11;	6-10;	7-9;	1-4;	2-3;	8-12
Day 6:	6-11;	7-10;	8-9;	1-5;	2-4;	3-12
Day 7:	7-11;	8-10;	1-6;	2-5;	3-4;	9-12
Day 8:	9-10;	1-7;	2-6;	3-5;	8-11;	4-12
Day 9:	9-11;	1-8;	2-7;	3-6;	4-5;	10-12
Day 10:	10-11;	1-9;	2-8;	3-7;	4-6;	5-12
Day 11:	1-10;	2-9;	3-8;	4-7;	5-6;	11-12;

Note: The answer is not unique. **59.** The smallest result is 785.

5.8 Cryptography, page 244

1. 14-5-22-5-18-29-19-1-25-29-14-5-22-5-18-28 **3.** 25-15-21-29-2-5-20-29-25-15-21-18-29-12-9-6-5-28 **5.** ARE WE HAVING FUN YET
7. FAILURE TEACHES SUCCESS **9.** Divide by 8. **11.** Subtract 2 and then divide by 20. **13.** Divide by 2, then subtract 2, then divide by 4.
15. MOHOY .CQ MOHOYZ **17.** ZFREIOPEZFRLE WQOC
19. HUMPTY DUMPTY IS A FALL GUY. **21.** MIDAS HAD A GILT COMPLEX.

23. D UPEOTEHEQAUXUJGEWAUOEHEQHGHEXAUNTDDCRZEDN UULEHRQECEPCLLED UPEVUJEHERCRNUOXJGTAB
25. ANYONE WHO SLAPS CATSUP, MUSTARD, AND RELISH ON HIS HOT DOG IS TRULY A MAN FOR ALL SEASONINGS.
27. CRYSTAL-CLEAR AIR OF ROCKY MOUNTAINS PROVIDES IDEAL ENVIRONMENT FOR WEATHER STATION.
29. $3{,}915 + 15 + 4{,}826 = 8{,}756$

Chapter 5 Review Questions, page 246

1. -19 **2.** $\frac{71}{63}$ **3.** $\frac{1{,}396}{3{,}465}$ **4.** -10 **5.** 2 **6.** $\frac{7}{72}$ **7.** $-\frac{7}{9}$ **8.** $\frac{-3+\sqrt{33}}{4}$
9. $\frac{8}{3}$ (*Note:* $2\frac{2}{3}$ is mixed-number form, but $\frac{8}{3}$ is reduced.) **10.** $\frac{8}{9}$
11. $\frac{4}{33}$ **12.** $\frac{8}{9}$ **13.** $\frac{3}{7}$ **14.** 0.375, rational **15.** $2.\overline{3}$, rational
16. $0.\overline{428571}$, rational **17.** 6.25, rational **18.** $0.\overline{230769}$, rational
19. prime **20.** prime **21.** prime **22.** $7 \cdot 11 \cdot 13$
23. $3 \cdot 5^2 \cdot 7 \cdot 13$ **24.** $x \equiv 2$, (mod 8) **25.** $x \equiv 5$, (mod 7)
26. $x \equiv 1$, (mod 2) **27.** 7 **28.** 343,343 **29.** 119 **30.** 2 **31.** For $b \neq 0$, multiplication is defined as: $a \times b$ means $\underbrace{b + b + b + \cdots + b.}_{a \text{ addends}}$

If $a = 0$, then $0 \times b = 0$. **32.** $a - b = a + (-b)$ **33.** $\frac{a}{b} = m$ means $a = bm$ where $b \neq 0$. **34.** If we use the definition of division, $\frac{x}{0} = m$, then $0 \cdot m = x$. If $x \neq 0$, then there is no solution because $0 \cdot m = 0$ for all numbers m. Also, if $\frac{0}{0} = m$, then $0 = 0 \cdot m$ which is true for *every* number m. Thus, $\frac{0}{0} = 0$ checks, and $\frac{0}{0} = 1$ checks, and since two numbers equal to the same number must also be equal, we obtain the statement $0 = 1$; thus, we say $\frac{0}{0}$ is indeterminate. **35.** 34.1011011101111011 . . .
36. See p. 228. **37.** It is not a group. **38.** BMI $= \frac{703w}{h^2}$ **a.** 27.5
b. 25.1 **c.** $w = 155$ lb **39.** There are 31 doors left open. **40.** 12 steps are necessary; length of segments is 20 ft; length of diagonal is $4\sqrt{13}$ ft.

CHAPTER 6

6.1 Polynomials, page 257

9. $-x - 8$; 1st-degree binomial **11.** $3x - 6y - 4z$; 1st-degree trinomial
13. $5x^2 - 7x - 7$; 2nd-degree trinomial **15.** $-x^2 - 5x + 3$; 2nd-degree trinomial **17.** $x - 31$; 1st-degree binomial **19.** $16x^2 + 9x - 3$; 2nd-degree trinomial **21.** $-3x^2 + 15x - 17$; 2nd-degree trinomial
23. a. $x^2 + 5x + 6$ **b.** $y^2 + 6y + 5$ **c.** $z^2 + 4z - 12$ **d.** $s^2 + s - 20$
25. a. $c^2 - 6c - 7$ **b.** $z^2 + 2z - 15$ **c.** $2x^2 - x - 1$ **d.** $2x^2 - 5x + 3$
27. a. $x^2 + 2xy + y^2$ **b.** $x^2 - 2xy + y^2$ **c.** $x^2 - y^2$ **d.** $a^2 - b^2$
29. a. $x^2 + 8x + 16$ **b.** $y^2 - 6y + 9$ **c.** $s^2 + 2st + t^2$
d. $u^2 - 2uv + v^2$ **31.** $6x^3 + x^2 - 12x + 5$ **33.** $5x^4 - 9x^3 + 13x^2 + 3x$
35. $-4x^3 + 25x^2 - 19x + 22$ **37.** $7x^2$
39.

$x + 2$	x^2	x	x	x	x
	x	1	1	1	1
	x	1	1	1	1

$x + 4$ (top)

$(x + 2)(x + 4) = x^2 + 6x + 8$

41.

$x + 3$	x^2	x	x	x	x
	x	1	1	1	1
	x	1	1	1	1
	x	1	1	1	1

$x + 4$ (top)

$(x + 3)(x + 4) = x^2 + 7x + 12$

43.

$3x + 2$ (top)

$2x + 3$	x^2	x^2	x^2	x	x
	x^2	x^2	x^2	x	x
	x^2	x^2	x^2	x	x
	x	x	x	1	1
	x	x	x	1	1
	x	x	x	1	1

$(2x + 3)(3x + 2) = 6x^2 + 13x + 6$

45. $(x - 1)^3 = x^3 - 3x^2 + 3x - 1$
47. $(x + y)^6 = x^6 + 6x^5y + 15x^4y^2 + 20x^3y^3 + 15x^2y^4 + 6xy^5 + y^6$
49. $(x - y)^8 = x^8 - 8x^7y + 28x^6y^2 - 56x^5y^3 + 70x^4y^4 - 56x^3y^5 + 28x^2y^6 - 8xy^7 + y^8$ **51.** $(2x - 3y)^4 = 16x^4 - 96x^3y + 216x^2y^2 - 216xy^3 + 81y^4$

53. $91x^2y^{12} + 14xy^{13} + y^{14}$ **55.** $(6x + 2)(51x - 7) = 306x^2 + 60x - 14$
57. $(6b + 15)(10 - 2b) = 150 + 30b - 12b^2$

6.2 Factoring, page 263

3. $2x(5y - 3)$ **5.** $2x(4y - 3)$ **7.** $(x - 3)(x - 1)$ **9.** $(x - 3)(x - 2)$
11. $(x - 4)(x - 3)$ **13.** $(x - 6)(x + 5)$ **15.** $(x - 7)(x + 5)$
17. $(3x + 10)(x - 1)$ **19.** $(2x - 1)(x - 3)$ **21.** $(3x + 1)(x - 2)$
23. $(2x + 1)(x + 4)$ **25.** $(3x - 2)(x + 1)$ **27.** $x(5x - 3)(x + 2)$
29. $x^2(7x + 3)(x - 2)$ **31.** $(x - 8)(x + 8)$ **33.** $25(x^2 + 2)$
35. $(x - 1)(x + 1)(x^2 + 1)$ **37.** $x^2 + 5x + 6 = (x + 2)(x + 3)$
39. $x^2 + 4x + 3 = (x + 1)(x + 3)$ **41.** $x^2 + 6x + 8 = (x + 2)(x + 4)$
43. $x^2 - 1 = (x - 1)(x + 1)$ **45.** $x^2 + x - 2 = (x - 1)(x + 2)$
47. $x^2 - x - 2 = (x + 1)(x - 2)$ **49.** The dimensions are $x - 13$ feet by
$x + 11$ feet.   **51.** The time is $2x - 1$ hours.   **53.** $(3x + 2)(2x + 1)$
55. $x^2(x - 3)(x + 3)(x - 2)(x + 2)$ **57.** $x^2(4y + 5z)(5y - 2z)$
59. Let $x - 1$, x, and $x + 1$ be the three integers. Then
$(x - 1)(x + 1) = x^2 - 1$ so the square of the middle integer is one more
than the product of the first and third.

6.3 Evaluation, Applications, and Spreadsheets, page 271

5. a. $+(2/3)*A1^2$ **b.** $+5*A1^2 - 6*A2^2$ **7. a.** $+12*(A1^2+4)$
b. $+(15*A1+7)/2$ **9. a.** $+(5 - A1)*(A1+3)^2$
b. $+6*(A1+3)*(2*A1 - 7)^2$ **11. a.** $+(1/4)*A1^2-(1/2)*A1+12$
b. $+(2/3)*A1^2+(1/3)*A1 - 17$ **13. a.** $4x + 3$ **b.** $5x^2 - 3x + 4$
15. a. $\frac{5}{4}x + 14^2$ **b.** $(\frac{5}{4}x + 14)^2$ **17. a.** $\frac{x}{y}(z)$ **b.** $\frac{x}{yz}$ **19.** $A = 13$
21. $C = 8$ **23.** $E = 21$ **25.** $G = 19$ **27.** $I = 2$ **29.** $K = 4$
31. $M = 9$ **33.** $P = 20$ **35.** $R = 11$ **37.** $T = 17$ **39.** $V = 48$
41. $X = 100$ **45. a.** 8   **b.** 5   **c.** 9   **d.** 3.5

47. a.

	A	B	C	D	E
1	1	3	4	5	6
2	1	3	3	3	3
3					
4					
5					

b.

49. a.

	A	B	C
1	7	0	5
2	2	4	6
3	3	8	1

b.

	A	B	C
1	107	100	105
2	102	104	106
3	103	108	101

51.

	A	B	C	D	E
1	NAME	SALES	COST	PROFIT	COMMISSION
2				+B2-C2	+.08*D2
3	Replicate Row	2 for Rows 3 to 21.			
4					
5					

53. Genotype: black, 42.25%; black (recessive brown), 45.5%; brown,
12.25% Phenotype: black, 87.75%; brown, 12.25%   **55.** Genotypes and
phenotypes are the same: red, 4%; pink, 32%; white, 64%   **57.** $B = 50\%$
and $b = 50\%$ **59.** Answers vary. For the general population, FF is 49%,
Ff is 42%, and ff is 9%; free hanging is 91% and attached is 9%. In other
words, F is 70% and f is 30%.

6.4 Equations, page 281

3. a. 15   **b.** 8   **c.** −4   **d.** −8   **5. a.** 0   **b.** 0   **c.** 8   **d.** 2   **7. a.** $\frac{1,111}{10,000}$
b. $\frac{47}{90}$ **9. a.** $\frac{13}{33}$ **b.** $\frac{28}{45}$ **11. a.** $X = \frac{1}{5}$ **b.** $C = 10$ **13. a.** $F = 1$
b. $G = 6$ **15. a.** $J = 15$ **b.** $K = 9$ **17. a.** $N = -6$ **b.** $P = -8$
19. $S = 8$ **21.** $U = 3$ **23.** $W = -15$ **25.** $Z = 14$ **27.** 0, 10

29. 11, −6   **31.** 0, 2, −2   **33.** $-\frac{3}{2}, \frac{3}{2}$ **35.** $\frac{-7 \pm \sqrt{41}}{2}$ **37.** $\frac{5 \pm \sqrt{37}}{2}$
39. $3 \pm \sqrt{2}$ **41.** $\frac{-5 \pm \sqrt{73}}{6}$ **43.** no real values   **45.** 4, $-\frac{1}{3}$ **47.** 0, $\frac{5}{6}$
49. 1.41, 2.83   **51.** 0.91, −2.33   **53.** −41.54, −0.01   **55. a.** 45.5 mg
b. 20 mg   **57.** On the last step, dividing by $a + b - c$ is not allowed
because $a + b = c$ so $a + b - c = 0$; cannot divide by 0.
59. a. −13, 3   **b.** 3

6.5 Inequalities, page 287

3.
5.
7.
9.
11.
13.
15.

17. $x \geq -4$ **19.** $x \geq -2$ **21.** $y > -6$ **23.** $s > -2$ **25.** $m < 5$
27. $x > -1$ **29.** $x \leq 1$ **31.** $s < -6$ **33.** $a \geq 2$ **35.** $s > 2$ **37.** $u \leq 2$
39. $w < -1$ **41.** $A > 0$ **43.** $C > \frac{19}{2}$ **45.** $E < -1$ **47.** $G > 7$
49. $I > \frac{5}{4}$ **51.** any number greater than −5   **53.** any number less
than −4   **55.** 2   **57.** less than 2   **59.** height and width must be 18 in. or
less and the length is 36 in. or less

6.6 Algebra in Problem Solving, page 297

3. a. $3 + 2 \times 4 = 11$ **b.** $3(2 + 4) = 18$ **5. a.** $8 \times 9 + 10 = 82$
b. $8(9 + 10) = 152$ **7. a.** $3^2 + 2^3 = 17$ **b.** $3^3 - 2^2 = 23$
9. a. $4^2 + 9^2 = 97$ **b.** $(4 + 9)^2 = 169$ **11. a.** $3(n + 4) = 16$; $n = \frac{4}{3}$;
open, conditional   **b.** $5(n + 1) = 5n + 5$; open, identity
13. a. $3^2 + 4^2 = 25$; true   **b.** $1^2 + 2^2 + 3^2 = n$; $n = 14$; open, conditional
15. a. $6n + 12 = 6(n + 2)$; open, identity   **b.** $n(7 + n) = 0$; $n = 0, -7$;
open, conditional   **17.** $A = bh$ **19.** $A = \frac{1}{2}pq$ **21.** $V = s^3$
23. $V = \frac{1}{3}\pi r^2 h$ **25.** $V = \frac{4}{3}\pi r^3$ **27.** $2(\text{NUMBER}) - 12 = 6$; The number
is 9.   **29.** $3(\text{NUMBER}) - 6 = 2(\text{NUMBER})$; the number is 6.
31. EVEN INTEGER + NEXT EVEN INTEGER = 94; The integers are 46 and 48.
33. INTEGER + NEXT INTEGER + THIRD CONSECUTIVE INTEGER + FOURTH
CONSECUTIVE INTEGER = 74; the integers are 17, 18, 19, and 20.
35. PRICE OF FIRST CABINET + PRICE OF SECOND CABINET = 4,150; the prices
of the cabinets are $830 and $3,320.   **37.** 4(AMOUNT OF MONEY TO START)
− 72 = 48; the gambler started with $30.   **39.** $8^2 + 14^2 = (\text{LENGTH OF}$
BRACE$)^2$. The exact length of the brace is $2\sqrt{65}$; this is approximately 16 ft.
41. DIST FROM N TO M + DIST FROM M TO C + DIST FROM C TO D = TOTAL
DISTANCE; it is 250 mi from Cincinnati to Detroit.   **43.** DIST OF SLOWER
RUNNER + HEAD START = DIST OF FASTER RUNNER; the faster runner will
catch the slower one in 12.5 seconds.   **45.** DIST OF CAR + HEAD START
= DIST OF POLICE CAR; it will take the police car 6 minutes to catch the
speeder.   **47.** DIST OF 1ST JOGGER + DIST OF 2ND JOGGER = TOTAL DISTANCE;
the jogger's rates are 6 mph and 8 mph.   **49.** The length of the shorter side
is 5 cm.   **51.** The base is 3.6 ft and the height is 1.6 ft.   **53.** Need to obtain
about 41.4% interest.   **55.** The center would be approximately 10.5 ft
above the ground.   **57.** There are 120 lilies.   **59.** The second monkey
jumped 50 cubits into the air.

6.7 Ratios, Proportions, and Problem Solving, page 306

5. 20 to 1   **7.** 53 to 50   **9.** 18 to 1   **11. a.** yes   **b.** yes   **c.** yes
13. a. yes   **b.** no   **c.** no   **15. a.** >   **b.** <   **c.** >   **17. a.** <   **b.** >
c. <   **d.** <   **19.** $A = 30$ **21.** $C = 10$ **23.** $E = 8$ **25.** $G = 21$
27. $I = 16$ **29.** $K = \frac{15}{2}$ or 7.5   **31.** $M = 4$ **33.** $P = 3$ **35.** $R = 9$
37. $T = \frac{1}{4}$ or 0.25   **39.** $V = \frac{5}{2}$ or 2.5   **41.** $Y = 22$ **43.** $0.91
45. 2 gallons   **47.** 27 minutes   **49.** 2,475 calories   **51.** 159.25
53. $\frac{2}{3}$ **55.** $3\frac{1}{3}$ ft or 3 ft, 4 in.   **57.** $780   **59.** Since she started with

32 gallons and ended with 1 pt (of pure soft drink), the amount of soft drink served was 31 gal, 3 qt, and 1 pt.

6.8 Percents, page 316

1. $\frac{3}{4}$; 75%   **3.** $\frac{2}{5}$; 0.4   **5.** $0.\overline{3}$; $33\frac{1}{3}$%   **7.** $\frac{17}{20}$; 85%   **9.** 0.375; 37.5%
11. $\frac{6}{5}$; 1.2   **13.** $\frac{1}{20}$; 5%   **15.** $0.1\overline{6}$; $16\frac{2}{3}$%   **17.** $\frac{2}{9}$; $0.\overline{2}$ **19.** $\frac{7}{40}$; 17.5%
21. $\frac{1}{400}$; 0.25% *Estimates in Problems 22–28 may vary.*   **23. a.** 9,500
b. 8.56   **25. a.** 200   **b.** 200   **27. a.** 40   **b.** 8,100   **29.** $\frac{15}{100} = \frac{A}{64}$; 9.6
31. $\frac{14}{100} = \frac{21}{W}$; 150   **33.** $\frac{P}{100} = \frac{10}{5}$; 200%   **35.** $\frac{P}{100} = \frac{4}{5}$; 80%
37. $\frac{P}{100} = \frac{9}{12}$; 75%   **39.** $\frac{35}{100} = \frac{49}{W}$; 140   **41.** $\frac{120}{100} = \frac{16}{W}$; $13\frac{1}{3}$
43. $\frac{33\frac{1}{3}}{100} = \frac{12}{W}$; 36   **45.** $\frac{6}{100} = \frac{A}{8,150}$; $489   **47.** 23.1 million   **49.** $10.86
51. 5%   **53.** 40%   **55.** The tax withheld is $2,624.   **57.** 90%
59. The old wage was $1,250 and the new wage is $1,350.

6.9 Modeling Uncategorized Problems, page 323

3. A   **5.** A   **7.** A   **9.** B   **11.** D   **13.** C   **15.** A   **17.** A   **19.** A
21. C   **23.** C   **25.** C   **27.** B   **29.** A   **33.** 15 and 17   **35.** 1 and 2
37. a. 55%   **b.** 122%   **39.** Standard Oil bldg., 1,136 ft; Sears, 1,454 ft.
41. 10,100   **43.** 70   **45.** 180 hours   **47.** $x = 2\ell - \frac{1}{30}c\ell - 40$ **49.** Should invest $64,000 in savings and $36,000 in annuities.   **51.** Cut off 2 in.; the box is $8 \times 9 \times 12$ in.   **53.** The wind speed is 21 mph.   **55.** $2,350 with 30 additional persons   **57.** The reading would not change.
59. 24,000.

Chapter 6 Review Questions, page 327

1. a. Algebra refers to a structure as a set of axioms that forms the basis for what is accepted and what is not.   **b.** The four main processes are *simplify* (carry out all operations according to the order-of-operations agreement and write the result in a prescribed form), *evaluate* (replace the variable(s) with specified numbers and then simplify), *factor* (write the expression as a product), and *solve* (find the replacement(s) for the variable(s) that make the equation true).   **2. a.** $x^3 + x^2 + 6x - 8$ **b.** $x^4 - x^3y - x^2y + xy$
3. a. −19   **b.** −19   **4. a.** $3(x-3)(x+3)$ **b.** $(x-6)(x+1)$
5. a. $\frac{3}{2}$ **b.** $-2 \pm \sqrt{10}$
6.

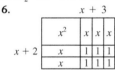

$$x^2 + 5x + 6 = (x+3)(x+2)$$

7. a. 4   **b.** $\frac{1}{4}$ **8. a.** 9   **b.** $-\frac{7}{3}$ **9. a.** $P = 15$ **b.** $W = 3.75$ **10.** 5, −1
11. $\frac{3 \pm \sqrt{5}}{4}$ **12.** $x < -3$ **13.** $x \le -2$ **14.** $x \le 2$ **15.** $x < 3$
16. a. <   **b.** =   **c.** <   **d.** <   **e.** >   **17.** $12\frac{1}{2}$ cups of flour
18. The integers are 22, 24, 26, and 28.   **19.** Genotypes: 27% tall, 50% tall (recessive short), 23% short; Phenotypes: 77% tall, 23% short
20. The distance from New York to Chicago is 720 mi, from Chicago to San Francisco is 1,860 mi, and from San Francisco to Honolulu is 2,400 mi.

CHAPTER 7

7.1 Geometry, page 337

1. both   **3.** Answers vary; the point that is being made is that although we may use a figure in geometry to help us understand a problem, we cannot use what we see in a figure as a basis for our reasoning.
9. reflection
11. P Q   **13.** P Q   **15.** P Q
17. P Q   **19.** P S
21. symmetric   **23.** symmetric   **25.** symmetric   **27.** not symmetric
41. not symmetric   **43.** symmetric (except for the words)
45. symmetric   **47.** symmetric

49.   **51.**   **53.**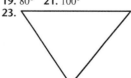

55. C   **57.** C   **59.** (1) letters with no symmetry; (2) letters with horizontal line symmetry; (3) letters with vertical line symmetry; (4) letters with symmetry around both vertical and horizontal lines

7.2 Polygons and Angles, page 346

9. a. quadrilateral   **b.** pentagon   **11. a.** triangle   **b.** hexagon
13. a. quadrilateral   **b.** heptagon   **15. a.** T   **b.** T   **17. a.** T   **b.** F
19. a. F   **b.** F   **21. a.** yes   **b.** yes   **c.** yes   **d.** yes   **e.** yes
23. a. no   **b.** no   **c.** no   **d.** no   **e.** no
25.   **27.**

29.

31. a. acute   **b.** right   **33. a.** right   **b.** obtuse   **35. a.** acute   **b.** acute
37. adjacent and supplementary   **39.** adjacent and supplementary
41. vertical   **43.** alternate interior angles   **45.** F   **47.** T   **49.** F
51. $m\angle 1 = m\angle 3 = m\angle 5 = m\angle 7 = 115°$; $m\angle 2 = m\angle 4 = m\angle 6 = m\angle 8 = 65°$
53. $m\angle 1 = m\angle 3 = m\angle 5 = m\angle 7 = 153°$; $m\angle 2 = m\angle 4 = m\angle 6 = m\angle 8 = 27°$ **55.** $m\angle 1 = m\angle 3 = m\angle 5 = m\angle 7 = 163°$; $m\angle 2 = m\angle 4 = m\angle 6 = m\angle 8 = 17°$ **57. a.** obtuse
b. obtuse   **c.** acute   **d.** acute   **e.** straight   **f.** right   **g.** acute
h. straight   **i.** acute   **j.** $\angle AOC$
59.

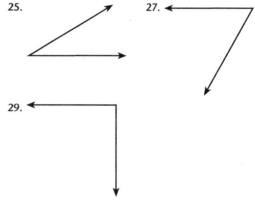

7.3 Triangles, page 354

5. $\overline{AB} \cong \overline{ED}$; $\overline{AC} \cong \overline{EF}$; $\overline{CB} \cong \overline{FD}$; $\angle A \cong \angle E$; $\angle B \cong \angle D$; $\angle C \cong \angle F$
7. $\overline{RS} \cong \overline{TU}$; $\overline{RT} \cong \overline{TR}$; $\overline{ST} \cong \overline{UR}$; $\angle SRT \cong \angle UTR$; $\angle S \cong \angle U$; $\angle STR \cong \angle URT$ **9.** $\overline{JL} \cong \overline{PN}$; $\overline{LK} \cong \overline{NM}$; $\overline{JK} \cong \overline{PM}$; $\angle J \cong \angle P$; $\angle L \cong \angle N$; $\angle K \cong \angle M$ **11.** 88°   **13.** 145°   **15.** 56°   **17.** 75°
19. 80°   **21.** 100°
23.   **25.**

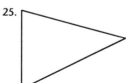

27.

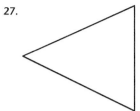

29. 20°   **31.** 21°   **33.** 6°   **35.** 60°; 60°; 60°   **37.** 50°; 60°; 70°
39. 13°; 53°; 114°   **41.** 50°   **43.** 120°   *Answers to Problems 45–52
may vary.*

53.   **55.**

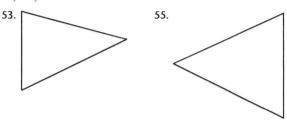

57. a. $x = 135°, y = 45°$ **b.** $x = 132.5°; y = 47.5°$ **c.** $x = 136°$;
$y = 44°$ **59.** 540°

7.4 Similar Triangles, page 359

3. similar   **5.** not similar   **7.** similar
9. $m\angle A = m\angle A' = 25°; m\angle B = m\angle B' = 75°; m\angle C = m\angle C' = 80°$
11. $m\angle A = m\angle D = 38°; m\angle B = m\angle E = 68°; m\angle C = m\angle F = 74°$
13. $m\angle A = m\angle A' = 54°; m\angle B = m\angle B' = 36°; m\angle C = m\angle C' = 90°$
15. $|AC| = |AB| = 11; |A'C'| = |A'B'| = 22; |BC| = 5; |B'C'| = 10$
17. $|GH| = 14; |HI| = 12; |GI| = 16; |DF| = 20; |DE| = 17.5;$
$|EF| = 15$ **19.** $|AB| = 10; |AC| = 6; |BC| = 8; |B'C'| = 5;$
$|A'B'| = 6.25; |A'C'| = 3.75$ **21.** $\sqrt{80}$ or $4\sqrt{5}$ **23.** 4   **25.** $\frac{16}{3}$
27. $\frac{8}{3}$ **29.** 22   **31.** 7.8   **33.** 13.7   **39.** The lake is 125 ft long.
41. The height of the building is 24 ft.   **43.** The building is 45 ft tall.
45. The bell tower is 70 ft tall.   **47.** The tree is 17 ft tall.   **49.** The tree
is 6 ft 8 in. tall.   **51.** Denver to New Orleans is 1,080 mi. and Chicago to
Denver is 1,020 mi.   **53. a.** ΔHSP and ΔBTP **b.** yes; answers vary.
c. The footbridge is 21 ft above the base.

7.5 Right-Triangle Trigonometry, page 368

1. For any right triangle with sides with lengths a and b and hypotenuse
with length c, $a^2 + b^2 = c^2$. Also, if a, b, and c are lengths of sides of a
triangle so that $a^2 + b^2 = c^2$, then the triangle is a right triangle.   **3.** In
a right triangle ABC with right angle at C, $\cos A = \frac{\text{length of adjacent side of } A}{\text{length of hypotenuse}}$.
5. Rope A would form a right triangle.   **7.** b **9.** a **11.** $\frac{a}{c}$ **13.** $\frac{b}{c}$
15. $\frac{a}{b}$ **17.** 0.8290   **19.** 0.8746   **21.** 0.5878   **23.** 0   **25.** 0.4452
27. 3.7321   **29.** 30°   **31.** 45°   **33.** 60°   **35.** 56°   **37.** 37°
39. Yes; $\sin A = \frac{12}{13}$; $\cos A = \frac{5}{13}$; $\tan A = \frac{12}{5}$ **41.** No   **43.** Yes;
$\sin A = \frac{1}{6}$; $\cos A = \frac{\sqrt{35}}{6}$; $\tan A = \frac{1}{\sqrt{35}}$ **45.** Yes; $\sin A$; $\cos A = \frac{\sqrt{3}}{2}$;
$\tan A = \frac{1}{\sqrt{3}}$ **47.** No   **49.** The height is 109 ft.   **51.** The distance is 199 m.
53. The top of the ladder is 12 ft 7 in.   **55.** The chimney stack is
1,251 ft tall.   **57.** $\cos 30° = \frac{\sqrt{3}}{2}$, $\sin 30° = \frac{1}{2}$, and $\tan 30° = \frac{\sqrt{3}}{3}$ **59.** 12 in.

7.6 Mathematics, Art, and Non-Euclidean Geometries, page 380

5. The divine proportion is the relationship $\frac{h}{w} = \frac{w}{h + w}$.   **7.** It is the
number $\frac{1 + \sqrt{5}}{2}$.   **9.** Answers vary; for example, start with 4 and 4.
a. The sequence is 4, 4, 8, 12, 20, 32, ...   **b.** The ratios are
$\frac{4}{4} = 1, \frac{8}{4} = 2, \frac{12}{8} = 1.5, \frac{20}{12} = 1.\overline{6}, \frac{32}{20} = 1.6$. It seems that these ratios
oscillate around $\tau \approx 1.62$.   **11.** $1.61\overline{6}$; it is close to τ.   **13.** $\frac{b}{2}$ to h is 1.62,
about the same; b to s is 1.7, close   **15.** 2.17, not too close
17. Euclidean   **19.** Euclidean   **21.** elliptic   **23.** hyperbolic   **25.** It is a
Saccheri quadrilateral.   **27.** It is not a Saccheri quadrilateral.

29. a. 5 in. by 3 in.   **b.** 1.67; about the same   **31. a.** 10.25 in. by 8 in.
b. 1.28; not close   **33.** Answers vary   **35. a.** 2   **b.** 8   **c.** 144
d. 1, 2, 1.50, 1.67, 1.60, 1.63, 1.62, . . . ; close to τ.   **37.** close
39. 3.1 ft or 8.1 ft   **41.** 15 cm   **43.** B   **45.** C   **47.** Their sum is greater
than 180°.   **49. a.** A great circle is a circle on a sphere with a diameter
equal to the diameter of the sphere.   **b.** ℓ is a line (a great
circle), but m is not.   **c.** yes   **51.** Lines are great circles, and the circle
labeled m is not a great circle.   **53.** True; answers vary.
55. The length-to-width ratio will remain unchanged if $\frac{L}{W} = \sqrt{2}$.
57. a. $x = \frac{1 \pm \sqrt{5}}{2}$ **b.** They are negative reciprocals.   **59.** Just down
from the North Pole there is a parallel that has a circumference of
exactly one mile. If you begin anywhere on the circle that is 300 feet north
of this parallel, the conditions are satisfied.

Chapter 7 Review Questions, page 384

1. a. 0   **b.** 8   **c.** 24   **d.** 24   **e.** 8   **2.** two men (rotate the picture 180°)
3. rotation   **4.** the photograph   **5.** the photograph   **6. a.** Flag is symmetric; picture is not (if you include the flagpole).   **b.** no   **c.** no   **d.** yes
7. a. a rectangle satisfying the divine proportion   **b.** yes
8. 173 ft   **9.** $C = \frac{\ell w}{15}$ **10. a.** obtuse angle   **b.** adjacent angles or
supplementary angles   **c.** vertical angles   **d.** acute angle   **e.** obtuse
angle   **f.** vertical angles   **11. a.** 41°   **b.** 131°   **c.** 41°   **12.** 36°
13. The width is about 6 in.   **14.** The other leg is 5 in.   **15.** $5\sqrt{2}$ in.
16. a. 0.8572   **b.** 0   **c.** 0.9511   **d.** 7.1154   **17.** The distance is
about 753 ft.
18.

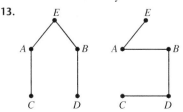

19. A Saccheri quadrilateral is a quadrilateral $ABCD$ with base angles A
and B right angles and with sides AC and BD with equal lengths.
20. If the summit angles C and D of a quadrilateral $ABCD$ are right angles,
then the result is Euclidean geometry. If they are acute, then the result is
hyperbolic geometry. If they are obtuse, the result is elliptic geometry.

CHAPTER 8

8.1 Euler Circuits and Hamiltonian Cycles, page 397

7. not an Euler circuit; traversable   **9.** not an Euler circuit; not traversable
11. not an Euler circuit; not traversable   **13.** Hamiltonian cycle;
$A \to B \to C \to D \to A$ **15.** Hamiltonian cycle; $A \to B \to C \to G \to$
$H \to F \to E \to D \to A$ **17.** Hamiltonian cycle; $A \to B \to C \to D \to A$
Possible paths in Problems 18–23 may vary.   **19.** not traversable
21. not traversable   **23.** traversable   **25.** not an Euler circuit; not
traversable   **27.** not an Euler circuit; not traversable   **29.** no Hamiltonian cycle   **31.** no Hamiltonian cycle   **33.** Answers may vary. $1 \to 2 \to$
$3 \to 10 \to 11 \to 12 \to 4 \to 5 \to 14 \to 13 \to 19 \to 18 \to 17 \to 9 \to 8 \to$
$7 \to 16 \to 20 \to 15 \to 6 \to 1$ **35.** no   **37.** It is traversable; begin at either Queens or Manhattan.   **39.** yes; 2 odd vertices   **41.** No; there are
8 odd vertices.   **43. a.** NYC to Boston to Washington, D.C. to NYC; 892
mi; forms a loop without including Cleveland   **b.** NYC to Boston to
Washington, D.C. to Cleveland to NYC; 1,513 mi   **45.** 4,627 mi
47. 2,699 mi   **49.** 720°   **51. a.** Room 1: 1 path; room 2: 2 paths;
room 3: 3 paths; room 4: 5 paths   **b.** 89   **c.** 377   **53. a.** Start at the top
(or at the right) at one of the two odd vertices.   **b.** The chance that you
will choose one of the two odd vertices at random is small.   **55.** The
result is a twisted band twice as long and half as wide as the band with
which you began.   **57.** The result is two interlocking pieces, one twice as
long as the other.   **59.** One edge; one side; after cutting, you will have a
single loop with a knot.

8.2 Trees and Minimum Spanning Trees, page 409

5. no   **7.** no   **9.** no   **11.** yes
13.

15.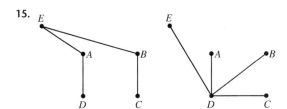

17.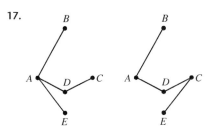

19.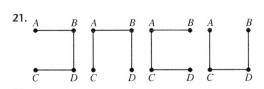

21.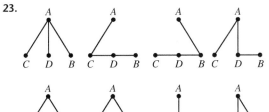

23.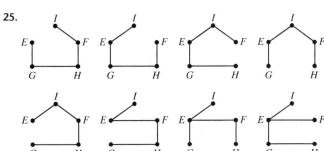

25.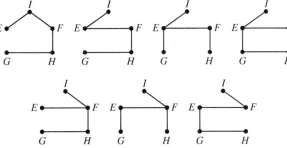

27. The propane molecule is a tree.

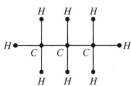

29. The isobutane molecule is a tree.

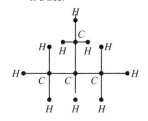

31. Not a tree; because there is a circuit.

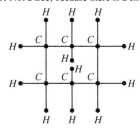

33. 60   **35.** 45   **37.** 180   **39.** 65   **41.** 30   **43.** 64   **45.** no

47.

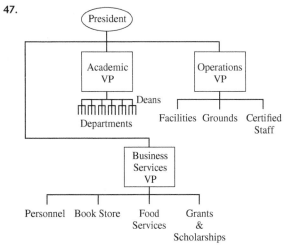

49. 49   **51.** $38,500   **53.** 375 miles

55. a.   **b.**   **c.** $4,000,000

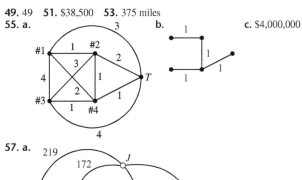

57. a.

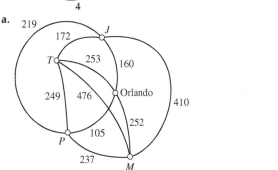

b.

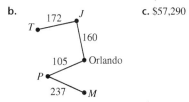

c. $57,290

59. a. $E = v - 1$; a tree with n vertices has $n - 1$ edges **b.** 0
c. one edge **d.** two edges

8.3 Topology and Fractals, page 418

3. A and F; B and G; C, D and H **5.** A and F are simple closed curves.
7. C, E, F, G, H, I, J, K, L, M, N, S, T, U, V, W, X, Y, and Z are the same
class; A, D, O, P, Q, and R are another class; B is a third class. **9.** A, C, E,
and F are the same class; B and D are the same class; G is different.
11. *A* and *C* are inside; *B* is outside. **13.** *A* and *B* are inside; *C* is outside.
15. It will need only two colors.

19.

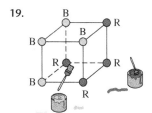

21.

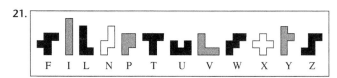

25. Answers vary.

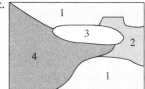

29. a. No, it will now fit the left hand. **b.** yes

Chapter 8 Review Questions, page 422

1. no **2.** yes **3.** yes **4.** yes **5. a.** no **b.** yes
6. a.

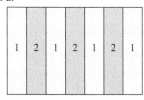

b.

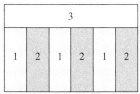

c.

d. No such map exists.

7. 20,160 ways **8.** 1,596 miles **9.** 635

10. Weighted graph: The minimum spanning tree is:

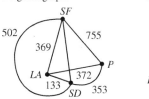
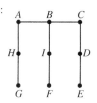

The minimum distance is 855 miles.
11. yes **12.** no **13.** 20 **14.** 47 **15.** 4.3589×10^{10} **16.** 39
17. no **18.** yes
19. Answers vary; here is one:

20. There are two edges and two sides; the result after cutting is two
interlocking loops.

CHAPTER 9

9.1 Perimeter, page 433

3. $P = 4s$; $P = 2(\ell + w)$; $P = 3s$; $P = 5s$ **5.** The number π is the
ratio of the circumference to the diameter of a circle.
7. a. —————————— **b.**
c. ——— **9.** A **11.** B **13.** A **15.** C **17.** B **19.** B **21.** C
23. C **25.** C **27.** A **29.** C **31.** A **33.** A **35. a.** 3 cm
b. 3.4 cm **c.** 1 in. **d.** $1\frac{3}{8}$ in. **37.** 18 in. **39.** 9 dm **41.** 15.08 m
43. 397.08 ft **45.** 46 ft **47.** 15.2 cm **49.** 35.7 in. **51.** 11.14 cm
53. 300 m **55.** The sides are 26 in., 39 in., and 52 in. **57.** probably
smaller **59.** The approximate measurements of the ark are 158 m long,
26 m wide, and 16 m high.

9.2 Area, page 442

3. a. 3 cm^2 **b.** 3 cm^2 **5.** 8 cm^2 **7.** 11 cm^2 **9.** C **11.** A **13.** C
15. A **17.** C **19.** 15 in.^{2} **21.** 1,196 m^2 **23.** 100 mm^2 **25.** 7,560 ft^2
27. 136.5 dm^2 **29.** 5,550 cm^2 **31.** 28 in.^{2} **33.** 314.2 in.^{2}
35. 78.5 in.^{2} **37.** 307.9 in.^{2} **39.** 7.6 cm^2 **41.** A; $2.86/ft^2 for Lot A
and $3.19/ft^2 for Lot B. **43.** 22.2 acres **45.** 216 in.^{2} **47.** $93\frac{1}{2}$ in.^{2}
49. 20 pounds are necessary; $117 **51.** $s = 11.5$; $A \approx 20$ ft^2
53. $s = 230$; area of triangle $\approx 9{,}591.66$; area of figure $\approx 52{,}792$ ft^2
55. 172 in.^{2} **57.** 483 in.^{2} **59.** 79 in.^{2}

9.3 Surface Area, Volume, and Capacity, page 453

5. A liter is a bit larger than a quart. **7.** 60 cm^3 **9.** 125 ft^3
11. 8,000 cm^3 **13.** 24 ft^3 **15.** 96,000 cm^3 **17. a.** 2 c **b.** 16 oz
19. a. 13 oz **b.** 380 mL **21. a.** 25 mL **b.** 75 mL **c.** 75 mL **23.** B
25. A **27.** C **29.** B **31.** B **33.** 112 kL **35.** 3,125 cm^2
37. 780 cm^2 **39.** 35,000 cm^2 **41.** 36π cm^2 ≈ 113.1 cm^2
43. 7.8 in.^{2} **45.** 29,375 m^2 **47.** 4.3 gal **49.** 4 L **51.** 9 L
53. 500 L **55. a.** 45.375 ft^3 **b.** 26.375 ft^3 **57.** 2.5 yd^3
59. a. 560,000 people/mi^2 **b.** 11,071 mi^2; this is about the size of the
state of Maryland. **c.** about 5.4 acres per person

9.4 Miscellaneous Measurements, page 464

5. a. centimeter **b.** meter **7. a.** liter **b.** kiloliter **9. a.** Celsius
b. Celsius **11.** C **13.** C **15.** B **17.** C **19.** A **21.** B **23.** C
25. B **27.** B **29.** A **31.** 0.000063 kiloliter; 0.00063 hectoliter;
0.0063 dekaliter; 0.063 liter; 0.63 deciliter; 6.3 centiliter; **63 milliliter**
33. 0.0035 kiloliter; 0.035 hectoliter; 0.35 dekaliter; **3.5 liter;**
35 deciliter; 350 centiliter; 3,500 milliliter **35.** 0.08 kiloliter;
0.8 hectoliter; **8 dekaliter;** 80 liter; 800 deciliter; 8,000 centiliter;
80,000 milliliter **37.** 0.31 kiloliter; **3.1 hectoliter;** 31 dekaliter;

310 liter; 3,100 deciliter; 31,000 centiliter; 310,000 milliliter **39. a.** 0.001
b. 0.000001 **c.** 1,000 **d.** 100 **41. a.** 1,000 **b.** 10 **c.** 0.001
d. 1,000,000 **43.** 71 cm² **45.** 2,827 cm² **47.** 30 ft³ **49.** 600 cm³
51. $S = 452$ in.²; $V = 905$ in.³ **53.** The area is increased six-fold.
55. The area is increased nine-fold. **57.** The area is increased four-fold.
59. Answers vary; use the formula $F = \frac{9}{5}C + 32$ in the column headed
Fahrenheit.

Chapter 9 Review Questions, page 468

1. a. ─────────────────────────
b. 1.9 cm **2. a.** feet and meters **b.** Answers vary; 40°C; 100°F
c. Answers vary; $\frac{1}{2}$ in.; 1.5 cm **3. a.** one-thousandth **b.** capacity
c. 1,000,000 cm **4.** s 43 in. **5.** 105 in.² **6.** less than **7.** 1,262 in.³
8. a. 4π ft² **b.** 12.6 ft² **9. a.** $\frac{4}{3}\pi$ ft³ **b.** 4.2 ft³ **10. a.** 30 dm³
b. 30 L **11.** 56 dm² **12. a.** 30 cm × 20 cm × 50 cm **b.** 130 gal
13. 76 cm³ **14. a.** The best value is the large size. **b.** Answers vary;
$17.95. **15.** 2,400 ft² **16.** 7,200 ft³ **17.** 53,856 gal **18.** You need to
purchase 20 square yards.
19. a.

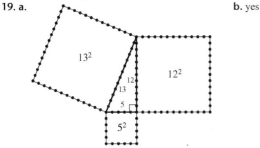

b. yes

20. The diagram gives a geometric justification of the distributive law.

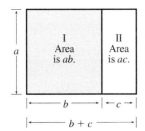

Area of rectangle I: ab
Area of rectangle II: ac
Area of I + II is $ab + ac$
Area of large rectangle is
$a(b+c)$

CHAPTER 10

10.1 Exponential Equations, page 480

5. a. $\log N$ is the exponent on a base 10 that gives N. **b.** $\ln N$ is the
exponent on a base e that gives N. **c.** $\log_b N$ is the exponent on a base b
that gives N. **7.** An exponential equation is an equation where the variable
appears as an exponent. **9. a.** $6 = \log_2 64$ **b.** $2 = \log 100$
c. $p = \log_n m$ **11. a.** $-1 = \log \frac{1}{10}$ **b.** $2 = \log_6 36$ **c.** $n = \log_t s$
13. a. 1 **b.** 3 **c.** -5 **15. a.** -3 **b.** -1 **c.** 1 **17. a.** 1 **b.** 3
c. -6 **19. a.** -2 **b.** $\log_5 8$ **c.** $\log_6 4.5$ **d.** $\log_4 5$ **21. a.** $\frac{2}{3}$
b. $\log 2.5$ **c.** $\log 45$ **d.** $\log 15$ **23. a.** 0.63 **b.** 2.00 **c.** 3.00 **d.** 2.30
25. a. 4.85 **b.** 2.00 **c.** 0.00 **d.** 6.91 **27. a.** 0.82 **b.** 2.82
c. 1.99 **d.** -1.14 **29.** 3.4650 **b.** 2.8028 **31. a.** 1.3181 **b.** 9.1189
33. a. -7.4804 **b.** 2.1991 **35. a.** 2.0686 **b.** 3.4396
37. a. 0.528320834 **b.** 0.386988016 **39. a.** 1.623249290
b. -1.630784143 **41. a.** -2.07944154168 **b.** -2.09691001301
43. a. 2.129072048 **b.** 1.855903615 **45.** 3.07 **47.** 2.16 **49.** 2015
51. 2016 **53.** 3 **55.** 8.665302427 **57.** $t = \frac{1}{r} \ln \frac{P}{P_0}$ **59.** 1 hour, 18 min

10.2 Logarithmic Equations, page 488

5. F **7.** F **9.** T **11.** F **13.** F **15.** F **17.** F **19.** F **21. a.** 23
b. 3.4 **c.** x **d.** x **23. a.** 2 **b.** 7 **c.** 4 **d.** 3 **25. a.** 10^5 **b.** e **c.** e^2
d. e^3 **27. a.** $\log 24$ **b.** $\log 2$ **c.** $\ln \frac{x^2 y^3}{z^4}$ **29. a.** $\ln \frac{3}{2}$ **b.** $\ln \frac{1}{48}$
c. $\ln \frac{3}{1,024}$ **31.** 3.5 **33.** 6.2 **35.** 3,572 **37. a.** 8 **b.** 10^8 **39. a.** 2

b. 25 **41. a.** 2 **b.** $\frac{\sqrt{2}}{e^2}$ **43. a.** 2 **b.** e^2 **45.** 10^{10} **47.** 1, -1
49. $4.8 \cdot 10^{18}$ **51.** $8e^{12}$ **53.** 0 **55.** $\frac{3 \pm \sqrt{409}}{2}$ **57. a.** 13 sec
b. $t = e^{(80-R)/27}$ **59. a.** 3.89 **b.** 8.8 **c.** $10^{23.8}$ **d.** $10^{1.5M + 11.8}$

10.3 Applications of Growth and Decay, page 497

5. 30 dB **7.** 107 dB **9.** 114 dB **11.** 896,716 **13.** -0.023104906
15. The half-life is about 28 years. **17.** 6.7 **19.** An earthquake with
magnitude 6 is 100 times stronger than an earthquake of magnitude 4.
21. $10^{24.25}$ ergs **23.** The artifact is about 10,500 years old. **25.** The
elapsed time is about 7 years. **27.** 63 times more energy **29.** The
artifact is about 1,300 years old. **31.** 1.41 times more energy
33. 31.6 times more energy **35.** The cookies are about 128° F.
37. 37°C **39.** 5,313 ft **41.** The satellite will operate for about
128 days. **43. a.** 1.5% **b.** 674,161 **d.** 802,673 **45. a.** 1.1%
b. 510,478 **d.** 582,976 **47. a.** 8.8% **b.** 518,429 **d.** 1,482,201
49. a. 0.5% **b.** 278,106 **d.** 296.490 **51. a.** Growth rate of about 1.6%;
predict the 2004 population to be 4,049,258. **b.** Growth rate of about
-0.27%; predict the 2004 population to be 3,357,957. **c.** Growth rate of
about 1.07%; predict the 2004 population to be about 3,838,310.
53. a. February 2003 **b.** The actual growth rate is greater than the
assumed growth rate. **c.** April 2011 **55.** 1,583 yr **57.** In 1988, the
Shroud was about 662 years old. **59.** When $x = 75$, $y \approx 0.16$ or no
O-ring failures; when $x = 32$, $y \approx 4.80$ or 5 O-ring failures.

Chapter 10 Review Questions, page 500

1. $2\frac{1}{2}$ **2.** 543 **3.** 4.3 **4.** 0.5 **5.** 3 **6. a.** 0.93 **b.** 3.99 **7. a.** 0.69
b. -2.08 **8. a.** 3.32 **b.** -1 **9.** 1.929418926 **10.** 6.214608098
11. 1.1178328654 **12.** 0.935554163 **13.** 6^4 **14.** $\frac{\log_2 6 + 1}{3}$ **15.** $\frac{\log 5}{2}$
16. $\frac{101}{99}$ **17.** 5 **18.** $\log_{(1+i)} \frac{A}{P}$ **19.** about 7 days **20.** Equation is
$A = A_0 e^{0.59t}$, where A_0 is the number of teens infected and t is the
number of years after 1992.

CHAPTER 11

11.1 Interest, page 514

7. C; interest rate is not stated, but you should still recognize a
reasonable answer. **9.** B is the most reasonable. **11.** A **13.** D
15. B **17.** $1,500 **19.** $4,200 **21.** $1,028.25 **23.** $16,536.79
25. $1,132,835.66 **27.** $1,661.44 **29.** $165,298.89 **31. a.** $28,940.57
b. $29,222.27 **c.** $29,367.30 **d.** $29,465.60 **e.** $29,513.58
f. $29,515.24 **g.** $29,515.24 **h.** $22,800 **33.** $1,548.13 **35. a.** $2.74
b. $1.96 **c.** $3.06 **d.** $4.63 **e.** $2,509.30 **f.** $29,797.93
g. $43,912.74 **h.** $25,092.99 **37.** $1,220.19 **39.** $11,023.18
41. $5,219.84 **43.** $279,064 **45.** $17,072.71 **47.** $P = $101,500$
49. $800,000 **51.** $200,000 **53.** 4 years, 61 days **55.** 7 years, 49 days
57. a. 3 years, 3 months **b.** 10 years **c.** The interest rate is about 14%.
59. $Y = \left(1 + \frac{r}{n}\right)^n - 1$

11.2 Installment Buying, page 523

7. B **9.** B **11.** B **13.** B **15.** B **17.** B **19.** C **21.** A **23.** B
(it should be the least expensive) **25.** 15% **27.** 18% **29.** 8%
31. a. $4.50 **b.** $3.75 **c.** $3.95 **33. a.** $37.50 **b.** $36.88 **c.** $36.58
35. $14,181 **37.** $18,975 **39.** 23.4% **41.** 21.1% **43. a.** $344.17
b. $349.69 **c.** 4.9% **d.** 0% is better **45. a.** $711.67 **b.** $705.00
c. 4.9% **d.** 2.5% is better **47. a.** $11,430 **b.** $2,430 **c.** 0.09
d. 17.5% **49. a.** $23,443.20 **b.** $9,093.20 **c.** 0.1584181185
d. 31.0% **51. a.** $8,886.48 **b.** $2,088.48 **c.** 0.08702 **d.** 17.0%
53. 8% add-on rate; APR is about 15.7% **55.** 11% add-on rate; APR is
about 21.6% **57.** previous balance method, $45; adjusted balance
method, $40.50; average daily balance method, $43.35 **59.** $67.58

11.3 Sequences, page 536

7. a. geometric **b.** $r = 2$ **c.** 32 **9. a.** arithmetic **b.** $d = 10$ **c.** 35
11. a. Fibonacci-type **b.** $s_1 = 5, s_2 = 15$ **c.** 35 **13. a.** geometric
b. $r = \frac{1}{5}$ **c.** $\frac{1}{5}$ **15. a.** geometric **b.** $r = 3$ **c.** 27 **17. a.** none of the
classified types **b.** differences are $-2, 1, -2, 1, -2, \ldots$ **c.** 5

19. a. geometric **b.** $r = 2$ **c.** 96 **21. a.** both arithmetic and geometric
b. $d = 0$ or $r = 1$ **c.** 10 **23. a.** Fibonacci-type **b.** $s_1 = 3, s_2 = 6$
c. 24 **25. a.** geometric **b.** $r = \frac{3}{2}$ **c.** $\frac{81}{2}$ **27. a.** geometric
b. $r = 4^{-1}$ or $\frac{1}{4}$ **c.** 4 **29. a.** arithmetic **b.** $d = \frac{1}{10}$ **c.** $\frac{3}{5}$
31. a. arithmetic **b.** $d = \frac{1}{12}$ **c.** $\frac{11}{12}$ **33. a.** 0, 3, 6 **b.** arithmetic; $d = 3$
35. a. 1, 0, −1 **b.** arithmetic; $d = −1$ **37. a.** 0, −10, −20 **b.** arith-
metic; $d = −10$ **39. a.** $0, \frac{1}{2}, \frac{2}{3}$ **b.** neither **41. a.** 1, 3, 6
b. neither **43. a.** −1, 1, −1 **b.** geometric, $r = −1$ **45. a.** $\frac{2}{3}, \frac{2}{3}, \frac{2}{3}$
b. both; $d = 0$ or $r = 1$ **47. a.** −2, 3, −4 **b.** neither **49.** −200
51. 625 **53.** $3, 1, \frac{1}{3}, \frac{1}{9}, \frac{1}{27}$ **55.** 1, 2, 3, 5, 8 **57.** It is Fibonacci.
59.

1st number:	x
2nd number:	y
3rd number:	$x + y$
4th number:	$x + 2y$
5th number:	$2x + 3y$
6th number:	$3x + 5y$
7th number:	$5x + 8y$
8th number:	$8x + 13y$
9th number:	$13x + 21y$
10th number:	$21x + 34y$
SUM:	$55x + 88y = 11(5x + 8y)$

11.4 Series, page 546

5. 30 **7.** 150 **9.** −1 **11.** 12 **13.** 90 **15.** 10 **17.** 33 **19.** 2
21. $\frac{3}{2}$ **23.** $-\frac{40}{3}$ **25.** 25 **27.** 15 **29.** 110 **31.** 10,000 **33.** 5,050
35. $n(n + 1)$ **37.** 11,500 **39.** 2,030 **41.** 120 **43.** 56; 64
45. 9,330 **47.** 3,828 blocks **49.** 200 cm **51.** 1,500 **53.** 190 ft
55. 1,024,000,000 present after 10 days **57.** 31 games **59.** 364 games

11.5 Annuities, page 554

7. $1,937.67 **9.** $2,026.78 **11.** $41,612.93 **13.** $74,517.97
15. $15,528.23 **17.** $18,294.60 **19.** $170,413.86 **21.** $540,968.11
23. $56,641.61 **25.** $59,497.67 **27.** $99,386.46 **29.** $38,754.39
31. $2,204.31 **33.** $252,057.07 **35.** $1,193.20 **37.** $1,896.70
39. $7,493.53 **41.** $8,277.87 **43.** $2,261.06 **45.** $36.89
47. $915,239.29 **49.** $27,298.98 **51.** $2,880.97 **53.** $1,666,454.24
55. $831,706 **57.** Answer depends on your age. **59.** $255,309.73

11.6 Amortization, page 560

3. m is the amount of a periodic payment (usually a monthly payment);
n is the number of payments made each year; t is the number of years;
r is the annual interest rate; A is the future value; and P is the present value
5. $2,586.28 **7.** $27,942.24 **9.** $20,442.52 **11.** $175,131.20
13. $297.46 **15.** $1,100.65 **17.** $1,316.36 **19.** $2,092.02
21. $6,882.42 **23.** $10,827.33 **25.** $5,429.91 **27.** $12,885.18
29. $7,407.76 **31.** $5,999.44 **33.** $6.38 **35.** $148.31 **37.** $430.73
39. $73.35 **41.** $780.54 **43.** $10,186.47 **45.** $117,238
47. $367,695.71 **49.** The annuity is the better choice.
51. $12,462,210.34 **53.** $206,029.43 **55. a.** decreases **b.** increases
c. decreases **57.** $1,510.92; $543,931.20; $213,046.20 **59.** price range
of $175,322.31 to $204,386.77

11.7 Summary of Financial Formulas, page 565

5. $m = \dfrac{P\left(\frac{r}{n}\right)}{1 - \left(1 + \frac{r}{n}\right)^{-nt}}$; the unknown is m **7.** present value **9.** annuity
11. amortization **13.** present value of an annuity **15.** amortization
17. annuity; $5,264.62 **19.** sinking fund; $1,574.10 **21. a.** annuity
b. $5,264.62 **23. a.** sinking fund **b.** $1,670.92 **25. a.** future value
b. $27,081.62 **27. a.** present value of an annuity **b.** $5,756.94
29. a. amortization **b.** $1,028.61 **31. a.** annuity **b.** $23,193.91
33. a. present value **b.** $7,215.46 **35. a.** annuity **b.** $21,867.63
37. a. present value **b.** $165,134.88 **39. a.** amortization **b.** $1,317.40
41. a. annuity **b.** $228,803.04 **43. a.** future value **b.** $884.12
45. a. future value **b.** $9,506.04 **47. a.** present value **b.** $3,655.96
49. a. present value **b.** $148,348 **51. a.** present value **b.** $500,420

53. $1,328.94 **55.** $179,986.40, total; $112,932 savings **57.** $726,624
59. Take $10,000 now and $45,000 in one year.

Chapter 11 Review Questions, page 567

1. A sequence is a list of numbers having a first term, a second term,
and so on; a series is the indicated sum of the terms of a sequence.
An arithmetic sequence is one that has a common difference,
$a_n = a_1 + (n − 1)d$; a geometric sequence is one that has a common
ratio, $g_n = g_1 r^{n−1}$; and a Fibonacci-type sequence, $s_n = s_{n−1} + s_{n−2}$, is
one that, given the first two terms, the next is found by adding the
previous two terms. The sum of an arithmetic sequence is $A_n = n\left(\frac{a_1 + a_n}{2}\right)$ or
$A_n = \frac{n}{2}[2a_1 + (n − 1)d]$, and the sum of a geometric sequence is
$G_n = \frac{g_1(1 − r^n)}{1 − r}$. **2.** A good procedure is to ask a series of questions.
Is it a lump-sum problem? If it is, then what is the unknown? If FUTURE
VALUE is the unknown, then it is a *future value* problem. If PRESENT VALUE
is the unknown, then it is a *present value* problem. **Is it a periodic
payment problem?** If it is, then is the periodic payment known? If the
PERIODIC PAYMENT IS KNOWN and you want to find the future value, then it
is an *ordinary annuity* problem. If the PERIODIC PAYMENT IS KNOWN and
you want to find the present value, then it is a *present value of an annuity*
problem. If the PERIODIC PAYMENT IS UNKNOWN and you know the future
value, then it is a *sinking fund* problem. If the PERIODIC PAYMENT IS
UNKNOWN and you know the present value, then it is an *amortization* problem. **3. a.** arithmetic; $a_n = 5n$ **b.** geometric; $g_n = 5 \cdot 2^{n−1}$
c. Fibonacci-type; $s_1 = 5, s_2 = 10, s_n = s_{n−1} + s_{n−2}, n \geq 3$ **d.** none of
these (add 5, 10, 15, 20, . . .); 55, 80 **e.** geometric; $g_n = 5 \cdot 10^{n−1}$
f. none of these (alternate terms); 5, 50 **4. a.** 5 **b.** $\frac{43}{30}$ or $1.4\overline{3}$ **5.** There
are a minimum of 2,047 people. **6.** 2^{82} **7.** You should offer $19,500 for
the car. **8. a.** The total interest is $783, and the monthly payment
is $595.13. **b.** The APR is 5.568%. **9.** The APR is about 23.5%.
10. The adjusted balance method is most advantageous to the consumer.
The previous balance method's finance charge is $3.94. The adjusted bal-
ance method's finance charge is $3.19. The average daily balance
method's finance charge is $3.42. **11.** Deposit $11,297.10 to have
a million dollars in 50 years. **12. a.** The monthly payments are $1,288.12.
b. The price of the home is $192,500. **c.** $639,122.51 **13.** $80,834.49
14. $97,178.53 **15.** $1,246,454.24 **16.** $302,821.47 **17.** You need to
set aside $97,178.53. **18.** $10,000 **19.** Take installments. **20.** Take
the one-time payment.

CHAPTER 12

12.1 Permutations, page 580

3. 9 **5.** 72 **7.** 3,024 **9.** 132,600 **11.** 95,040 **13.** 1,680 **15.** 1
17. 2,520 **19.** 210 **21.** 5,527,200 **23.** 336 **25.** 7,920
27. $\frac{g!}{(g − h)!}$ **29.** $\frac{5!}{(5 − r)!}$ **31.** 5,040 **33.** 360 **35.** 34,650
37. 4,989,600 **39.** 831,600 **41.** 120 **43.** 720 **45.** 16 **47.** 336
49. 6,400,000 **51.** 10,000 **53.** 40,320 **55.** 720 **57.** 64 **59.** 4,459

12.2 Combinations, page 588

3. 9 **5.** 84 **7.** 1 **9.** 22,100 **11.** 1 **13.** 35 **15.** 1,225
17. $\frac{g!}{h!(g − h)!}$ **19.** $\frac{k!}{(k − 4)!}$ **21.** $\frac{m!}{n!(m − n)!}$ **23.** 4,200
25. 1,260 **27.** 105 **29.** 792 **31.** 6 **33.** 1,287 **35.** 24 **37.** 10
39. 128 **41.** combination; $\binom{30}{5}$; 142,506 **43.** combination; $\binom{20}{2}$; 190
45. combination; $\binom{31}{3}$; 4,495 **47.** neither; distinguishable permutation;
1,260 **49.** permutation; $_{10}P_2$; 90 **51.** permutation; $_6P_5$; 720
53. combination; $\binom{7}{4}$; 35 **55.** permutation; $_7P_2$; 42 **57.** $\binom{n}{5}$
59. $_{16}P_2 \cdot {}_{19}P_2 \cdot \binom{31}{6}$; approximately $6.043394448 \times 10^{10}$

12.3 Counting without Counting, page 595

3. 15 **5.** 786,240 **7.** 21 **9.** 78,960,960 **11.** 1,296 **13.** 31
15. 127 **17.** 2,730 **19.** 1.95×10^{11} **21.** 135 **23.** 27,405

25. permutation; 120 **27.** combination; 286 **29.** combination; 1,191,052,400 **31.** permutation; 720 **33.** distinguishable permutation; 24
35. FCP, permutation, and combination; 57,600 **37.** permutation; 24
39. combination; 66 **41.** Subsets: $\{a, b\}$; Arrangements: $(a, b), (b, a)$
43. Subsets: $\{a, b, c, d\}$; 24 arrangements **45.** 810,000,000
47. 3,486,784,401 **49.** 26! **51.** 9,134.2 centuries **53.** Subtract each pair of billiard balls to find the value of the ball located below the pair.
55. 0 **57.** 524,800 **59.** 6,161,805

12.4 Rubik's Cube and Instant Insanity, page 601

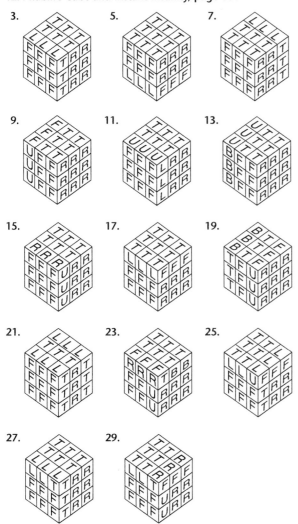

31. yes **33.** no **35.** no **37.** yes **39.** U^{-1} **41.** B **43.** U^2 or $(U^{-1})^2$
45. B or $(B^{-1})^3$ **47.** $U^{-1}B^{-1}$ **49.** TF^{-1} **51.** BF **53.** no **55.** No, answers vary. **57.** 41,472

Chapter 12 Review Questions, page 603

1. 40,314 **2.** 2 **3.** 120 **4.** 24 **5.** 28! **6.** 10 **7.** 336 **8.** 1
9. 1,001 **10.** 970,200 **11.** They can form 220 different committees.
12. They can form 120 different lineups at the teller's window.
13. happy: 60; college: 1,260 **14.** At least one red ball can be drawn in 100 ways. **15.** The 100 senators can be formed into 75,287,520 different five-member committees. **16.** The claim is correct. **17. a.** 1,024
b. 59,049 **c.** 9,765,625 **18. a.** 7,962,624 **b.** The result is more than 92 days (nonstop). **19.** It is not possible. **20.** The number of arrangements is $_{10}P_{10} = 10! = 3,628,800$. This is almost 10,000 years, so that day will never come for the members of this club.

CHAPTER 13

13.1 Introduction to Probability, page 616

5. a. $\frac{1}{4}$ **b.** $\frac{1}{4}$ **c.** $\frac{1}{2}$ **7. a.** $\frac{1}{2}$ **b.** $\frac{1}{3}$ **c.** $\frac{2}{3}$ **9.** about 0.05 **11.** 0.19
13. P(royal flush) ≈ 0.00001539077169 **15.** P(four of a kind) $\approx$ 0.0002400960384 **17.** P(flush) ≈ 0.00196540155 **19.** P(three of a kind) ≈ 0.02112845138 **21.** P(one pair) ≈ 0.42256902761
23. a. P(five of clubs) $= \frac{1}{52}$ **b.** P(five) $= \frac{1}{13}$ **c.** P(club) $= \frac{1}{4}$
25. a. P(five and a jack) $= 0$ **b.** P(five or a jack) $= \frac{2}{13}$ **27. a.** $\frac{1}{12}$
b. $\frac{7}{12}$ **c.** $\frac{1}{12}$ **29. a.** $\frac{1}{4}$ **b.** $\frac{3}{4}$ **31.** P(five) $= \frac{1}{9}$ **33.** P(seven) $= \frac{1}{6}$
35. P(nine) $= \frac{1}{9}$ **37.** P(four or five) $= \frac{7}{36}$ **39.** P(eight or ten) $= \frac{2}{9}$
41. Pick A. **43.** Pick D. **45.** Pick F. **47.** Pick F. **49.** Answers vary.
51. Answers vary; yes **53.** 10% **55. a.** $\frac{2}{9}$ **b.** $\frac{1}{9}$
57. a.

	1	2	3	4
1	(1, 1)	(1, 2)	(1, 3)	(1, 4)
2	(2, 1)	(2, 2)	(2, 3)	(2, 4)
3	(3, 1)	(3, 2)	(3, 3)	(3, 4)
4	(4, 1)	(4, 2)	(4, 3)	(4, 4)

b. $\frac{1}{16}$ **c.** $\frac{1}{8}$ **d.** $\frac{3}{16}$ **e.** $\frac{1}{4}$ **f.** $\frac{3}{16}$ **g.** $\frac{1}{8}$ **59.** $\frac{2}{3}$

13.2 Mathematical Expectation, page 624

7. B **9.** B **11.** B **13.** $0.08 **15.** $7.20 **17.** $0.25 for two plays of the game **19.** $1.50 **21.** $-$0.05 **23.** $-$0.05 **25.** $-$0.05
27. $-$0.05 **29.** $-$0.05 **31.** fair game **33.** not a fair game
35. $2.84 **37.** play **39.** $6,415 **41.** $6,875; yes **43.** $0.02; yes
45. $0.05 **47.** 1.82 **49.** no **51.** yes **57.** $1.50 **59.** $500.00

13.3 Probability Models, page 634

3. 15,120 ways **5.** The probability of event E is the ratio of s (success) to n (total number), whereas the odds in favor of that same event is the ratio of s (success) to f (failure) where $s + f = n$. **7.** C **9.** B **11.** B
13. $\frac{1}{5}$ **15.** 0.995 **17.** $\frac{4}{5}$ **19.** $\frac{15}{16}$ **21.** 15 to 1 **23.** 9 to 2
25. $P(\#1) = \frac{1}{19}$; $P(\#2) = \frac{2}{5}$; $P(\#3) = \frac{1}{3}$; $P(\#4) = \frac{5}{12}$; $P(\#5) = \frac{1}{2}$
27. $\frac{33}{34}$ **29.** $\frac{4}{11}$ **31.** 1 **33.** $\frac{1}{3}$ **35.** $\frac{1}{2}$ **37.** $\frac{4}{51}$ **39.** $\frac{4}{17}$ **41.** $\frac{26}{51}$
43. 51.5% **45.** 36.1% **47. a.** 0.3125 **b.** 0.675 **c.** 0.389
d. 0.70 **49. a.** 0 **b.** 1 **51. a.** $\frac{1}{5}$ **b.** $\frac{1}{5}$ **c.** 0

53. $\frac{P(\overline{E})}{P(E)} = \frac{\frac{f}{n}}{\frac{s}{n}} = \frac{f}{n} \cdot \frac{n}{s} = \frac{f}{s} =$ odds against **55. a.** $\frac{2}{7}$ **b.** $\frac{5}{7}$ **c.** $\frac{9}{34}$

d. $\frac{25}{34}$ **e.** $\frac{5}{17}$ **f.** $\frac{12}{17}$ **g.** $\frac{2}{7}$

h. *First selection* *Second selection*

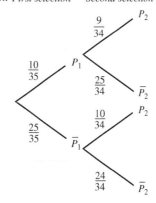

13.4 Calculated Probabilities, page 646

3. $P(E \cap F) = P(E) \cdot P(F)$, provided E and F are independent. **5.** $\frac{1}{2}$
7. $\frac{5}{6}$ **9.** $\frac{1}{12}$ **11.** $\frac{2}{3}$ **13.** $\frac{4}{9}$ **15.** $\frac{11}{12}$ **17.** $\frac{1}{3}$ **19.** $\frac{5}{9}$ **21.** $\frac{35}{36}$ **23.** no
25. yes **27.** yes **29.** $\frac{1}{6}$ **31.** $\frac{1}{2}$ **33.** $\frac{11}{36}$ **35. a.** 0.000455
b. 0.01229 **c.** 0.01229 **d.** 0.1538 **e.** 0.0237 **37.** $-$0.08
39. $-$1.42 **41.** $-$0.92 **43.** 2.7% **45.** $\frac{1}{32}$ **47. a.** $\frac{25}{64}$; $\frac{5}{14}$

b. $\frac{9}{64}$; $\frac{3}{38}$ **c.** $\frac{15}{32}$; $\frac{15}{28}$ **d.** $\frac{15}{64}$; $\frac{15}{56}$ **49. a.** play   **b.** play   **53.** $-\$0.44$
55. $-\$0.55$ **57.** one spot   **59.** First bet: 0.5177; second bet: 0.4914

13.5 The Binomial Distribution, page 653

3. 0.132   **5.** 0.128   **7.** 0.016   **9.** 1.701×10^{-4} **11.** 0.3125   **13.** .234375
15. 0.161   **17.** 0.3125   **19.** 0.044   **21.** 0.0107   **23.** 0.296   **25.** 0.222
27. 0.656   **29.** 0.0001   **31.** 0.9477   **33.** 0.512   **35.** 0.096   **37.** 0.488
39. 0.2109   **41.** 0.4019   **43.** 0.3025   **45.** 0.1699   **47.** 0.1028
49. 0.2765   **51.** 0.0837   **53.** 16   **55. a.** 0.109375   **b.** 0.114265
57. 0.75   **59.** 0.3125

Chapter 13 Review Questions, page 655

1. C   **2.** B   **3.** 0.004   **4.** $\frac{1}{2}$ **5.** $\frac{5}{36}$ **6.** $\frac{4}{13}$ **7.** $\frac{1}{17}$ **8. a.** $\frac{11}{36}$ **b.** $\frac{5}{9}$
c. $\frac{1}{18}$ **9. a.** 0.99   **b.** 9 to 1   **c.** $\frac{1}{1,001}$ **10.** \$2   **11. a.** $\frac{3}{5}$ **b.** $\frac{1}{2}$
12. $\frac{2}{15}$ **13.** $P(X = x) = \binom{n}{x}(0.001)^x(0.999)^{n-x}$ **14.** 0.138   **15.** 0.522
16. $\frac{2}{3}$ **17.** 0.821   **18.** Choose C; $P(C \text{ wins}) = \frac{5}{8}$ **19.** $\frac{1}{5}$ **20.** $\frac{1}{25}$

CHAPTER 14

14.1 Frequency Distributions and Graphs, page 667

5. a. October   **b.** August   **7. a.** U.S. trade with Canada for 1990–2005
b. more imports   **9. a.** 121 kwh   **b.** 44 kwh   **c.** 209 kwh   **d.** 55 kwh
11. C   **13.** Graph is meaningless without a scale.   **15.** Graphs are based
on height, but the impression is that of area.   **17.** Three-dimensional bars
are used to represent linear data, which is not appropriate.   **19.** 25 times
21. Maybe DUI (illegal if under 18 yr old)   **23.** no

25.

Number of Cars	Tally	Frequency
0	|	1
1	||||	4
2	|||| |||	8
3	||	2
4	|	1

27.

Temperature	Tally	Frequency
39	|	1
40	|	1
41		
42		
43	||	2
44	|	1
45	||	2
46		
47	|	1
48		
49	||||	4
50	||||	4
51	|	1
52	||	2
53	||	2
54	||	2
55	||	2
56		
57	||	2
58	||	2
59	|	1

29.

0	0 1 1 1 1 2 2 2 2 2 2 2 3 3 4

31.

3	9
4	0 3 3 4 5 5 7 9 9 9 9
5	0 0 0 0 1 2 2 3 3 4 4 5 5 7 7 8 8 9

33.

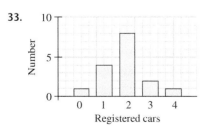

35.

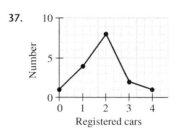

37.

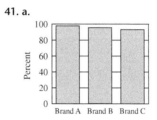

39.

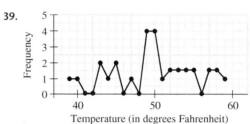

41. a.   **b.**

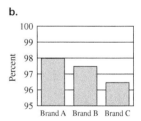

c. The graph in part **b**.

43.

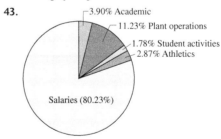

45. Each figure represents 30 managing directors.

Paine Webber: 46 out of 465, or about 10%.

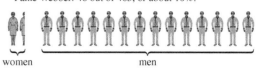

Goldman, Sachs: 9 out of 173, or about 5%.

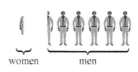

Merrill Lynch: 76 out of 694, or about 11%

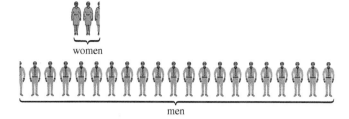

women

men

47. −$32 billion **49.** CBS **51.** The ratings for all three
networks (except for FOX) have generally declined from 1986 to 2008.
53. 2.4 persons **55.** 2036 **57.** The line graph at the right begins at
50 rather than 0. **59.** The advertisement says that the car is 57 in. wide on
the outside, but a full 5 ft across on the inside.

14.2 Descriptive Statistics, page 681

11. The data values are all the same. **13.** mean = 19; median = 19;
no mode **15.** mean = 767; median = 767; no mode **17.** mean = 11;
median = 9; no mode **19.** mean = 82; median = 81; no mode
21. mean = 6; median = 2.5; mode = 1 **23.** range = 4; var. = 2.5;
$s \approx 1.58$ **25.** range = 4; var. = 2.5; $s \approx 1.58$ **27.** range = 24;
var. = 93.5; $s \approx 9.67$ **29.** range = 25; var. = 83; $s \approx 9.11$
31. range = 21; var. = 62.86; $s \approx 7.93$ **33.** median = 432.51;
$Q_1 = 427.48$; $Q_3 = 442.28$

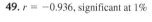

35. mean = 13; median = 11; mode = 10 **37.** mean = 68;
median = 70; mode = 70; range = 50 **39.** mean ≈ 366; median = 365; no
mode **41.** A **43.** C **45. a.** mean = 105.25 **b.** median = 12
c. mode = 42 **47.** 5 **49.** 12 **51.** 15 **53.** mean = 19,200;
range = 4,000; $s \approx 1,483$ **57. a.** $\bar{x}$ = 6.5; H.M. = 4.7
b. $\bar{x}$ = 56.5 mph; H.M. = 56.1 mph

14.3 The Normal Curve, page 692

5. The mean is to the right of the median. **7.** 5%, 16%, 45%, 79%, 94%,
99%, 100%; $\bar{x}$ = 2.62, median = 3, mode = 3 **9.** 1%, 12%, 47%, 68%,
88%, 94%, 97%, 99%, 100%; $\bar{x}$ = 2.94, median = 3, mode = 2
11. 28%, 40%, 75%, 81%, 100%; $\bar{x}$ = 7.84; median = 8; mode = 8
13. 41.92% **15.** 49.25% **17.** 49.99% **19.** 49.01% **21.** 17.72%
23. 48.68% **25. a.** 34 people **b.** 34 people **27.** 91.92%
29.

Height	Number	Cumulative
155		0.1%
160	1	2.3%
165	7	15.9%
170	17	50.0%
175	17	84.1%
180	7	97.7%
185	1	99.9%
190		100.0%

31. 60 or above **33.** 25 **35.** 87

37. 69 **39.**

Grade	Score	Cumulative
A	87 and above	6%
B	80–86	22%
C	70–79	78%
D	65–69	94%
F	64 and below	100.0%

41. mode

43. x = 98.0675 **45.** x = 68.919 **47.** 0.1587 **49.** 42.07%
51. 0.0228 or 2.28% **53.** 0.3085 **55. a.** 50% **b.** 12.4 oz
57. Graph **a** has less variance and graph **b** has more variance.

59.

−4	0.00001
−3	0.00195
−2	0.06250
−1	0.50000
0	1.00000
1	0.50000
2	0.06250
3	0.00195
4	0.00001

14.4 Correlation and Regression, page 699

3. $r = \dfrac{n\Sigma xy - (\Sigma x)(\Sigma y)}{\sqrt{n(\Sigma x^2) - (\Sigma x)^2} \cdot \sqrt{n(\Sigma y)^2 - (\Sigma y)^2}}$ **5.** Strong positive
correlation **7.** no **9.** yes **11.** no **13.** yes **15.** yes **17.** no
19. $r = -0.765$ **21.** $r = -0.954$ **23.** $r = -0.890$
25. $y' = -1.95x + 4.146$ **27.** $y' = -2.7143x + 30.0571$
29. $y' = -2.380x + 270.00$ **31.** D **33.** A **35.** C **37.** $y' = 6$; $r = 0$
39. $y' = x + 2$; $r = 1$ **41.** $r = 0.8830$, significant at 5%
43. $r = 0.8421$, significant at 1%
45. $y' = 2.4545x + 6.0909$

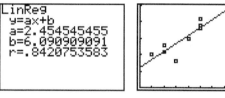

47. $r = 0.358$, no significant
correlation

49. $r = -0.936$, significant at 1%

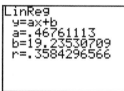 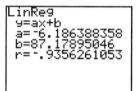

51. $y' = 0.468x + 19.235$ **53.** $y' = -6.186x + 87.179$

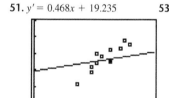 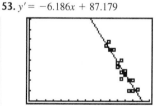

55. a. Time 27:31 or 27 hr 31 min; the difference is 4 hr 29 min.
57. a. Time is 44:21 or 44 hr 21 min. **59.** $r \approx 0.380$, significant at the
5% level

14.5 Sampling, page 706

5. B **7.** B **9.** D **11.** A **13.** D **25.** (1) You accept that 72 is the
mean, and it is the mean. (2) You accept that 72 is the mean, and it is not
the mean. This is Type II error (accept a false hypotheses). (3) You do not
accept that 72 is the mean, and it is the mean. This is Type I error (reject a
true hypothesis). (4) You do not accept that 72 is the mean, and it is not the
mean.

Chapter 14 Review Questions, page 709

1. Heads: ||||| ||||| ||||| ||| (18); Tails ||||| ||||| ||||| ||||| || (22)

2.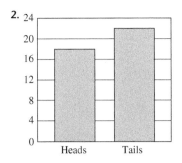

3.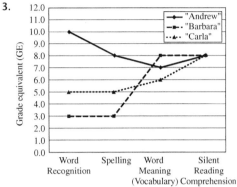

4. $23\frac{2}{3}$ **5.** 23   **6.** 21   **7.** 35   **8.** 11.59   **9.** mean = 11; median = 12; mode = 12; mode is the most appropriate measure.   **10.** mean = 79; median = 74; no mode; mean is the most appropriate measure.
11. mean = \$113,423; median = \$110,750; no mode; the median is the most appropriate measure.

12. a. yes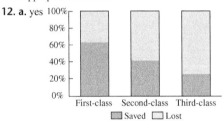

b. yes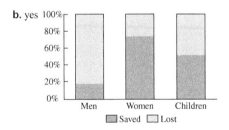

13. a. LTL   **b.** Courier Air   **c.** October
14.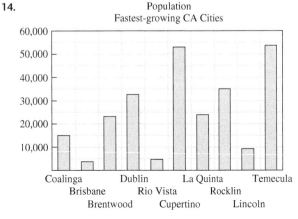

15. mean = $\dfrac{255{,}585}{10}$ = 25,558.5; median = 23,675; no mode
16. 18,091
17. a.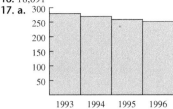

b.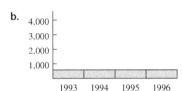

c.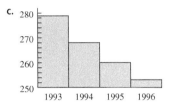

d. Impressions can be greatly influenced by using faulty or inappropriate scale (or even worse, no scale at all).

18.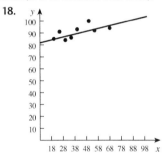

The best-fitting line is $y' = 0.22x + 81.8$.
19. $r = 0.658$; not significant at 1% or 5% levels   **20.** Approximately 1 in 1,000 pregnancies will have a 314-day duration.

CHAPTER 15

15.1 Cartesian Coordinates and Graphing Lines, page 722

1. a. Aphrodite   **b.** Maxwell Montes   **c.** Atalanta Planitia   **d.** Rhea Mons   **e.** Lavina Planitia   *Ordered pairs in Problems 7–18 may vary.*
7. (0, 5), (1, 6), (2, 7)   **9.** (0, 5), (1, 7), (−1, 3)   **11.** (0, −1), (1, 0), (2, 1)   **13.** (0, 1), (1, −1), (−1, 3)   **15.** (0, 1), (1, 3), (2, 5)   **17.** (0, 2), (2, $\frac{1}{2}$), (4, −1)
19. 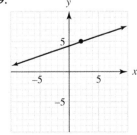   **21.**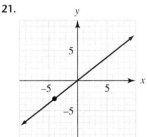

23.

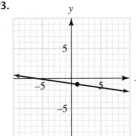

25.

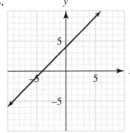

51. a. nearly   **b.** $y = -0.14x + 5.8$ **c.** 0.9

53. a.

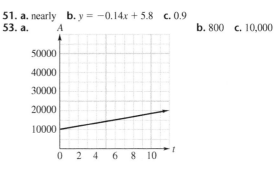

b. 800   **c.** 10,000

27.

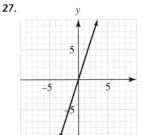

29.

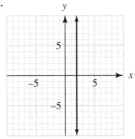

55. a.

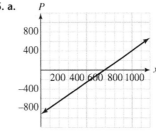

31.

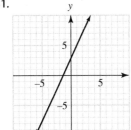

33.

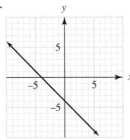

b. loss of $850   **c.** 1.25; it is the profit increase corresponding to each unit increase in number of items sold   **57.** 22.3 million

15.2 Graphing Half-Planes, page 725

3. F   **5.** F   **7.** T   **9.** T   **11.** T

13.

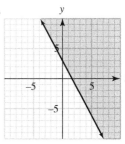

15.

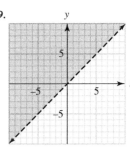

35.

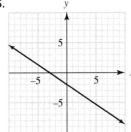

37.

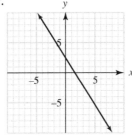

39.

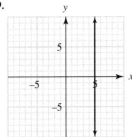

41.

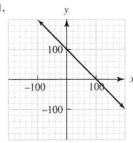

17.

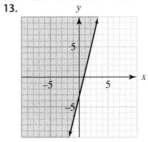

19.

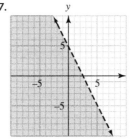

43.

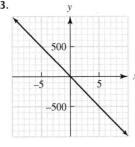

45. C   **47.** A   **49.** E

21.

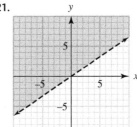

23.

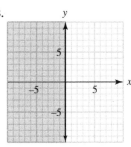

25.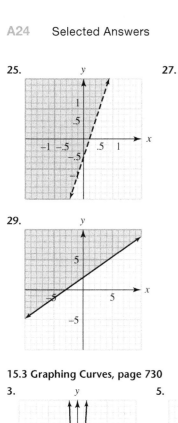

27.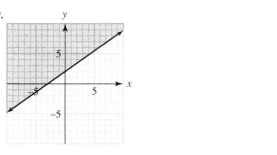

29.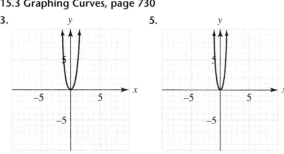

15.3 Graphing Curves, page 730

3. **5.**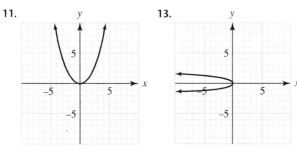

7. **9.**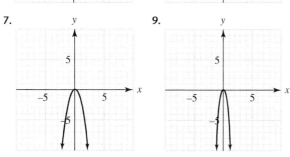

11. **13.**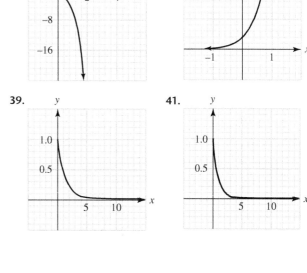

15. **17.**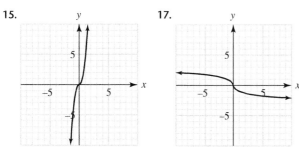

19. **21.** **23.** **25.** **27.** **29.** **31.** **33.** **35.** **37.** **39.** **41.**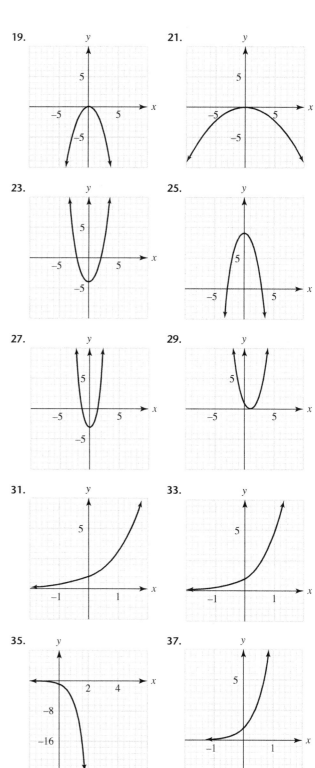

43. a.

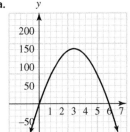

b. downward

c.

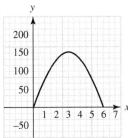

45.

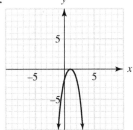

47.

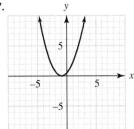

49.

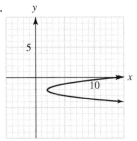

51.

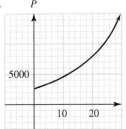

53.

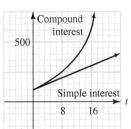

If $x = 4,000$, $y = 1,560$, positive; $x = 4,700$, $y = 188$, positive; $x = 5,000$, $y = -550$, negative. The crossover point $(y = 0)$ is between 4,700 and 5,000, so he will make it across.

55.

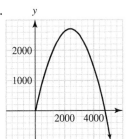

57.

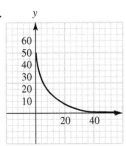

59.

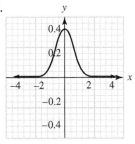

15.4 Conic Sections, page 743

9. A and C have opposite signs.   **11.** $A = 0$ and $C \neq 0$, or $A \neq 0$ and $C = 0$ **13.** $A = C = 0$

15.

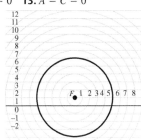

17.

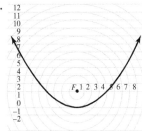

19.

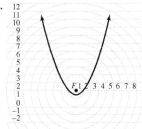

21.

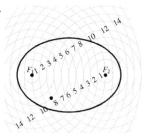

23.

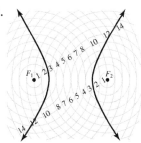

25. a. line **b.** ellipse **c.** parabola   **27. a.** parabola **b.** hyperbola **c.** ellipse

29.

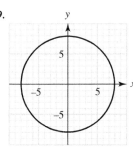

31.

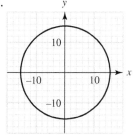

33.

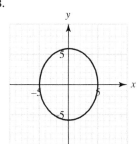

35.

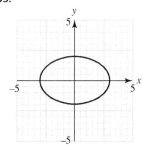

37.

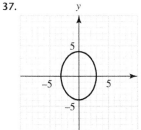

39.

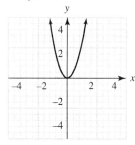

41.

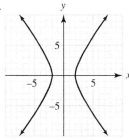

43.

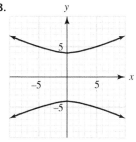

45.

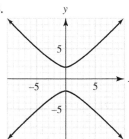

47.

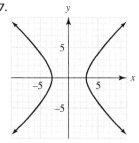

49.

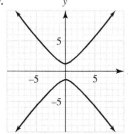

51.

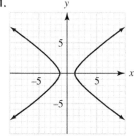

53. aphelion is 1.5×10^8 mi; perihelion is 1.3×10^8 mi.   **55.** $\epsilon \approx 0.053$
57. 2.25 m   **59.** 8 in.

15.5 Functions, page 750

3. function   **5.** function   **7.** not a function   **9.** function   **11.** function
13. not a function   **15. a.** 18   **b.** 22   **c.** -6 **d.** 11   **e.** $2(t + 5)$
17. a. 17   **b.** 37   **c.** 65   **d.** $1\frac{1}{4}$ **e.** $t^2 + 1$ **19. a.** 7   **b.** 11   **c.** -17
d. 0   **e.** $2t - 1$ **21. a.** 8   **b.** -16 **c.** $p - 7$ **23. a.** -1 **b.** -31
c. $3a - 1$ **25. a.** 5   **b.** -2 **c.** $\frac{3}{2}$ **27.** not a function; domain:
$-1 \le x \le 1$; range: $-3 \le y \le 3$ **29.** not a function; domain: $x \ge -3$;
range: $\mathbb{R}$ **31.** function; domain: $-2 \le x \le 3$; range: $-8 \le y \le 4$

33. quadratic

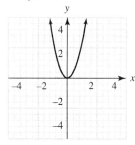

35. logarithmic

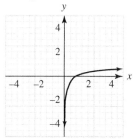

37. probability

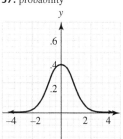

39. 3   **41.** $3x^2 + 3xh + h^2$

43. $\dfrac{-1}{x(x + h)}$ **45. a.** 64   **b.** 96   **c.** 128   **d.** 256   **e.** 512
47. a. 1,430   **b.** 1,050   **c.** 670   **d.** 290   **e.** 100   **49. a.** 4   **b.** 0
c. 25   **51.** $y = 3x - 5$; domain: $\mathbb{R}$ **53.** $y = \sqrt{5 - x}$; domain: $x \le 5$
55. Toss a rock into the well and measure the time it takes to hit the
bottom. It will take 18 seconds.   **57.** $f(x) = 10x + 25$
59. $A = \left(\frac{P}{4}\right)^2$

Chapter 15 Review Questions, page 753

1.

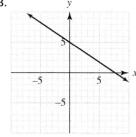

2.

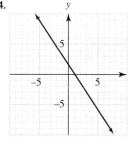

3.

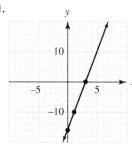

4.

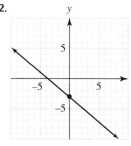

5.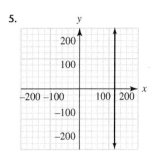

6.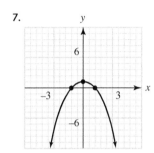

20.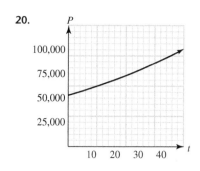

7.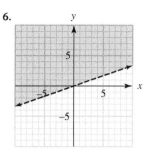

8.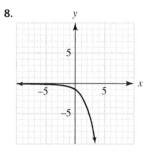

9.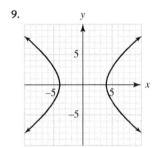

10.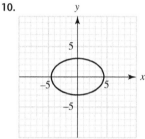

11.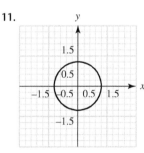

12.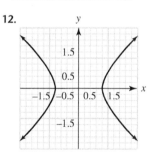

13. Yes   **14.** 20   **15.** −3   **16.** 75   **17.** 5

18.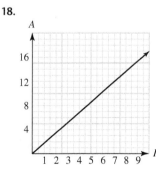

19.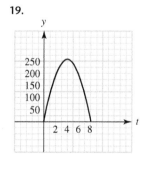

CHAPTER 16

16.1 Systems of Linear Equations, page 761

7. $(4, -1)$ **9.** inconsistent   **11.** $(-1, 1)$ **13.** $(1, 1)$ **15.** $(-5, -3)$
17. $(-1, -2)$ **19.** $(2, 10)$ **21.** $(9, -4)$ **23.** $(4, -1)$ **25.** $(6, -2)$
27. $(525, 35)$ **29.** $(5, -2)$ **31.** dependent   **33.** $(s_1, s_2) = (3, 4)$
35. $(u, v) = (5, -2)$ **37.** $\left(\frac{3}{5}, \frac{1}{2}\right)$ **39.** $(5, -3)$ **41.** $(3, 1)$ **43.** $(3, 1)$
45. $(4, -1)$ **47.** $\left(\frac{1}{3}, -\frac{2}{3}\right)$ **49.** $(1, 1)$ **51.** inconsistent   **53.** $(8, 2)$
55. $\left(-\frac{8}{5}, -\frac{21}{5}\right)$
57. 2,601 days after the cat's birth—namely, June 2, 1999.
59. $\left(\dfrac{a + \sqrt{a^2 - 4}}{2}, \dfrac{a - \sqrt{a^2 - 4}}{2}\right), \left(\dfrac{a - \sqrt{a^2 - 4}}{2}, \dfrac{a + \sqrt{a^2 - 4}}{2}\right)$

16.2 Problem Solving with Systems, page 770

1. The box has 31 nickels and 56 dimes.   **3.** There are 18 nickels.
5. The plane's speed in still air is 390 mph.   **7.** The equilibrium point for
the system is $(50, 250\,000)$.   **9.** The optimum price for the items is $3.
11. Goldie Hawn was born in 1945.   **13.** Mixture **a** has 7 lb of micoden.
15. Mixture **c** has $0.5p$ L of bixon.   **17.** Mixture **a** contains $46\frac{2}{3}\%$
micoden.   **19.** There are 40 oz of the base metal.   **21.** Mix 45 gal of
milk with 135 gal of cream.   **23.** The equilibrium point is $(58, 9200)$.
25. The equilibrium point is $(2, 10{,}000)$.   **27.** There are 14 dimes
and 28 quarters.   **29.** Clint Eastwood was born in 1930.
31. Matt Damon was born in 1970.   **33.** Add $\frac{1}{3}$ gal water.   **35.** TX is
262,134 sq mi and FL is 54,090 sq mi.   **37.** There are 37 quarters.
39. There are 30 dimes.   **41.** The robbery included 14 $5 bills,
70 $10 bills, and 31 $20 bills.   **43.** The plane's speed is 304.5 mph.
45. Mix together 28.5 gal of milk with 1.5 gal of cream.   **47.** The Bank
of America building is 779 ft and the Transamerica Tower is 853 ft.
49. The length of the Verrazano Narrows bridge is 4,260 ft.   **51.** The
equilibrium point is $3.50 for 4,000 items.   **53.** Mix 20 g of pure silver
and 80 g of sterling silver.   **55.** Add in 25 gallons of cream.
57. Replace $\frac{5}{8}$ qt of the punch with 7-UP.   **59. a.** 125 items would be
supplied; 75 would be demanded   **b.** No items would be supplied at
$200.   **c.** No items would be demanded at $400.   **d.** The equilibrium
price is $233.33.   **e.** The number of items produced at the equilibrium
price is 83.

16.3 Matrix Solution of a System of Equations, page 781

5. false   **7.** true   **9.** true   **11.** false   **13.** false

15. a. $\begin{cases} 6x + 7y + 8z = 3 \\ x + 2y + 3z = 4 \\ y + 3z = 4 \end{cases}$ **b.** $\begin{cases} x_1 = 3 \\ x_2 + 2x_3 = 4 \end{cases}$ **c.** $\begin{cases} x_1 = 32 \\ x_2 = 27 \\ x_3 = -5 \\ 0 = 3 \end{cases}$

17. RowSwap([B], 1, 2); $\begin{bmatrix} 1 & 0 & 2 & | & -8 \\ -2 & 3 & 5 & | & 9 \\ 0 & 1 & 0 & | & 5 \end{bmatrix}$ **19.** *Row(1/5, [D], 1);

$$\begin{bmatrix} 1 & 4 & 3 & | & \frac{6}{5} \\ 7 & -5 & 3 & | & 2 \\ 12 & 0 & 1 & | & 4 \end{bmatrix}$$
21. *Row+(3, [B], 1, 2);
$$\begin{bmatrix} 1 & 3 & -5 & | & 6 \\ 0 & 13 & -14 & | & 20 \\ 0 & 5 & 1 & | & 3 \end{bmatrix}$$

23. *Row+(-2, [D], 1, 2), Row+(-3, [Ans], 1, 3);
$$\begin{bmatrix} 1 & 5 & 3 & | & 2 \\ 0 & -7 & -7 & | & 0 \\ 0 & -13 & -8 & | & -6 \end{bmatrix}$$
25. *Row(1/3, [B], 2);
$$\begin{bmatrix} 1 & 5 & -3 & | & 5 \\ 0 & 1 & 3 & | & -5 \\ 0 & 2 & 1 & | & 5 \end{bmatrix}$$

27. *Row+(-1, [D], 3, 2);
$$\begin{bmatrix} 1 & 3 & -2 & | & 0 \\ 0 & 1 & -4 & | & 8 \\ 0 & 3 & 6 & | & 1 \end{bmatrix}$$

29. *Row+(-3, [B], 2, 1), *Row+(2, [Ans], 2, 3);
$$\begin{bmatrix} 1 & 0 & 12 & | & 27 \\ 0 & 1 & -2 & | & -5 \\ 0 & 0 & -2 & | & -4 \end{bmatrix}$$

31. *Row+(-5, [D], 2, 1), *Row+(-1, [Ans], 2, 3),
*Row+(-2, [Ans], 2, 4);
$$\begin{bmatrix} 1 & 0 & -26 & -8 & | & 8 \\ 0 & 1 & 5 & 2 & | & 0 \\ 0 & 0 & -1 & -2 & | & 5 \\ 0 & 0 & -13 & -3 & | & 7 \end{bmatrix}$$

33. *Row(1/8, [B], 3);
$$\begin{bmatrix} 1 & 0 & 4 & | & -5 \\ 0 & 1 & 3 & | & 6 \\ 0 & 0 & 1 & | & 1.5 \end{bmatrix}$$

35. *Row(1/2, [D], 3);
$$\begin{bmatrix} 1 & 0 & -8 & 2 & | & 8 \\ 0 & 1 & -1 & 3 & | & 2 \\ 0 & 0 & 1 & 0 & | & 5 \\ 0 & 0 & -2 & 1 & | & 6 \end{bmatrix}$$

37. *Row+(-4, [B], 3, 2), *Row+(3, [Ans], 3, 1);
$$\begin{bmatrix} 1 & 0 & 0 & | & 7 \\ 0 & 1 & 0 & | & -7 \\ 0 & 0 & 1 & | & 3 \end{bmatrix}$$

39. *Row+(8, [D], 3, 1), *Row+(-4, [Ans], 3, 2),
*Row+(1, [Ans], 3, 4);
$$\begin{bmatrix} 1 & 0 & 0 & 2 & | & 24 \\ 0 & 1 & 0 & 2 & | & -8 \\ 0 & 0 & 1 & 0 & | & 2 \\ 0 & 0 & 0 & 1 & | & 9 \end{bmatrix}$$
41. $(5, -3)$ **43.** $(3, 1)$ **45.** $(4, -1)$

47. $(4, -1)$ **49.** $(2, 0, 1)$ **51.** $(3, 2, 5)$ **53.** $(2, -3, -1)$ **55.** $(2, -3, 2)$
57. $\left(1, 2, -\frac{1}{2}\right)$ **59.** Mix 3 containers of Spray I with 4 containers of Spray II.

16.4 Inverse Matrices, page 794

9. a. $\begin{bmatrix} 2 & 4 & 2 \\ 6 & -2 & 4 \\ 2 & 2 & 5 \end{bmatrix}$ **b.** $\begin{bmatrix} -6 & -1 & -2 \\ 3 & -7 & -3 \\ 4 & -7 & -2 \end{bmatrix}$ **11. a.** $\begin{bmatrix} 20 & 21 & 34 \\ 29 & 16 & 15 \\ 7 & 48 & 5 \end{bmatrix}$

b. $\begin{bmatrix} -1 & 37 & 32 \\ 4 & 14 & 45 \\ 27 & 9 & 28 \end{bmatrix}$ **13. a.** $\begin{bmatrix} 14 & 14 \\ -7 & 7 \end{bmatrix}$ **b.** $\begin{bmatrix} 1 & 0 & 0 & 0 \\ 0 & 1 & 0 & 0 \\ 0 & 0 & 1 & 0 \\ 0 & 0 & 0 & 1 \end{bmatrix}$

15. a. not conformable   **b.** not conformable   **17.** $\begin{cases} x + 2y + 4z = 13 \\ -3x + 2y + z = 11 \\ 2x + z = 0 \end{cases}$

19. $[A][B] = [B][A] = \begin{bmatrix} 1 & 0 \\ 0 & 1 \end{bmatrix}$ **21.** $\begin{bmatrix} 2 & 7 \\ 1 & 4 \end{bmatrix}$ **23.** $\begin{bmatrix} 9 & -4 & -2 \\ -18 & 9 & 4 \\ -4 & 2 & 1 \end{bmatrix}$

25. $\begin{bmatrix} 1 & 0 & -1 & 0 \\ 0 & \frac{1}{2} & 0 & 0 \\ -2 & 0 & 2 & 1 \\ 0 & 0 & 1 & 0 \end{bmatrix}$ **27.** $(3, 2)$ **29.** $(5, -4)$ **31.** $(38, 21)$

33. $(3, -2)$ **35.** $(3, -5)$ **37.** $(-4, 1)$ **39.** $(3, 1)$ **41.** $(-2, 2)$

43. $(1, -8)$ **45.** $(5, 6, 1)$ **47.** $(-26, 52, 15)$ **49.** $(88, -176, -38)$

51. $(1, 1, 1)$ **53.** $(2, -4, -1)$ **55. a.** $P = \begin{bmatrix} 1 & 0 & 0 & 0 & 0 \\ -1 & 1 & 0 & 0 & 0 \\ 1 & -2 & 1 & 0 & 0 \\ -1 & 3 & -3 & 1 & 0 \\ 1 & -4 & 6 & -4 & 1 \end{bmatrix}$

b. It is the same as the Pascal's matrix except that the signs of the terms alternate.   **57.** $[A]^3 = \begin{bmatrix} 2 & 4 & 1 & 3 \\ 4 & 2 & 3 & 4 \\ 1 & 3 & 0 & 1 \\ 3 & 4 & 1 & 2 \end{bmatrix}$ **59. a.** Riesling costs 24;

Charbono, 25; and Rosé, 51   **b.** Outside bottling, 230; produced and bottled at winery, 520; estate bottled, 280   **c.** It is the total cost of production of all three wines.

16.5 Modeling with Linear Programming, page 804

5. a. 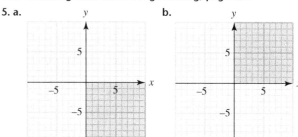   **b.**

7. 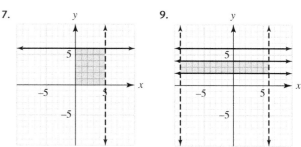   **9.**

11. 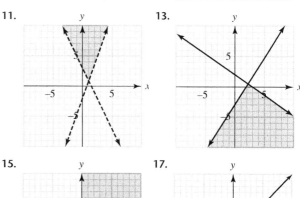   **13.**

15. 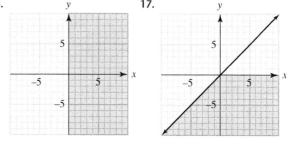   **17.**

19. a. no   **b.** yes   **c.** no   **d.** no   **e.** no   **f.** no

21. 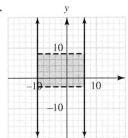   **23.**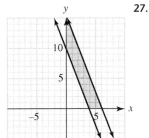

25. 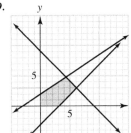   **27.**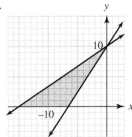

29.   **31.**

33.   **35.** $(0, 0), \left(0, \frac{9}{2}\right), (5, 2), (6, 0)$

37. $(0, 0), (0, 4), (2, 3), (4, 0)$ **39.** $(0, 0), (0, 4), (4, 4), (6, 2), (6, 0)$
41. $(0, 0), \left(0, \frac{8}{5}\right), \left(\frac{24}{13}, \frac{16}{13}\right), \left(\frac{8}{3}, 0\right)$ **43.** $(50, 0), \left(\frac{200}{7}, \frac{60}{7}\right), (8, 24),$

$(0, 40)$ **45.** $(3, 2), (5, 5), (7, 5), \left(\frac{10}{3}, \frac{4}{3}\right)$ **47.** maximum $W = 190$ at

$(5, 2)$ **49.** maximum $P = 500$ at $(2, 3)$ **51.** minimum $A = -12$ at $(0, 4)$
53. Let $x =$ number of grams of food A, $y =$ number of grams of food B;

Minimize $C = 0.29x + 0.15y$, Subject to $\begin{cases} x \geq 0, y \geq 0 \\ 10x + 5y \geq 200 \\ 2x + 5y \geq 100 \\ 3x + 4y \geq 20 \end{cases}$

55. Let $x =$ amount invested in stock (in millions of dollars),
$y =$ amount invested in bonds (in millions of dollars); Maximize
$T = 0.12x + 0.08y$,

Subject to $\begin{cases} x \geq 0, \\ x \leq 8, y \geq 2 \\ x + y \leq 10 \\ x \leq 3y \end{cases}$ **57.** The maximum profit $P = \$14,300$ is

achieved with all 100 acres planted in corn.   **59.** $70,000 in stocks and
$30,000 in bonds for a yield of $17,000

Chapter 16 Review Questions, page 807

1. $\begin{bmatrix} 4 & -5 & 0 \\ 7 & -1 & 2 \\ -1 & -2 & 4 \end{bmatrix}$ **2.** $\begin{bmatrix} 3 & -2 \\ 5 & -5 \end{bmatrix}$ **3.** not conformable

4. $\begin{bmatrix} 4 & -2 & 0 \\ 8 & -5 & -2 \\ 1 & -1 & -1 \end{bmatrix}$ **5.** $\begin{bmatrix} 1 & 0 \\ 2 & -1 \end{bmatrix}$ **6.** $\begin{bmatrix} -1 & -2 \\ 3 & 4 \end{bmatrix}$

7. $\begin{bmatrix} 7 & -3 & -3 \\ -1 & 1 & 0 \\ -1 & 0 & 1 \end{bmatrix}$ **8.** $(3, 4)$ **9.** $(0, 1)$ **10.** $(-1, 3)$ **11.** $(-1, 2, 1)$

12. $(-33, 79)$ **13.** $(-3, 1)$ **14.** $(5, 0)$ **15.** $(4, 2, -1)$ **16.** $(11, 9)$
17.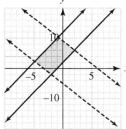

18. Use 7 bars of Product I and 3 bars of Product II.   **19.** The number of
product I to be manufactured is 100; product II, 150; and product III, 250.
20. Plant 100 acres of corn and 200 acres of wheat (200 acres are left
unplanted).

CHAPTER 17

17.1 Voting, page 822

13. 12   **15. a.** "(ACB)" means that the voter ranks three candidates in the
order of A first, C next, and candidate B last.   **b.** It means that in the
election there were 4 voters who ranked the candidates in the order ACB.
17. a. "(BCA)" means that the voter ranks three candidates in the order of
B first, C next, and candidate A last.   **b.** It means that in the election
there were no voters who ranked the candidates in the order BCA.
19. 10   **21. a.** "(ADBC)" means the voter picks A as the first choice, followed by D, then B, with C in last place.   **b.** It means that in the election
there were 8 voters who ranked the candidates in the order ADBC.
23. a. 24   **b.** (ABCD), (ABDC), (ACBD), (ACDB), (ADCB), (BACD),
(BCAD), (BCDA), (BDAC), (CABD), (CADB), (CBAD), (CBDA),
(CDAB), (CDBA), (DABC), (DBAC), (DBCA), (DCBA)   **25. a.** 6
b. 24   **c.** 120   **27.** $n!$ **29.** A wins   **31.** A wins   **33.** A wins
35. snacks   **37.** Howard Dean   **39.** no winner   **41.** A wins
43. A wins   **45.** no winner   **47.** C wins   **49.** C wins   **51. a.** B
b. plurality vote   **53. a.** C   **b.** plurality vote   **55.** 120   **57.** C wins
59. D wins

17.2 Voting Dilemmas, page 836

11. a. California Teachers Association   **b.** no   **13. a.** There is no
majority winner; A wins plurality.   **b.** A   **c.** no   **15. a.** A wins
b. C wins   **c.** yes   **17. a.** A   **b.** There is no majority winner; B wins
plurality. This violates the Condorcet criterion.   **19. a.** A wins
b. B wins   **c.** yes   **21.** There is no majority winner; C wins plurality.
This violates the Condorcet criterion.   **23.** C wins; yes   **25.** A is the
Condorcet candidate.   **27.** A wins; no   **29.** A wins; no   **31.** E wins
33. E wins; no   **35.** M wins; yes   **37.** Lillehammer wins; no
39. a. Beijing wins   **b.** no   **41. a.** Chirac and Le Pen   **b.** Answers
vary.   **c.** Answers vary.   **43.** Betty wins; no   **45.** Betty wins; none
47. D (Dave) wins; no   **49.** D; no   **51. a.** no winner   **b.** A, C, or D
could win depending on the way they are paired.   **c.** Yes, both of these
methods violate the condition of decisiveness.   **53. a.** B wins   **b.** yes
55. a. no majority; C wins plurality   **b.** There is no winner because B
and C tie.   **c.** B wins   **d.** C wins; yes

17.3 Apportionment, page 856

7. a. 3; 4 **b.** 3.5 **c.** 3.46 **d.** 4; 4 **9. a.** 1; 2 **b.** 1.5 **c.** 1.41
d. 1; 2 **11. a.** 2; 3 **b.** 2.5 **c.** 2.45 **d.** 2; 3 **13. a.** 1,695; 1,696
b. 1,695.5 **c.** 1,695.50 **d.** 1,695; 1,695 **15.** 6,500 **17.** 126
19. 120,833.33 **21.** 184,000

	Year	d	Manhattan	Bronx	Brooklyn	Queens	Staten Island
23.	1800	10,125	6.02	0.20	0.59	0.69	0.49
25.	1900	429,750	4.30	0.47	2.72	0.36	0.16
27.	1990	915,500	1.63	1.32	2.51	2.13	0.41

29. a. 11,600 **b.** 3.02, 1.81, 1.03, 4.14 **c.** 9 **d.** 10,000
31. a. 80,000 **b.** 1.69, 2.89, 1.48, 3.95 **c.** 7 **d.** 65,000
33. a. 11,600 **b.** 3.02, 1.81, 1.03, 4.14 **c.** 13 **d.** 13,000
35. a. 80,000 **b.** 1.69, 2.89, 1.48, 3.95 **c.** 11 **d.** 110,000

CT	DE	GA	KY	ME	MD	MA	NH	NJ	NY	NC	PA	RI	SC	VT	VA
37. 6.41 1.59 2.23 1.99 2.61 8.62 10.21 3.83 4.97 9.17 10.65 11.69 1.86 6.72 2.30 20.16

39. 96 **41.** N, 3; S, 2; E, 3; W, 2 **43.** N, 4; S, 2; E, 3; W, 1 **45.** N, 4; S, 2; E, 3; W, 1 **47.** N, 8; S, 5; E, 7; W, 6 **49.** N, 8; S, 5; E, 7; W, 6 **51.** N, 5; S, 3; E, 4; W, 4 **53.** N, 5; S, 3; E, 5; W, 3 **55.** N, 5; S, 3; E, 5; W, 3 **57.** N, 52; NE, 84; E, 50; SE, 57; S, 34; SW, 71; W, 95; NW, 32 **59.** N, 52; NE, 84; E, 50; SE, 57; S, 34; SW, 71; W, 94; NW, 33

17.4 Apportionment Paradoxes, page 863

5. State A violates the quota rule. **7.** State A violates the quota rule.
9. State D violates the quota rule. **11.** State A illustrates the Alabama paradox. **13.** State B illustrates the Alabama paradox. **15.** State C illustrates the population paradox. **17.** State C illustrates the population paradox. **19.** State A illustrates the new states paradox. **21.** State B illustrates the new states paradox. **23. a.** 62.78 **b.** A: 199.43; B: 72.55; C: 12.93; D: 15.08 **c.** A: 199, 200; B: 72, 73; C: 12, 13; D: 15, 16 **d.** modified quota is 62.4; A: 200, B: 72, C: 13, D: 15 **e.** no **25. a.** 203.3 **b.** Uptown (U): 83.52; Downtown (D): 16.48 **c.** U: 84; D: 16 **d.** U: 83; D: 17; New: 12 **e.** yes **27.** yes **29.** Adams' or Webster's plan gives the correct apportionment of the horses.

Chapter 17 Review Questions, page 866

1. no majority; plurality vote goes to C **2.** 3 **3.** A **4.** B **5.** Hare method violates the Condorcet criterion. **6.** A **7.** yes, B **8.** Carr (280), Crouch (770), Dorsey (638), Freeney (42), Grossman (708), Harrington (364), McKinnie (116), Peppers (41), El (267), Williams (146); Crouch wins **9.** A **10.** A **11.** C; yes **12.** 7.9 **13.** EA: 11.39; MC: 27.22; M: 33.92; P: 16.84; SR: 10.63. The lower and upper quotas are EA: 11, 12; MC: 27, 28; M: 33, 34; P: 16, 17 SR: 10, 11.
14. EA: 12; MC: 27; M: 33; P: 17; SR: 11 **15.** EA: 11; MC: 28; M: 34; P: 17; SR: 10 **16.** EA: 11; MC: 27; M: 34; P: 17; SR: 11 **17.** EA: 11; MC: 27; M: 34; P: 17; SR: 11 **18.** EA: 11; MC: 27; M: 34; P: 17; SR: 11 **19.** no **20.** Downtown: 70; Fairground: 29; Columbus Square: 28; Downtown West: 27; Peabody: 26

CHAPTER 18

18.1 What Is Calculus?, page 879

5. $\frac{1}{3}$ **7.** 1 **9.** π **11.**

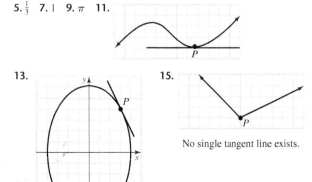

13.

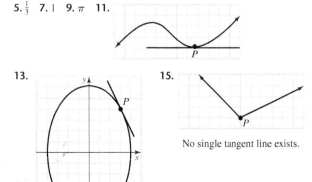

15.

No single tangent line exists.

17. $\frac{2}{3}$ **19.** $\frac{1}{2}$ **21.** $\frac{3}{2}$ **23.** 20 **25.** 4 or 5 **27.** 3

18.2 Limits, page 855

3. 0, 2, 0, 2, 0 **5.** $\frac{4}{3}, \frac{7}{4}, 2, \frac{13}{6}, \frac{16}{7}$ **7.** 8,000 **9.** $\frac{2}{3}$ **11.** 5 **13.** 4
15. 0 **17.** 0 **19.** 0.7 **21.** 0 **23.** ∞ **25.** -3 **27.** 3 **29.** 0.75 mg; $24\left(\frac{1}{2}\right)^n$ mg

18.3 Derivatives, page 895

1. a. 5.71 ft/s **b.** 15 ft/s **c.** 40 ft/s **d.** 40 ft/s **3. a.** 59 mph
b. 18 mph **c.** 36 mph **d.** 38 mph **5.** Let \$ be trillions of dollars.
a. 0.198 \$/yr **b.** 0.255 \$/yr **c.** 0.307 \$/yr **d.** 0.348 \$/yr **e.** 0.371 \$/yr
f. It is changing at the rate of \$371 billion per year (or greater).

7.

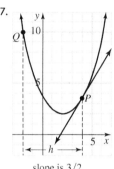

slope is 3/2

9.

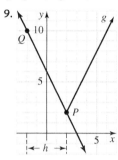

slope is -2

11.

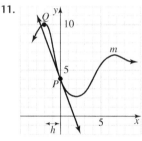

slope is -2

13. a. 0 **b.** 0

15. a. -25 **b.** -15 **17.** x^2 **19.** $-6e^{-6x}$ **21.** $2 - 6x$
23. $16x - y - 32 = 0$ **25.** $4x - y = 0$ **27. a.** The height of the tower is 176 ft. **b.** The velocity is $-32t + 96$. **29. a.** \$8,900/item
b. \$6,200/item **c.** \$5,930/item **d.** $5,900 + 30h$

18.4 Integrals, page 904

1. 40 **3.** 24 **5.** 19.5 **7.** $6x + C$ **9.** $\frac{1}{2}x^2 + 5x + C$
11. $\frac{3}{2}x^2 + 4x + C$ **21.** $242\frac{2}{3}$ **23.** 82.5 **25.** $2e - 2$
27. 76 **29.** 58,965.3; this represents the increase in the number of bacteria after 10 hours.

Chapter 18 Review Questions, page 906

1. limits, derivatives, and integrals **2.** The closer the measurements are together, the better the approximation at a particular point. **3.** 0
4. does not exist **5.** $\frac{3}{7}$ **6.** ∞ **7.** e **8.** 0 **9.** -2 **10.** 1 **11.** $-8x$
12. $22e^{0.5x}$ **13.** $8x^2 + C$ **14.** $\pi x + C$ **15.** 33 **16.** -6 **17.** 4.67
18. $2x - y - 1 = 0$ **19.** 7 mph **20.** Oil reserves will be depleted in 2014.

Epilogue Problem Set, page E10

3. a. social science **b.** natural science **c.** natural science
d. humanities **e.** social science **5. a.** social science **b.** natural science
c. social science **d.** social science **e.** natural science
f. natural science **7.** all natural science **9.** 1.46×10^8
11. Venus and Neptune **13.** 54 oz.
15. genotype $SS = 0.3025$; genotype wS or $Sw = 0.4950$; genotype $ww = 0.2025$

17. 0.45 cm² **19.**

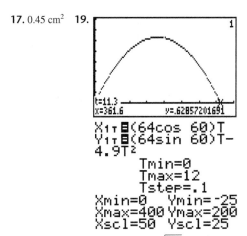

$$X_{1T} = (64\cos 60)T$$
$$Y_{1T} = (64\sin 60)T-$$
$$4.9T^2$$
Tmin=0
Tmax=12
Tstep=.1
Xmin=0   Ymin=-25
Xmax=400 Ymax=200
Xscl=50 Yscl=25

21. a. 0.0996 **b.** Let each unit be $\sqrt{10^{16}} = 10^8$. **23.** 24

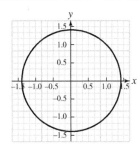

25. a.

$$\begin{array}{c}
 & A & B & C & D \\
a & (1,2) & (3,1) & (4,1) & (2,2) \\
b & (2,3) & (4,4) & (3,2) & (1,1) \\
c & (2,4) & (3,3) & (4,4) & (1,3) \\
d & (3,1) & (2,2) & (4,3) & (1,4)
\end{array}$$

b. Answers vary.

27.

Y₁=8sin (360*261
.626X)+4sin (720
*261.626X)
Xmin=0   Ymin=-15
Xmax=.02 Ymax=15
Xscl=.001 Yscl=1

29. A. 6 **b.** 3

Index